MATHEMATICS TODAY

FOR ICSE

CLASS – VII

Based on the latest syllabus and guidelines of the Council for the Indian School Certificate Examinations.

MATHEMATICS TODAY

FOR ICSE
CLASS – VII

O.P. MALHOTRA
M.A. (*Gold Medallist*)
Head of the Maths Department (*Retd.*)
The Doon School, *Dehra Dun*

S.K. GUPTA
Principal (Retd.)
Birla Vidya Mandir
Nainital

ANUBHUTI GANGAL
M.A. (*Gold Medallist*) M.Ed.
Formerly, Senior Faculty Member
The Daly College, Indore
Birla Vidya Mandir, *Nainital*

S. CHAND & COMPANY LTD.
(AN ISO 9001: 2000 COMPANY)
RAM NAGAR, NEW DELHI -110 055

S. CHAND & COMPANY LTD.

(An ISO 9001 : 2000 Company)

Head Office: 7361, RAM NAGAR, NEW DELHI - 110 055
Phone: 23672080-81-82, 9899107446, 9911310888
Fax: 91-11-23677446
Shop at: **schandgroup.com**; e-mail: **info@schandgroup.com**

Branches :

AHMEDABAD	: 1st Floor, Heritage, Near Gujarat Vidhyapeeth, Ashram Road, **Ahmedabad** - 380 014, Ph: 27541965, 27542369, ahmedabad@schandgroup.com
BENGALURU	: No. 6, Ahuja Chambers, 1st Cross, Kumara Krupa Road, **Bengaluru** - 560 001, Ph: 22268048, 22354008, bangalore@schandgroup.com
BHOPAL	: Bajaj Tower, Plot No. 243, Lala Lajpat Rai Colony, Raisen Road, **Bhopal** - 462 011, Ph: 4274723. bhopal@schandgroup.com
CHANDIGARH	: S.C.O. 2419-20, First Floor, Sector - 22-C (Near Aroma Hotel), **Chandigarh** -160 022, Ph: 2725443, 2725446, chandigarh@schandgroup.com
CHENNAI	: 152, Anna Salai, **Chennai** - 600 002, Ph: 28460026, 28460027, chennai@schandgroup.com
COIMBATORE	: No. 5, 30 Feet Road, Krishnasamy Nagar, Ramanathapuram, **Coimbatore** -641045, Ph: 0422-2323620 coimbatore@schandgroup.com **(Marketing Office)**
CUTTACK	: 1st Floor, Bhartia Tower, Badambadi, **Cuttack** - 753 009, Ph: 2332580; 2332581, cuttack@schandgroup.com
DEHRADUN	: 1st Floor, 20, New Road, Near Dwarka Store, **Dehradun** - 248 001, Ph: 2711101, 2710861, dehradun@schandgroup.com
GUWAHATI	: Pan Bazar, **Guwahati** - 781 001, Ph: 2738811, 2735640 guwahati@schandgroup.com
HYDERABAD	: Padma Plaza, H.No. 3-4-630, Opp. Ratna College, Narayanaguda, **Hyderabad** - 500 029, Ph: 24651135, 24744815, hyderabad@schandgroup.com
JAIPUR	: A-14, Janta Store Shopping Complex, University Marg, Bapu Nagar, **Jaipur** - 302 015, Ph: 2719126, jaipur@schandgroup.com
JALANDHAR	: Mai Hiran Gate, **Jalandhar** - 144 008, Ph: 2401630, 5000630, jalandhar@schandgroup.com
JAMMU	: 67/B, B-Block, Gandhi Nagar, **Jammu** - 180 004, (M) 09878651464 **(Marketing Office)**
KOCHI	: Kachapilly Square, Mullassery Canal Road, Ernakulam, **Kochi** - 682 011, Ph: 2378207, cochin@schandgroup.com
KOLKATA	: 285/J, Bipin Bihari Ganguli Street, **Kolkata** - 700 012, Ph: 22367459, 22373914, kolkata@schandgroup.com
LUCKNOW	: Mahabeer Market, 25 Gwynne Road, Aminabad, **Lucknow** - 226 018, Ph: 2626801, 2284815, lucknow@schandgroup.com
MUMBAI	: Blackie House, 103/5, Walchand Hirachand Marg, Opp. G.P.O., **Mumbai** - 400 001, Ph: 22690881, 22610885, mumbai@schandgroup.com
NAGPUR	: Karnal Bag, Model Mill Chowk, Umrer Road, **Nagpur** - 440 032, Ph: 2723901, 2777666 nagpur@schandgroup.com
PATNA	: 104, Citicentre Ashok, Govind Mitra Road, **Patna** - 800 004, Ph: 2300489, 2302100, patna@schandgroup.com
PUNE	: 291/1, Ganesh Gayatri Complex, 1st Floor, Somwarpeth, Near Jain Mandir, **Pune** - 411 011, Ph: 64017298, pune@schandgroup.com **(Marketing Office)**
RAIPUR	: Kailash Residency, Plot No. 4B, Bottle House Road, Shankar Nagar, **Raipur** - 492 007, Ph: 09981200834, raipur@schandgroup.com **(Marketing Office)**
RANCHI	: Flat No. 104, Sri Draupadi Smriti Apartments, East of Jaipal Singh Stadium, Neel Ratan Street, Upper Bazar, **Ranchi** - 834 001, Ph: 2208761, ranchi@schandgroup.com **(Marketing Office)**
SILIGURI	: 122, Raja Ram Mohan Roy Road, East Vivekanandapally, P.O., **Siliguri**-734001, Dist., Jalpaiguri, (W.B.) Ph. 0353-2520750 **(Marketing Office)**
VISAKHAPATNAM	: Plot No. 7, 1st Floor, Allipuram Extension, Opp. Radhakrishna Towers, Seethammadhara North Extn., **Visakhapatnam** - 530 013, (M) 09347580841, visakhapatnam@schandgroup.com **(Marketing Office)**

First Edition 1979 with Subsequent Edition and Reprints
First ICSE Edition 2006
Subsequent Editions and Reprints 2007, 2008
Revised Edition 2009, Reprint 2010
Reprint 2011

ISBN : 81-219-2715-3   **Code :** 14C 514

PRINTED IN INDIA
By Rajendra Ravindra Printers Pvt. Ltd., 7361, Ram Nagar, New Delhi -110 055
and published by S. Chand & Company Ltd., 7361, Ram Nagar, New Delhi -110 055.

PREFACE TO THE REVISED EDITION

It gives us great satisfaction to be able to bring out this new version of our old Maths Today series for classes VI to VIII. The old series has been rehashed and redesigned incorporating the current global trends and International practices and the latest philosophy and policy of providing stress free education.

The **salient features** of this series are :

1. It follows strictly the new syllabus of the ICSE council.

2. All the mathematical concepts have been presented in a very simple and lucid form and loading the course content with unnecessary and irrelevant details has been avoided. The approach and orientation is to lay a strong foundation for the students through adequate emphasis on the fundamentals.

3. It aims at complete involvement of the pupils in the learning process. The emphasis throughout the text is on a student-centered performance and the **activity approach** is freely used relating the mathematical concepts to real life situations.

4. Every unit is introduced by a motivating paragraph or story.

5. To facilitate easy and better understanding each unit is divided into a number of subunits with short & separate practice exercises on each subunit.

6. **An attempt has been made to expose the children more fully to the 'Why' of various operations and made abundant use of diagrams, illustrations, cartoons, tables and charts to stimulate the student's interest in the subject and to clarify more difficult concepts.**

7. Colour panels are used throughout as a teaching aid to emphasize important terms and relationships and present useful tips.

8. The problems given in the books avoid tedious calculations and help in strengthening the understanding of basic principles honing the faculties of thinking and reasoning.

9. Each chapter contains a **unit summary of key points** at the end. It reviews the main points covered and helps the students in remembering them.

10. **Unit review exercises** help in evaluating the assimilation of the concepts learnt in a unit.

11. **Mental maths** exercises have been given to help the students acquire speed and sharpen their intellect.

12. **Historical Notes, Quizzes , Just For Fun, Puzzles and Enrichment Material** offer further intellectual challenge to sharp students and help them not only to maintain their interest in the subject and widen their horizon of knowledge but would also be of immense help in preparing for such competitions such as Mathematics Olympiad at various levels.

It is hoped that this series of books will meet more than adequately, the needs of the students they are meant for. Any suggestions for the improvement of the books would be most welcome and gratefully acknowledged.

AUTHORS

A NOTE ON THE NEW 2009 EDITION

The text matter and answers have been thoroughly re-checked.

AUTHORS

A NOTE ON THE NEW 2008 EDITION

The authors wish to express their satisfaction and gratitude for the warm welcome accorded to this series.

1. The text matter has been completely revised to help better understanding and the number of questions and exercises have been reduced wherever it was felt to be advisable to do so.

2. Keeping in view the age group for which the books are meant, the layout and font size has been changed to facilitate easy reading.

3. The books have been thoroughly checked for any printing mistakes and all the answers have been checked by the authors themselves after solving each and every question. Hopefully, the books will now be error-free.

4. The authors are grateful to all those teachers and students who have provided valuable feedback for the improvement of the series.

A NOTE FOR THE TEACHERS

Dear friends,

We feel happy to be able to present for your perusal and consideration the new and thoroughly revised and updated edition of our **Mathematics Today Series for classes VI, VII and VIII**. It has no doubt been possible as a result of the motivation and feedback received in the form of valuable comments, suggestions and criticism from the learned teacher. We strongly feel that a textbook howsoever good it may be is only a tool to help teachers to teach effectively. It is the teacher and only the teacher who is competent to decide his/her teaching strategies in the classroom and is the best judge of how to use the textbook to meet the special needs of his/her class. It is earnestly hoped that this series will be able to supplement your efforts effectively to create interest of your pupils in the subject and make the study of mathematics interesting and enjoyable and gain mastery over the subject.

Howsoever best one performs or creates there is always scope for improvement.

We would be very happy rather grateful to receive your comments, appreciation/criticism and suggestions for further improvement of the books.

With regards

Yours sincerely,
Authors

A NOTE FOR STUDENTS

Wishing you the best in life, dear students. You are the best judge to evaluate whether the book you are studying fulfills your needs and satisfies your thirst for knowledge or not. Please do not hesitate to write individually through the publishers or directly to the authors at the following address if you come across any discrepancies or if you have some suggestions to make.

S.K. Gupta
502/8, Rajendra Nagar
Dehra Dun 248001

e.mail:skgupta2k@rediffmail.com
e.mail:anubhutigangal@hotmail.com

SYLLABUS

Teaching Points	Teaching Notes

1. Sets Concepts

Review of work done in Class VI - idea of notation, equal sets, equivalent sets, the empty set, the universal set, cardinal property of a set, finite and infinite sets. Union and intersection of sets, disjoint sets, overlapping sets, complement set; Venn diagrams.

Examples should be drawn for the number systems with which the pupil is familiar and from real life situations; Operations on sets should be confined to the universal set and one or two of its subsets or two disjoint or overlapping sets.

2. Numbers

Review of work done in class VI.

Natural numbers, whole numbers, the four fundamental operations, factors, repeated factors, exponents, prime factorisation, properties of exponents (confined to integral exponents); H.C.F. or G.C.D.; multiples, even and odd numbers, L.C.M.; perfect square natural numbers and their square roots.

Integers : the four fundamental operations.

Fractions : classification and comparison of fractions; the four fundamental operations with fractions; simplification, percentages; ratio.

Decimals : the four fundamental operations; recurring decimals; approximation (rounding off). Powers and roots - elementary treatment, based on the multiplication tables and drilling in the most frequently used powers and roots e.g. powers and roots - e.g. powers of 2 up to 2^8, powers of 3 up to 3^4; squares of all numbers up to 20 and cubes of all numbers up to 10; square roots of the perfect square natural numbers and perfect cube natural numbers corresponding to the previous item.

3. Arithmetic Problems

Unitary method

Speed, time and distance, simple problems

Ratio, sharing in a ratio

Profit and loss

Simple interest

Averages (direct problems to be emphasized).

Note : pupils may be introduced to the idea of a multiplying ratio to prepare them for direct and inverse proportion in higher classes.

4. Algebra

Fundamental concepts

Review of class VI work; concept of degrees and coefficients; like and unlike terms; polynomials with rational coefficients.

Fundamental operations

Addition, subtraction, multiplication of a polynomial by a monomial, binomial and trinomial (up to degree 2 only); division of a polynomial, in one variable only, by a monomial and binomial in one variable only. Using the rule; Dividend = Divisor times Quotient plus Remainder to check the result of division.

Formula

Translation from words to symbols (construction of a formula) and from symbols to words. Use of formulae in real life situations as in simple interest, mensuration, geometry, physics etc. Changing the subject of a formula (simple other than the common factor). Substitution in formula. Substitution in an expression in which the variables are only up to power 2.

Exponents

the following laws of indices - integral exponents only. Proofs are **not** required. $X^m \cdot X^n = X^{m+n}$; $X^m / X^n = X^{m-n}$; $(X^m)^n = X^{mn}$; $X^0 = 1$

Here x may be a rational number.

Products

Special products as identities :

(i) $(x + a)(x + b) = x^2 + (a + b)x + ab$

(ii) $(x + a)^2 = x^2 + 2xa + a^2$

(iii) $(x - a)^2 = x^2 - 2xa + a^2$

	(iv) $(x + a)(x - a) = x^2 - a^2$
Factors	Factors of -
(a)	polynomials with a common monomial
(b)	difference of two squares
Simplification	Simplification, addition and subtraction of algebraic expressions with integral denominators.
Relations and mapping	To be done through arrow diagrams, leading to listing of the matching pairs.
	Classification of functions not included.
	Note : In the teaching scheme, the section on formulae and / or graphs or ordered pairs should be linked with this section.
Equations and inequations	A mathematical sentence; an open mathematical sentence in one variable. Simple equations (in one variable) and the graphical representation of the solution. Problems leading to simple equations. Simple inequations in one variable and the graphical representation of the solution.
Graphs	Terms : rectangular coordinates, ordered pairs, abscissa ordinate; plotting.
	Representing a linear (first degree) equation in two variables, graphically.

5. Geometry

Lines, rays, line segments planes, angles	Review of work done in Class VI; lines, rays, segments, planes, angles.
	Linear pair, vertically opposite angles; parallel lines, corresponding angles; alternate angles, allied (interior opposite) angles. Problems on the above mentioned topics.
Basic constructions	Constructions ; bisection of a line segment and of an angle; construction of an angle congruent to given angle. Construction of perpendiculars and parallels.
Trianlges	Classification; construction of triangles; appreciation of the fact that the sum of the three angles of a triangle is two right angles or 180°; related problems.
Symmetry, Reflection, Rotation	Simple, direct cases only
Congruency of triangles;	Conditions for the congruency of two triangles namely, SAS, ASA, SSS, RHS - **no formal proofs** (practical approach, use of movements e.g. sliding, turning to make congruent triangles coincide); using congruency - single cases only ; some idea of similarity.
Polygons	Quadrilaterals - different kinds of quadrilaterals and their properties.
	Polygons; sum of the interior angles of a polygon in the case of a polygon of a given number of sides.
Construction of rectangles and squares	Construction of a rectangle, given (i) a pair of adjacent sides (ii) one side and a diagonal.
	Construction of a square given (i) one side (ii) one diagonal.
Circles	Revising terms associated with circles e.g. radius, diameter, secant, chord and arc.
	Questions based on multiple radii and simple questions associated with angles of a triangle and angle at a point.
	(Concept : Ability to identify radii of the circle.)

6. Mensuration

Perimeter and area	Perimeter and area of a rectangle and a square.
Volume and surface area	Volume and surface area of cubes and cuboids. Units of area and volume : cm², cm³; m², m³

7. Statistics

Handling of raw data, Making a frequency distribution table and calculating mean. Drawing a pie graph, column graph and line graph based on the data.

CONTENTS

UNIT I : SET THEORY

UNIT II : PURE ARITHMETIC

UNIT III : COMMERCIAL MATHEMATICS

UNIT IV : ALGEBRA

UNIT I : SET THEORY

1. Set Concepts

1.1 Revision

We help you to revise here the basic set concepts that you have studied in Class VI.

1. The word set is used for a collection of objects of any kind whatsoever, whereby given any object, we can say with certainity whether the object belongs to that collection or not. In other words,

> *A set is a collection of well defined objects.*

The following are some examples of sets :

(*i*) a set of animals;

(*ii*) the set of teachers teaching you;

(*iii*) the set of letters in the word "CRICKET".

The following are not well defined collections and are, therefore, not sets :

(*i*) the books that are a fun to read;

(*ii*) the movies that are good.

2. **Sets can be specified by any of the following methods :**

(*i*) *Description method*

(*ii*) *Tabular form or the Roster method*

(*iii*) *Rule method or Set Builder form*

1.2 Notations

1. The sets are usually denoted by capital letters *A, B, C*, etc., and the members of the set are denoted by small letters *a, b, c, ..., x, y, z*, etc.

2. The symbol $x \in S$ means *x* is an element of set *S* or *x* belongs to *S* whereas the symbol $x \notin S$ means *x* is not an element of *S* or *x* does not belong to *S*. For example, let *C* be the set of all countries in Asia. Then we have : India $\in C$, Ceylon $\in C$, Japan $\in C$

whereas, England $\notin C$, Canada $\notin C$, France $\notin C$.

$\in$	$\notin$
Belongs to	Does not belong to

1.3 Description Method

In this method, we write a description of the members of the set stating clearly their common property. The description is usually enclosed in braces '{ }'

Ex. 1. *Write the following sets in description form :*

(*i*) **0, 2, 4, 6, 8, 10**

(*ii*) *a, e, i, o, u*

Sol. (*i*) {even numbers less than 12}

(*ii*) {vowels of the English alphabet}

1.4 Tabulation Form or the Roster Method

In this method, we list all the members of the set and separate them by commas. The list is enclosed within the braces '{ }'.

1

The order in which elements are listed is unimportant. Also, repetition is not done while listing the elements. Thus, if S is the set of letters in the word 'PAPER' it will be specified as $S = \{ p, a, e, r \}$

Ex. 2. *Write each of the following sets in Roster form :*

    (i) *The set of prime numbers less than 15.*

    (ii) *The set of colours of the rainbow.*

    (iii) *The set of letters in the word 'REMEMBER '.*

Sol. The given sets can be written as

    (i) $A = \{2, 3, 5, 7, 11, 13\}$

    (ii) $B = \{$violet, indigo, blue, green, yellow, orange, red$\}$

    (iii) $C = \{R, E, M, B\}$

If the number of elements is large, we can write a few elements, then indicate the pattern by putting three dots and then in the end, write the last element.

Ex. 3. *Write the set A of the set of non-zero multiples of 2 less than 100.*

Sol. The set of non-zero multiples of 2 less than 100 is $A = \{2, 4, 6, ..., 98\}$

Ex. 4. *Write the set P of the integers greater than – 5.*

Sol. $P = \{-4, -3, -2, -1, 0, 1, 2, ...\}$.

1.5 Rule Method or Set Builder form

In this method, we write a variable (say x) representing any member of the set, put the vertical '|' or the colon ':' which stands for the words **'such that'**. Then we state the property which is characteristic of all the objects of the set.

| or :
Symbol for such that

Thus, if the members of a set S possess a property P and x is any element of S, then we write the set S as

$$S = \{ x \mid x \text{ has property } \textbf{P} \} \text{ or } S = \{x : x \text{ has property } \textbf{P} \}$$

Ex. 5. *Write the following sets in the set builder form :*

    1. *The set E of days of the week.*

    2. *The set A of natural numbers less than 20.*

    3. *{–9, –6, –3, 0, 3, 6, 9, 12, 15, 18}.*

Sol.   1. $E = \{d \mid d$ is a day of the week$\}$

       2. $A = \{x \mid x \in N, x < 20\}$

       3.   Given set $= \{x \mid x = 3n, n \in Z$ and $-3 \leq n \leq 6\}$

Ex. 6. *Write the following sets in roster form and also in set builder form :*

    (a) *The set of integers which lie between –5 and 4 (both inclusive).*

    (b) *The set of natural numbers which are divisible by 8 and less than 60.*

Sol.   *(a)* $\{-5, -4, -3, -2, -1, 0, 1, 2, 3, 4\}$ or $\{x \mid x \in Z, -5 \leq x \leq 4\}$

      (b) $\{8, 16, 24, 32, 40, 48, 56\}$ or $\{x : x = 8n, n \in N$ and $x < 60\}$.

Ex. 7. *Write the following sets both in roster form and description form :*

    1. $\{x : x = n^2, n \in N$ and $n \leq 7\}$.   **2.** $\{x : x$ is a Ocean$\}$

    3. $\{x : x$ is a letter in the word 'EXAMINATION'$\}$.

    4. $\{y \mid y = 2x - 7, x \in W$ and $x < 7\}$.

Sol. 1. Natural numbers ≤ 7, i.e., less than or equal to 7 are 1, 2, 3, 4, 5, 6, 7.

    The squares of these numbers are 1, 4, 9, 16, 25, 36, 49

∴ The given set can be written as {1, 4, 9, 16, 25, 36, 49}   [*Roster form*]

or {squares of first seven natural numbers}   [*Description form*]

2. {Pacific, Atlantic, Indian, Arctic}   [*Roster form*]

{Oceans of the world}   [*Description form*]

3. {E, X, A, M, I, N, T, O}   [*Roster form*]

or {letters of the word 'Examination'}   [*Description form*]

4. Whole numbers less than 7 are 0, 1, 2, 3, 4, 5, 6.

Putting $x = 0, 1, 2, 3, 4, 5, 6$ respectively in $2x - 7$ we get $y = -7, -5, -3, -1, 1, 3, 5$. So the given set can be written as

{−7 −5, −3, −1, 1, 3, 5}   [*Roster form*]

or {odd integers lying between −8 and 6}   [*Description form*]

Ex. 8. *Write the following sets in builder form :*

$$\left\{ \frac{1}{3}, \frac{1}{5}, \frac{1}{7}, \dots\dots, \frac{1}{31} \right\}$$

Sol. Since 3, 5, 7, ... are odd numbers and general odd number can be written as $2n + 1$ where $n \in N$, we have

Given set $= \left\{ x : x = \dfrac{1}{2n+1}, n \in N \text{ and } n \leq 15 \right\}$

EXERCISE 1 (a)

I. List the members of the sets in questions 1 to 8.

(1) {the first three months of the year}.

(2) {first 4 prime numbers}.

(3) {odd numbers smaller than 8}.

(4) {even numbers smaller than 10}.

(5) {the letters of the word 'SCHOOL'}.

(6) {even positive integers that are divisible by 5}.

(7) {the angles of ∆ABC}.

(8) {the numbers that differ from 5 by 1}.

II. Write down the following sets in the descriptive form in questions 1 to 6.

(1) {1, 3, 5, 7}

(2) {0, 1, 2, 3, 4, 5}

(3) {5, 10, 15, 20, 25}

(4) {Tuesday, Thursday}

(5) {2, 3, 5, 7, 11}

(6) {1, 4, 9, 16...}

III. List the following sets in Roster form.

(1) $A = \{x/x$ is a non-zero multiple of 2 less than 11}.

(2) $B = \{x/x$ is the shortest month of the year}.

(3) $C = \{x/x$ is a square number less than 20}.

(4) $D = \{x/x$ is a prime number which is even}.

(5) $E = \{x/x$ is a vowel}.

IV. List the following sets in set-builder form

(1) {2, 3, 5, 7, 11, 13, 17, 19}.

(2) {3, 5, 7, 9, 11, 13, 15, 17, 19, 21, 23, 25}.

(3) {1, 4, 9, 16, 25, 36, 49, 64}.

(4) {January, March, May, July, August, October, December.}.

(5) {1, 2, 3, 4, 6, 9, 12, 18, 36}.

(6) {1, 8, 27, 64, 125, 216, 243, 512}.

(7) $\left\{ \dfrac{1}{3}, \dfrac{1}{4}, \dfrac{1}{5}, \dots, \dfrac{1}{10} \right\}$

V. Fill in the blanks with the symbol '∈' or ∉ to make the statements true.

(1) 2 .... {set of even numbers}

(2) Carrot .... {fruits}

(3) e .... {set of vowels}

(4) 7.......... $\{x \mid x$ is a multiple of 7}

(5) m .... {m, a, t}

(6) 1 .... $\{x \mid x$ is a prime number}

(7) 0 .... {5 − 5, 5 + 5, 5 × 5, 5 ÷ 5}

(8) b .... {c, o, p, y}.

1.6 Types of Sets

1. **Finite set.** A set whose members can be counted, *i.e.*, in which the process of counting its member comes to an end, is called a *finite set*.

For example :

The following are all finite sets :

(*i*) $A = \{a, e, i, o, u\}$ (*ii*) $B = \{x \mid x = 2n, n \in N, n \leq 30\}$

(*iii*) The set of all persons on earth.

2. **Infinite set.** A set which contains unlimited number of elements, *i.e.*, in which the counting of element does not come to an end, is called an infinite set.

For example :

The following are all infinite sets.

(*i*) The set of prime numbers   (*ii*) The set of integers less than 0.

(*iii*) The set of points on a line segment.

3. **Singleton set.** A set containing only one element is called a singleton set.

For example :

$\{5\}$ is a singleton set, containing only one element, namely 5.

4. **Empty set or Null set**

The set containing no elements at all is called the *empty set*. It is denoted by the symbol '{ }' or, by the symbol ϕ. The latter symbol is more commonly used.

For example :

(*i*) $\phi = \{$pupils in your class over 70 years old$\}$

(*ii*) $\phi = \{$integers greater than 3 and less than 4$\}$

(*iii*) $\phi = \{$squares with five sides$\}$

Cardinal number of a set

The number of distinct elements in a finite set A is called its **Cardinal number** and is denoted by $n (A)$

For example :

1. For the set A, shown in the picture $n (A) = 4$.

2. Let P = set of letters of the word 'NANNY'. Then

   $P = \{N, A, Y \}$ has 3 distinct elements, and so $n (P) = 3$.

3. Let $B = \{x \mid x \in W, -3 < x < -1\}$. Then $B = \phi$, since there is no whole number between -3 and -1.

   Since, ϕ contains no elements at all therefore $n(B) = n (\phi) = 0$

> **Remark :** The cardinal set of an infinite set is not defined.

5. **Equal sets**

Two sets A and B are said to be **identical** or equal, written : $A = B$ when they have exactly the same elements. To be more precise, A and B are equal if every element of A is an element of B and conversely every element of B is also an element of A.

$$A = \left\{ \text{🍎 🥒 🥭} \right\}, B = \left\{ \text{🥒 🥭 🍎} \right\}$$

$$A = B$$

6. Equivalent Sets

If the two sets contain the same number of elements which may not be exactly the same elements, they are called *equivalent sets*. Obviously the equivalent sets have the same cardinal number.

If two sets A and B are equivalent, we indicate it by writing $A \leftrightarrow B$.

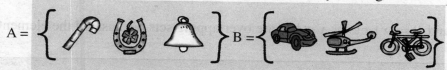

$$A \leftrightarrow B$$

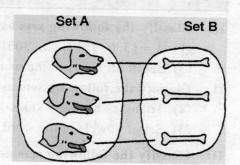

Note 1. It is easy to observe that **all equal sets are equivalent sets** while **all equivalent sets are not equal sets**.

2. The sets on the right **match one-to-one.** For every member of A there is a member of B and for every member of B there is a member of A, A and B are **equivalent sets**.

Ex. 1. Let A = set of the letters of the word 'FOLLOW'.
B = set of the letters of the word 'WOLF'.
C = set of the letters of the word 'FLOW'.
D = set of the letters of the word 'SLOW'.
Then $A = \{F, O, L, W\}$, $B = \{W, O, L, F\}$, $C = \{F, L, O, W\}$,
$D = \{S, L, O, W\}$.

Sol. Since the sets A, B, and C contain exactly the same elements, we have $A = B = C$. The set does not contain exactly the same elements as the set A or set B or set C, but the number of elements is the same in all these four sets, i.e., $n(A) = n(B) = n(C) = n(D)$ so they are equivalant sets, i.e., $A \leftrightarrow D$, $B \leftrightarrow D$, $C \leftrightarrow D$.

Caution : Note that $A \neq D$, $B \neq D$, $C \neq D$.

Ex. 2. *Show that* ϕ, *{0} and 0 are all different.*

Sol. ϕ is a set containing **no elements** at all
$\{0\}$ contains one element, namely 0, and so is a singleton set.
0 is a number and not a set.
$\therefore$ ϕ, $\{0\}$ and 0 are all different.

8. Disjoint sets.

Sets which do not contain any element in common are called **disjoint sets**.

 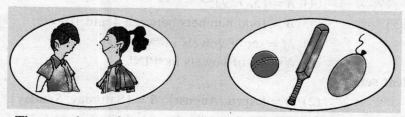

The members of set A are not in set B. The members of set B are not in set A. The sets A and B are disjoint sets.

9. Overlapping sets.

Two sets are called *overlapping* sets, if they have at least one element in common.

Ex. 3. (1) Let $A = \{1, 3, 5\}$, $B = \{2, 4, 6\}$. Since, the sets A and B have no elements in common, they are disjoint sets.

(2) The sets $A = \{$Sunday, Monday, Tuesday$\}$ and $B = \{$Thursday, Friday, Saturday$\}$ are disjoint sets.

(3) The sets $A = \{4, 8, 12\}$, $B = \{6, 12, 18\}$ are overlapping sets since one element, namely 12, is common to them.

(4) The sets $A = \{1, 3, 5, 7\}$ and $B = \{x \mid x \in N, x < 10\}$ are overlapping sets because all the elements of A are common to them.

EXERCISE 1 (b)

I. **Classify the following sets as finite or infinite sets :**

(1) $A = \{3, 6, 9, 12, ... 300\}$

(2) The set of natural numbers.

(3) Set of all rivers in the world.

(4) Set of square numbers greater then 10,000.

II. **Classify the following sets as the empty or singleton sets :**

(1) Triangles having 4 sides.

(2) Whole numbers less than 0.

(3) Set of vowels in the word 'MAN'.

(4) $\{x \mid x$ is a capital of Assam$\}$

III. **Classify the following sets as finite, empty or singleton sets.**

(1) The set of natural numbers.

(2) $\{x/x$ is a composite number $< 13\}$.

(3) $\{$Natural numbers that are less than 40 and are multiples of 7$\}$

(4) The set of square numbers.

(5) The set of stars in the sky.

(6) The set of students more than 3 metres tall.

(7) $\{$Months having more than 32 days$\}$

(8) $\{$Fractions between 2 and 3$\}$.

(9) $\{$Whole numbers less than 1$\}$

(10) $\{$Two digit numbers greater than 98$\}$.

IV. **State the cardinal number of the following sets.**

(1) $A = $ set of letters in the word 'LOOK'.

(2) $B = \{$Triangle, quadrilateral, pentagon$\}$.

(3) $C = \{0\}$.

(4) $\{$Prime numbers less than 6$\}$.

(5) $D = \{$colours of a rainbow$\}$.

(6) $E = \{$square numbers less than 6$\}$.

(7) $F = \{$quadrilateral with five sides$\}$.

(8) $G = \{x/x \in N, x$ lies between 5 and 9 i.e., $5 < x < 9\}$.

V. **Which of the following pairs are equal sets ?**

(1) $A = \{3, 6, 9, 12\}$, $B = \{$Multiples of 3$\}$

(2) $A = \{2, 3, 5, 7, 11\}$, $B = \{$Prime numbers $< 12\}$.

(3) $P = \{0, 1, 2, 3, 4\}$, $Q = \{$Positive integers less than 5$\}$

(4) $A = \{5, 7, 9\}$, $B = \{$odd numbers between 4 and 10$\}$

(5) $A = \{s, a, t\}$, $B = \{t, a, b\}$

(6) $M = $ set of vowels in 'MAN', $N = $ set of vowels in 'PIN'.

VI. **Which of the following are equivalent sets?**

(1) $A = \{1\}$, $B = \{0\}$

(2) $A = \{$April, August$\}$, $B = \{$Saturday, Sunday$\}$

(3) $X = $ set of letters in the word 'LADDER' $Y = $ set of vowels in the English alphabet.

(4) $M = \{a, b, c, d\}$, $N = \{a, b, c, d, e\}$

(5) $A = $ set of letters in the word 'FREE' $B = $ set of letters in the word 'PET'

VII. **Classify as disjoint or overlapping sets :**

(1) $A = \{1, 3, 5\}$, $B = \{2, 4, 6\}$

(2) $A = \{p, q, r\}$, $B = \{r, a, t\}$

(3) $M = $ set of even number < 20, $N = $ set of square numbers less than 17.

(4) $A = $ set of multiples of 3, $B = $ set of multiples of 5.

(5) $A = $ set of letters in the word 'INK', $B = $ set of letters in the word 'BOY'.

1.7. Subsets

is a subset of

Any part of a set is also a set. The set of pupils in your class is "*a part of*" the set of all pupils in your school. If we have two sets

$$B = \{a, b, c, d, e\}, A = \{a, b, c\},$$

we see that every element of set A is contained in set B. In other words, the set A is part of the set B. Sets which are part of another set are called subsets of the original set. The set A above is a subset of the set B.

If every member of one set is also a member of a second set, then the first set is a subset of the second set.

We use the symbol $\subseteq$ to mean "is a subset of ". Thus, A is a subset of B will be written as $A \subseteq B$. In other words, A is **contained** in B.

If set A is not a subset of set B then we write $A \nsubseteq B$. Thus if $A = \{5, 7, 9\}$, $B = \{5, 7, 10, 12\}$ then $A \nsubseteq B$. This means that A is **not contained** in B.

Remarks :

(1) If A is any set, then $A \subseteq A$, *i.e.*, every set is a subset of itself.

(2) The empty set is a subset of every set. Thus if A is any set, then $\phi \subseteq A$.

1. *Every set is a subset of itself.*
2. *Null set is a subset of every set.*

For example :

(1) If $F = \{5, 7, 9\}$, $G = \{9, 11, 5, 7, 13\}$, then $F \subseteq G$.

(2) If $X = \{3, 7, 11\}$ and $Y = \{3, 7, 13\}$, then X is not a subset of Y, because not every element of X is also an element of Y. We write $X \nsubseteq Y$.

(3) If A = set of vowels and B = set of alphabets then clearly all the elements of set A viz. a, e, i, o, u are contained in set B therefore $A \subseteq B$. Note that $B \nsubseteq A$.

1.8 Proper Subset

The subsets of a given set other than itself are called proper subsets of the given set and the symbol '$\subset$' is used to denote a proper subset.

For example :

(1) If $A = \{a, b, c\}$ and $B = \{a, b\}$, $C = \{a\}$, the $B \subset A$, $C \subset A$, $C \subset B$.

(2) Let $P = \{$Prime numbers less than 10$\}$, $Q = \{2, 3\}$ then $Q \subset P$.

1.9 Number of subsets of a given set

(1) Let $A = \{a\}$. All possible subsets of A are ϕ and $\{a\}$.

Number of all possible subsets of $A = 2 = 2^1$.

(2) Let $A = \{a, b\}$. All possible subsets of A are ϕ, $\{a\}$, $\{b\}$, $\{a, b\}$.

The number of all possible subsets of $A = 4 = 2^2$.

(3) If $A = \{a, b, c\}$, then all the possible subsets of A are ϕ, $\{a, b, c\}$ $\{a, b\}$, $\{a, c\}$ $\{b, c\}$ $\{a\}$, $\{b\}$, $\{c\}$.
Note that the number of possible subsets of the set A which has 3 elements is 8, i.e., 2^3.

(4) Consider the set $A = \{1, 3, 5, 7\}$. It has 4 elements. Its possible subsets are ϕ, $\{1, 3, 5, 7\}$, $\{1, 3, 5\}$, $\{1, 3, 7\}$, $\{1, 5, 7\}$, $\{3, 5, 7\}$, $\{1, 3\}$, $\{1, 5\}$, $\{1, 7\}$, $\{3, 5\}$, $\{3, 7\}$, $\{5, 7\}$, $\{1\}$, $\{3\}$, (5), $\{7\}$. Here, the number of possible subsets is 16, i.e., 2^4.

If there are 'n' elements in a set, the total number of subsets is 2^n.

Remark : The number of proper subsets is $2^n - 1$., since the set whose subsets are being found out is itself excluded.

For example :

All possible proper subsets of the set
$A = \{a, b, c\}$ are ϕ, $\{a, b\}$, $\{a, c\}$, $\{b, c\}$, $\{a\}$, $\{b\}$, $\{c\}$.
Their number = 7 = $2^3 - 1$. Exclude the subset $\{a, b, c\}$.

1.10 Superset

If $A \subseteq B$, then set B is called the superset of set A. We express the same by writing $B \supseteq A$. {Reverse the direction of the symbol $\subseteq$}., i.e; B contains A.

For example :

Let A = {vowels}, B = {alphabets} then since all the elements of set A, viz. a, e, i, o, u are contained in set B, therefore, we have $A \subseteq B$, but $B \not\subseteq A$. Also set B is a superset of A, so, $B \supseteq A$.

1.11 Equal Sets

Let $A = \{1, 3, 5, 7\}$, $B = \{7, 3, 1, 5\}$

Since every element of A is in B, we have $A \subseteq B$. Also, since every element of B is in A, we have $B \subseteq A$. The elements of the two sets being the same it is obvious that $A = B$.

In general, whenever $A = B$ then $A \subseteq B$ and $B \subseteq A$.

1.12. Universal Set

A universal set is the set of elements from which elements may be chosen to form sets for a particular discussion. Thus the set of even numbers is a subset of the universal set of whole numbers. The set of mangoes in a fruit seller's shop is a subset of the universal set of fruits in the shop. We denote a universal set by the letter ξ. The symbol U is also used to denote universal sets.

For example :

(1) *The set of letters of the alphabet is the universal set from which the letters of any word may be chosen to form a set.*

(2) *$A = \{March, April\}$ is a subset of the universal set $\xi = \{Months of the year\}$.*

(3) *Suppose we have to solve the equation $x + 3 = 0$, x, being a positive integer.*

If the universal set were the set of integers, then the solution set would be $\{-3\}$. But, here it is given that the universal set is the set of positive integers, therefore, the solution set is ϕ.

This example shows that different universal sets may lead to different solutions.

1.13 Complement Set

(1) Consider the set of the family members of Mr. Sharma.

Mr. Sharma   Mrs. Sharma   Anil   Sudha

The set of the family members is the universal set

$$U = \{\text{Mr. Sharma, Mrs. Sharma, Anil, Sudha}\}$$

Its subsets are the set of parents A = {Mr. Sharma, Mrs. Sharma} and the set of children B = {Anil, Sudha}.

If we consider the subset A, then the set of the remaining elements of the universal set U, i.e, the set B is called the **complement set** of set A. The complement of a given set A is denoted by A'. Thus, we have A' = {Anil, Sudha}.

(2) Let the universal set be the set of all letters in the English alphabet. Let the set of vowels $V = \{a, e, i, o, u\}$ be its subset. Then the set C of the remaining letters in the alphabet, that is, consonants is the complement set of the set of vowels. $V' = C$. Also, $C' = V$.

(3) Let the universal set U be the set of all students of a school and B the set of all boys in the school. Then, the set of girls is the complement of the set of boys in the school and vice versa. $B' = G$ and $G' = B$

> *Complement of the given set is the set of elements in the Universal Set, other than the given set.*

For example :

(1) *If $\xi = \{0, 3, 6, 9, 12\}$ and $A = \{0, 6\}$, then*

    A' = set of elements of ξ other than A = {3, 9, 12}.

(2) If $\xi = \{2, 4, 6, 8, 10, 12, 14, 16\}$, $A = \{2, 4, 6\}$, B = {multiples of 3}, C = {multiples of 4}.

    Then, since $B = \{6, 12\}$, $C = \{4, 8, 12, 16\}$ therefore $A' = \{8, 10, 12, 14, 16\}$,

    $B' = \{2, 4, 8, 10, 14, 16\}$, $C' = \{2, 6, 10, 14\}$.

(3) If ξ = set of natural numbers, E = set of even natural numbers, then E' = set of odd natural numbers.

I. **Write all the possible subsets of the following sets.**

(i) {7} (ii) {5, 8} (iii) {4, 9, 13} (iv) φ.

II. **Write the proper subsets of the following sets.**

(i) {p} (ii) {3, 7} (iii) φ (iv) {p, q, r}

III. **How many subsets do the following sets have ?**

(i) A set containing 4 elements. (ii) A set of vowels. (iii) A set containing 8 elements.

IV. **How many proper subsets in all are there if a set contains**

(i) 3 elements (ii) 6 elements.

V. **Suggest a universal set for each of the following.**

(i) {Monday, Tuesday} (ii) {June, July} (iii) {apples, oranges, bananas} (iv) {a, e, i, o, u}

(v) {3, 6, 9, 12, 15}.

VI. Let $U = \{1, 2, 3, 4, 5, 6, 7, 8\}$ $A = \{5, 6, 7\}$, $B = \{1, 4, 8\}$, $C = \{1, 3, 5, 7\}$

$D = \{$prime numbers less then $10\}$. Find :

(i) A' (ii) B' (iii) C' (iv) D'

VII. Let $U = \{1, 2, 3, 4, 5\}$, $A = \{1, 3, 5\}$, $B = \{1, 4\}$

Find : (i) $n(A')$ (ii) $n(B')$.

VIII. Suppose there is co-education in your school. Find B' if $B = $ the set of boys in your school.

IX. If $\xi = \{$colours of rainbow$\}$ $A = \{$Violet, indigo, red$\}$, find A'.

X. If $\xi = \{$alphabets$\}$, $A = \{$consonants$\}$, find A'.

(Chapter Review)

I. **Answer true or false :**

1. $\{a\} \subset \{a, b\}$ **2.** $\{1, 3, 5\} \subset$ set of odd numbers. **3.** $\{a, c\} \subset \{a, b, d\}$ **4.** $\{p, q, r\} \subseteq \{q, r, p\}$

5. $\phi \in \{p, q, r\}$ **6.** $\{p, i, n\} \subset \{n, i, b\}$ **7.** $\{\ \} \not\subset \{0\}$ **8.** $0 \in \phi$

9. $\{0\} \subset \{1\}$ **10.** $\{5, 8, 11\} \subset \{8, 11, 5\}$ **11.** $\phi \not\subset \{x, y\}$

12. The set of even numbers $\subset$ the set of whole numbers

II. **Answer whether the given statement is true or false :**

1. {Natural numbers} $\subseteq$ {whole numbers} **2.** {vowels} $\subseteq$ {consonants}

3. Set of vowels in 'CONTINENT $\subseteq$ {vowels}. **4.** {Triangles} $\subseteq$ {Quadrilaterals}

5. Set of consonants in 'WORLD' $\subseteq$ Set of letters in 'WELDER'. **6.** {Squares} $\subseteq$ {Rectangles}

7. {Tokyo, London, Chennai} $\subseteq$ {world capitals}

8. Set of vowels in 'PARROT' = set of vowels in 'SPARROW'.

III. **Let** $A = \{1, 2, 3, 4\}$. **List the subsets as directed.**

1. All the subsets with one element. **2.** All the subsets with two elements.

3. All the subsets with three elements. **4.** All the subsets of A.

IV. **How many subsets do the following sets have ?**

1. $\{a, b\}$ **2.** $\{x, y, z\}$ **3.** $\{0, 3, 6, 9\}$

4. Set of letters in 'MUMBAI' [**Hint.** The set is $\{M, U, B, A, I\}$. Recall that each element of a set is written once and only once.

5. Set of letters in 'AUSTRALIA'.

V. List the proper subsets of the following sets :
  1. {5, 10}   **2.** {7}   **3.** Set of letters of 'BOOK'.

VI. Let ξ = set of first 10 natural numbers. List the following subsets of ξ.
  1. Set of prime numbers.   **2.** Set of composite numbers.   **3.** Set of odd numbers.
  4. Set of even numbers.   **5.** Set of multiples of 2.   **6.** Set of multiples of 5.
  7. Set of multiples of 4.   **8.** Set of multiples of 12.

VII. Name the following subsets :
  1. Vegetables in {carrots, beans, peaches, pears, bread}
  2. Let D = set of digits of the number 34013. List the subsets of D of the numbers having 2 digits.

VIII. Match the universal set on the right to the set on the left.
  1. {0, 3, 6, 9, 12, 15} A = {odd numbers}
  2. {1, 3, 5, 7, 9, 11} B = {mountains}
  3. {pine, oak, deodar} C = {fractional numbers}
  4. {Himalayas, Alps, Andes} D = {trees}
  5. $\left\{\dfrac{1}{3}, \dfrac{1}{5}, \dfrac{1}{9}, \dfrac{1}{4}, \dfrac{1}{11}\right\}$. E = {multiples of 3}

IX. Solve the following equations
  1. $x - 3 = 0$, x being a whole number.   **2.** $x + 1 = 0$, x being a positive integer.
  3. $7x - 14 = 0$, x being a whole number.   **4.** $3x + 7 = 0$, x being a whole number.

X. Let ξ = {1, 2, 3, 4, 5, 6, 7, 8}, A = {5, 6, 7}, B = {1, 4, 8}, C = {1, 3, 5, 7}, D = { 2, 4, 6, 8},
  E = {1, 2, 3, 4, 5, 6, 7}, find :
  (i) A' (ii) B' (iii) C' (iv) D' (v) E' (vi) $n(A')$ (vii) $n(C')$ $(viii)$ $n(E')$.

ANSWERS

EXERCISE 1 (a)

I. **(1)** {January, February, March}   **(2)** {2, 3, 5, 7,}   **(3)** {1, 3, 5, 7}   **(4)** {2, 4, 6, 8}   **(5)** {s, c, h, o, l}
  (6) {10, 20, 30 ------}   **(7)** {∠A, ∠B, ∠C}   **(8)** {4, 6}

II. **(1)** The set of odd numbers less than 8.
  (2) The set of whole numbers less than 6.
  (3) The set of non-zero multiples of 5 less than 26.
  (4) The set of days of the week beginning with the letter T.
  (5) The set of prime numbers less than 12.
  (6) The set of square numbers.

III. **1.** A = {2, 4, 6, 8, 10}   **2.** B = {February}   **3.** C = {1, 4, 9, 16}   **4.** D = {2}   **5.** E = {a, e, i, o, u}

IV. **(1)** {$x|x$ is a prime number less than 20}   **(2)** {$x|x = 2n + 1, n \in N$ and $1 \le n \le 12$}
  (3) {$x : x = n^2, n \in N$ and $n \le 8$}   **(4)** {$x : x$ is a month having 31 days}
  (5) {$x : x$ is non-zero factor of 36}   **(6)** {$x : x = n^3, n \in N$ and $1 \le n \le 8$}
  (7) {$x : x = \dfrac{1}{n+1}, n \in N$ and $2 \le n \le 9$}

V. **(1)** ∈   **(2)** ∉   **(3)** ∈   **(4)** ∈   **(5)** ∈   **(6)** ∉   **(7)** ∈   **(8)** ∉

EXERCISE 1 (b)

I. **(1)** Finite   **(2)** Infinite   **(3)** Finite   **(4)** Infinite
II. **(1)** Empty   **(2)** Empty   **(3)** Singleton   **(4)** Singleton
III. **(1)** Infinite   **(2)** Finite   **(3)** Finite   **(4)** Infinite   **(5)** Infinite   **(6)** Empty   **(7)** Empty   **(8)** Infinite
  (9) Singleton   **(10)** Singleton

IV. (1) 3   (2) 3   (3) 1   (4) 3   (5) 7   (6) 2   (7) 0   (8) 3

V. (1) Unequal   (2) Equal   (3) Unequal [Note that 0 is considered as neither positive nor negative].
       (4) Equal   (5) Unequal   (6) Unequal

VI. (1) Equivalent   (2) Equivalent   (3) Equivalent   (4) Non-equivalent   (5) Equivalent

VII. (1) Disjoint   (2) Overlapping   (3) Overlapping   (4) Overlapping   (5) Disjoint

EXERCISE 1 (c)

I. (*i*) φ, {7}   (*ii*) φ, {5}, {8}, {5, 8}   (*iii*) φ {4}, {9}, {13}, {4, 9}, {9, 13}, {4, 13} {4, 9, 13}   (*iv*) φ

II. (*i*) φ   (*ii*) φ {3}, {7}   (*iii*) None   (*iv*) φ {p}, {q}, {r}, {p, q}, {q, r}, {p, r}

III. (*i*) 16.   (*ii*) 32   (*iii*) 256

IV (*i*) 7   (*ii*) 63

V. (*i*) {days of a week}   (*ii*) {Months of the year}   (*iii*) {fruits}   (*iv*) {letters of the alphabet}   (*v*) {multiples of 3}

VI. (*i*) {1, 2, 3, 4, 8}   (*ii*) {2, 3, 5, 6, 7}   (*iii*) {2, 4, 6, 8}   (*iv*) {1, 4, 6, 8}

VII. (*i*) 2   (*ii*) 3   **VIII.** The set of girls   **IX.** {blue, green, yellow, orange}   **X.** {vowels}

EXERCISE 1 (d)

I. 1. True   2. True   3. False   4. True   5. False
    6. False   7. False   8. False   9. False   10. False
   11. False   12. True

II. 1. True   2. False   3. True   4. False   5. True
    6. True   7. False   8. True

III. 1. {1}, {2}, {3}, {4}.   2. {1, 2}, {1, 3}, {1, 4}, {2, 3}, {2, 4}, {3, 4}   3. {1, 2, 3}, {1, 2, 4}, {2, 3, 4}, {3, 4,
   4. φ, {1}, {2}, {3}, {4}, {1, 2}, {1, 3} {1, 4}, {2, 3}, {2, 4}, {3, 4} {1, 2, 3}, {1, 2, 4}, {2, 3, 4}, {3, 4, 1}, {1, 2, 3,

IV. 1. $2^2 = 4$ 2. $2^3 = 8$ 3. $2^4 = 16$ 4. $2^5 = 32$ 5. $2^7 = 128$

V. 1. φ, {5}, {10}   2. φ   3. φ, {b}, {0}, {k}, {b, 0}, {b, k}

VI. 1. {2, 3, 5, 7}   2. {4, 6, 8, 9, 10}   3. {1, 3, 5, 7, 9}   4. {2, 4, 6, 8, 10}   5. {2, 4, 6, 8, 10}
    6. {5, 10}   7. {4, 8}   8. φ

VII. 1. {carrots, beans}   2. {34}, {40}, {13}, {43}, {31}, {41}, {30}, {14}, {10}

VIII.   1. 1 → E,   2. 2 → A,   3. 3 → D,   4. 4 → B   5. 5 → C

IX. 1. $x = 3$ 2. φ   3. $x = 2$.   4. φ

X. (*i*) {1, 2, 3, 4, 8}   (*ii*) {2, 3, 5, 6, 7}   (*iii*) {2, 4, 6, 8}   (*iv*) {1, 3, 5, 7}   (*v*) {8}
    (*vi*) 5   (*vii*) 4   (*viii*) 1

2. Operations on Sets and Venn Diagrams

You studied the two operations of union and intersection in class 6. We help you to revise and strengthen your understanding of the two topics further.

2.1. Union of Sets

The union of two sets *is the set whose elements occur either in one set or in the other (or in both the sets.)*

The symbol $A \cup B$ is used to name the union of set A and set B. It is read as "A union B". We write $C = A \cup B$.

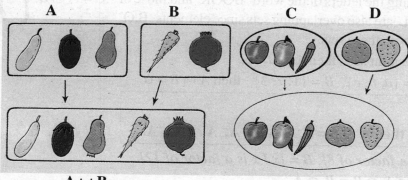

Examples :

1. Let $A = \{1, 3, 5\}$, $B = \{0, 2, 4, 6\}$. Then $A \cup B = \{0, 1, 2, 3, 4, 5, 6\}$.
2. Let $A = \{a, b, c\}$, $B = \{b, c, d, e\}$. Then $A \cup B = \{a, b, c, d, e\}$

   {Include common elements in A and B only once in $A \cup B$}

3. Let A = set of letters of the word 'BOOK'.

   B = set of letters of the word 'BANK'

   and C = set of letters of the word 'INDIAN', then

   $A = \{B, O, K\}$, $B = \{B, A, N, K\}$, $C = \{I, N, D, A\}$

   So, $A \cup B = \{B, O, K, A, N\}$, $B \cup A = \{B, A, N, K, O\}$

   $B \cup C = \{B, A, N, K\} \cup \{I, N, D, A\} = \{B, A, N, K, I, D\}$.

   Since, $A \cup B$ and $B \cup A$ contain the same elements, we have **$A \cup B = B \cup A$.**

4. Let $\xi = \{1, 2, 3, 4, 5, 6, 7, 8, 9, 10\}$ be the universal set and $A = \{1, 3, 5, 7, 9\}$, $B = \{2, 3, 4, 9, 10\}$ be its subsets, then

   $A' = \{2, 4, 6, 8, 10\}$, $B' = \{1, 5, 6, 7, 8\}$

   $A' \cup B = \{2, 4, 6, 8, 10\} \cup \{2, 3, 4, 9, 10\} = \{2, 3, 4, 6, 8, 9, 10\}$

   $A \cup B' = \{1, 3, 5, 7, 9\} \cup \{1, 5, 6, 7, 8\}\quad = \{1, 3, 5, 6, 7, 8, 9\}$

   $A' \cup B' = \{2, 4, 6, 8, 10\} \cup \{1, 5, 6, 7, 8\}\quad = \{1, 2, 4, 5, 6, 7, 8, 10\}$

Remarks :

  If A is any set then   1. $A \cup \phi = A$ 2. $A \cup \xi = \xi$ 3. $A \cup A = A$

2.2 Intersection of Sets

The intersection of two sets *is the set whose elements are common to both the sets.*

Set C is the set that contains members common to set A and set B.

Set C is the **intersection** of set A and set B. In symbols, we write

$$C = A \cap B$$

For example :

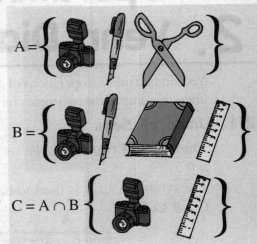

$A = \{\ \}$

$B = \{\ \}$

$C = A \cap B \{\ \}$

Let $A = \{f, l, o, r\}$, $B = \{f, l, o, w, e, r\}$

then $A \cap B = \{f, l, o, r\}$.

Sets which have at least one element in common are called **overlapping** or **intersecting sets.**

Thus If $P = \{2, 4, 6, 8\}$, $Q = \{3, 6, 9, 12\}$, Then $P \cap Q = \{6\}$ and P and Q are overlapping sets.

The sets containing the letters of the word 'BOOK' and those of the word 'BOWL' are also overlapping sets since elements 'B,O' are common to both these sets.

If A and B are disjoint sets, then $A \cap B = \phi$.

For example : If $A = \{a, b, c\}$, $B = \{1, 2, 3\}$ then $A \cap B = \phi$.

Remarks :

If A is any set, then $A \cap \phi = \phi$, $A \cap \xi = A$, $A \cap A = A$.

Ex. 1. *Let A = {x|x is a factor of 8}, B = {x / x is a factor of 12}.*
Then prove that $A \cap B = B \cap A$.

Sol. $A = \{1, 2, 4, 8\}$, $B = \{1, 2, 4, 6, 12\}$

$A \cap B = \{1, 2, 4, 8\} \cap \{1, 2, 4, 6, 12\} = \{1, 2, 4\}$

$B \cap A = \{1, 2, 4, 6, 12\} \cap \{1, 2, 4, 8\} = \{1, 2, 4\}$

$\therefore A \cap B = B \cap A$

Ex. 2. *Let $\xi = \{1, 2, 3, 4\}$, A = {1, 2}, B = {1, 3} and C = {1, 4}*

  (a)   **(i)**   *Find $A' \cap B$ and $A \cup B'$.*

      (ii)   *$(A \cup B)' = A' \cap B'$*

      (iii) *$(A \cap B)' = A' \cup B'$*

      (iv) *$n(A) + n(B) = n(A \cup B) + n(A \cap B)$.*

Sol. **(a)** (i) $A' = \{3, 4\}$ $\therefore A' \cap B = \{3, 4\} \cap \{1, 3\} = \{3\}$.

      $B' = \{2, 4\}$ $\therefore A \cup B' = \{1, 2\} \cup \{2, 4\} = \{1, 2, 4\}$.

    (ii) $A \cup B = \{1, 2\} \cup \{1, 3\} = \{1, 2, 3\}$ $\therefore (A \cup B)' = \{4\}$

        $A' \cap B' = \{3, 4\} \cap \{2, 4\} = \{4\}$

      $\therefore (A \cup B)' = A' \cap B'$.

    (iii) $(A \cap B) = \{1, 2\} \cap \{1, 3\} = \{1\}$ $\therefore (A \cap B)' = \{2, 3, 4\}$

      $A' \cup B' = \{3, 4\} \cup \{2, 4\} = \{2, 3, 4\}$

      $\therefore (A \cap B)' = A' \cup B'$.

    (iv) $n(A) = n\{1, 2\} = 2$, $n(B) = n\{1, 3\} = 2$

      $n(A \cup B) = n\{1, 2, 3\} = 3$, $n(A \cap B) = n\{1\} = 1$

      $\therefore n(A) + n(B) = 2 + 2 = 4$, $n(A \cup B) + n(A \cap B) = 3 + 1 = 4$

      Hence, $n(A) + n(B) = n(A \cup B) + n(A \cap B)$.

1. Let A = {2, 4, 7, 11}, B = {3, 5}, C = {2, 4, 6, 8, 10}, D = {1, 9, 11}, find
   (i) A ∪ B (ii) A ∪ C (iii) A ∪ D (iv) B ∪ C (v) B ∪ D (vi) C ∪ D

2. Let P = {a, b, c}, Q = φ, what is P ∪ Q ?

3. Let L = {letters 'BOAT}, M = {letters of 'BROWN'}. Write = L ∪ M.

4. Let E = {6, 8, 10, 12,}   F = {2, 4, 6, 8}   G = {7, 8, 9, 10}
   Prove that :
   (i) E ∪ F = F ∪ E   (ii) F ∪ G = G ∪ F   (iii) E ∪ G = G ∪ E

5. **Let ξ = set of factors of 36**, A = set of factors of 6, B = set of factors of 18 find :
   (i) A ∪ ξ   (ii) B ∪ ξ   (iii) A' ∪ B   (iv) A ∪ B'   (v) A' ∪ B'

6. List the elements of A ∩ B if
   (i) A = { 1, 2, 3, }, B = {2, 3, 5, 7}   (ii) A = {1, 3, 5, 7}, B = {2, 3, 5, 8}
   (iii) A = {multiples of 4 less than 20}, B = {multiples of 6 less than 20}
   (iv) A = {rectangle, square}, B = {rhombus, square}   (v) A = {1, 3, 5}, B = {2, 4, 6}
   (vi) A = {letters of INDIA}, B = {letters of INK}

7. Given ξ = {1, 2, 3, 4, 5, 6, 7, 8}, A = {1, 2, 3, 6}, B = {1, 2, 4, 7} and C = {1, 3, 5, 7}, list the elements of
   (i) A'   (ii) B'   (iii) A' ∩ B'   (iv) (A ∩ B)'   (v) (A ∩ C)'   (vi) (B ∩ C)'

2.3 Venn Diagrams

Sets can be shown pictorially on a Venn diagram. The universal set is usually represented by a rectangle and its subsets are shown as circles, ovals etc. Within the rectangle, the elements of the set are written inside the curve. If the number of elements is large we can write the letter name outside the curve and a brief description inside.

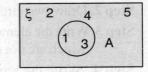

Type 1. Given : A universal set and its subset.

Ex. 1. *Let ξ = {1, 2, 3, 4, 5}, A = {1, 3}. Illustrate this information on a Venn diagram.*

Sol.

Step 1 : Draw a rectangle to represent the universal set.

Step 2 : Draw a circle (or any closed curve) inside the rectangle to represent A.

Step 3 : Write the elements of A (here 1 and 3} inside the circle and the remaining elements of ξ (here 2, 4 and 5) outside it.

Fig. Ex. 1

Remark : Clearly, the complement set A' = {2, 4, 5} will be represented by the shaded region.

Type 2. Given : A universal set and its intersecting subsets

Ex. 2. *If ξ = {1, 2, 3, 4, 5, 6}, A = {1, 3, 5} and B = {2, 3, 5}, illustrate this information on a Venn diagram.*

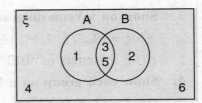

Sol.   Step 1. Draw a rectangle to represent the universal set.

Step 2. Since A and B are overlapping sets, draw two overlapping circles.

Step 3. In the common portion of the overlapping circles write the elements common to both A and B, i.e. 3 and 5.

Fig. Ex. 2

Step 4. In the remaining portions of circles A and B, write the remaining elements of sets A and B, viz., 1 in circle A and 2 in circle B.

Step 5. Two elements, viz., 4 and 6 remain in the universal set which are not in set A or B. Write them in the rectangle anywhere outside these circles.

Ex. 3. *Let ξ = {1, 2, 3, 4, 5, 6, 7, 8}, A = {1, 3, 5}, B = {1, 3, 4, 6} C= {2, 6}. Illustrate this information on a Venn diagram.*

Sol. The Venn diagram is as shown.

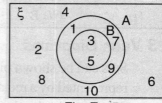

Fig. Ex. 3

Type 3. Given : A universal set and its disjoint subsets.

Ex. 4. *Let ξ = {1, 2, 3, 4, 5, 6, 7, 8, 9, 10} A = {1, 3, 5}, B = {2, 4, 6}. Illustrate this information on a Venn diagram.*

Sol. Step 1. Draw a rectangle to represent the universal set.

Step 2. Draw two non-intersecting circles to represent the disjoint sets A and B.

Step 3. Write the elements of A and B in their respective circles.

Step 4. Write the remaining elements of ξ in the rectangle outside the circles. The Venn diagram is show below.

Fig. Ex. 4

Type 4. Given : A universal set and its two subsets, one of which is a subset of the other set.

Ex. 5. *Let ξ = {1, 2, 3, 4, 5, 6, 7, 8, 9, 10}, A = {1, 3, 5, 7, 9}, B = {3, 5}. Illustrate this information on a Venn diagram.*

Sol. Step 1. Draw a rectangle to represent the universal set.

Step 2. Draw two circles one within the other to show B ⊂ A.

Step 3. Write the elements of B inside the inner circle and the remaining elements of A which are not in B, inside the outer circle and outside the inner circle.

Step 4. Write the remaining elements of ξ which are neither in A, nor in B in the rectangle outside these circles.

Fig. Ex. 5

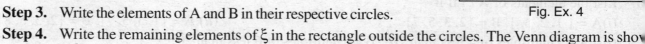

EXERCISE 2 (b)

1. **Show each group of sets on a Venn diagram.**

    (i) ξ = {4, 5, 6, 7, 8}, A = {5, 6}   (ii) ξ = {Set of vowels}, A = {Vowels in 'Hare'}

    (iii) ξ = {letters in 'Chennai'}, A = {letters in 'Chin'}

2. **Show each group of sets on a Venn diagram**

    (i) ξ = {1, 2, 3, 4, 5, 6}, A = {1, 2, 6}, B = {2, 4, 6} (ii) ξ = {1, 2, 3, 4, 5, 6, 7}, A = {1, 3, 4}, B = {2, 3, 6}

    (iii) ξ = {letters of 'BANGALORE'}, A = {letters of 'BEAR'}, B = {letters of 'NEAR'}

    (iv) ξ = {1, 2, 3, 4, 5, 6, 7, 8, 9, 10}, A = {1, 4, 7, 8}, B = {2, 4, 7, 9}, C = {2, 3, 9}

    (v) ξ = {First ten letters of the alphabet}, A = {letters of 'BED'}, B = {letters of 'FACE'}
       C = {letters of 'FIG'}

3. **Show on a Venn diagram**

    (i) ξ = {2, 3, 5, 7, 11, 13, 17, 19}, A = {2, 5, 7}, B = {3, 11}

    (ii) ξ = {letters of 'HELICOPTER'}, A = {letters of 'HEEL'} B = {letters of 'TOP'}

4. **Show each group on a Venn diagram**

    (i) ξ = {3, 6, 9, 12, 15, 18, 21} A = {3, 6, 9, 12, 15}, B = {3, 6, 9}

    (ii) ξ = {letters of 'EAGLE'}, A = {letters of 'AGE'}, B = {letters of 'EGG'}

    (iii) ξ = {letters of 'MATHEMATICS'}, A = {letters of 'THAMES'}, B = {letters of 'TEA'}

Type 5. Finding the sets from the given Venn diagrams.

Ex. 6. *Describe the sets represented by the shaded regions for each diagrams.*

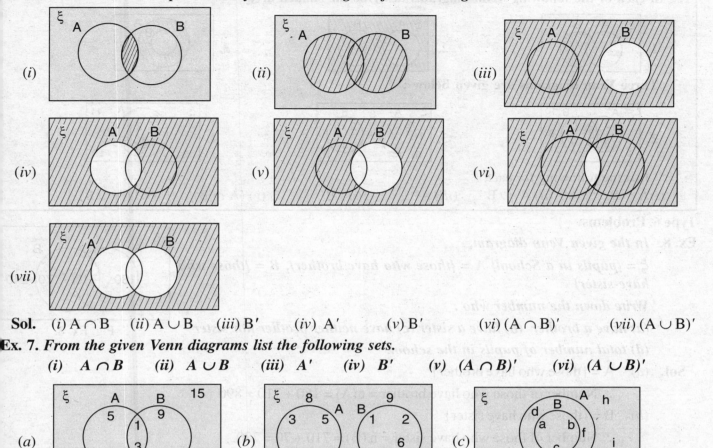

Sol. (i) $A \cap B$ (ii) $A \cup B$ (iii) B' (iv) A' (v) B' (vi) $(A \cap B)'$ (vii) $(A \cup B)'$

Ex. 7. *From the given Venn diagrams list the following sets.*

    (i) $A \cap B$ (ii) $A \cup B$ (iii) A' (iv) B' (v) $(A \cap B)'$ (vi) $(A \cup B)'$

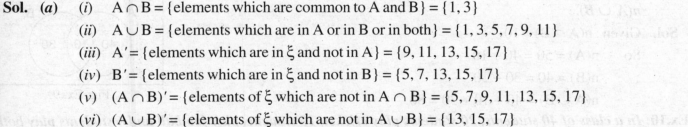

Fig. Ex. 7.

Sol. **(a)**   (i) $A \cap B = \{$elements which are common to A and B$\} = \{1, 3\}$

       (ii) $A \cup B = \{$elements which are in A or in B or in both$\} = \{1, 3, 5, 7, 9, 11\}$

       (iii) $A' = \{$elements which are in ξ and not in A$\} = \{9, 11, 13, 15, 17\}$

       (iv) $B' = \{$elements which are in ξ and not in B$\} = \{5, 7, 13, 15, 17\}$

       (v) $(A \cap B)' = \{$elements of ξ which are not in $A \cap B\} = \{5, 7, 9, 11, 13, 15, 17\}$

       (vi) $(A \cup B)' = \{$elements of ξ which are not in $A \cup B\} = \{13, 15, 17\}$

    (b)   (i) $A \cap B = \phi$ since there are no elements of ξ common to A and B.

       (ii) $A \cup B = \{3, 5, 7, 11, 1, 2, 4, 6\}$ (iii) $A' = \{1, 2, 4, 6, 8, 9, 10, 12\}$

       (iv) $B' = \{3, 5, 7, 11, 8, 9, 10, 12\}$ (v) $(A \cap B)' = \xi$, since $A \cap B = \phi$.

       (vi) $(A \cup B)' = \{$elements of ξ while are not in $A \cup B\} = \{8, 9, 10, 12\}$

    (c)   (i) $A \cap B = \{a, b, c\}$ (ii) $A \cup B = \{a, b, c, d, e, f\}$

       (iii) $A' = \{g, h, i, j, k\}$ (iv) $B' = \{d, e, f, g, h, i, j, k\}$

       (v) $(A \cap B)' = \{d, e, f, g, h, i, j, k\}$ (vi) $(A \cup B)' = \{g, h, i, j, k\}$

EXERCISE 2 (c)

1. **In each of the following Venn diagrams describe the shaded area.**

    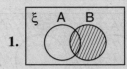 1.

    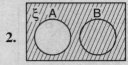 2.

    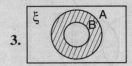 3.

    Three Venn diagrams are given below :

    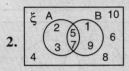 2.

    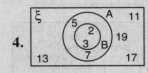 3.

    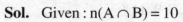 4.

    List the following for each :

    (*i*) A ∩ B   (*ii*) A ∪ B   (*iii*) A′   (*iv*) B′   (*v*) (A ∩ B)′   (*vi*) (A ∪ B)′

Type 6. Problems.

Ex. 8. *In the given Venn diagram,*

ξ = {pupils in a School} A = {those who have brother}, B = {those who have sister}

Write down the number who :

(a) have a brother (b) have a sister (c) have neither brother nor sister

(d) total number of pupils in the school.

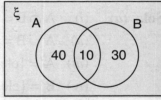

Fig. Ex. 8.

Sol. (*a*)   A = {those who have brother}

     ∴ Number of those who have brother = n(A) = 180 + 710 = 890

   (*b*)   B = {those who have sister}

     ∴ Number of those who have sister = n (B) = 710 + 70 = 780.

   (*c*)   Number of those who have neither brother nor sister = 240.

   (*d*)   Total number of pupils = 180 + 710 + 70 + 240 = 1200.

Ex. 9. *If n(A) = 50, n(B) = 40 and n(A ∩ B) = 10, draw a Venn diagram to find n(A ∪ B).*

Sol. Given : n(A ∩ B) = 10

   So   n(A) = 50 = 40 + 10

        n(B) = 40 = 30 + 10

   ∴   n(A ∪ B) = 40 + 10 + 30 = 80.

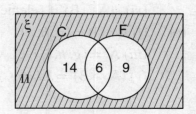

Fig. Ex. 9.

Ex.10: *In a class of 40 students, 20 students play cricket, 15 students play football and 6 students play both the games. Draw a Venn diagram and find the number of students who play.*

(i) either cricket or football   (ii) neither cricket nor football

Sol. Let ξ = all students of the class, C = students who play cricket, F = students who play football.

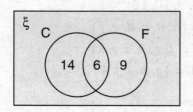

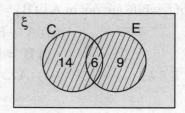

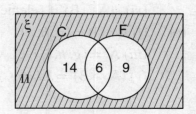

Since 6 students play both games, these are intersecting sets. Write 6 in the common region. Then $20 - 6$, i.e., 14 will be written in the remaining region of C and $15 - 6$ i.e., 9 will be written in the remaining region of F.

(i) Number of students who play either cricket or football (shown by shaded region) $= 14 + 6 + 9 = 29$.

(ii) Number of students who do not play any of the two games (shown by shaded region) $= 40 - (14 + 6 + 9)$
$$= 40 - 29 = 11.$$

EXERCISE 2 (d)

. In the given Venn diagram,
$\xi = \{\text{pupils in a class}\}$, $A = \{\text{pupils who play cricket}\}$, $B = \{\text{pupils who play hockey}\}$.
How many pupils :

(a) are there in the class.   (b) play cricket   (c) play both cricket and hockey.

(d) play hockey.   (e) play neither cricket nor hockey ?

. If $n(\xi) = 40$, $n(A) = 28$, $n(B) = 19$, and $n(A \cap B) = 14$, draw a Venn diagram to find :

(a) $n(A \cup B)$ (b) $n(A \cup B)'$ (c) $n(A \cap B')$ (d) $(A' \cap B)$.

. In a sample of 200 people, 150 liked tea, 75 liked coffee and 11 liked neither. How many people liked both tea and coffee ?

EXERCISE 2 (e) (Miscellaneous)

. **Let $\xi = \{1, 2, 3, 4, 5, 6, 7, 8\}$, $A = \{5, 6, 7\}$, $B = \{1, 4, 8\}$, $C = \{1, 3, 5, 7\}$, $D = \{2, 4, 6, 8\}$,**

$E = \{1, 2, 3, 4, 5, 6, 7\}$ Find :

(a) (i) A' (ii) B' (iii) C' (iv) D' (v) E'

(b) (i) $A' \cup B'$ (ii) $A' \cap B'$ (iii) $B' \cup C'$ (iv) $B' \cap C'$ (v) $C' \cup D'$ (vi) $C' \cap D'$

(vii) $D' \cap E'$ (viii) $(A \cup B)'$

. **For the sets in 1 above verify that :**

(i) $A \cup A' = \xi$ (ii) $A \cap A' = \phi$ (iii) $(A \cup B)' = A' \cap B'$

(iv) $n(B') = n(\xi) - n(B)$ (v) $(B \cap C)' = B' \cup C'$ (vi) $n(D) + n(D') = n(\xi)$

. **Let $A = \{\text{letters of CONTINENT}\}$ and $B = \{\text{letters of COUNTRY}\}$,**

Find : 1. $A \cup B$ 2. $A \cap B$ 3. Verify that : $n(A) + n(B) = n(A \cup B) + n(A \cap B)$.

. **Let $\xi = \{x / x \in N, x \le 20\}$,**

$A = \{x \text{ is a multiple of } 2, x < 20\}$, $B = \{x/x \text{ is a multiple of } 3, x < 20\}$, $C = \{x/x \text{ is prime, } x < 20\}$

$D = \{x/x \text{ is a perfect square number, } x < 20\}$,

Verify that : (i) $C \cap D = D \cap C$ (ii) $A \cap A' = \phi$ (iii) $D \cup D' = \xi$

(iv) $(A \cup B)' = A' \cap B'$ (v) $(B \cap C)' = B' \cup C'$ (vi) $n(C \cup D) = n(C) + n(D) - n(C \cap D)$.

. **Use a similar diagram to illustrate by shading the region.**

(i) $A \cup B$ (ii) $(A \cap B)'$ (iii) $A' \cap B'$

. Draw a Venn diagram to show the relationship between the following sets :

$\xi = \{\text{Integers}\}$, $A = \{\text{Natural numbers}\}$ and $B = \{\text{Whole numbers}\}$.

. If $n(\xi) = 1000$, $n(A) = 550$, $n(B) = 530$, and $n(A \cap B) = 385$, draw a Venn diagram to find :

(a) $n(A \cup B)$ (b) $n(A \cup B)'$.

LOOKING BACK
Summary of Key Facts (Chapter 1, 2)

1. A **set** is a well defined collection of objects.

2. Each thing in a set is called a **member** or an **element** of the set.

3. The symbol '∈' is used to denote '*is a member of*' or '*belongs to*'. Thus, if x is a member of set A, we write $x ∈$ A.

4. If x does not belong to set A, we write $x ∉$ A.

5. Sets are specified by any of the following methods :

   (*i*) **Description method** : By writing the description in braces, viz. A = { colours of rainbow }, B = {vowels}, etc.,

   (*ii*) **Roster method** : By listing the names of the elements in braces,

   > For example, the set of letters in the word 'NAINITAL' is written as A = {N, A, I,T, L}.

   Repetition is not done while listing the elements.

   (*iii*) **Set-builder form :** A set is specified in the form {x : statement of property which x satisfies}.

   For example, {$x \,|\, x$ is a prime number, $x < 20$}.

6. A set containing only one element is called a **singleton set**.

7. Two sets are called **overlapping sets**, if, they have at least one element in common. Thus, A and B are overlapping sets if A = {letters of 'TEN'}, B = {letters of 'TEAR'},

8. If two sets have no elements in common, they are called **disjoint sets**. For example, if A = {1, 3, 5}, B = {2, 4,6}, then A and B are disjoint sets.

9. A set which contains a definite number of objects is called a **finite set,** otherwise it is called an **infinite set**.

10. A set which contains no elements is called *the* **empty set**. It is denoted by the symbol φ or { }. We may write φ = { }.

11. Sets containing equal number of elements are called **equivalent sets**. Sets containing the same elements are called **equal sets**.

    For example, if A = {3, 5, 7, 9}, B = {7, 5, 3, 9}, C = {1, 3, 4, 5} then A and B are equal sets, while A and C, B and C are equivalent sets.

12. The number of members in a set is called the **cardinal number** of the set and is denoted by the symbol **n (A)**. Thus, if A = {p, q, r, s}, then n (A) = 4.

13. If every member of a set A is also a member of a second set B, then the set A is called a **subset** of set B. This is expressed by writing A ⊆ B.

    If a set E is a part of a set F, then the set E is called a **proper subset** of set F. This is expressed by writing E ⊂ F.

    For example, If A = {1, 2, 3, 4, 5}, B = {2, 4, 5,}, C = {2, 4}, D = {5, 4, 3, 1,2}, then B ⊂ A, C ⊂ B, A ⊆ D, D ⊆ A.

    The symbol ⊈ is used to denote '*is not a subset of*' and to ⊄ to denote ' *not a proper subset of*'.

14. If A ⊆ B, then B is called the **superset** of A. It is indicated by writing B ⊇ A.

15. (1) Every set is a subset of itself, i.e. A ⊆ A.

    (2) The Null set is a subset of every set, i.e. φ ⊆ A, where A is any set.

16. The total number of subsets of a set containing n elements is 2^n. The total number of proper subsets is $2^n - 1$.

    For example, if A = {1, 3, 5, 7, 9}, then it has 2^5, i.e. 32 subsets. The number of proper subsets is $2^5 - 1$, i.e. 32 − 1 = 31.

17. A **universal set** is the set of elements from which elements may be chosen for a particular discussion. It is denoted by the symbol 'ξ' or U.

18. Let ξ be a universal set and A is its any subset. Then the **complement** of the set A is the set consisting of all elements of ξ which do not belong to A. It is denoted by A′ or $\overline{A}$ and is read as '*complement of set A*'.

Thus, if ξ = {letters of CONTINENT} = {c,o, n, t, i, e} and A ={c, o, t}, then A′ = {n, i, e}.

19. The **union** of two sets A and B, denoted by A ∪ B, is the set of all those elements which are either in A or in B or in both.

For example, if A = {a,b, c,d}, B = {e, f, g}, C = {a, c, e, f}, then

A ∪ B = {a, b, c, d, e, f, g}, A ∪ C = {a, b, c, d, e, f}, B ∪ C = {e, f, g, a, c}.

| A ∪ φ = A, A ∪ ξ = ξ |
| A ∪ A = A, A ∪ A′ = ξ |

20. The **intersection** of two sets A and B, denoted by A ∩ B, is the set of elements common to A and B.

For example, if A = {days of the week}, B = {Tuesday, Wednesday} then A ∩ B = {Tuesday, Wednesday}. In this case, A and B are overlapping sets. If E = {Even numbers < 20}, F = {odd numbers < 20} then E ∩ F = φ. In this case, E and F are disjoint sets.

| A ∩ ξ = A, A ∩ A = A |
| A ∩ φ = φ, A ∩ A′ = φ |

21. A ∪ B = B ∪ A   **22.** A ∩ B = B ∩ A   **23.** (A ∪ B)′ = A′ ∩ B′   **24.** (A ∩ B)′ = A′ ∪ B′

25. **Venn Diagrams** are diagrams used to express various ideas about sets and relationships between them. Usually, a universal set is represented by a rectangle and its subsets by closed figures such as circles or ovals.

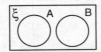

UNIT REVIEW – 1

1. **Write the following sets in (i) Description form, (ii) Roster form, (iii) Set-Builder form ;**

   (*a*)   The set of prime numbers less than 20.

   (*b*)   The set of integers which lie between – 4 and 3, both inclusive.

   (*c*)   The set of factors of 24.

   (*d*)   The set of whole numbers which are multiples of 5 and less than 41.

2. **Write the following sets in Roster form and also in Description form.**

   (*i*) $\{x : x = n^2, n \in \mathbf{N} \text{ and } n \le 8\}$.   (*ii*) $\{y \mid y = 3x - 7, x \in \mathbf{W} \text{ and } x < 4\}$.

   (*iii*)   {x : x is a letter in the word POPULATION}.

3. **State which of the following are equivalent sets ?**

   (*a*)   A = { a, e, i, o, u}, B = {1, 2, 3, 4, 5}.   (*b*)   A = {letters of INDIA}, B = {letters of IDEA}.

   (*c*)   A = { Months having 30 days}, B = {letters of TEA}.

4. Let A = {vowels in the word SECULAR}, B = {vowels in the word PEANUT}. Are the two sets equal ?

5. Let A = {Days of a week}, B = {x | x ∈ N, x ≤ 7}. Is A = B? Are A and B equivalent sets?

6. **Answer true or false :**

   (1) All equal sets are equivalent sets.   (2)   All equivalent sets are equal sets.

   Illustrate your answer is each case by giving an example.

7. **State which of the following is the empty set ?**

   (*a*)   {prime numbers which are even}   (*b*)   {odd numbers divisible by 2}

8. **Find which pairs of sets are disjoint and which are overlapping :**

   (*i*)   A = {months of a year}, B = {months whose names start with J}.

   (*ii*)   A = {letters of MUMBAI}, B = {letters of MADAM}.

   (*iii*)   A = {Prime numbers}, B = {Composite Numbers}.

9. **Write all the subsets of the following sets.**

   (*i*)   {p, q}   (*ii*)   {consonants in the word WOMAN}.   (*iii*)   {x | 3x – 9 = 12, x ∈ N}

10. (a) How many subsets does the set {0, 1, 2, 3, 4, 5, 6} have ?
    (b) How many proper subsets does the set A = {colours of rainbow} have?

11. **Give a suitable universal set to include the subset**
    (a) {apples, oranges, bananas}   (b) {Male students of a co-ed. school.}

12. **Let A = {x : x = 3n, n < 10}, find A when**
    (i) ξ = N   (ii) ξ = W   (iii) ξ = Z.

13. **Let ξ = {all digits in our number system}, A = {prime numbers} and B = {factors of 24}. Find :**
    (i) A $\cup$ B   (ii) A $\cap$ B   (iii) A′   (iv) B′   (v) A $\cap$ B′   (vi) B $\cap$ A′.
    Also, verify that
    (a) (A $\cap$ B)′ = A′ $\cup$ B′   (b) (A $\cup$ B)′ = A′ $\cap$ B′   (c) n (A $\cup$ B) + n (A $\cap$ B) = n (A) + n (B)
    (d) n (A′) = n (ξ) – n (A)   (e) n (B) + n (B′) = n (ξ).

14. **Let ξ = {1, 2, 3, 4, 5, 6, 7}, A = {2, 3, 7}, B = {1, 2, 4}. Show this group of sets on a Venn diagram.**

15. **Using the adjoining Venn diagram list the elements of the following sets :**
    (i) A $\cap$ B   (ii) A $\cup$ B   (iii) A′   (iv) B′
    (v) (A $\cap$ B)′   (vi) (A $\cup$ B)′

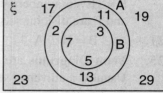

Fig. Q. 15

16. **If n (A) = 18, n (B) = 15 and n (A $\cup$ B) = 24, find n (A $\cap$ B).**

17. **In a class of 62 students, 30 students like cricket, 25 students like football and 10 students like both the games. Draw a Venn diagram and find the number of students who**
    (i) like either cricket or football;
    (ii) like neither cricket nor football.

ANSWERS

EXERCISE 2 (a)

1. (i) {2, 3, 4, 5, 7, 11}   (ii) {2, 4, 6, 7, 8, 10, 11}   (iii) {1, 2, 4, 7, 9, 11}   (iv) {2, 3, 4, 5, 6, 8, 10}
   (v) {1, 3, 5, 9, 11}   (vi) {1, 2, 4, 6, 8, 9, 10, 11}

2. {a, b, c}   3. {b, o, a, t, r, w, n}

5. (i) ξ = {factors of 36}   (ii) ξ = {factors of 36}   (iii) {1, 2, 3, 4, 6, 9, 12, 18, 36}   (iv) {1, 2, 3, 4, 6, 12, 36}
   (v) {4, 9, 12, 18, 36}.

6. (i) {2, 3,}   (ii) {3, 5}   (iii) {12}   (iv) {square}   (v) ϕ (vi) {I, N}.

7. (i) {4, 5, 7, 8}   (ii) {3, 5, 6, 8}   (iii) {5, 8}   (iv) {3, 4, 5, 6, 7, 8}   (v) {2, 4, 5, 6, 7, 8}   (vi) {2, 3, 4, 5, 6, 8}

EXERCISE 2 (b)

1. (i) 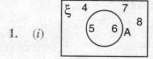   (ii) 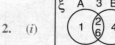   (iii)

2. (i)   (ii) 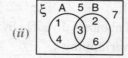   (iii) 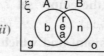   (iv)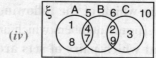

   (v)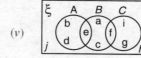

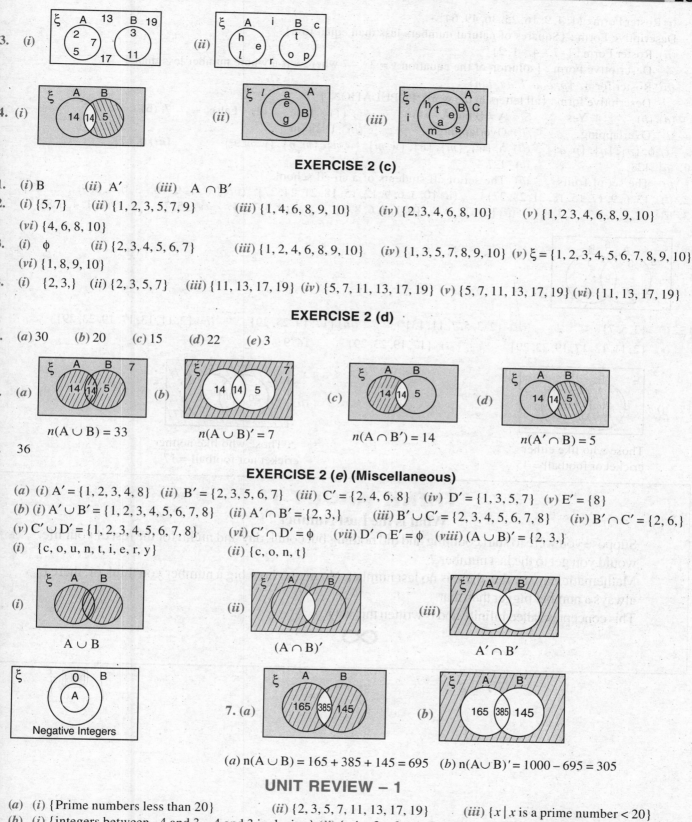

3. (i) ... (ii) ...

4. (i) ... (ii) ... (iii) ...

EXERCISE 2 (c)

1. (i) B (ii) A′ (iii) A ∩ B′

2. (i) {5, 7} (ii) {1, 2, 3, 5, 7, 9} (iii) {1, 4, 6, 8, 9, 10} (iv) {2, 3, 4, 6, 8, 10} (v) {1, 2 3, 4, 6, 8, 9, 10} (vi) {4, 6, 8, 10}

3. (i) φ (ii) {2, 3, 4, 5, 6, 7} (iii) {1, 2, 4, 6, 8, 9, 10} (iv) {1, 3, 5, 7, 8, 9, 10} (v) ξ = {1, 2, 3, 4, 5, 6, 7, 8, 9, 10} (vi) {1, 8, 9, 10}

4. (i) {2, 3,} (ii) {2, 3, 5, 7} (iii) {11, 13, 17, 19} (iv) {5, 7, 11, 13, 17, 19} (v) {5, 7, 11, 13, 17, 19} (vi) {11, 13, 17, 19}

EXERCISE 2 (d)

(a) 30 (b) 20 (c) 15 (d) 22 (e) 3

(a) $n(A \cup B) = 33$

(b) $n(A \cup B)' = 7$

(c) $n(A \cap B') = 14$

(d) $n(A' \cap B) = 5$

36

EXERCISE 2 (e) (Miscellaneous)

(a) (i) A′ = {1, 2, 3, 4, 8} (ii) B′ = {2, 3, 5, 6, 7} (iii) C′ = {2, 4, 6, 8} (iv) D′ = {1, 3, 5, 7} (v) E′ = {8}

(b) (i) A′ ∪ B′ = {1, 2, 3, 4, 5, 6, 7, 8} (ii) A′ ∩ B′ = {2, 3,} (iii) B′ ∪ C′ = {2, 3, 4, 5, 6, 7, 8} (iv) B′ ∩ C′ = {2, 6,}

(v) C′ ∪ D′ = {1, 2, 3, 4, 5, 6, 7, 8} (vi) C′ ∩ D′ = φ (vii) D′ ∩ E′ = φ (viii) (A ∪ B)′ = {2, 3,}

(i) {c, o, u, n, t, i, e, r, y} (ii) {c, o, n, t}

(i) A ∪ B

(ii) (A ∩ B)′

(iii) A′ ∩ B′

Negative Integers

7. (a) (b)

(a) n(A ∪ B) = 165 + 385 + 145 = 695 (b) n(A ∪ B)′ = 1000 − 695 = 305

UNIT REVIEW – 1

(a) (i) {Prime numbers less than 20} (ii) {2, 3, 5, 7, 11, 13, 17, 19} (iii) {x | x is a prime number < 20}

(b) (i) {integers between −4 and 3, −4 and 3 inclusive} (ii) {−4, −3, −2, −1, 0, 1, 2, 3, } (iii) {x | x, x ∈ Z and −4 ≤ x ≤ 3}

(c) (i) {factors of 24} (ii) { 1, 2, 3, 4, 6, 8, 12, 24} (iii) {x | x is a factor of 24}

(d) (i) {whole numbers which are multiples of 5 and less than 41} (ii) {0, 5, 10, 15, 20, 25, 30, 35, 40}

(iii) { x | x = 5n where n ∈ W and 0 < n < 9}

2. *(i)* Roster Form : { 1, 4, 9, 16, 25, 36, 49, 64}

Descriptive Form : {Squares of natural numbers less than equal to 8}

(ii) Roster Form : {–7, –4, –1, 2}

Descriptive Form : {solution of the equation $y = 3x - 7$ where x is a whole number less than 4

(iii) Roster form, {$p, o, u, l, a t, i, n$}

Descriptive form : {all letters in the word 'POPULATION'}

3. *(a)*, *(b)*   4. Yes   5. A ≠ B but A ↔ B   6. (1) True   (2) False   7. (b)

8. *(i)* Overlapping   *(ii)* Overlapping   *(iii)* Disjoint

9. *(i)* φ, {p}, {q}, {p, q}   *(ii)* φ, {w}, {m}, {n}, {w, m}, {w, n}, {m, n}, {w, m, n}   *(iii)* φ, {7}.

10. *(a)* 128   *(b)* 127

11. *(a)* The set of fruits   *(b)* The set of all students of a co-ed school.

12. *(i)* {3, 6, 9, 12, 15, 18, 21, 24, 27}   *(ii)* {0, 3, 6, 9, 12, 15, 18, 21, 24, 27}   *(iii)* {....., –9, –6, –3, 0, 3, 6, 9, ...27}

13. *(i)* {1, 2, 3, 4, 5, 6, 7, 8,}   *(ii)* {2, 3}   *(iii)* {0, 1, 4, 6, 8, 9}   *(iv)* {0, 5, 7, 9}   *(v)* {5, 7}   *(vi)* {1, 4, 6, 8}

14.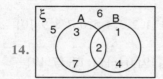

15. *(i)* {3, 5, 7}   *(ii)* {2, 3, 5, 7, 11, 13}   *(iii)* {17, 19, 23, 29}   *(iv)* {2, 11, 13, 17, 19, 23, 29}

    (v) {2, 11, 13, 17, 19, 23, 29}   *(vi)* {17, 19, 23, 29}   16. 9

17. *(i)*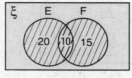

Those who like either
cricket or football = 45

(ii)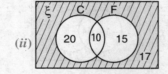

∴ Those who like neither
cricket nor football = 17

THINK ABOUT IT
What is the Last Number ?

Suppose you were to start counting and did nothing but count, day and night, for the rest of your life, would you get to the last number ?

Mathematicians say that there is no last number. No matter how big a number you think of, there is always a number bigger than that.

This concept is called infinity and is written this way :

3. Number System

3.1 Revision

Numbers, as well as numerals, are inventions of man. Let us recall some of the types of numbers, about which we have studied so far and then further extend our knowledge of numbers.

Natural Numbers

The numbers used for counting are called natural numbers. Thus,

$N = \{1, 2, 3, 4, ...\}$ is the set of natural numbers.

Two consecutive natural numbers differ by 1.

Even Natural Numbers

Natural numbers exactly divisible by 2 are called even natural numbers. Thus,

$E = \{2, 4, 6, 8, 10, ...\}$ is the set of even natural numbers. Here two consecutive numbers differ by 2. Thus an even natural number can be represented by $2n$ where $n \in N$.

Odd Natural Numbers

Natural numbers which are not exactly divisible by 2 are called odd natural numbers. Thus,

$O = \{1, 3, 5, 7, 9, ...\}$ is the set of odd natural numbers. Here two consecutive numbers differ by 2. Thus an odd natural number can be represented by $2n - 1$ where $n \in N$ or $2n + 1$ where $n \in W$.

Whole Numbers

The set of natural numbers together with 0 form the set of whole numbers. Thus,

$W = \{0, 1, 2, 3, ...\}$ is the set of whole numbers. The smallest whole number is 0. Consecutive numbers of the set differ by 1. Therefore,

(i) Each natural number is a whole number.

(ii) Each even natural number is an even whole number.

(iii) Each odd natural number is an odd whole number.

Prime Numbers

All natural numbers greater than 1 which are divisible only by 1 and by itself are called prime numbers. Thus,

2, 3, 5, 7, 11, 13, 17, 19, 23, ... are all prime numbers. In other words a prime number is a natural number which has only two factors 1 and itself. 2 is the smallest prime number and also the only even prime number.

Composite Numbers

All natural numbers (greater than 1) which are not prime, i.e., which have more than two factors are called composite numbers. Thus,

4, 6, 8, 9, 10, 12, 14, ... etc. are all composite numbers.

Integers

The set of natural numbers, 0, and the negatives of natural numbers form the set of integers. Thus,

$Z = \{..., -3, -2, -1, 0, 1, 2, 3, ...\}$ is the set of integers. Zero is neither negative nor positive.

PROPERTIES OF OPERATIONS ON WHOLE NUMBERS

We have already studied the basic operations of addition, subtraction, multiplication and division on who numbers. Now we study the properties of operations on whole numbers.

3.2 Closure Property

The offsprings of human beings are human beings. The wheat seeds when sown produce wheat. The sum of a two whole numbers is a whole number. Thus, $2 + 4 = 6$ and 6 is a whole number.

> *A set is closed under an operation when*
> *the result of the operation on any two members*
> *in the set is also in that set.*

The set of odd numbers is not closed under the operation of addition, since the sum of any two odd numbe such as 3 and 5 is not an odd number.

*3.3 Commutative Property

Walk 5 blocks E and 2 N.   Walk 2 blocks N and 5 E.

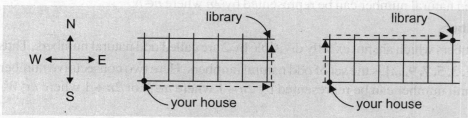

The order in which you walk from your house to the library does not affect the result. You get to the libra either way.

> *An operation is commutative if you can change the*
> *order (commute) without affecting the result.*

Illustrations

1. 'Putting on your hat; putting on your coat' is a commutative operation.
2. 'Taking off in an aeroplane; starting the engine' is not a commutative operation.

3.4 Associative Property

Using the same quantities make two cups of coffee by adding
(a) sugar and milk first, and then coffee,.
(b) sugar first, then milk and coffee.

We shall end up with two cups of coffee which are exactly the same. So

$$(S + M) + C = S + (M + C)$$

In the above operation of preparing coffee, out of the three things sugar, milk and coffee you may combine or associate any two of them first. Such a property is called **associative property.**

---

* The office-goers are called, 'commuters' because in the morning they change 'home', for the 'office', and th evening they change 'office' for the 'home'.

3.5 Properties of Addition

> **Property 1.** Addition of whole numbers is a **closed** operation, i.e. *If a and b are two whole numbers then a + b is also a whole number.*

Thus, the sum of the whole numbers 5 and 7 is 12, which is also a whole number. You may try any two pairs of whole numbers and verify that the property is true in all cases.

> **Property 2.** The addition of two whole numbers is **commutative,** i.e. changing the order of any two addends does not affect the sum. *If a and b are two whole numbers then a + b = b + a.*

For example :

$3 + 2 = 2 + 3 = 5$, $17 + 0 = 0 + 17 = 17$, $39 + 84 = 84 + 39 = 123$.

> **Property 3.** The addition of whole numbers is **associative.**
> *If a, b, c are any whole numbers, then $(a + b) + c = a + (b + c)$.*

For example :

(*i*) $(4 + 3) + 5 = 4 + (3 + 5)$, because left side = $7 + 5 = 12$, right side = $4 + 8 = 12$

(*ii*) Consider the addition problem $4 + 5 + 3$.

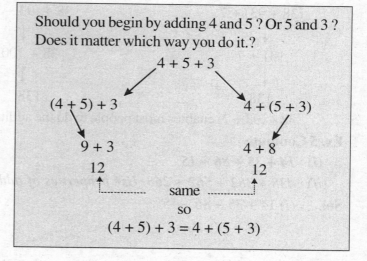

Addition property of zero

Look at these additions :

$4 + 0 = 4, 0 + 4 = 4$ Therefore, $4 + 0 = 0 + 4 = 4$
$0 + 15 = 15, 15 + 0 = 15$ Therefore, $0 + 15 = 15 + 0 = 15$

The result of adding a number to 0 is equal to the number itself. Since zero added to any number does no change the identity of that number, we call zero the **identity element** with respect to addition. It is also calle the **additive identity**.

> *** Property 4.** If a is a whole number then, $a + 0 = 0 + a = a$.

Ex. 1 *Fill in the blanks to make each of the following a true statement.*

(i) $1005 + 283 =$ _____ $+ 1005$ (ii) $300507 + 0 =$ _____

(iii) $12345 + (679 + 321) = (679 +$ _____ $) + 321$

Sol. (i) $1005 + 283 = 283 + 1005$. (ii) $300507 + 0 = 300507$. (iii) $12345 + (679 + 321) = (679 + 12345) + 321$

Ex. 2 *Find the sum*

(i) $5628 + 39784$ (ii) $39784 + 5628$ *and check property 2 of addition.*

Sol. (i) $5628 + 39784 = 45412$ and   (ii) $39784 + 5628 = 45412$, so property 2 of addition is verified.

Ex. 3 *Find each of the sums*

(i) $(15409 + 112) + 591$ (ii) $15409 + (112 + 591)$ *and check property 3 of addition.*

Sol. (i) $(15409 + 112) + 591 = 15521 + 591 = 16112$

(ii) $15409 + (112 + 591) = 15409 + 703 = 16112$ so property 3 of addition is verified.

Ex. 4 *Tell which method of associating makes the computation easier*

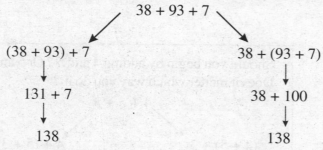

$38 + (93 + 7)$ enables most people to do the addition mentally.

Ex. 5 Compute

(i) $14 + 35 + 86 + 15$

(ii) $438 + 382 + 562 + 268.$ *Use properties of addition to make the computation as easy as possible.*

Sol.   (i) $14 + 35 + 86 + 15$

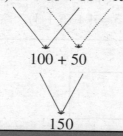

$100 + 50$

150

(ii) $438 + 382 + 562 + 268$
$= (438 + 562) + (382 + 268)$
$= 1000 + 650 = \mathbf{1650.}$

> It is easy to add zeros as $0 + 0 = 0$, so combine 14 and 86 as their sum has 0 in the units place. Combine 35 and 15. $14 + 86$ is 100 and $35 + 15$ is 50. Now $100 + 50 = 150$.

EXERCISE 3 (a)

1. **Fill in the blanks to make each of the following a true statement.**

    (i) $529 +$ _____ $= 398 + 529$ (ii) $0 + 815 =$ _____ (iii) $10,000 + 0 =$ _____ (iv) _____ $+ 204 = 204$

    (v) $39 + (201 + 18) = (39 + 201) +$ _____

2. **Find the sums :**

    (i) $834679 + 2573$ (ii) $2573 + 834679$ and check property 2 of addition.

---

*   Zero is called the *identity element* for addition because zero when added to a number does not change the 'identity' i.e., the value of the number.

3. **Find each of the following sums and check by reversing the order of addends.**
   (*i*) 739 + 826   (*ii*) 2983 + 7216   (*iii*) 839 + 785 + 609
4. **Find each of the sums**
   (*i*) (39208 + 386) + 726   (*ii*) 39208 + (386 + 726) and check property 3 of addition.
5. **Compute the following : Use properties of addition to make the computation as easy as possible**
   (*i*) 27 + 52 + 73 + 10   (*ii*) 137 + 24 + 63 + 66
6. **Determine each of the following sums by suitable arrangement.**
   (*i*) 867 + 1000 + 133   (*ii*) 235 + 600 + 765   (*iii*) 637 + 908 + 363   (*iv*) 2062 + 353 + 1438 + 547

3.6 Subtraction

Operation of Subtraction

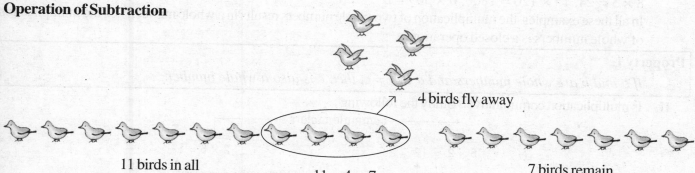

4 birds fly away

11 birds in all   11 – 4 = 7   7 birds remain

When a part or whole of a group is taken away from a given group we subtract to find how much is left. Subtraction can be shown on a number line.

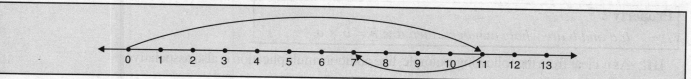

The '–' in 11 – 4 is read "minus" and means subtract. Remainder is also called **difference.**

You know that the operations of addition and subtraction are inverse of each other. Subtracting 7 from 18 can be considered as finding a number which when added to 7 gives 18.

$$18 - 7 = 11 \Rightarrow 7 + 11 = 18$$

If we subtract a whole number from itself, we get the whole number 0. Thus, 17 – 17 = 0.

Ex. 1. *For the addition sentence, 6 + 3 = 9, write two subtraction sentences.*

Sol.   Since addition of whole numbers is commutative.

$$6 + 3 = 3 + 6 = 9, \qquad 6 + 3 = 9 \Rightarrow 9 - 3 = 6 \qquad 3 + 6 = 9 \Rightarrow 9 - 6 = 3$$

Ex. 2. *Perform the subtraction 7839 – 983 and check your results by corresponding addition.*

Sol.   7839 – 983 = 6856,   *Check :* 6856 + 983 = 7839.

EXERCISE 3 (b)

1. **For each addition sentence, write two subtraction sentences :**
   (*i*) 8 + 17 = 25   (*ii*) 75 + 59 = 134   (*iii*) 101 + 278 = 379
2. **Perform the following subtractions and check your result by corresponding addition :**
   (*i*) 13407 – 10999   (*ii*) 100000 – 95673   (*iii*) 3030301 – 676767   (*iv*) 80093000 – 989996

3. **Complete the following :**
   (i) 9538 – ------------ = 3762   (ii) 8019 – ------------ = 5784   (iii) 72035 – ---------- = 30019

4. Sheela brought a Hindi novel from the library which had 378 pages. She read 152 pages on the first tw
   days. If she read 79 pages on the third day, how many pages would remain unread?

5. Find the difference between the largest number of 5 digits and the smallest number of 6 digits.

6. The population of a village is 1500. If 489 are men and 472 are women, find the number of children.

3.7 Properties of Multiplication

I. Consider the following multiplications :
   $8 \times 3 = 24$, $15 \times 120 = 1800$, $0 \times 309 = 0$

   In all these examples, the multiplication of two whole numbers results in a whole number, i.e., the multiplicati
   of whole numbers is a closed operation.

Property 1

If a and b are whole numbers and $a \times b = c$, then c is also a whole number.

II. Is multiplication commutative ? Study the following :

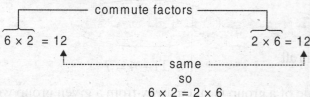

Yes, multiplication is commutative.

Property 2

If a and b are whole numbers, then $a \times b = b \times a$.

III. As is clear from the following example, like addition, multiplication is also associative.

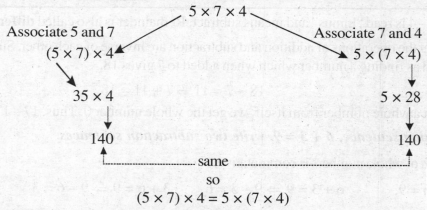

Similarly, we have $(23 \times 30) \times 89 = 23 \times (30 \times 89) = 61410$.

Property 3

If a, b and c are three whole numbers, then $(a \times b) \times c = a \times (b \times c)$
The common value of the product is denoted by $a \times b \times c$.

Note: We may make use of the above property in making multiplication of three or more whole numbers simpler

---

For example : Suppose we have to multiply 8, 987 and 25. It would be easier to multiply 8 and 25 first and the
multiply the product and 987. Thus,
$8 \times 987 \times 25 = (8 \times 25) \times 987 = 200 \times 987 = 197400$.

> Multiply 987 by 2 mentally and put tw
> zeros at the right.

IV. Look at these multiplications :

$$5 \times 1 = 5, \quad 1 \times 5 = 5 \qquad\qquad 17 \times 1 = 17, \quad 1 \times 17 = 17$$

*The result of multiplying a number by 1 is equal to the number itself. We say that 1 is the **identity element** with respect to multiplication. It is also called the **multiplicative identity.**

Property 4

The whole number 1 is such that $1 \times a = a \times 1 = a$ for every whole number a. The number 1 is the only number having this property.

V. Like 1, the number 0 also has a special property in relation to multiplication.

We have $5 \times 0 = 0 + 0 + 0 + 0 + 0 = 0$ and so $0 \times 5 = 5 \times 0 = 0$.

Likewise, $0 \times 3092 = 0$, $0 \times 10000 = 0$, $893762 \times 0 = 0$

Property 5

The whole number 0 is such that $0 \times a = a \times 0 = 0$ for every whole number a. The number 0 is the only number with this property.

VI. We now take up an important property of multiplication which connects the operations of addition and multiplication.

From the diagram it is clear that

$$4 (3 + 7) = 4 \times 3 + 4 \times 7$$

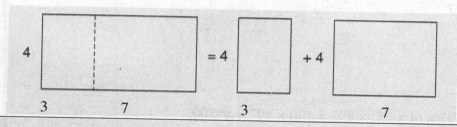

Property 6

If a, b and c are three whole numbers, then

$$a \times (b + c) = a \times b + a \times c, \text{ and } (b + c) \times a = b \times a + c \times a.$$

If instead of two numbers, we have the sum of three or more numbers, then also this property holds, i.e.,

$$a \times (b + c + d) = a \times b + a \times c + a \times d,$$

and $\quad (a + b + c + d) \times p = a \times p + b \times p + c \times p + d \times p.$

VII. Like that for addition, the distributive property of multiplication holds in case of subtraction also. Thus,

$$5 \times (7 - 3) = 5 \times 4 = 20 \text{ and } 5 \times 7 - 5 \times 3 = 35 - 15 = 20$$

so $\quad 5 \times (7 - 3) = 5 \times 7 - 5 \times 3 = 20.$

Property 7

If a, b and c are three whole numbers and $b > c$, then

$$a \times (b - c) = a \times b - a \times c \text{ and } (b - c) \times a = b \times a - c \times a.$$

Note : Calculations can be much simplified by using properties 6 and 7.

VIII. Consider the whole numbers 8, 5 and 12.

Here, $8 > 5$ and 12 is a number other than 0. If we multiply both 8 and 5 by 12, we have $8 \times 12 = 96$ and $5 \times 12 = 60$. Clearly, $96 > 60$.

Property 8

If a, b and c are whole numbers $a > b$ and c is not equal to 0, then $a \times c > b \times c$.

---

*   1 is called the *identity element* for multiplication because multiplication of a number by 1 does not change the 'identity' i.e., the value of the number.

Ex. 1 *Fill in the blanks :*

    (i) $8357 \times 1 =$ _____   (ii) $289 \times 0 =$ _____   (iii) $789 \times 835 = 835 \times$ _____

    (iv) $65 \times 48 = 65 \times 50 - 65 \times$ _____

Sol. (i) $8357 \times 1 = $ **1,** as the product of any number and 1 is the number itself.

    (ii) $289 \times 0 = $ **0**

    (iii) $789 \times 835 = 835 \times 789$ ('×' commutative)

    (iv) $65 \times 48 = 65 \times (50 - 2) = 65 \times 50 - 65 \times 2.$

Ex. 2 *Find the product of :*

    (i) *8, 9, 25, 3*   (ii) *4, 25, 897*   (iii) *4, 250, 2986*   (iv) *5873, 625, 16*   (v) *125, 40, 8, 25*

Sol. Since the numbers may be grouped in any order we group those numbers which make the calculations mos
convenient.

    (i) $8 \times 9 \times 25 \times 3$

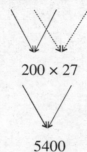

    200×27

    5400

> We group 8 and 25 since their product contain 2 zeros. It is easy to multiply 200 and 27.

    (ii) $4 \times 25 \times 897 = (4 \times 25) \times 897 = 100 \times 897 = $ **89700.**

    (iii) $4 \times 250 \times 2986 = (4 \times 250) \times 2986 = 1000 \times 2986 = $ **2986000.**

    (iv) $5873 \times 625 \times 16 = 5873 \times (625 \times 16) = 5873 \times 10000 = $ **58730000.**

    (v) $125 \times 40 \times 8 \times 25 = (125 \times 40) \times (8 \times 25) = 5000 \times 200 = $ **1000000.**

Ex. 3 *Find the value of the following using properties of multiplication.*

    $37 \times 865 + 18 \times 865 - 49 \times 865 - 6 \times 865.$

Sol. $37 \times 865 + 18 \times 865 - 49 \times 865 - 6 \times 865$

        $= 865 \times (37 + 18 - 49 - 6) = 865 \times (55 - 55) = 865 \times 0 = $ **0.**

Ex. 4 *Find 854×96, using properties of addition and multiplication.*

Sol. $854 \times 96 = (800 + 50 + 4) \times 96 = 800 \times 96 + 50 \times 96 + 4 \times 96 = 76800 + 4800 + 384 = $ **81984.**

EXERCISE 3 (*c*)

1. Fill in the blanks with a whole number to make each of the following a true statement.

    (i) $23987 \times 0 =$ _____   (ii) $59083 \times 1 =$ _____   (iii) $879 \times 56 = 56 \times$ _____   (iv) $100 \times 100 \times$ _____ $= 10000$

    (v) $27 \times 98 \times 35 = 35 \times$ ____ $\times 27$ (vi) $87 \times 19 = 19 \times (80 +$ _____) (vii) $205 \times 69 = 69 \times 200 + 69 \times$ ___

2. Fill in the blanks :

    (i) $56 \times 39 = 56 \times 30 + 56 \times$ _____   (ii) $37 \times 19 = 37 \times 10 + 37 \times 5 + 37 \times$ _____

    (iii) $18 \times 47 = 18 \times 50 - 18 \times$ _____   (iv) $76 \times 88 = 76 \times 90 - 76 \times$ _____

3. What number should replace each *n* ?

    (i) $3 (n + 6) = (3 \times 5) + (3 \times 6)$ (ii) $(7 \times 4) + (n \times 3) = 7 (4 + 3)$ (iii) $(9 \times 8) + (8 \times 8) = (9 + 8)n$

4. **Multiply by suitable arrangement :**
   (*i*) 20, 5, 8, 7   (*ii*) 25, 4, 598   (*iii*) 4, 2893, 250   (*iv*) 2, 2867, 50   (*v*) 8, 786, 125
   (*vi*) 3982, 625, 16 (*vii*) 394, 5, 80

5. **Find each of the following products by using properties of multiplication :**
   (*i*) $972 \times 8 + 972 \times 2$ (*ii*) $593 \times 999 + 593$ (*iii*) $46 \times 982 + 56 \times 982 - 58 \times 982 - 43 \times 982$

6. A security checkpoint can check up to 250 people per hour. What is the greatest number of people that can be checked in 5 days ?

7. The temperature dropped by 2 degrees an hour during the night. At midnight the temperature was 31 degrees. What was the temperature at 6 a.m?

8. Determine the product of the greatest number of 5 digits and the smallest number of 4 digits.

3.8 Operation of Division

Prabha wants to re-arrange a group of 8 girls into groups of 2 girls each. How many groups will there be ?
You know that $4 \times 2 = 8$. Therefore, she can make 4 groups of 2 each.

Prabha could also find how many groups of 2 are contained in 8 by subtracting as shown below :

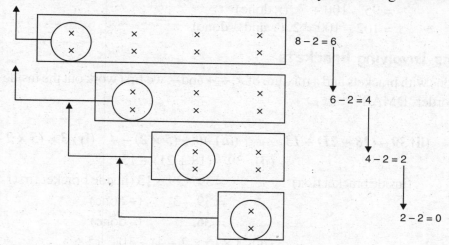

$8 - 2 = 6$

$6 - 2 = 4$

$4 - 2 = 2$

$2 - 2 = 0$

By using different methods (*i*) a multiplication fact and (*ii*) the idea of repeated subtraction you have seen that a set or group of 8 can be separated into 4 groups of equal size.

Another but short way of saying that there are 4 groups of 2 in 8 is

$$8 \div 2 = 4$$

It is read :

Eight divided by two is equal to 4.

We think of it as : How many 2's are there in 8 ?

Multiplication relates to joining a number of equal sized groups. Division relates to the separation of a bigger group into smaller groups of equal size. Multiplication can be thought of as repeated addition. Division can be thought of as repeated subtraction.

Checking Division : Look at the division carried out here. Here, the dividend is 739, the divisor is 54 and the remainder is 37.

Do you notice that

739 = 54 × 13 + 37

$$\begin{array}{r} 13 \\ 54\overline{)739} \\ -54\downarrow \\ \hline 199 \\ -162 \\ \hline 37 \end{array}$$

| **i.e., Dividend = Divisor × quotient + remainder** |

The above relation is very useful in checking the division result.

Note : 1. Division by 0 is a meaningless operation. You cannot divide by 0.

    2. If you divide any number by the number 1, the result is the number itself, i.e., $a \div 1 = a$,

    3. If you divide any number ($\neq 0$) by itself, result is 1, i.e., $a \div a = 1$ $(a \neq 0)$.

3.9 Mixed Operations

When a calculation involves a mixture of the operations +, –, ×, ÷, we always perform these operations in the following order :

| 1. First Division, then 2. Multiplication and finally addition and subtraction. | **DMAS** rule |

Ex.1 *Simplify :*

  (i) *3 + 7 × 5 – 10 ÷ 2*   **(ii)** *95 – 20 × 15 ÷ 3 + 7.*

Sol.(*i*) $3 + 7 \times 5 - 10 \div 2$ = 3 + 35 – 5   (÷ and × are done first)

                 = 38 – 5 = **33.** (+ and – done)

  (*ii*) $95 - 20 \times 15 \div 3 + 7$ = 95 – 20 × 5 + 7 (÷ done first)

                   = 95 – 100 + 7 (× done)

                   = 102 – 100 = **2.** (+ and – done)

3.10 Calculations Involving Brackets

For calculations with brackets and a mixture of ×, ÷, + and –, we first work out the inside of the brackets, then we do in the order 'DMAS'

Ex. 2 *Find :*

  (i) *5 × (3 + 7)*   **(ii)** *39 – (18 + 21) ÷ 13*   **(iii)** *40 ÷ (5 × 2) – 4* **(iv)** *3 × (5 × 2 – 4) + 10 – 15 ÷ 5*

Sol. (*i*) 5 × (3 + 7)

        = 5 × 10   (inside bracket first)

        = **50.**

  (*ii*) 39 – (18 + 21) ÷ 13

        = 39 – 39 ÷ 13 (inside bracket first)

        = 39 – 3   (÷ done)

        = **36.**   (– done)

  (*iii*) 40 ÷ (5 × 2) – 4

        = 40 ÷ 10 – 4 (inside bracket first)

        = 4 – 4   (÷ done)

        = **0.**   (– done)

  (*iv*) 3 × (5 × 2 – 4) + 10 – 15 ÷ 5

        = 3 (10 – 4) + 10 – 3 (Inside bracket first, ÷ also done)

        = 3 × 6 + 10 – 3

        = 18 + 10 – 3 = **25.** (×, + and –done)

EXERCISE 3 (*d*)

1. Find the value of each of the following :

  (*i*) 0 ÷ 39 (*ii*) 0 ÷ 975   (*iii*) 5 ÷ 5 (*iv*) 701 – (1869 ÷ 1869) (*v*) (3278 ÷ 3278) – (5098 ÷ 5098)

2. What must 789 be multiplied by to give 78,97,890 ?

3. Find the number of pages in a book which has on an average 207 words on a page, and contains 2,01,411 words altogether.

4. In a sum, the divisor is 173, the quotient is 2,544 and the remainder is 60. What is the dividend ?

5. A cinema hall is to be constructed in which each row must have 36 seats. Determine the minimum number of rows required to seat 600 persons at a time.

(A)

Find :

1. $8 + 2 \times 6$ 2. $7 - 14 \div 2$ 3. $5 \times 8 \div 4$ 4. $25 + 7 \times 25 \div 5$ 5. $1 - 35 \div 35$ 6. $6 + 6 \div 6 \times 6$

7. $10 - 10 \times 28 \div 28$ 8. $30 - 5 \times 2 + 3 - 8 \div 2$ 9. $15 \div 5 \times 4 \div 2$ 10. $18 \div 9 \times 10 + 5 \times 4 \div 2 - 300 \div 10$

(B)

Find :

11. $14 \div (3 + 4)$ 12. $5 \times (7 - 3)$ 13. $(5 + 3) \div 2$ 14. $(5 - 4) \times (2 + 7)$

15. $(7 - 1) \div (5 - 3)$ 16. $3 \times (6 - 1) \div (27 - 12)$ 17. $8 + (3 \times 4 - 10) - 2$ 18. $15 \div 3 + 28 \div (10 - 3)$

19. $8 \div (9 - 5) \times 3$ 20. $(16 \div 4 + 4) \div (3 \times 3 - 1)$ 21. $54 \div (7 \times 8 - 47) \times 20 - 15 \times 8$

22. $(19 - 9 \times 2) \div (10 \div 5 - 1)$ 23. $(45 \div 5) \div 3 - (18 \div 6) \times 4 + (14 \div 7) \times (48 \div 8)$

24. $125 \div (7 \times 8 - 31) \times 8 - 3 \times 15 \div 15$

LOOKING BACK

Summary of Key Facts

1. **If a, b, c are whole numbers, then**

   (*i*) $a + b$ is a whole number $\rceil$
   (*ii*) $a \times b$ is a whole number $\rfloor$ **Property of closure**
   (*iii*) $a - b$ may or may not be a whole number.
   (*iv*) $a \div b$ may or may not be a whole number.

2. **Commutative property**

   (*i*) $a + b = b + a$
   (*ii*) $a \times b = b \times a$ e.g., $3 + 4 = 4 + 3$, $3 \times 4 = 4 \times 3$

3. **Associative property**

   (*i*) $(a + b) + c = a + (b + c)$, e.g., $(5 + 7) + 2 = 5 + (7 + 2) = 14$
   (*ii*) $(a \times b) \times c = a \times (b \times c)$, e.g., $(5 \times 7) \times 2 = 5 \times (7 \times 2) = 70$

4. **Distributive property**

   (*i*) $a \times (b + c) = a \times b + a \times c$ (*ii*) $a \times (b - c) = a \times b - a \times c$

5. **Property of 0 and 1.**

   (*i*) $a + 0 = a$ (*ii*) $a - 0 = a$ (*iii*) $a \times 0 = 0$ (*iv*) $0 \div a = 0$
   (*v*) $a \div 0$ is not possible   (*vi*) $a \times 1 = a$ (*vii*) $a \div 1 = a$ (*viii*) $a \div a = 1, a \neq 0$.

6. **If a is dividend, b divisor, q quotient and r remainder, then $a = bq + r$,**

   e.g. in
   $$\begin{array}{r} 3 \\ 4\overline{)14} \\ -12 \\ \hline 2 \end{array}$$

   $\boxed{14 = 4 \times 3 + 2}$ $\boxed{\textbf{Dividend = Divisor} \times \textbf{quotient + remainder}}$

7. Mixed operations involving brackets, $+, -, \times, \div$ are done in the following order :
   Brackets, Division, Multiplication, Addition, Subtraction.

MENTAL MATHS-1

Complete the following :

1. $537 \times 1 = $ _____
2. $39 \times 0 = $ _____
3. $0 \times 352 = $ _____
4. $0 \times 0 = $ _____

5. $0 \div 38 = $ _____
6. $29 \div 29 = $ _____
7. $28 \times 59 = 59 \times $ _____

8. $7 \times (3 + 5) = 7 \times 3 + 7 \times $ _____
9. $259 \times 75 = 259 \times (70 + $ _____ $)$

Calculate :

10. $(8 \div 8) - (275 \div 275)$
11. $13 \times 59 \times 0$
12. $(5 + 8) \times 7$
13. $35 \div 7 \times 2$

14. $59837 \div 1 - 59837$
15. $0 \div 876 + 519$
16. $105 \div 7 \times 1 - 3 \times 5$

ANSWERS

EXERCISE 3 (a)

1. (i) 398 (ii) 815 (iii) 10,000 (iv) 0 (v) 18 **2.** 837252 **3.** (i) 1565 (ii) 10,199 (iii) 2233 **4.** 40,320
5. (i) 162 (ii) 290 **6.** (i) 2000 (ii) 1600 (iii) 1908 (iv) 4400

EXERCISE 3 (b)

1. (i) $25 - 8 = 17, 25 - 17 = 8$ (ii) $134 - 75 = 59, 134 - 59 = 75$ (iii) $379 - 101 = 278, 379 - 278 = 101$
2. (i) 2408 (ii) 4327 (iii) 2353534 (iv) 79103004 **3.** (i) 5776 (ii) 2235 (iii) 42016 **4.** 147 Pages **5.** 1
6. 539 children

EXERCISE 3 (c)

1. (i) 0 (ii) 59083 (iii) 879 (iv) 10 (v) 98 (vi) 7 (vii) 5
2. (i) 9 (ii) 4 (iii) 3 (iv) 2
3. (i) 5 (ii) 7 (iii) 8
4. (i) 5600 (ii) 59800 (iii) 2893000 (iv) 286700 (v) 786000 (vi) 39820000 (vii) 157600
5. (i) 9720 (ii) 593000 (iii) 982
6. 30,000 people **7.** 19° C **8.** 99999000

EXERCISE 3 (d)

1. (i) 0 (ii) 0 (iii) 1 (iv) 700 (v) 0
2. 10010 **3.** 973 pages **4.** 440172 **8.** 17 rows

EXERCISE 3 (e)

1. 20 **2.** 0 **3.** 10 **4.** 60 **5.** 0 **6.** 12 **7.** 0 **8.** 19 **9.** 6 **10.** 0 **11.** 2 **12.** 20 **13.** 4
14. 9 **15.** 3 **16.** 1 **17.** 8 **18.** 9 **19.** 6 **20.** 1 **21.** 0 **22.** 1 **23.** 3 **24.** 37

MENTAL MATHS – 1

1. 537 **2.** 0 **3.** 0 **4.** 0 **5.** 0 **6.** 1 **7.** 28 **8.** 5 **9.** 5 **10.** 0 **11.** 0 **12.** 91 **13.** 10 **14.** 0
15. 519 **16.** 0

ENRICHMENT

MAGIC SQUARE

A magic square is a square in which the numbers are arranged in such a manner that the sums of numbers in each row, in each column, and along each diagonal is the same. For example, in the magic square shown here,

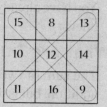

In each row
15 + 8 + 13 = 36
10 + 12 + 14 = 36
11 + 16 + 9 = 36

In each column
15 + 10 + 11 = 36
8 + 12 + 16 = 36
13 + 14 + 9 = 36

Along each diagonal
15 + 12 + 9 = 36
13 + 12 + 11 = 36

Complete the following magic squares by filling in the blanks :

8	1	6
3	7	
		2

1	14	15	
8	11		
		6	9
13			16

4. Integers

Introduction

You have already studied in detail about integers in your previous class. Here we shall revise the same again in brief.

4.1 What are Integers ?

The sum of two whole numbers is always a whole number, so the set of whole numbers is closed under addition, but is this true for subtraction also? The answer is no. For example when 4 is subtracted from 9, the answer is 5, which is a whole number. But when we subtract 9 from 4 what do we get? We get $-5 \notin W$. Thus this operation cannot be performed if we have only the set of whole numbers to work with. So we extend this set of whole numbers and include negative natural numbers also. This new set comprising whole numbers and negative natural numbers is called the set of integers. Thus

I or Z = {....–3, –2, –1, 0, 1, 2, 3,.....} is the set of integers.

The numbers +1, +2, +3, ... etc. are called positive integers.

The numbers –1, –2, –3, ... etc. are called negative integers.

Zero is neither negative nor positive.

Both the positive and negative integers are called **directed numbers** since they indicate direction. Another name given to them is **signed numbers** because of the + or – sign which is a part of them.

Note: 1. For every positive natural number '+ a' there exists an opposite number called the negative of 'a' represented by '– a'.

2. The sum of any integer and its negative is always zero. i.e. $a + (-a) = 0.$

For the sake of simplicity we omit the +sign and write it as **a** instead of **+ a**, where **a** is a positive integer.

4.2 Representing Integers on a Number Line

We draw a line and mark a point O in the middle of that line. This point denotes the number 0. Since negative numbers are opposites of positive numbers, therefore if positive numbers +1, +2, +3, +4, ... are marked at 1 unit, 2 units, 3 units, 4 units and so on from the 0-mark to the right of it, then the points at distances 1 unit, 2 units, 3 units, 4 units and so on from the 0-mark to the left of it shall represent negative integers –1, –2, –3, – 4, ... and so on.

Negative Integers	Zero	Positive Integers
–7 –6 –5 –4 –3 –2 –1	0	+1 +2 +3 +4 +5 +6 +7

4.3 Predecessor and Successor

- **Predecessor:** One less than a given integer is called its *predecessor*. Thus, on the number line each integer is the predecessor of the integer just on the right of it.

- **Successor:** One more than a given integer is called its *successor*. Thus on the number line each integer is the successor of the integer just on the left of it.

4.4 Comparison of Integers

For any two integers represented on the number line the one indicated on the right is greater, e.g., $-4 > -5$, $-1 > -2$, $0 > -1$, $2 > 1$, $7 > 4$, and so on.

Note : 1. Every positive integer is greater than the negative integer, e.g., $1 > -1, 5 > -5, 8 > -11$, and so on.

2. Zero is less than every positive integer, e.g., $0 < 1, 0 < 5, 0 < 8$, and so on.

3. Zero is greater than every negative integer, e.g., $0 > -3, 0 > -16, 0 > -37$, and so on.

4. The greater the number, the lesser is its opposite i.e. if a and b are two integers such that $a > b$, then $-a < -b$. Likewise if $a < b$ then $-a > -b$, e.g., if $5 > 3$, then $-5 < -3$ and if $2 < 5$ then $-2 > -5$.

> *In other words the operation of a negative sign (–) on both sides of an inequality reverses the sign of inequality.*

4.5 Absolute Value of an Integer

The absolute value of an integer is the numerical value of the integer regardless of its sign. The symbol '| |' is used to represent the absolute value of an integer. Thus $|+8| = 8, |-8| = 8$. This shows that the absolute value of an integer is either equal to or greater than the integer, but never less than the integer.

> *If a represents an integer, then*
> $|a| = a$ *if a is + ve or 0*
> $= -a$ *if a is –ve.*

EXERCISE 4 (a)

1. Write all the integers between (*i*) –6 and 3.   (*ii*) – 8 and – 1   (*iii*) – 23 and – 15

2. Replace each blank by < or > to make given statement true :

(*i*) – 8 .... – 18   (*ii*) –4 0   (*iii*) – 357 .... – 537   (*iv*) –71 .... 17.

3. State the successor of (*i*) – 91   (*ii*) –1   (*iii*) –105

4. State the predecessor of   (*i*) –380   (*ii*) 0   (*iii*) – 99

5. Arrange the following integers in ascending order.

(*i*) –7, 4, –3, 0, –1 (*ii*) –8, –17, –3, 0, –25 (*iii*) –28, 17, –40, –5, –19, 2 (*iv*) –8, –4 , 0 –11, 9, 4, 6, 13, –27, 19.

6. Arrange the following integers in descending order.

(*i*) 0, –3, 5, –2, –1 (*ii*) –17, –1, 3, –9 (*iii*) –8, 0, –4, –12, 1 (*iv*) –6, –11, 12, –32, –23, 14, 0, 32, 16, –19, –18

7. Evaluate:

(*i*) $|-3| + |5|$ (*ii*) $|18 - 3| \div |-5|$ (*iii*) $|-4 + 3| \times |-6|$ (*iv*) $|-317| + |0| - |317|$

8. Fill in the blanks.

(*i*) The greatest negative integer is _____ .   (*ii*) 0 is greater than every _____ integer.

(*iii*) The absolute value of an integer is either _____ or_____ than the integer, but never _____ than the integer.

OPERATIONS ON INTEGERS

.6 Addition of Integers

Using the concept of absolute value, we state the rules for addition of integers as under.

> **Rule 1.** *To add two integers of like signs, find the sum of their absolute values and place the common sign before the sum.*

> **Rule 2.** *To add two integers of unlike signs, find the difference of their absolute values and place the sign of the integer which has the larger absolute value before the difference.*

xamples : (*i*) $(+ 6) + (+ 3) = 9$ Absolute values of addends are 6 and 3. Sum = 9. Both addends are + ve \ Sum is also +ve.

(*ii*) $(- 9) + (- 3) = -12$ Absolute values of addends are 9 and 3. Sum = 12. Both addends are –ve \ Sum is also –ve.

(*iii*) $(+ 8) + (-11) = -3$ Difference between 11 and 8 is 3. The greater absolute value is of 11 and it has –ve sign ∴ Sum is – ve.

4.7 Properties of Addition of Integers

1. **Closure Property:** *If a and b are integers then a + b is also an integer.*
   $a \in Z, b \in Z \Rightarrow a + b \in Z.$

2. **Addition is commutative:** *If a and b are integers than a + b = b + a.*

3. **Addition is associative:** *If a, b and c are integers then a + (b + c) = (a + b) + c.*

4. **Existence of additive identity:** *The sum of any integer a and the integer 0 is that integer itself.*
   i.e. if $a \in$ **Z**, then $a + 0 = a.$ 0 is additive identity.

5. **Additive Inverse Property:** *The sum of any integer and its negative is zero.*
   For $a \in Z, a + (-a) = 0.$

6. *If a > b, then a + c > b + c and if a < b, then a + c < b + c for a, b, c $\in$ Z.*

4.8 Subtraction of Integers

If a and b are two integers, then a–b is equal to a + (–b), i.e. to subtract b from a, change the sign of and add it to a.

$$a - b = a + (-b)$$

For example :

(a) $(+4) - (+2) = (+4) + (-2) =$ **2.**
   Change '–' to '+'
   opposite of + 2 is –2

(b) $(+6) - (-4) = (+6) + (+4) =$ **10.**
   Change '–' to '+'
   opposite of – 4 is + 4

(c) $(-11) - (-8) = (-11) + (+8) =$ **–3.**
   Change '–' to '+'
   opposite of –8 is 8

(d) $(-3) - (+7) = (-3) + (-7) =$ **–10.**
   Change '–' to '+'
   opposite of +7 is –7

EXERCISE 4 (b)

1. **Add the integers in each of the following:**
   (i) – 18, 14 (ii) – 26, – 3   (iii) 46, – 46 (iv) 6, – 3   (v) – 111, 413, – 317
   (vi) – 613, – 421, – 700   (vii) 400, – 31, – 71   (viii) 27, –18, –51, –79, 15

2. **Find the additive inverse of:** (i) – 26   (ii) 12   (iii) 0   (iv) –1

3. **Simplify:** (i) 48 + (– 55) + 30 + (– 16) (ii) (– 16) + 10 + (– 3) + 11 + (– 4)

4. The temperature at 9 a.m on a certain day was – 3°C. It rose by 6 degrees in the next hour. What did the thermometer register at 10 a.m.?

5. **Verify the following :**
   (i) (– 6) + (+ 9) = (+ 9) + (– 6)   (ii) (–2) + [(– 13) + (+ 4)] = [(– 2) + (– 13)] + (+ 4).

6. **Subtract the first integer from the second in each case :**
   (i) 6, 18   (ii) – 3, 6   (iii) –27, – 54   (iv) 12, –7   (v) –95, 95

7. **Fill in the blanks :** (i) 6 + _____ = 0.   (ii) (–12) + (12) = _____ .   (iii) (+5) + _____ = 14.

8. **Find the value of:**
   (i) – 37 – (– 15) – 2   (ii) 16– [14 – (–2) – (–6)].   (iii) 98 – (14) – (–32). (iv) – 10 + (– 9) + (– 6)

9. Add (i) – 63 to the difference of – 19 from – 43 (ii) –105 to the difference of –25 from –75.

10. Subtract the sum of – 400 from – 310 from the sum of – 230 and – 110.

11. The sum of two integers is 63. If one of them is – 37, find the other.

12. **Calculate the Sum :**   (– 6) + (6) + (– 6) + (6) + ...
   (i) if the numbers of terms is 70.   (ii) if the number of terms is 203.

4.9 Multiplication of Integers

> **Rule 1.** *To determine the product of two integers with like signs, i.e. with same signs, find the product of their absolute values and give a plus sign to the product.*

For example : (i) $(+ 4) \times (+ 12) = 48$ (ii) $(- 3) \times (- 7) = + 21$

> **Rule 2.** *To determine the product of two integers with unlike signs (Opposite signs), find the product of their absolute values and give a minus sign to the product.*

For example :   (i) $(-3) \times (+ 5) = -15$ (ii) $(+7) \times (-4) = -28$

4.10 Properties of Multiplication of Integers

1. **Closure Property:** *If a and b are integers, then a × b is also an integer.*
$$a \in Z, b \in Z \Rightarrow a \times b \in Z.$$

2. **Multiplication is commutative:** *For any integers a and b, a × b = b × a.*

3. **Multiplication is associative:** *If a, b and c are integers then a × (b × c) = (a × b) × c.*

4. **Multiplicative Identity:** *For any integer a, a × 1 = 1 × a = a. 1 is the multiplicative identity.*

5. **Multiplicative property of 0 :** *For any integer a, a × 0 = 0 × a = 0.*

6. **Distributive property :** *If a, b and c are integers then a × (b + c) = (a × b) + (a × c).*

7. **Inequalities:** *If a, b and c are integers such that a > b, then.*
   (i) $a \times c > b \times c$ *if c is positve, e.g.,* $6 > 2 \Rightarrow 6 \times 4 > 2 \times 4.$
   (iii) $a \times c < b \times c$ *if c is negative, e.g.,* $6 > 2 \Rightarrow 6 \times -4 < 2 \times -4.$

EXERCISE 4 (c)

1. **Calculate :**
   (i) $(- 6) \times (- 11)$ (ii) $-14 \times (-3) \times (+2)$ (iii) $(- 145) \times 6$ (iv) $(- 21) \times 0 \times 0 (+ 16)$ (v) $64 \times (- 14)$

2. **Find the products :**
   (i) $(-4) \times (-7) \times (-11).$ (ii) $(-8) \times (-148) \times (-160) \times 64 \times 0.$ (iii) $6 \times (- 4) \times (- 7).$ (iv) $(-15) \times (+17) \times 11.$

3. **Fill in the missing numbers :**
   (i) _____ $\times (-6) = 12.$ (ii) $3 \times$ _____ $= -18.$ (iii) $(-6) \times$ _____ $= 0.$ (iv) $(-2) \times$ _____ $= -14.$

4. **Find the value of :** (i) $6893 \times 103 - 6893 \times 3$ (ii) $175 \times 997 + 25 \times 997$ (iii) $2673 \times (- 4) + (- 2673) \times 96$
   (iv) $327 \times 928 + 327 \times (-728) - 327 \times 228$

5. **Verify and name the property used:**
   (i) $(- 63) \times (- 43) = (- 43) \times (- 63)$ (ii) $(- 20) \times [(- 4) + (- 3)] = (- 20) \times (- 4) + (- 20) \times (- 3)$

6. **Fill in the blanks:**
   (i)   Product of 11 negative integers and 3 positive integers is _____.
   (ii)   Every integer when multiplied by –1 gives its _____ inverse.
   (iii)   If a, b and c are integers and $a > b$, then $a \times c < b \times c$ if c is _____.
   (iv) $– 1 \times$ _____ $= 25.$

4.11 Division of Integers

> **Rule 1.** *When the dividend and divisor are both positive or both negative, then the quotient is positive and is obtained by dividing the absolute value of the dividend by the absolute value of divisor*

For example : (i) $(-12) \div (-6) = +2$ (ii) $(+6) \div (+3) = +2$.

> **Rule 2.** *When the dividend and divisor are with unlike signs, then the quotient is negative and is obtained by dividing the absolute value of the dividend by the absolute value of the divisor.*

For example : (i) $(-14) \div (+7) = -2$ (ii) $(+16) \div (-4) = -4$.

EXERCISE 4 (d)

1. **Find the quotient :**
   (i) $(-18) \div (+3)$ (ii) $(-16) \div (-8)$ (iii) $(+24) \div (-8)$ (iv) $(+634) \div (-634)$
   (v) $0 \div (-8000)$ (vi) $(-48000) \div (-1600)$ (vii) $(-792) \div (-792)$

2. **Fill in the Blanks :**
   (i) _____ $\times -7 = 28$.   (ii) $69 \div$ _____ $= -23$.   (iii) $-144 \div$ _____ $= 12$.
   (iv) _____ $\div -698 = -1$.   (v) _____ $\div 999 = 0$.

3. **Simplify :**
   (i) $|-12 -|-4|| \div |40 - |-36||$ (ii) $|15 \div (-3)| + |25 \div |-5||$

4.12 Simplification of Numerical Expressions

To simplify a numerical expression involving two or more operations, there are rules about the order in which the operations have to be performed. We remember the order with the help of the word **'BODMAS'** which has been coined for the sequence *'Brackets, of, Division, Multiplication, Addition, Subtraction'*.

The *brackets* used in a numerical expression are handled in the order : '−' ( ), { } and [ ]. This sequence of brackets is from innermost to outermost.

Note: 1. There is no change in the sign of the integer inside the bracket if there is a + sign before the bracket.

For example : $6 + (16 \div 4) = 6 + 4 = 10$.

2. The sign of integer (obtained on simplification) inside the bracket changes if there is a – ve sign before the bracket.

For example : $6 - (16 \div -4) = 6 - (-4) = 6 + 4 = 10$.

3. Multiplication sign is often not written before a bracket so if there is an integer before the bracket we multiply the integer obtained on (simplification) inside the bracket by the outside integer.

For example : $6 + 4(12 - 10) = 6 + 4 \times 2 = 6 + 8 = 14$.

Ex 1. Simplify :

$$-8 - \{-6\ (9 - 11) + 18 \div -3\}$$

Sol:
$= -8 - \{-6\ (9 - 11) + 18 \div -3\}$
$= -8 - \{-6 \times -2 + 18 \div -3\}$
$= -8 - \{12 + (-6)\}$
$= -8 - \{12 - 6\}$
$= -8 - \{6\} = -8 - 6 = \mathbf{-14}$.

Ex 2. Simplify :

$$\{6\ (24 \div \overline{12 - 9}) - 12\} - (3 \times 10 + 4).$$

Sol.
$= \{6\ (24 \div \overline{12 - 9}) - 12\} - (3 \times 10 + 4)$
$= \{6\ (24 \div 3) - 12\} - (30 + 4)$
$= \{6 \times 8 - 12\} - 34 = \{48 - 12\} - 34 = 36 - 34 = \mathbf{2}.$

EXERCISE 4 (e)

Simplify

1. $-6 -(-64 \div -8) + [-4 \times 7]$ 2. $4- [6-\{7 - (8 - \overline{6-3})\}\,]$ 3. $25 -[20 - \{8 \div 4 - (15 - 25 \div 5) \div 2\}]$
4. $(-8) - (-28) \div (-4) + (-4) \times 7$ 5. $45 \div \{8 -(-2 \text{ of } 5 + 3)\}$ 6. $-16 + 11(-15 \div 5)$
7. $3\{7 - (15 \div 3)\}$ 8. $\{63 \div (-15 + 8)\} - (-3 \times 7)$ 9. $\{5 + (5 \times 8) \div 2 - 3\} \div -(11)$

LOOKING BACK
Summary of Key Facts

1. The set Z = { ..., –4, –3, –2, –1, 0, 1, 2, 3, 4, ...} is the set of integers.

2. (i) 1, 2, 3, 4, ... are called positive integers.

   (ii) –1, –2, –3, –4, ... are called negative integers.

   (iii) Zero is neither positive nor negative.

3. For comparison, the integers on the left of zero on the number line are less than the integers on the right of zero on the number line.

4. The absolute value of an integer a is its numerical value regardless of its sign and is denoted by $|a|$.

5. The sum of two integers with like signs is the sum of the absolute values of the addends having the sign of the addends, e.g. 7 + 5 = 12, –7 + –5 = –12

6. The sum of two integers with unlike signs is the difference of the absolute values of the addends having the sign of the integer with greater numerical value, e.g., –5 + 7 = 2 and –8 +2 = – 6.

7. The operation of addition has closure, commutative, associative, addition of zero, additive inverse and successor properties.

8. To subtract b from a, we add the additive inverse of b, to a, i.e., $a – b = a + (– b)$, e.g., –7 –5 = –7 + (–5) = – 12, –7–(–5) = –7 + (5) = –2.

10. The product of two integers with like signs is the product of the absolute values, with a positive sign. e.g., 8 × 6 = 48 and –8 × –6 = 48.

10. The product of two integers with unlike signs is the product of the obsolute values, with a negative sign. e.g. –7 × 5 = –35 and 8x –9 = – 72.

11. The operation of multiplication has closure, commutative, associative properties and also the properties of 0 and 1.

12. The quotient of two integers with the same sign is a positive integer obtained by dividing the absolute value of the dividend by the absolute value of the divisor. e.g., 8 ÷ 2 = 4 and –10 ÷ –5 = 2.

13. The quotient of two integers with unlike signs is a negative integer obtained by dividing the absolute value of the dividend by the absolute value of the divisor. –8 ÷ 2 = –4 and 15 ÷ –3 = –5.

14. Division by zero is not allowed.

15. Expressions involving brackets and arithmetical operations are simplified using BODMAS rule. Brackets are simplified in the order '–', ( ) { } and [ ].

MENTAL MATHS - 2

Simplify:

1. 48 ÷ – 16.
2. – 6 – (72 ÷ – 9).
3. 16 – (–12 ÷ $\overline{6 – 3}$).
4. (– 20) of (– 3) + 56 ÷ – 8.
5. $|20 ÷ (–4) + 11| ÷ (–3)$.
6. 650 ÷ 5 of 13.
7. (– 8) ÷ (– 4) × 2.
8. 90 ÷ (– 6 × 3) of 5.
9. 0 ÷ (2000).
10. 25 ÷ (–15 ÷ 3).
11. Additive inverse of –23 is _____.
12. Find the predecessor of $–|5^2 –4^2|$.
13. $(–1)^{103} + (–1)^{104} = 0$; True or False.
14. (– 6) ÷ (2) = (2) ÷ (– 6); True of False.
15. Which number divided by any integer will give the value 0 ?

ANSWERS

EXERCISE 4 (a)

1. *(i)* –5, –4, –3, –2, –1, 0, 1, 2. *(ii)* –7, –6, –5, –4, –3, –2 *(iii)* –22, –21, –20, –19, –18, –17, –16.
2. *(i)* > *(ii)* < *(iii)* > *(iv)* <.
3. *(i)* – 90 *(ii)* 0 *(iii)* – 104 4. *(i)* – 381 *(ii)* – 1 *(iii)* – 100
5. *(i)* –7, –3, –1, 0, 4 *(ii)* –25, –17, –8, – 3, 0 *(iii)* –40, –28, –19, –5, 2, 17 *(iv)* –27, –11, –8, –4, 0, 4, 6, 9, 13, 19.
6. *(i)* 5, 0, –1, –2, –3 *(ii)* 3, –1, –9, –17 *(iii)* 1, 0, –4, –8, –12 *(iv)* 32, 16, 14, 12, 0, –6, –11, –18, –19, –23, –32.
7. *(i)* 8 *(ii)* 3 *(iii)* 6 *(iv)* 0 8. *(i)* – 1 *(ii)* negative. *(iv)* equal, greater, less.

EXERCISE 4 (b)

1. *(i)* – 4, *(ii)* – 29 *(iii)* 0 *(iv)* 3 *(v)* –15 *(vi)* – 1734 *(vii)* 298 *(viii)* –106
2. *(i)* 26, *(ii)* – 12 *(iii)* 0 *(iv)* 1 3. *(i)* 7 *(ii)* – 2 4. 3°C
6. *(i)* 12 *(ii)* 9 *(iii)* –27 *(iv)* –19 *(v)* 190 7. *(i)* –6 *(ii)* 0 *(iii)* 9
8. *(i)* –24 *(ii)* –6 *(iii)* 116 *(iv)* –25 9. *(i)* –87 *(ii)* –155
10. 370 11. 100 12. *(i)* 0 *(ii)* – 6

EXERCISE 4 (c)

1. *(i)* 66 *(ii)* 84 *(iii)* –870 *(iv)* 0 *(v)* –896
2. *(i)* –308 *(ii)* 0 *(iii)* 168 *(iv)* –2805
3. *(i)* –2 *(ii)* –6 *(iii)* 0 *(iv)* +7
4. *(i)* 689300 *(ii)* 199400 *(iii)* –267300 *(iv)* –9156
5. *(i)* Commutative property of Multiplication. *(ii)* Distributive property.
6. *(i)* negative *(ii)* additive *(iii)* negative *(iv)* – 25

EXERCISE 4 (d)

1. *(i)* – 6 *(ii)* 2 *(iii)* – 3 *(iv)* –1 *(v)* 0 *(iv)* 30 *(vii)* 1
2. *(i)* – 4 *(ii)* – 3 *(iii)* – 12 *(v)* 698 *(v)* 0
3. *(i)* 4 *(ii)* 10

EXERCISE 4 (e)

1. – 42 2. 0 3. 2 4. – 43 5. 3 6. – 49 7. 6 8. 12 9. – 2

MENTAL MATHS –2

1. – 3 2. 2 3. 20 4. 53 5. – 2 6. 10 7. 4 8. –1 9. 0 10. – 5 11. 23 12. –10 13. True 14. False 15. 0.

FUN WITH MATHS

PUZZLERS

1. One particular year of the last century (1880-1899) if viewed in a mirror, it increased exactly 4.5 times. Which was that year ?
2. The number of my car is such that if you divide it by 2, 3, 4, 5, 6, 7, 8, 9 and 10, you will get remainder as 1, 2, 3, 4, 5, 6, 7, 8, and 9 respectively. But if you divide by 11, then the remainder is nil. Can you tell the number of my car ?
3. If you reverse a number then the difference of the two numbers is 9999. What is that number ?
4. Which is the largest number that you can write with two nines ?
5. Can you insert plus and minus signs to obtain 40 ?
   1, 2, 3, 4, 5, 6, 7 = 40

ANSWERS

1. 1818. 2. 2519 3. 21211 or 11212 4. No 99, but 9⁹.; this is 387, 420, 489; much more (3,900,000 times) than 99.
5. 12 + 34 – 5 + 6 – 7 = 40.

5. H.C.F. and L.C.M. of Numbers

5.1 Factor

If a number x divides another number y exactly (i.e. remainder = 0) then x is a factor of y. Thus *factor of a number is an exact divisior of that number.*

For example:

6 divides 24 exactly so 6 is a factor of 24. 7 divides 21 exactly so 7 is a factor of 21.

Similarly, the numbers 1, 3, 5 and 15 all divide 15 exactly so they are all factors of 15:

1, 2, 4, 5, 10 and 20 are all possible factors of 20.

5.2 Multiple

The number y in the above definition is the multiple of x. *A multiple of any natural number is a number obtained by multiplying that number by any whole number.*

Remark : Here, whenever we shall talk about multiples we shall be talking about non-zero multiples.

Thus the multiples of 2 are 0, 2, 4, 6, 8, ...

The non-zero multiples of 2 are 2, 4, 6, 8, ...

5.3 Prime Numbers

A prime number is a whole number greater than 1, which is divisible only by 1 and by the number itself. A natural number greater than 1 which is not a prime number is called a **composite number.** 1 is neither prime nor composite. 2 is the smallest and the only even prime number.

Two natural numbers which do not have a *common prime factor are called co-primes.*

Prime numbers that differ by 2 are called **twin primes.**

The process of writing a composite number as the product of prime factors is called **prime factorisation** of the given number.

In the mathematical sentence $2 \times 8 = 16$.

2 and 8 are the factors of 16 and 16 is the multiple of 2 as well as of 8.

Similarly 5 is a factor of 20 and 20 is a multiple of 5.

1. *1 is a factor of every number.*
2. *Every number is a factor of itself (except 0).*
3. *The factors of a number are smaller or equal to the number.*
4. *Since a factor is less than or equal to the number there are only a finite number of factors of a given number.*
5. *There is no number which has no factors since 1 and the number itself are the factors of every number.*
6. *Since every number is a multiple of itself, therefore every multiple of a number is greater than or equal to itself.*
7. *Every number has an infinite number of multiples.*

5.4 Highest Common Factor H.C.F.

Common Factor : *When two or more numbers have the same number as factor, it is called a **Commo** Factor *of those numbers.*

Thus   3 is a common factor of 12 and 27.

7 is a common factor of 14 and 49.

Highest Common Factor (H.C.F.) *The greatest number which is a common factor of two or more numbers called the **highest common factor** or **H.C. F.** , i.e., it is the greatest number that divides each of th numbers exactly.*

For example :

Let us take the numbers 12 and 30.

Factors of 12 = 1, 2, 3, 4, 6, 12.

Factors of 30 = 1, 2, 3, 5, 6, 10, 15, 30.

Common Factors of 12 and 30 = 1, 2, 3, 6. Out of these 6 is the highest or the greatest.

∴   **The highest common factor** or **H.C.F.** of 12 and 30 = **6.**

There are **two methods** which are commonly used to find the H.C.F. of two or more numbers.

(1) *Prime Factorisation Method*   (2) *Continued Division Method*

5.5 H.C.F. by Prime Factorisation Method

Step 1 : *Express the given numbers in terms of their prime factors.*

Step 2 : *Write down the smallest power which appears of each of the prime factors, which are common to all the given numbers.*

Step 3: *The continued product of these gives us the H.C.F.*

Ex. 1 *Write down the H.C.F. of 108, 162 and 270.*

Sol.   Prime factorising each of the given numbers.

2	108
2	54
3	27
3	9
	3

2	162
3	81
3	27
3	9
	3

2	270
3	135
3	45
3	15
	5

$108 = 2^2 \times 3^3$

$162 = 2 \times 3^4$

$270 = 2 \times 3^3 \times 5$

∴ H.C.F. $= 2 \times 3^3 = 2 \times 27 =$ **54.**

Explanation : The only prime factors common to the three given numbers are 2 and 3. The smallest powers of these numbers which appear are 2 and 3^3. ∴ The product 2×3^3 is the H.C.F.

Ex. 2 *Write down the H.C.F. of 189, 882 and 1071.*

Sol.   Prime factorising each of the given numbers.

3	189
3	63
3	21
	7

3	1071
3	357
7	119
	17

2	882
3	441
3	147
7	49
7	7
	1

$189 = 3^3 \times 7, \ 882 = 2 \times 3^2 \times 7^2, \ 1071 = 3^2 \times 7 \times 17$

$\therefore$ H.C.F. $= 3^2 \times 7 = 9 \times 7 = $ **63.**

> **Explanation :** Common factor are 3 and 7 and their smallest powers are 3^2 and 7. The product $3^2 \times 7$ is the H.C.F.

5.6 H.C.F. by Continued Division Method

To find the H.C.F. of two given numbers by continued division method follow the sequence of steps given below.

> **Step 1 :** *Divide the larger number by the smaller number and get a remainder.*
>
> **Step 2 :** *Divide the previous divisor by the remainder last obtained.*
>
> **Step 3 :** *Repeat Step 2 until the remainder becomes 0.*

The last divisor is the H.C.F. of the two numbers.

Ex. 3 *Find the H.C.F. of 429 and 715 by division method.*

Sol.

$$429 \ ) \ \overline{715} \ (\ 1$$
$$\underline{429}$$
$$286 \ ) \ 429 \ (\ 1$$

> Last divisor is the H.C.F.

$$\underline{286}$$
$$\rightarrow \ 143 \ ) \ 286 \ (\ 2$$
$$\underline{286}$$
$$0 \ \leftarrow \text{Remainder} = 0$$

$\therefore$ **143** is the H.C.F. of 429 and 715.

> **To find the H.C.F. of more than two numbers,** *first find the H.C.F. of two numbers then find the H.C.F. of the result and the third number and so on . The final H.C.F. is the required H.C.F.*

Ex. 4 *Find the H.C.F. of 343, 5929 and 7007 by division method.*

Sol.

$$343 \ ) \ \overline{5929} \ (\ 17$$
$$\underline{343 \downarrow}$$
$$2499$$
$$\underline{2401}$$
$$98 \ ) \ 343 \ (\ 3$$
$$\underline{294}$$
$$49 \ ) \ 98 \ (\ 2$$
$$\underline{98}$$
$$0$$

H.C.F. of 343 and 5929 is 49

Now we find the H.C.F. of 49 and 7007

$$49 \ ) \ \overline{7007} \ (\ 143$$
$$\underline{49 \downarrow}$$
$$210$$
$$\underline{196 \downarrow}$$
$$147$$
$$\underline{147}$$
$$0$$

Therefore H.C.F. of 343, 5929 and 7007 is **49.**

5.7 Problems on H.C.F.

Ex. 5 *Find the greatest number which divides 120, 165 and 210 exactly leaving remainder 5, 4 and 3 respectively.*

Sol. Required number should divide $(120-5)$, $(165-4)$ and $(210-3)$, i.e., 115, 161 and 207 exactly.

Therefore, we find the H.C.F. of 115, 161 and 207.

```
115 ) 161 ( 1              23 ) 207 ( 9
      115                       207
    ─────                       ───
    46 )115 ( 2                   0
        92
       ─────
       23 )46 ( 2
           46
          ───
           0
```

∴ Required number = H.C.F. of 115, 161 and 207 = **23.**

Ex. 6 *What is the largest number of persons among whom 128 ice - creams and 324 chocolates can b*
equally divided and what will be each person's share ?

Sol : The greatest number by which 128 and 324 are divisible will be the number of persons, i.e., we have to find the
H.C.F. of 128 and 324.

```
128 ) 324 ( 2
      256
     ─────
     68 ) 128 ( 1
          68
         ────
         60 ) 68 ( 1
              60
             ────
              8 ) 60 ( 7
                  56
                 ────
                  4 ) 8 ( 2
                      8
                     ───
                      0
```

∴ The number of persons is equal to 4 and each person's share is

128 ÷ 4 = 32 ice creams

324 ÷ 4 = 81 chocolates.

Ex. 7 *Two tankers contain 245 litres and 385 litres of oil respectively. Find the maximum capacity of*
container that can measure the oil of either tanker exact number of times.

Sol. The maximum capacity of a container that can measure the oil of either tanker exact number of time
= H.C.F. of 245 and 385.

```
245 ) 385 ( 1
      245
     ─────
     140 ) 245 ( 1
           140
          ─────
          105 ) 140 ( 1
                105
               ─────
                35 ) 105 ( 3
                     105
                    ─────
                      0
```

∴ The maximum capacity of a container = **35 litres.**

EXERCISE 5 (a)

1. **Find the H.C.F. of the following by prime factorisation method:**
   (*i*) 65, 78, 104   (*ii*) 176, 220, 1331   (*iii*) 546, 882, 924   (*iv*) 175, 315, 425   (*v*) 63, 483, 777
   (*vi*) 72, 96, 120 and 384.

2. **Find the H.C.F. of the following by division method:**
   (*i*) 703, 1387   (*ii*) 2914, 3782.   (*iii*) 2619, 7663   (*iv*) 39, 403 and 182
   (*v*) 910, 1442 and 7245   (*vi*) 1976, 2340 and 1742.

3. Find the largest number which will divide 4352 and 9039 leaving a remainder of 9 in each case.

4. A farmer wishes to put 39 kg of wheat, 403 kg of oats and 182 kg of barley into the largest bags of equal size that will hold exactly of each kind. How many kgs must each bag hold ?

5. What is the greatest number so that if 6 is subtracted from it, the difference will exactly divide 84 and 180 ?

6. The length, breadth and height of a room are 7 m 25 cm, 9m 25 cm and 8 m 25 cm respectively. Determine the length of the largest tape which can measure the three dimensions of the room exactly.

7. Find the H.C.F. of 1 hour 17 minutes and 2 hours 12 minutes.

8. Find the greatest number of girls among whom, 105 rings, 81 bracelets and 324 earrings will be shared. Also find the share of each girl.

5.8 Least Common Multiple or L.C.M.

Common Multiple *A number which is a multiple of two or more given numbers is called a common multiple of three numbers.*

For example :

First 8 multiples of 6 are 6, 12, 18, 24, 30, 36, 42, 48

First 8 multiples of 8 are 8, 16, 24, 32, 40, 48, 56, 64

Common multiples of 6 and 8 are 24, 48.

Least Common Multiple or L.C.M. : *The smallest number which is a common multiple of two more given numbers is called their least common multiple or L.C.M.* In the above example among the first 8 multiples of 6 and 8, common multiples are 24 and 48. The smallest of these is 24 ∴ L.C.M. of 6 and 8 = **24.**

Similarly for 6 and 9, we have

Multiples of 6 = 6, 12, 18, 24, 30, 36, 42, 48.

Multiples of 9 = 9, 18, 27, 36, 45, 54, 63, 72.

∴ L .C.M. of 6 and 9 = **18.**

There are two methods commonly used for finding the L.C. M. of two or more given numbers.

(*i*) *Prime Factorisation*   (*ii*) *Common Division Method*

5.9 L.C.M. by Prime Factorisation Method

Step 1 : *Express each number as a product of prime factors.*

Step 2 : *Select the greatest power of every prime factor.*

Step 3 : *The product of these prime factors with their greatest power is the L.C.M. of the given numbers.*

Ex. 1 *Find the L.C.M of 132, 165 and 220.*

Sol. Prime factorising the given numbers :

2	132
2	66
3	33
	11

3	165
5	55
	11

2	220
2	110
5	55
	11

$132 = 2^2 \times 3 \times 11$, $165 = 3 \times 5 \times 11$, $220 = 2^2 \times 5 \times 11$

∴ L.C.M $= 2^2 \times 3 \times 5 \times 11$ (Product of all prime factors, each raised to highest power) = **660.**

5.10 L.C.M. by Common Division Method

Step 1: *Arrange the given numbers in a row in any order.*

Step 2: *Now divide by a number which divides exactly at least two of the given numbers and carry forward the numbers which are not divisible.*

Step 3: *Repeat this process till no two numbers have a common factor other than 1.*

Step 4: *The product of the divisors and the remaining numbers is the L.C.M of the given numbers.*

Ex. *Find the L. C. M. of 38, 57, 36, 76.*

Sol.

2	38, 57, 36, 76
2	19, 57, 18, 38
3	19, 57, 9, 19
19	19, 19, 3, 19
1	1, 1, 3, 1

∴ L.C.M. $= 2 \times 2 \times 3 \times 19 \times 3$
    $= 684.$

5.11 Problems on L.C.M

Ex. 3 *What is the lowest number which when divided separately by 15, 20, 48 and 36, will leave a remainder of 9 in each case.*

Sol. Required No = (L.C.M of 15, 20, 48 and 36) + 9

2	15, 20, 48, 36
2	15, 10, 24, 18
3	15, 5, 12, 9
5	5, 5, 4, 3
	1, 1, 4, 3

L.C.M. $= 2 \times 2 \times 3 \times 5 \times 4 \times 3 = 720$

∴ Required No. $= 720 + 9 = $ **729.**

Ex. 4 *There are 45 boys and 54 girls in a class. Determine the minimum number of chocolates required so that they can be distributed equally among girls or boys.*

Sol. Required minimum no. of chocolates

$= $ L.C.M of 45 and 54

$= 3 \times 3 \times 5 \times 6$

$= 270.$

3	45, 54
3	15, 18
	5, 6

5.12 Relationship between H.C.F and L.C.M

It can be summarized as under :

1. The *H.C.F.* of two numbers a and b is a *factor of the L.C.M. of a and b. Likewise LCM of a and b is a multiple of the HCF of a and b.*
2. *The L.C.M of two co-primes is equal to the product of the numbers.*
3. *The product of the H.C.F. and the L.C.M. of two numbers a and b is equal to their product a × b.*

Ex. 5 *The H.C.F. of two numbers is 13 and their L.C.M. is 1014. If one of the numbers is 169, find the other number.*

Sol. H.C.F × L.C.M = Product of the numbers

$$13 \times 1014 = 169 \times x \Rightarrow x = \frac{13 \times 1014}{169} = \textbf{78}$$

∴ The other number is **78**.

Ex. 7 *Can two numbers have 26 as their H.C.F. and 2628 as their L.C.M. ?*

Sol. ∵ H.C.F. is a factor of L.C.M ∴ H.C.F. should divide L.C.M. exactly.

Dividing 2628 by 26 we have

```
26 ) 2628 ( 101          Remainder = 2
     26
     028
      26
       2
```

∴ The two given numbers cannot have 26 as their H.C.F. and 2628 as their L.C.M.

EXERCISE 5 (b)

1. **Find the L.C.M of the following by prime factorisation method.**
   (*i*) 64, 144, 576   (*ii*) 250, 115, 325   (*iii*) 132, 176, 407   (*iv*) 112, 280, 504   (*v*) 72, 168, 108

2. **Find the LCM of the following by common division method.**
   (*i*) 36, 63, 77, 147 (*ii*) 36, 64, 96, 100   (*iii*) 132, 165, 220   (*iv*) 87, 69, 116, 92 (*v*) 60, 50, 144, 35, 18.

3. What is the least number which when divided by 16, 21 and 42 leaves a remainder of 10 in each case ?

4. The rims of the wheel of a tractor and van are 5m and 4m 50cm. What is the least distance in which both rotate an exact number of times ?

5. One side of a road is planted with trees 24 m apart. On the other side are lamps 32 m apart. If the first tree is opposite the first lamp, how far off is the next tree that has a lamp opposite to it.

6. 4 Alarm clocks beep at intervals of 4, 6, 12 and 18 minutes. They beep simultaneously at 6 A.M. At what time shall they beep together again ?

7. The H.C.F. and L.C.M. of two numbers are 131 and 8253 respectively. If one of the numbers is 917, find the other number.

8. The product of two numbers is 2560. The H.C.F. is 16. What is the L.C.M.?

9. Can two numbers have 21 as the H.C.F. and 443 as the L.C.M.?

LOOKING BACK

Summary of Key Facts

1. A factor of a number is an exact divisor of that number.
2. A multiple of a number is exactly divisible by that number.
3. The **H.C.F.** of two or more numbers is the greatest number that divides each one of them exactly.
4. The **L.C.M** of two or more numbers is the least common number that is exactly divisible by each one of them.
5. **H.C.F.** of two numbers divides the L.C.M. of the same numbers exactly.
6. The product of two numbers is equal to the product of their L.C.M. and H.C.F.

MENTAL MATHS – 3

1. Three logs of wood 42 m, 49 m and 63 m long have to be divided into planks of same length. What is the greatest possible length of each plank ?
2. If the product of the H.C.F. and L.C.M of two numbers is a perfect square, then the two numbers must be equal. True or False ?
3. The L.C.M. of 7 and 16 is —
4. The L.C.M and H.C.F of two numbers are 240 and 8 respectively. If one of the numbers is 40, find the other.
5. Two numbers are co-prime. Their L.C.M. is 336. If one number is 16, find the other number.
6. Find the H.C.F. of $2^2 \times 3$; $2^4 \times 3^3$ and $2^2 \times 3^2 \times 11$ in the exponential form.
7. The L.C.M. of two numbers is 324. Which one of the following cannot be the H.C.F. of the two numbers (a) 27 (b) 18 (c) 24 (d) 54 ?
8. Find the L.C.M. of $2^3 \times 3^2 \times 5$; $2^2 \times 3$; $2 \times 3^2 \times 5^2$ in exponential form.

ANSWERS

EXERCISE 5 (a)

1. (i) 13	(ii) 11	(iii) 42	(iv) 5	(v) 21	(vi) 24
2. (i) 19	(ii) 62	(iii) 97	(iv) 13	(v) 7	(vi) 26
3. 43	4. 13 kg		5. 18	6. 25 cm	7. 11 minutes

8. 3 girls, Each girl gets 35 rings, 27 bracelets and 108 earrings.

EXERCISE 5 (b)

1. (i) 576	(ii) 74750	(iii) 19536	(iv) 5040	(v) 1512
2. (i) 19404	(ii) 14400	(iii) 660	(iv) 8004	(v) 25200
3. 346	4. 45 m	5. 96 m	6. 6:36 a.m	7. 1179 8. 160

13. No.

MENTAL MATHS - 3

1. (i) 7 m	2. True	3. 112	4. 48	5. 21	6. $2^2 \times 3$ 7. (c)

8. $2^3 \times 3^2 \times 5^2$

6. Fractions

6.1 Introduction

Fraction is a part of the whole. It is represented by $\frac{a}{b}$, where a and b are whole numbers and $b \neq 0$.

The number above the horizontal line (also known as the division line) is called the **numerator** and the number below it is called the **denominator**. *a* is the numerator, *b* is the denominator.

For example :

$\frac{6}{11}, \frac{7}{15}, \frac{3}{4}$ are all fractions with 6, 7 and 3 respectively as numerators and 11, 15 and 4 as denominators.

$$\therefore \text{ Fraction} = \frac{\text{Numerator}}{\text{Denominator}}$$

$$= \frac{\text{The number of parts to be taken}}{\text{The number of parts into which the whole is divided}}$$

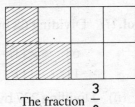

The fraction $\frac{3}{8}$

6.2 Types of Fractions

1. **Decimal Fraction:** A fraction whose denominator is 10,100, 1000 or any other higher power of 10 is called a decimal fraction.

For example :

$\frac{4}{10}, \frac{33}{100}, \frac{65}{1000}, \frac{731}{10000}$ are all decimal fractions.

2. **Vulgar Fraction:** A fraction whose denominator is a whole number other than 10 or any other power of 10 is called a vulgar fraction.

For example :

$\frac{6}{11}, \frac{23}{351}, \frac{69}{1009}$ are all vulgar fractions.

3. **Proper Fraction:** A fraction $\frac{a}{b}$ ($b \neq 0$) where $a > 0$ and $a < b$, i.e., the numerator is less than the denominator is called a proper fraction.

For example :

$\frac{2}{3}, \frac{5}{13}, \frac{39}{451}$ are all proper fractions.

4. **Improper Fraction:** A fraction $\frac{a}{b}$ ($b \neq 0$) where $a = b$ or $a > b$, i.e., the numerator is greater than or equal to the denominator is called an improper fraction.

For example :

$\frac{6}{5}, \frac{5}{5}, \frac{9}{7}, \frac{46}{41}$ are all improper fractions.

5. **Mixed Fraction:** A fraction like $a\frac{b}{c}$, i.e., a combination of a whole number a and a proper fraction $\frac{b}{c}$ is called a mixed fraction (or mixed number).

$$a\frac{b}{c} = a + \frac{b}{c}.$$

For example : $2\frac{1}{3}, -6\frac{2}{5}, 8\frac{5}{11}, -13\frac{16}{41}$ are all mixed fractions.

Note : In fact every mixed fraction can be written as an improper fraction and every improper fraction can be written as a mixed fraction.

Ex. 1 *Convert each of the following into improper fraction.*

(i) $12\frac{6}{7}$ 　　　　　　(ii) $3\frac{8}{23}$.

Sol. (i) $12\frac{6}{7} = \frac{12 \times 7 + 6}{7} = \frac{90}{7}$. 　　(ii) $3\frac{8}{23} = \frac{3 \times 23 + 8}{23} = \frac{77}{23}$.

Ex. 2 *Convert each of the following into mixed fraction.*

(i) $\frac{68}{11}$ 　　　　　　(ii) $\frac{237}{21}$.

Sol. (i) Dividing 68 by 11, we get

$\therefore \frac{68}{11} = \frac{6 \times 11 + 2}{11} = 6\frac{2}{11}$.

(ii) Dividing 237 by 21, we get

$\therefore \frac{237}{21} = \frac{11 \times 21 + 6}{21} = 11\frac{6}{21}$.

$$11\overline{)68}(6$$
$$\underline{66}$$
$$2$$

$$21\overline{)237}(11$$
$$\underline{21}$$
$$27$$
$$\underline{21}$$
$$6$$

Note : A fraction does not alter its value if you multiply or divide both numerator and denominator by the same non-zero number.

For example : $\frac{3}{7} = \frac{3 \times 2}{7 \times 2} = \frac{6}{14}$ and $\frac{15}{25} = \frac{15 \div 5}{25 \div 5} = \frac{3}{5}$.

6.3 Simplest Form of a Fraction

A fraction $\frac{a}{b}$ is said to be in its simplest form or lowest terms *when a and b do not have any other common factor except 1. i.e., the H.C.F. of a and b is 1.*

Reduction of a fraction to its lowest terms

Method 1: A fraction is reduced to lowest terms by dividing both numerator and denominator by all the factors common to both.

Ex. 3 *Reduce* $\frac{45}{105}$ *to its lowest terms.*

Sol. The common factors are 5 and 3 $\therefore$ Cancelling by 5 and then 3, we have $\frac{45}{105} = \frac{45}{105} = \frac{3}{7}$.

Method 2: To reduce any fraction $\frac{a}{b}$ $(b \neq 0)$ to its lowest terms, the second method is to find the H.C.F. of a and b and divide both by the H.C.F.

Ex. 4 *Reduce* $\frac{65}{117}$ *to the lowest terms.*

$$65 = 13 \times 5$$
$$117 = 13 \times 9$$
$$\therefore \quad \text{HCF} = 13$$

Sol. The H.C.F. of 65 and 117 is 13. Dividing both by 13, we have $\frac{65}{117} = \frac{65 \div 13}{117 \div 13} = \frac{5}{9}$.

- **Equivalent Fractions:** Fractions having equal values (in their simplest form) are called equivalent fractions. To check whether two fractions are equivalent or not we reduce both of them to the simplest form. If the two simplest forms are equal then the two fractions are equivalent.

For example :

$\frac{16}{36}$ and $\frac{4}{9}$ are equivalent fractions. Since $\frac{16}{36} = \frac{16 \div 4}{36 \div 4} = \frac{4}{9}$.

- **Simple Fraction:** A fraction $\frac{a}{b}$ ($b \neq 0$) where a and b both are whole numbers is called a simple fraction.

For example :

$\frac{4}{7}, \frac{6}{11}, \frac{2}{5}$ are all simple fractions, etc.

- **Complex Fraction:** A fraction whose numerator and denominator are either or both fractions is called a complex fraction.

For example :

$\dfrac{\frac{2}{3}}{\frac{4}{7}}, \quad \dfrac{\frac{2}{6}}{11}, \quad \dfrac{4\frac{2}{11}}{6}$ are all complex fractions.

EXERCISE 6 (a)

1. **Classify the following fractions as decimal, vulgar, proper, improper or mixed fractions.**
   (i) $\frac{4}{21}$ (ii) $\frac{301}{13}$ (iii) $\frac{29}{29}$ (iv) $\frac{64}{1000}$ (v) $\frac{23}{10^4}$ (vi) $3\frac{3}{7}$ (vii) $\frac{63}{8000}$

2. **Convert each of the following mixed fractions to an improper fraction.**
   (i) $5\frac{7}{8}$ (ii) $4\frac{11}{16}$ (iii) $19\frac{4}{15}$ (iv) $41\frac{17}{39}$ (v) $6\frac{15}{23}$

3. **Convert each of the following improper fractions to a mixed fraction :**
   (i) $\frac{91}{11}$ (ii) $\frac{29}{12}$ (iii) $\frac{234}{20}$ (iv) $\frac{94}{13}$ (v) $\frac{1234}{101}$.

4. **Reduce the following fractions to their lowest terms.**
   (i) $\frac{36}{48}$ (ii) $\frac{65}{91}$ (iii) $\frac{72}{272}$ (iv) $\frac{324}{396}$ (v) $\frac{330}{726}$.

5. **Write an equivalent fraction of $\frac{4}{7}$.**
   (i) with denominator 28   (ii) with numerator 48.

6. **Write an equivalent fraction of $\frac{36}{84}$ with**
   (i) numerator 3   (ii) denominater 21

7. **Which of the following fractions are complex fractions ?**

(i) $\dfrac{-7}{4\frac{1}{3}}$ (ii) $\dfrac{16}{21}$ (iii) $\dfrac{0}{-8}$ (iv) $\dfrac{2\frac{3}{11}}{8}$ (v) $\dfrac{27}{27}$ (vi) $\dfrac{\frac{6}{11}}{\frac{4}{7}}$ (vii) $\dfrac{-7\frac{3}{5}}{8\frac{2}{11}}$

6.4 Like and Unlike Fractions

Fractions having the same denominator but different numerators are called like fractions whereas fractions with different denominators are called unlike fractions.

For example : $\dfrac{1}{8}, \dfrac{4}{8}, \dfrac{2}{8}$ *are all like fractions whereas* $\dfrac{3}{8}, \dfrac{2}{7}, \dfrac{6}{11}$ *are unlike fractions.*

■ **To convert unlike fractions to like fractions.**

1. Find the L.C.M. of the denominator of the given fractions.
2. Convert each fraction into an equivalent fraction having denominator as the L.C.M. of the denominators of the given fractions.

Ex. 1. *Convert the fractions* $\dfrac{7}{12}, \dfrac{3}{4}, \dfrac{2}{3}$ *into like fractions.*

Sol.   L.C.M. of 12, 4, 3 is $3 \times 4 = 12$.

3	12, 4, 3
4	4, 4, 1
	1, 1, 1

Converting all the fractions to equivalent fractions with denominator 12,

$$\dfrac{7}{12} = \dfrac{7 \times 1}{12 \times 1} = \dfrac{7}{12}, \dfrac{3}{4} = \dfrac{3 \times 3}{4 \times 3} = \dfrac{9}{12}, \dfrac{2}{3} = \dfrac{2 \times 4}{3 \times 4} = \dfrac{8}{12}$$

$\therefore$ $\dfrac{7}{12}, \dfrac{9}{12}, \dfrac{8}{12}$ are the required like fractions.

6.5 Comparison of Two Fractions

We compare two fractions $\dfrac{a}{b}$ and $\dfrac{c}{d}$ as under :

(i) **If** $ad > bc$ **then** $\dfrac{a}{b} > \dfrac{c}{d}$ **(ii)** **If** $ad = bc$ **then** $\dfrac{a}{b} = \dfrac{c}{d}$ **(iii)** **If** $ad < bc$ **then** $\dfrac{a}{b} < \dfrac{c}{d}$

Ex. 1. *Compare the following pairs of fractions :*

(i) $\dfrac{3}{4}, \dfrac{5}{12}$ (ii) $\dfrac{2}{5}, \dfrac{10}{25}$ (iii) $\dfrac{1}{8}, \dfrac{3}{-32}$

Sol. (i) On finding the cross product of $\dfrac{3}{4}$ and $\dfrac{5}{2}$ as :

$\dfrac{3}{4} \bowtie \dfrac{5}{12}$ we have $3 \times 12 = 36$ and $4 \times 5 = 20$ $\because 36 > 20$ $\therefore \dfrac{3}{4} > \dfrac{5}{12}$.

(ii) On finding the cross product of $\dfrac{2}{5}$ and $\dfrac{10}{25}$ as :

$\dfrac{2}{5} \bowtie \dfrac{10}{25}$ we have $2 \times 25 = 50$ and $5 \times 10 = 50$

$\because 50 = 50$, $\therefore \dfrac{2}{5} = \dfrac{10}{25}$

(iii) First writing the given fractions in standard form, the given fractions are $\frac{1}{8}$ and $\frac{-3}{32}$. On finding their cross product

$$\frac{1}{8} \diagdown \frac{-3}{32} \text{ we have } 1 \times 32 = 32 \text{ and } 8 \times -3 = -24$$

$$\therefore \ 32 > -24 \ \therefore \ \frac{1}{8} > \frac{3}{-32}.$$

> Note that first we have written $\frac{3}{-32}$ in the standard form $\frac{-32}{3}$.

6.6 Comparison of More Than two Fractions

To compare more than two fractions we

(i) *Convert the fractions into equivalent fractions.*

(ii) *The fraction having the greater numerator is greater.*

> Fractions are said to be arranged in **Ascending Order** of *magnitude when each one is less than the one that follows it; in* **Descending Order** of *magnitude when each is greater than the one that follows it.*

Ex. 1. *Arrange* $\frac{13}{20}, \frac{5}{8}$ *and* $\frac{7}{10}$ *in ascending order of magnitude.*

Sol.   We first convert the unlike fractions to equivalent like fractions.

L.C.M. of 20, 8, 10 = $2 \times 2 \times 5 \times 2 = 40$

Now $\frac{13}{20} = \frac{13 \times 2}{20 \times 2} = \frac{26}{40}$; $\frac{5}{8} = \frac{5 \times 5}{8 \times 5} = \frac{25}{40}$; $\frac{7}{10} = \frac{7 \times 4}{10 \times 4} = \frac{28}{40}$

2	20, 8, 10
2	10, 4, 5
5	5, 2, 5
2	1, 2, 1
	1, 1, 1

Comparing numerators : $25 < 26 < 28$ $\therefore \ \frac{25}{40} < \frac{26}{40} < \frac{28}{40}$

$\therefore$ Given fractions in ascending order are $\frac{5}{8}, \frac{13}{20}, \frac{7}{10}$.

Ex. 2. *Arrange* $\frac{3}{5}, \frac{7}{10}, \frac{6}{25}, \frac{11}{30}$ *in descending order of magnitude.*

Sol.   First convert $\frac{3}{5}, \frac{7}{10}, \frac{6}{25}, \frac{11}{30}$ to like fractions

L.C.M. of 5, 10, 25, 30 = $5 \times 2 \times 5 \times 3 = 150$

Now $\frac{3}{5} = \frac{3 \times 30}{5 \times 30} = \frac{90}{150}$; $\frac{7}{10} = \frac{7 \times 15}{10 \times 15} = \frac{105}{150}$

5	5, 10, 25, 30
2	1, 2, 5, 6
	1, 1, 5, 3

$\frac{6}{25} = \frac{6 \times 6}{25 \times 6} = \frac{36}{150}$; $\frac{11}{30} = \frac{11 \times 5}{30 \times 5} = \frac{55}{150}$

Comparing numerators

$\frac{105}{150} > \frac{90}{150} > \frac{55}{150} > \frac{36}{150} \Rightarrow \frac{7}{10} > \frac{3}{5} > \frac{11}{30} > \frac{6}{25}$

$\therefore$ The given fractions in descending order of magnitude are $\frac{7}{10}, \frac{3}{5}, \frac{11}{30}, \frac{6}{25}$.

6.7 To Insert a Fraction between two given Fractions

> If $\frac{a}{b}$ and $\frac{c}{d}$ are two fractions, then $\frac{a+c}{b+d}$ lies between $\frac{a}{b}$ and $\frac{c}{d}$.

i.e. The numerator of the required fraction is the sum of the numerators of the given fractions and the denominator of the required fraction is the sum of the denominators of the given fractions.

Ex. 3. *Insert a fraction between $\frac{2}{3}$ and $\frac{6}{7}$.*

Sol. Fraction between $\frac{2}{3}$ and $\frac{6}{7}$ is $\frac{2+6}{3+7} = \frac{8}{10}$ $\therefore \frac{2}{3} < \frac{8}{10} < \frac{6}{7}$.

Ex. 4. *Insert 3 fractions between $\frac{1}{3}$ and $\frac{7}{9}$.*

Sol. Fraction between $\frac{1}{3}$ and $\frac{7}{9} = \frac{1+7}{3+9} = \frac{8}{12}$ $\therefore \frac{1}{3} < \frac{8}{12} < \frac{7}{9}$

Fraction between $\frac{1}{3}$ and $\frac{8}{12} = \frac{1+8}{3+12} = \frac{9}{15}$ $\therefore \frac{1}{3} < \frac{9}{15} < \frac{8}{12} < \frac{7}{9}$

Fraction between $\frac{8}{12}$ and $\frac{7}{9} = \frac{8+7}{12+9} = \frac{15}{21}$ $\therefore \frac{1}{3} < \frac{9}{15} < \frac{8}{12} < \frac{15}{21} < \frac{7}{9}$

$\therefore \frac{9}{15}, \frac{8}{12}, \frac{15}{21}$ are three fractions between $\frac{1}{3}$ and $\frac{7}{9}$.

EXERCISE 6 (b)

1. Convert $\frac{17}{20}, \frac{4}{5}, \frac{5}{6}, \frac{3}{4}$ into like fractions.

2. Fill in the blanks with <, > or = to make the statement true.

   (i) $\frac{12}{21}$ ...... $\frac{7}{12}$ (ii) $\frac{-3}{5}$ .... $\frac{4}{9}$ (iii) $\frac{15}{25}$ ..... $\frac{6}{10}$ (iv) $\frac{7}{19}$ .... $\frac{4}{21}$ (v) $\frac{6}{7}$ .... $\frac{12}{5}$ (vi) $\frac{5}{2}$ .... $\frac{-6}{9}$

3. Arrange the given fractions in ascending order of magnitude.

   (i) $\frac{2}{3}, \frac{9}{16}, \frac{3}{20}, \frac{1}{12}$ (ii) $\frac{5}{6}, \frac{5}{8}, \frac{2}{9}, \frac{13}{24}$ (iii) $\frac{8}{9}, \frac{9}{5}, \frac{6}{7}, \frac{2}{3}$ (iv) $\frac{8}{11}, \frac{2}{33}, \frac{5}{6}$.

4. Fill in the blanks to make the statements true.

   (i) $\frac{1}{5} = \frac{?}{30}$ (ii) $\frac{9}{16} = \frac{?}{96}$ (iii) $\frac{6}{7} = \frac{90}{?}$ (iv) $\frac{16}{36} = \frac{?}{9}$ (v) $\frac{32}{40} = \frac{4}{?}$

5. Insert a fraction between each of the given pairs of fractions.

   (i) $\frac{3}{5}, \frac{9}{11}$ (ii) $\frac{1}{5}, \frac{2}{13}$ (iii) $\frac{1}{4}, \frac{1}{3}$ (iv) $\frac{5}{7}, \frac{8}{13}$

6. Insert three fractions between each of the given pairs of fractions.

   (i) $\frac{7}{11}, \frac{3}{4}$ (ii) $\frac{1}{6}, \frac{1}{7}$ (iii) $\frac{5}{6}, \frac{4}{7}$ (iv) $\frac{7}{12}, \frac{9}{14}$

7. Write the first quantity as a fraction of the second quantity:

   (i) 36 minutes, 2 hours   (ii) 25 days, 5 weeks   (iii) 2 hours , 100 minutes   (iv) 75 cm, 1m.

OPERATIONS ON FRACTIONS

6.8 Addition and Subtraction

Rule 1. *To add or subtract two like fractions we add or subtract the numerator, the denominator remaining the same.*

For example : $\dfrac{3}{11} + \dfrac{7}{11} = \dfrac{3+7}{11} = \dfrac{10}{11}$; $\dfrac{7}{9} - \dfrac{2}{9} = \dfrac{7-2}{9} = \dfrac{5}{9}$

> **Rule 2.** *To add or subtract unlike fractions we convert them to equivalent like fractions and then add or subtract as in Rule 1.*

Ex. 1 *Find the sum :* $\dfrac{3}{4} + \dfrac{2}{5}$.

Sol. L. C. M. of 4 and 5 = 20

$$\therefore \dfrac{3}{4} + \dfrac{2}{5} = \dfrac{3\times 5 + 2\times 4}{20} = \dfrac{15+8}{20} = \dfrac{23}{20} = 1\dfrac{3}{20}.$$

Ex. 2 *Find the difference* $\dfrac{7}{8} - \dfrac{3}{4}$.

Sol. L. C. M of 4 and 8 = 8

$$\therefore \dfrac{7}{8} - \dfrac{3}{4} = \dfrac{7\times 1 - 3\times 2}{8} = \dfrac{7-6}{8} = \dfrac{1}{8}.$$

> **Note:** *To add or subtract mixed fractions, we can first convert them to improper fractions and then perform the operations as above. The second method is to add or subtract the whole number parts separately and fractional parts separately.*

Ex. 3 *Calculate* (a) $2\dfrac{1}{3} + 1\dfrac{1}{2}$ (b) $5\dfrac{1}{2} + 3\dfrac{2}{3}$.

Sol. (a) Converting to improper fractions we have $2\dfrac{1}{3} + 1\dfrac{1}{2} = \dfrac{7}{3} + \dfrac{3}{2}$

L.C.M. of 3 and 2 = 6

$$\therefore \dfrac{7}{3} + \dfrac{3}{2} = \dfrac{7\times 2 + 3\times 3}{6} = \dfrac{14+9}{6} = \dfrac{23}{6} = 3\dfrac{5}{6}.$$

Solving by second method

$$2\dfrac{1}{3} + 1\dfrac{1}{2} = (2+1) + \left(\dfrac{1}{3} + \dfrac{1}{2}\right)$$

$$= 3 + \dfrac{2+3}{6} \quad \text{(L.C.M. of 2 and 3 = 6)} = 3 + \dfrac{5}{6} = 3\dfrac{5}{6}.$$

(b) Converting to improper fractions we have $5\dfrac{1}{2} - 3\dfrac{2}{3} = \dfrac{11}{2} - \dfrac{11}{3}$

L.C.M. of 2 and 3 = 6 $\therefore \dfrac{11}{2} - \dfrac{11}{3} = \dfrac{11\times 3 - 11\times 2}{6} = \dfrac{33-22}{6} = \dfrac{11}{6} = 1\dfrac{5}{6}.$

Solving by second method

$$5\dfrac{1}{2} - 3\dfrac{2}{3} = (5-3) + \left(\dfrac{1}{2} - \dfrac{2}{3}\right) = 2 + \dfrac{1\times 3 - 2\times 2}{6} = 2 + \dfrac{3-4}{6}$$

$$= 2 + \left(-\dfrac{1}{6}\right) = \dfrac{2}{1} - \dfrac{1}{6} = \dfrac{2\times 6 - 1\times 1}{6} = \dfrac{12-1}{6} = \dfrac{11}{6} = 1\dfrac{5}{6}.$$

6.9 Multiplication

To multiply two or more fractions

(i) Convert the mixed fractions (if any) to improper fractions.

(ii) The numerator of the required fraction is the product of the numerators of the given fractions and the denominator of the required fraction is the product of the denominators of the given fractions.

If $\dfrac{a}{b}$ and $\dfrac{c}{d}$ are the given fractions then $\dfrac{a}{b} \times \dfrac{c}{d} = \dfrac{a \times c}{b \times d}$.

(iii) Reduce the answer to the lowest terms or while multiplying cancel the common factors (if any) from the numerators and denominators of the given fractions and then proceed as in (ii) above.

Ex. 4 *Calculate* (a) $1\dfrac{3}{4} \times \dfrac{2}{3} \times \dfrac{4}{28}$ (b) $\dfrac{2}{3} \times \dfrac{15}{24} \times \dfrac{4}{5}$.

Sol. (a) $\dfrac{7}{4} \times \dfrac{2}{3} \times \dfrac{4}{28} = \dfrac{1}{3 \times 2} = \dfrac{1}{6}$. (b) $\dfrac{2}{3} \times \dfrac{15}{24} \times \dfrac{4}{5} = \dfrac{1}{3}$.

6.10 Operating "of"

'of' works like multiplication

Ex. 5 *Evaluate* (a) $\dfrac{1}{9}$ *of 36* (b) $\dfrac{3}{5}$ *of 30* (c) $\dfrac{1}{4}$ *of* $\dfrac{12}{15}$ (d) $\dfrac{7}{8}$ *of Rs 56*.

Sol. (a) $\dfrac{1}{9}$ of $36 = \dfrac{1}{9} \times 36 = \mathbf{4}$. (b) $\dfrac{3}{5}$ of $30 = \dfrac{3}{5} \times 30 = 3 \times 6 = \mathbf{18}$.

(c) $\dfrac{1}{4}$ of $\dfrac{12}{15} = \dfrac{1}{4} \times \dfrac{12}{15} = \dfrac{1}{5}$. (d) $\dfrac{7}{8}$ of Rs $56 = \dfrac{7}{8} \times$ Rs $56 = $ Rs $(7 \times 7) = \mathbf{Rs\ 49}$.

6.11 Reciprocal of a given Fraction

Reciprocal of any non-zero fraction $\dfrac{a}{b}$ $(a \neq 0, b \neq 0)$ *is* $\dfrac{b}{a}$.

For example : The reciprocal of $\dfrac{4}{5}$ is $\dfrac{5}{4}$.

6.12 Division

If $\dfrac{a}{b}$ and $\dfrac{c}{d}$ are two fractions where $\dfrac{c}{d} \neq 0$ then $\dfrac{a}{b} \div \dfrac{c}{d} = \dfrac{a}{b} \times \dfrac{d}{c}$
i.e. the dividend is multiplied by the reciprocal of the divisor.

Ex. 6 *Work out :* (i) $\dfrac{2}{5} \div \dfrac{1}{2}$ (ii) $\dfrac{1}{4} \div \dfrac{2}{5}$ (iii) $1\dfrac{1}{2} \div 1\dfrac{3}{5}$ (iv) $2\dfrac{3}{4} \div \dfrac{4}{5}$ (v) $\dfrac{4}{5} \div 2$

Sol. (i) $\dfrac{2}{5} \div \dfrac{1}{2} = \dfrac{2}{5} \times \dfrac{2}{1} = \dfrac{4}{5}$. (ii) $\dfrac{1}{4} \div \dfrac{2}{5} = \dfrac{1}{4} \times \dfrac{5}{2} = \dfrac{5}{8}$.

(iii) $1\dfrac{1}{2} \div 1\dfrac{3}{5} = \dfrac{3}{2} \div \dfrac{8}{5} = \dfrac{3}{2} \times \dfrac{5}{8} = \dfrac{15}{16}$. (iv) $2\dfrac{3}{4} \div \dfrac{4}{5} = \dfrac{11}{5} \div \dfrac{4}{5} = \dfrac{11}{5} \times \dfrac{5}{4} = \dfrac{55}{20} = \dfrac{11}{4} = 2\dfrac{3}{4}$.

(v) $\dfrac{4}{5} \div 2 = \dfrac{4}{5} \div \dfrac{2}{1} = \dfrac{4}{5} \times \dfrac{1}{2} = \dfrac{2}{5}$.

6.13 Complex Fractions

To change a complex fraction to a simple fraction we proceed as under.

$$\therefore \dfrac{\dfrac{a}{b}}{\dfrac{c}{d}} = \dfrac{a}{b} \div \dfrac{c}{d} = \dfrac{a}{b} \times \dfrac{d}{c}.$$

x. 7 *Convert each of the following to a simple fraction.*

(a) $\dfrac{3\frac{1}{3}}{3\frac{1}{2}}$

(b) $\dfrac{9}{\frac{1}{5}}$

(c) $\dfrac{\frac{3}{8}}{4}$

(d) $\dfrac{\frac{2}{9}}{\frac{1}{8}}$

(e) $\dfrac{2\frac{1}{2}}{\frac{5}{7}}$

ol.

(a) $\dfrac{3\frac{1}{3}}{3\frac{1}{2}} = \dfrac{\frac{10}{3}}{\frac{7}{2}} = \dfrac{10}{3} \div \dfrac{7}{2} = \dfrac{10}{3} \times \dfrac{2}{7} = \dfrac{20}{21}$.

(b) $\dfrac{9}{\frac{1}{5}} = 9 \div \dfrac{1}{5} = 9 \times \dfrac{5}{1} = \mathbf{45}$.

(c) $\dfrac{3}{8} \div 4 = \dfrac{3}{8} \times \dfrac{1}{4} = \dfrac{3}{32}$.

(d) $\dfrac{\frac{2}{9}}{\frac{1}{8}} = \dfrac{2}{9} \div \dfrac{1}{8} = \dfrac{2}{9} \times \dfrac{8}{1} = \dfrac{16}{9} = 1\dfrac{7}{9}$

(e) $\dfrac{2\frac{1}{2}}{\frac{5}{7}} = \dfrac{\frac{5}{2}}{\frac{5}{7}} = \dfrac{5}{2} \div \dfrac{5}{7} = \dfrac{\overset{1}{\cancel{5}}}{2} \times \dfrac{7}{\underset{1}{\cancel{5}}} = \dfrac{7}{2} = 3\dfrac{1}{2}$.

EXERCISE 6 (c)

1. Evaluate

(a) $\dfrac{2}{7} + \dfrac{4}{7}$

(b) $\dfrac{2}{11} + \dfrac{5}{7}$

(c) $\dfrac{8}{15} + \dfrac{7}{45} + 4$

(d) $4\dfrac{3}{4} + 2\dfrac{5}{8}$

(e) $2\dfrac{5}{9} + 3\dfrac{2}{3} + 2\dfrac{2}{7}$

2. Calculate

(a) $\dfrac{11}{15} - \dfrac{7}{15}$

(b) $\dfrac{4}{5} - \dfrac{1}{3}$

(c) $3\dfrac{3}{4} - 1\dfrac{1}{4}$

(d) $1\dfrac{3}{4} - \dfrac{4}{25}$

(e) $2\dfrac{9}{10} - 1\dfrac{13}{15}$

3. Simplify

(a) $2\dfrac{1}{2} + 3\dfrac{1}{6} - 4\dfrac{1}{3}$

(b) $\dfrac{1}{60} - \dfrac{1}{42} + \dfrac{1}{90}$

(c) $2\dfrac{3}{4} + \dfrac{13}{8} + \dfrac{23}{10} - 3\dfrac{5}{24} + 1\dfrac{8}{15}$

(d) $2\dfrac{1}{5} + 1\dfrac{4}{7} - 4\dfrac{1}{2} - \dfrac{3}{5} + 2\dfrac{8}{35}$

4. What must be added to $15\dfrac{3}{5}$ to get a sum of $16\dfrac{7}{11}$?

5. What is the least number which should be added to $16\dfrac{7}{11}$ to make it an integer.

6. A box containing tomatoes has a total weight of $5\dfrac{7}{8}$ kg. The box when empty has a weight of $1\dfrac{1}{4}$ kg. What is the weight of the tomatoes?

7. Multiply

(a) $\dfrac{6}{5} \times \dfrac{25}{36}$

(b) $\dfrac{2}{5} \times \dfrac{10}{3}$

(c) $\dfrac{4}{5} \times \dfrac{3}{8}$

(d) $\dfrac{4}{5} \times \dfrac{3}{7} \times \dfrac{1}{8}$

(e) $1\dfrac{1}{6} \times \dfrac{3}{7}$

(f) $6\dfrac{9}{10} \times 1\dfrac{1}{23}$

(g) $\dfrac{4}{18} \times \dfrac{35}{20} \times \dfrac{9}{14}$

(h) $6\dfrac{3}{10} \times 2\dfrac{1}{7} \times \dfrac{5}{9}$

(i) $9\dfrac{2}{3} \times 1\dfrac{1}{29} \times \dfrac{6}{15} \times 7\dfrac{1}{5}$

8. Divide.

(a) $\dfrac{2}{5} \div \dfrac{3}{4}$

(b) $\dfrac{8}{9} \div 4$

(c) $4\dfrac{3}{5} \div \dfrac{2}{3}$

(d) $2\dfrac{3}{5} \div 3\dfrac{1}{2}$

(e) $\dfrac{5}{9} \div \dfrac{5}{6}$

(f) $6\dfrac{2}{5} \div 1\dfrac{1}{15}$

9. **Convert the following complex fractions to simple fractions.**

(a) $\dfrac{\frac{3}{10}}{\frac{1}{2}}$ (b) $\dfrac{\frac{7}{10}}{\frac{2}{5}}$ (c) $\dfrac{4\frac{2}{3}}{3\frac{1}{9}}$ (d) $\dfrac{2\frac{3}{4}}{\frac{4}{5}}$ (e) $\dfrac{3\frac{1}{4}}{13}$ (f) $\dfrac{8}{\frac{1}{4}}$

10. **Find the value of:**

(a) $\dfrac{3}{4}$ of 32 kg   (b) $\dfrac{5}{8}$ of 20 m   (c) $\dfrac{4}{5}$ of Rs 90   (d) $\dfrac{4}{9}$ of $\dfrac{1}{24}$ (e) $\dfrac{7}{9}$ of 45   (f) $4\dfrac{1}{5}$ of $\dfrac{1}{3}$

11. **Calculate the area of each of two rectangles.**

(a)   [rectangle] $1\frac{1}{2}$ cm   (b)   [rectangle] $2\frac{1}{2}$ cm

        4 cm $9\frac{2}{3}$ cm

12. A melon weighs $1\dfrac{3}{4}$ kg. Work out the total weight of $8\dfrac{1}{4}$ melons.

13. A company can repair $2\dfrac{1}{5}$ km of road in a day. How many days will it take to repair a road of length $24\dfrac{3}{5}$ km?

14. Find the difference between $\dfrac{3}{5}$ of 40 km and $\dfrac{2}{3}$ of 30 km.

6.14 Simplification of Numerical Expressions

To simplify numerical expressions the operations have to be performed according to the rule of **BODMAS**, i.e., in the order *brackets, of, division, multiplication, addition and subtraction.*

Ex. 8 Simplify :

(a) $\dfrac{1}{2} - \left(\dfrac{4}{5} \text{ of } \dfrac{5}{6}\right) + \dfrac{1}{4}$ (b) $\left(4\dfrac{2}{3} \times 5\dfrac{4}{7}\right) \div 3\dfrac{1}{4}$

Sol.

(a) $\dfrac{1}{2} - \left(\dfrac{4}{5} \text{ of } \dfrac{5}{6}\right) + \dfrac{1}{4} = \dfrac{1}{2} - \dfrac{\overset{2}{\cancel{4}}}{\cancel{5}} \times \dfrac{\cancel{5}}{\cancel{6}_{3}}^{1} + \dfrac{1}{4} = \dfrac{1}{2} - \dfrac{2}{3} + \dfrac{1}{4} = \dfrac{6-8+3}{12} = \dfrac{9-8}{12} = \dfrac{1}{12}.$

(b) $\left(4\dfrac{2}{3} \times 5\dfrac{4}{7}\right) \div 3\dfrac{1}{4} = \left(\dfrac{14}{\cancel{3}} \times \dfrac{39}{\cancel{7}}\right) \div \dfrac{13}{4} = 26 \div \dfrac{13}{4} = 26 \times \dfrac{4}{13} = 8.$

6.15 Handling Brackets

The brackets are handled or removed from the innermost to outermost which are normally in the following order :

(i) ‾ ; bar or vinculum   (ii) ( ); parentheses

(iii) { }; curly brackets   (iv) [ ]; square brackets

Ex. 9 *Simplify :*

(a) $\dfrac{3}{19}$ of $\left\{\dfrac{7}{9} + \left(\dfrac{3}{4} \div \overline{\dfrac{1}{2} - \dfrac{1}{3}}\right)\right\}$ (b) $\left(5\dfrac{1}{4} - 2\dfrac{1}{3}\right) + \dfrac{1}{3}$ of $\left(5\dfrac{1}{2} \div 2\dfrac{1}{5}\right)$

ol. (a) $\frac{3}{19}$ of $\left\{\frac{7}{9} + \left(\frac{3}{4} \div \overline{\frac{1}{2} - \frac{1}{3}}\right)\right\}$

$= \frac{3}{19}$ of $\left\{\frac{7}{9} + \left(\frac{3}{4} \div \frac{3-2}{6}\right)\right\} = \frac{3}{19}$ of $\left\{\frac{7}{9} + \left(\frac{3}{4} \div \frac{1}{6}\right)\right\}$

$= \frac{3}{19}$ of $\left\{\frac{7}{9} + \frac{3}{4} \times \frac{\overset{3}{\cancel{6}}}{1}\right\} = \frac{3}{19}$ of $\left\{\frac{7}{9} + \frac{9}{2}\right\} = \frac{3}{19}$ of $\frac{7 \times 2 + 9 \times 9}{18}$

$= \frac{3}{19}$ of $\frac{14 + 81}{18} = \frac{3}{19}$ of $\frac{95}{18} = \frac{\cancel{3}}{\cancel{19}} \times \frac{\cancel{95}}{\cancel{18}} = \frac{5}{6}$.

(b) $\left(5\frac{1}{4} - 2\frac{1}{3}\right) + \frac{1}{3}\left(5\frac{1}{2} \div 2\frac{1}{5}\right)$

$= \left(\frac{21}{4} - \frac{7}{3}\right) + \frac{1}{3}\left(\frac{11}{2} \div \frac{11}{5}\right) = \frac{21 \times 3 - 7 \times 4}{12} + \frac{1}{3} \times \frac{\overset{1}{\cancel{11}}}{2} \times \frac{5}{\underset{1}{\cancel{11}}}$

$= \frac{63 - 28}{12} + \frac{5}{6} = \frac{35}{12} + \frac{5}{6} = \frac{35 + 5 \times 2}{12} = \frac{\overset{15}{\cancel{45}}}{\underset{4}{\cancel{12}}} = \frac{15}{4} = 3\frac{3}{4}$.

EXERCISE 6 (d)

Simplify :

1. $5\frac{1}{4} - 2\frac{1}{3} + \frac{1}{3}$ of $5\frac{1}{2}$

2. $\left(4\frac{2}{3} \times 5\frac{4}{7}\right) \div 3\frac{1}{4}$

3. $\left\{\frac{3}{7} \div \left(\frac{1}{14} + \frac{13}{14}\right)\right\} \times \frac{7}{13}$

4. $4\frac{2}{3} + 6\frac{1}{5} - 2\frac{1}{5} \div \left(\frac{5}{6} - \frac{3}{5}\right)$

5. $\dfrac{\frac{1}{3}\left(\frac{1}{2} + \frac{1}{5}\right)}{\frac{1}{5}\left(\frac{1}{2} + \frac{1}{3}\right)}$

6. $\dfrac{3\frac{1}{2} + 2\frac{1}{3} + 2\frac{4}{5}}{\frac{1}{7} \text{ of } \frac{11}{12} \text{ of } \frac{14}{15}}$

7. $3\frac{4}{5} + \left\{4\frac{1}{2} - \left(\frac{6}{7} \times \overline{\frac{1}{5} - \frac{1}{6}}\right)\right\}$

8. $\left(\frac{16}{17} \text{ of } 6\frac{4}{5}\right) - 4\frac{1}{5} - \left\{1\frac{1}{14} \div \left(\frac{1}{2} + \frac{1}{7}\right)\right\}$

9. $\left\{10\frac{5}{6} + \left(49\frac{1}{2} \div 1\frac{2}{9}\right)\right\} \div \left\{30\frac{2}{3} - \left(47\frac{1}{4} \times \frac{20}{189}\right)\right\}$

10. $\left[10\frac{1}{4} - \left\{\frac{3}{7} \text{ of } 15\frac{3}{4} + \left(2\frac{2}{35} \div 1\frac{11}{25}\right)\right\}\right]$

6.16 Word Problems on Fractions

We can apply our knowledge of fractions to our every day life also.

While solving word problems, the whole quantity is always taken as 1.

Ex. 1 *A man bought $4\frac{1}{2}$ kg of apples, $2\frac{3}{4}$ kg of guavas and $3\frac{1}{5}$ kg of oranges. How many kg of fruits did he buy?*

Sol.   Total weight of the fruits

= wt. of apples + wt. of guavas + wt. of oranges.

$$= \left(4\frac{1}{2} + 2\frac{3}{4} + 3\frac{1}{5}\right) kg = (4 + 2 + 3) kg + \left(\frac{1}{2} + \frac{3}{4} + \frac{1}{5}\right) kg$$

$$= \left(9 + \frac{10 + 15 + 4}{20}\right) kg = \left(9 + \frac{29}{20}\right) kg = \left(9 + 1\frac{9}{20}\right) kg = \mathbf{10\frac{9}{20}\ kg.}$$

Ex. 2   *The perimeter of a triangular field is* $43\frac{1}{4}$ *m. If two sides measure* $16\frac{2}{5}$ *m and* $10\frac{1}{3}$ *m, what is th* *length of the third side ?*

Sol.   Perimeter of a triangle = Sum of the three sides

$$\therefore\ 43\frac{1}{4} = 16\frac{2}{5} + 10\frac{1}{3} + \text{Third side.}$$

Third side $= 43\frac{1}{4} - \left(16\frac{2}{5} + 10\frac{1}{3}\right) = \frac{173}{4} - \left(\frac{82}{5} + \frac{31}{3}\right) = \frac{173}{4} - \left(\frac{246 + 155}{15}\right)$

$$= \frac{173}{4} - \frac{401}{15} = \frac{2595 - 1604}{60} = \frac{991}{60} = \mathbf{16\frac{31}{60}\ m.}$$

Ex. 3   *The cost of 1 litre of petrol is Rs* $42\frac{4}{7}$*. What is the cost of* $10\frac{1}{2}$ *litres of petrol?*

Sol.   1 litre of petrol costs Rs $42\frac{4}{7}$

$$\therefore\ 10\frac{1}{2}\ \text{litres of petrol costs Rs}\ 42\frac{4}{7} \times 10\frac{1}{2} = \text{Rs}\ \frac{\overset{149}{\cancel{298}}}{\cancel{7}} \times \frac{\overset{3}{\cancel{21}}}{\cancel{2}} = \mathbf{Rs\ 447.}$$

Ex. 4   *A bag of flour has a weight of* $12\frac{1}{2}$ *kg. Two fifths of it was lost through a hole in the side. How muc* *of it was lost ?*

Sol.   Weight lost $= \frac{2}{5}$ of total wt $= \frac{2}{5}$ of $12\frac{1}{2}$ kg

$$= \frac{2}{5}\ \text{of}\ \frac{25}{2}\ kg = \frac{2}{5} \times \frac{25}{2} = \mathbf{5\ kg.}$$

Ex. 5   *A carpenter cuts off from a plank* $\frac{5}{12}$ *of its length and then* $\frac{6}{7}$ *of what remains. If the remaining* *piece is* $2\frac{1}{2}$ *m long, find the original length of the plank.*

Sol.   Whole is assumed as 1 ∴ Let us take the total length of the plank as 1m.

Portion of the plank cut off $= \frac{5}{12}$

∴ The portion of the plank left

$$= 1 - \frac{5}{12} = \frac{12 - 5}{12} = \frac{7}{12}\ m$$

∴ The portion of the plant cut next

$$= \frac{6}{7} \text{ of } \frac{7}{12} = \frac{6}{7} \times \frac{7}{12} = \frac{1}{2}$$

The remaining portion of the plank

$$= 1 - \left(\frac{5}{12} + \frac{1}{2}\right) = 1 - \frac{5}{12} - \frac{1}{2}$$

$$= \frac{12 - 5 - 6}{12} = \frac{12 - 11}{12} = \frac{1}{12}$$

Given, $\frac{1}{12}$ of the length of the plank $= 2\frac{1}{2}$ m

∴ Length of the plank $= 2\frac{1}{2} \div \frac{1}{12} = \frac{5}{2} \div \frac{1}{12} = \frac{5}{2} \times 12 = \textbf{30 m.}$

Ex.6 *A book has 860 pages. Three twentieths of the pages have pictures on them and the rest are worded. How many pages have on them (a) pictures (b) words?*

Sol (a) Number of pages having pictures $= \frac{3}{20}$ of 860 pages. $= \frac{3}{20} \times 860 = \textbf{129.}$

(b) Number of pages having words = Total number of pages – no. of pages having pictures

$$= 860 - 129 = \textbf{731 pages.}$$

EXERCISE 6 (e)

1. Three girls shared a cake. A gets $\frac{3}{8}$ of the cake, B gets $\frac{1}{4}$ of the remainder. How much does C get ?

2. From a rope $17\frac{1}{4}$ m long, three pieces of lengths $2\frac{3}{5}$ m, $4\frac{2}{7}$ m and $6\frac{1}{4}$ m are cut off. What is the length of the rope left?

3. The perimeter of a rectangular tile is 30 cm. If it is $6\frac{3}{4}$ cm long; find its width.

4. $\frac{2}{5}$ of a school are boys, what fraction of the school consists of girls? If there are 240 girls, what is the number of boys?

5. Add $1\frac{2}{3}$ to the difference of $3\frac{1}{2}$ and $1\frac{1}{6}$.

6. A boy spends $\frac{3}{4}$ of his pocket money and then gives $\frac{4}{5}$ of the remainder to his sister. If he has Rs 40 left, what did he have at first ?

7. A sum of money is divided among three boys so that the first gets one half of it and the second one third of the remainder. What fraction of the first boy's is the third boy's share?

8. I buy 24 mangoes, but $\frac{3}{8}$ of them are bad; how many are fit to eat ?

9. If you spent $1\frac{1}{2}$ hours on home work last night and $\frac{1}{4}$ of that time was spent on Mathematics, what fraction of an hour did you spend on mathematics ?

10. $\frac{3}{5}$ of a road is to be resurfaced. If the road is $2\frac{3}{5}$ km long, what length in kilometres is to be resurfaced

11. My friend has $2\frac{1}{3}$ litres of lemonade. I have $2\frac{1}{2}$ times more than he has, and I drink half of mine. Ho many litres do I drink.

12. $\frac{7}{12}$ of the total number of children in a school come by bus, $\frac{3}{10}$ walk and the rest of them come by car. there are 1020 children in the school, find how many come

      (a) by bus   (b) on foot   (c) by car.

13. The product of two fractions is 19. If one of them is $15\frac{5}{6}$, find the other.

14. After covering $\frac{3}{8}$ of her journey by train, Ranjana finds that she has travelled 144 km. What is the length o the journey still left.

15. $\frac{7}{15}$ of the water in a tank which is full is used on one day, and $\frac{5}{6}$ of the remainder on the next. If 80 litre are then left, how much water can the tank hold when full ?

LOOKING BACK
Summary of Key Facts

1.   Numbers of the form $\frac{a}{b}$ where $b \neq 0$ are called fractions. **a** is called the numerator and **b** is called the denominator.

2.   A fraction $\frac{a}{b}$ in which $a > 0$ and $a < b$ $\left(\text{ex}: \frac{4}{9}\right)$ is called a **Proper Fraction.**

3.   A fraction $\frac{a}{b}$ in which $a = b$ or $a > b$ $\left(\text{ex}: \frac{10}{3} \text{ or } \frac{3}{3}\right)$ is called an **Improper Fraction**.

4.   A fraction $\left(5\frac{3}{7} = 5 + \frac{3}{7}\right)$ which can be expressed as the sum of a natural number and a fraction is called a **Mixed Fraction.**

5.   A fraction where denominator is a multiple of 10 is called a **Decimal Fraction.**

6.   Fractions having denominators as whole numbers other than a power of 10, i.e., 10, 100, 1000 are called **Vulgar Fractions.**

7.   Fractions obtained on multiplying or dividing both numerator and denominator of a given fraction by a non zero number, and the given fraction are called **Equivalent Fractions.**

8.   An integer is a fraction with denominator 1. **Ex.** $-7 = \frac{-7}{1}$, $5 = \frac{5}{1}$ are integers.

9.   Fractions having the same denominator are called like fractions whereas those having different denominator are called unlike fractions. **Ex.** $\frac{5}{7}$ and $\frac{3}{7}$ are like fractions. $\frac{8}{3}$ and $\frac{7}{12}$ are unlike fractions.

10. A fraction of the form $\frac{a}{b}$, $b \neq 0$ where a and b are whole numbers is called a **Simple Fraction.** (Ex. $\frac{8}{11}$

11. A fraction of the form $\dfrac{a}{b}$ where a and b are fractions is called a **Complex Fraction.** $\left(\text{Ex. }\dfrac{\frac{3}{4}}{\frac{8}{9}}\right)$

12. A fraction $\dfrac{a}{b}$ is said to be in its lowest form if the H.C.F. of a and b is 1.

13. Comparing fractions $\dfrac{a}{b}$ and $\dfrac{c}{d}$:

   (i) If $ad > bc$ than $\dfrac{a}{b} > \dfrac{c}{d}$, (ii) If $ad = bc$ then $\dfrac{a}{b} = \dfrac{c}{d}$, (iii) If $ad < bc$ then $\dfrac{a}{b} < \dfrac{c}{d}$

> **Note:** Before applying the rule of cross multiplication, put the given fractions in standard form.
> Thus, $\dfrac{a}{-b}$ should be written in the form $\dfrac{-a}{b}$.

14. *(i)* For addition or subtraction of like fractions, numerators are added (or subtracted) denominator remaining the same.

   (ii) For addition or subtraction of unlike fractions first change them to equivalent like fractions (by finding the L.C.M. of denominators) and then do as in (i)

15. If $\dfrac{a}{b}$ and $\dfrac{c}{d}$ two fractions then $\dfrac{a}{b} \times \dfrac{c}{d} = \dfrac{a \times c}{b \times d}$.

16. Reciprocal of any fraction $\dfrac{a}{b} = \dfrac{b}{a}$.

17. If $\dfrac{a}{b}$ and $\dfrac{c}{d}$ are two fractions then $\dfrac{a}{b} \div \dfrac{c}{d} = \dfrac{a}{b} \times \dfrac{d}{c}$.

18. Before performing an operation, change mixed fractions to improper fractions.

   Note: To add or subtract mixed fractions, you may add or subtract the whole number parts separately.

19. The sequence of operations followed while solving a numerical expression is   **BODMAS**
   (i) Bracket (ii) of (iii) Division (iv) Multiplication (v) Addition (vii) Subtraction.

20. Brackets follow the sequence '—' ( ), { }, [ ], i.e., from innermost to outermost.

MENTAL MATHS– 4

. Which is greater $\dfrac{7}{8}$ or $\dfrac{9}{11}$? 2. Express $\dfrac{42}{5}$ as a mixed number.

. What fraction is 25 years of 1 century ? 4. Find the value of $\dfrac{1}{7} + \dfrac{1}{3}$.

. In a test total marks are 30. You get $\dfrac{3}{5}$ of the total marks. How many marks do you get?

. Simplify: $\dfrac{1}{6} \times \dfrac{18}{64} \times \dfrac{16}{20}$. 7. What is the reciprocal of $\dfrac{2}{9} \div \dfrac{1}{2}$?

. Simplify: $11\dfrac{2}{7} - 6\dfrac{2}{7}$ 9. $\dfrac{6}{9} + \dfrac{2}{5} \times \dfrac{5}{9}$ 10. $\dfrac{\frac{4}{4}}{7}$

1. $\dfrac{63}{800}$ is a decimal fraction. True or false ? 12. Find a fraction between $\dfrac{3}{5}$ and $\dfrac{4}{7}$.

3. A eats $\dfrac{1}{5}$ of a cake. Her sister eats $\dfrac{1}{4}$ of the cake. What fraction of the cake is left?

ANSWERS

EXERCISE 6 (a)

1. $\frac{4}{21}, \frac{301}{13}, \frac{63}{8000}, 3\frac{3}{7} \rightarrow$ vulgar fractions. $\frac{301}{13}, \frac{29}{29} \rightarrow$ Improper Fractions. $\frac{64}{1000}, \frac{23}{10^4} \rightarrow$ Decimal Fractions.

$\frac{4}{21}, \frac{63}{8000} \rightarrow$ Proper Fractions $3\frac{3}{7} \rightarrow$ mixed fraction

2. (i) $\frac{47}{8}$ (ii) $\frac{75}{16}$ (iii) $\frac{289}{15}$ (iv) $\frac{1616}{39}$ (v) $\frac{153}{23}$

3. (i) $8\frac{3}{11}$ (ii) $2\frac{5}{12}$ (iii) $11\frac{14}{20}$ (iv) $7\frac{3}{13}$ (v) $12\frac{22}{101}$

4. (i) $\frac{3}{4}$ (ii) $\frac{5}{7}$ (iii) $\frac{9}{34}$ (iv) $\frac{9}{11}$ (v) $\frac{5}{11}$

5. (i) $\frac{16}{28}$ (ii) $\frac{48}{84}$ 6. (i) $\frac{3}{7}$ (ii) $\frac{9}{21}$

7. (i), (iv), (vi) and (vii) are complex fractions.

EXERCISE 6 (b)

1. $\frac{51}{60}, \frac{48}{60}, \frac{50}{60}, \frac{45}{60}$

2. (i) <   (ii) <   (iii) =   (iv) >   (v) <   (vi) >

3. (i) $\frac{1}{12}, \frac{3}{20}, \frac{9}{16}, \frac{2}{3}$ (ii) $\frac{2}{9}, \frac{13}{24}, \frac{5}{8}, \frac{5}{6}$ (iii) $\frac{2}{3}, \frac{6}{7}, \frac{8}{9}, \frac{9}{5}$ (iv) $\frac{2}{33}, \frac{8}{11}, \frac{5}{6}$

4. (i) 6   (ii) 54   (iii) 105   (iv) 4   (v) 5

5. (i) $\frac{12}{16}$ (ii) $\frac{3}{18}$ (iii) $\frac{2}{7}$ (iv) $\frac{13}{20}$

6. (i) $\frac{17}{26}, \frac{10}{15}, \frac{13}{19}$ (ii) $\frac{3}{19}, \frac{2}{13}, \frac{3}{20}$ (iii) $\frac{14}{19}, \frac{9}{13}, \frac{13}{20}$ (iv) $\frac{23}{38}, \frac{16}{26}, \frac{25}{40}$

7. (i) $\frac{3}{10}$ (ii) $\frac{5}{7}$ (iii) $\frac{6}{5}$ (iv) $\frac{3}{4}$

EXERCISE 6 (c)

1. (a) $\frac{6}{7}$ (b) $\frac{69}{77}$ (c) $4\frac{31}{45}$ (d) $7\frac{3}{8}$ (e) $8\frac{32}{63}$

2. (a) $\frac{4}{15}$ (b) $\frac{7}{15}$ (c) $2\frac{1}{2}$ (d) $1\frac{59}{100}$ (e) $1\frac{1}{30}$

3. (a) $1\frac{1}{3}$ (b) $\frac{1}{252}$ (c) 5   (d) $\frac{9}{10}$

4. $1\frac{2}{55}$ 5. $\frac{4}{11}$ 6. $4\frac{5}{8}$ kg

7. (a) $\frac{5}{6}$ (b) $1\frac{1}{3}$ (c) $\frac{3}{10}$ (d) $\frac{3}{70}$ (e) $\frac{1}{2}$ (f) $7\frac{1}{5}$

    (g) $\frac{1}{4}$ (h) $7\frac{1}{2}$ (i) $28\frac{4}{5}$

8. (a) $\dfrac{8}{15}$ (b) $\dfrac{2}{9}$ (c) $\dfrac{69}{10}$ (d) $\dfrac{26}{35}$ (e) $\dfrac{2}{3}$ (f) 6

9. (a) $\dfrac{3}{5}$ (b) $1\dfrac{3}{4}$ (c) $1\dfrac{1}{2}$ (d) $3\dfrac{7}{16}$ (e) $\dfrac{1}{4}$ (f) 32

10. (a) 24 kg (b) $12\dfrac{1}{2}$ m (c) Rs 72 (d) $\dfrac{1}{54}$ (e) 35 (f) $1\dfrac{2}{5}$

11. (a) 6 cm² (b) $24\dfrac{1}{6}$ cm² 12. $14\dfrac{7}{16}$ kg 13. $11\dfrac{2}{11}$ days 14. 4 km

EXERCISE 6 (d)

1. $4\dfrac{3}{4}$ 2. 8 3. $\dfrac{3}{13}$ 4. $1\dfrac{46}{105}$ 5. $1\dfrac{2}{5}$ 6. $70\dfrac{7}{11}$

7. $8\dfrac{19}{70}$ 8. $\dfrac{8}{15}$ 9. 2 10. $2\dfrac{1}{14}$

EXERCISE 6 (e)

1. $\dfrac{15}{32}$ 2. $4\dfrac{4}{35}$ m. 3. $8\dfrac{1}{4}$ cm 4. $\dfrac{3}{5}$; 160 boys 5. 4 6. Rs 800

7. $\dfrac{2}{3}$ 8. 15 9. $\dfrac{3}{8}$ 10. $1\dfrac{14}{25}$ km 11. $2\dfrac{11}{12}$ litres

12. (a) 595 (b) 306 (c) 119. 13. $1\dfrac{1}{5}$ 14. 240 km 15. 900 litres.

MENTAL MATHS – 4

1. $\dfrac{7}{8}$ 2. $8\dfrac{2}{5}$ 3. $\dfrac{1}{4}$ 4. $\dfrac{10}{21}$ 5. 18 6. $\dfrac{3}{80}$

7. $\dfrac{9}{4}$ 8. 5 9. $\dfrac{8}{9}$ 10. 7 11. False 12. $\dfrac{7}{12}$ 13. $\dfrac{11}{20}$

MIND BENDERS

1. Take Roman's L, multiply by the number of lives a cat is supposed to have, divide by the Roman numeral X, and subtract the number of paise in a quarter rupee. What is left?

$$\text{Answer}: 20 \left(= 50 \times \dfrac{9}{10} - 25\right)$$

FUN WITH MATHS
A Special Magic Square

The square shown here is not an ordinary one.

1. You can add up the numbers, across, down or diagonally and the total is the same, in this case 34.

2. The four numbers in the centre add up to 34.

3. The middle numbers is the bottom row 15 $\begin{bmatrix} 10+11 \\ +6+7 \end{bmatrix}$ and 14, added to the two middle numbers in top row i.e., 3 and 2 total 34.

4. The two numbers 5 and 9 in the beginning of the second and third row, and the last two numbers 8 and 12 in the same two rows add up to 34.

5. And the four numbers in each quarter total 34.

16	3	2	13
5	10	11	8
9	6	7	12
4	15	14	1

This magic square was created by a great German artist Albrecht Durer.

7. Decimals

You have already studied decimals in class VI. Here we will first revise the four fundamental operations of decimals and then extend our study of decimals further.

7.1 Decimal Fractions:

A fraction whose denominator is 10 or a power of 10 is called a decimal fraction. Thus $\frac{4}{10}, \frac{3}{100}, \frac{17}{1000}, \frac{2}{1000}$ are all decimal fractions.

Another way of expressing a decimal fraction is by writing the numerator with a dot (at the proper place) removing the denominator.

Thus $\frac{2}{10}$ can be written as 0.2 ; $\frac{43}{100}$ can be written as 0.43. This dot (.) is known as a decimal point.

- Numbers of the form 1.18, 0.03, 4.435 are known as decimal numbers or simply decimals.
- A decimal has two parts–whole number part and decimal part. These two parts are separated by a dot called the decimal point. The whole number part is to the left of the decimal point and the decimal part to the right of the decimal point. Thus, in **63.82, 63** is the **whole number part** and **82** is the **decimal part.**
- The number of digits contained in the decimal part of a decimal gives the number of its decimal places. e.g. 6.23 has two decimal places ; 34.7834 has four decimal places.
- Decimals having the same number of decimal places are called **like decimals.** e.g. 43.346, 6.306, 0.423 are like decimals.
- Decimals having different number of decimal places are called **unlike decimals,** e.g., 3.23, 0.234, 1.1, 49.4834 are unlike decimals.

7.2 An Important Property

*A **very important property** of decimals is that adding zeros after the last digit of the decimal part of any decimal number does not change the value of the decimal.*
e.g. 1.1 = 1.10 = 1.100 = 1.1000

We use this property to convert unlike decimals to like decimals.

e.g. 4.3, 6.42, 19.343 can be converted to like decimals. The largest number of decimal places is 3. ∴ We convert each decimal into one having 3 decimal places.

4.3 = 4.300, 6.42 = 6.420 and 19.343 = 19.343. Now 4.300, 6.420 and 19.343 are like decimals.

OPERATIONS ON DECIMALS

7.3 Addition and Subtraction of Decimals Numbers

Method :
(i) *Write the given numerals one below the other with decimal points in a vertical line (same column).*
(ii) *Equal the number of decimal places in all the numbers by adding the required number of zeros to the right end, whenever needed.*
(iii) *Now add or subtract as for whole numbers placing the decimal point in the result directly under the other decimal points.*

Ex. 1: *Find the given decimals sum of 643.175, 25.2, 6.04, 5143.7004.*

Sol : Writing the given decimals one below the other and making the decimal places in all the numbers equal by adding zeros we have

$$
\begin{array}{r}
643.1750 \\
25.2000 \\
6.0400 \\
+ 5143.7004 \\
\hline
\text{Sum} = \quad 5818.1154
\end{array}
$$

Ex.2 : *Subtract 17.123 from 73.1.*

Sol : Arranging the numbers one below the other with point below the point and making the decimal places equal by adding zeros we have:

$$
\begin{array}{r}
73.100 \\
- 17.123 \\
\hline
\text{Difference} = \quad 55.977
\end{array}
$$

Ex.3 : *Simplify 4.346 – 1.16 + 3.402 – 2.3.*

Sol :
$$
\begin{array}{ll}
4.346 & 1.16 \\
+ 3.402 & + 2.30 \\
\hline
7.748 & 3.46 \\
- 3.460 & \\
\hline
4.288 &
\end{array}
$$

First add 4.346 and 3.402 and then 1.16, and 2.3. Subtract the 2nd sum from the 1st sum.

$\therefore \quad 4.346 - 1.16 + 3.402 - 2.3 = \mathbf{4.288}$

Ex. 4: *A tank 25.54 cm deep contains water to a depth of 18.5cm ; How far in cm is the water–level below the top of the tank ?*

Sol : Water level below the top of the tank
$= (25.54 - 18.5)$ cm
$= \mathbf{7.04 \ cm.}$

$$
\begin{array}{r}
25.54 \\
- 18.50 \\
\hline
7.04
\end{array}
$$

EXERCISE 7 (a)

1. **Convert the following decimals to like decimals.**
   (i) 4.3, 0.43, 161.345, 2.302   (ii) 1.1, 0.11, 11.011, 2.3589   (iii) 63.85, 5, 9.035, 101.3

2. **Add :**
   (i) 6.75, 4.3, 2.913   (ii) 0.872, 3.46, 4.009, 4.17   (iii) 16.32, 20.04, 5.207, 0.918
   (iv) 0.0804, 0.00924, 0.1072, 0.02065   (v) 53.07, 17.896, 3.5, 21.97   (vi) 24.341, 0.0462, 431.5, 9
   (vii) 7.1037, 0.00982, 0.0003, 12.35   (viii) 26.23, 4, 0.003, 9.01

3. **Subtract :**
   (i) 6.473 from 17.589   (ii) 17.182 from 360.05   (iii) 3.2103 from 5.23
   (iv) 13.9807 from 34.25   (v) 127.323 from 133.6549   (vi) 0.0093 from 0.045
   (vii) 0.376 from 1   (viii) 43.937 from 100   (ix) .011 from 1.1

4. **Simplify :**
   (i) 4.105 + 2.37– 5.2   (ii) 11.001 – 2.36 + 4.965 – 5.7   (iii) 9.95 + 6.389–2.367–7.8
   (iv) 100 – 3.067 – 33.0689 – 21.2

5. Shreya sells newspapers. She received Rs 43.56 on Monday, Rs 57.93 on Tuesday and Rs 63.75 on Wednesday. How much did she get in total for the three days ?

6. Raj buys a Rs 7.65 metro ticket with a Rs 20 note. How much change does he get ?

7. A baby increases in weight from 5.46 kg to 6.18 kg. How much weight has the baby gained ?

8. Subtract the difference of 43.875 and 53.9 from the sum of 29.358 and 2.3023.

7.4 Multiplication of Decimal Numbers

Type 1. To multiply a decimal number by 10 or any power of 10.

Rule. *Move the decimal point as many places to the right as there are zeros in the multiplier*

Ex: 1 *Find the products :*

(i) **6.943 × 10**   (ii) **29.62 × 100**   (iii) **0.89345 × 1000.**

Sol :   (*i*) $6.943 \times 10 = 69.43$

       (*ii*) $29.62 \times 100 \Rightarrow 29.62 = 2962$

       (*iii*) $0.89345 \times 1000 \Rightarrow 0.89345 = 893.45$

> The movement of the decimal point is shown by the arrow.

Ex: 2   *Multiply*

       (*i*)   **6.54 × 1000**   (*ii*)   **29.8 × 100**   (*iii*) **0.3 × 1000**

> Decimal point has to be shifted 3 places to the right so we add one zero at the right end.

Sol :   (*i*) 6.54×1000 =   6540

       (*ii*) 29.8×100 =   2980

> Here again one zero is added.

       (*iii*) 0.3×1000 =   300

> To shift three places to the right 2 zeros have to be added.

Type 2. **To multiply a decimal number by a whole number or by a decimal number.**

> **Rule.** *Multiply in the usual way as in whole numbers. Place the decimal point so that the number of decimal places in the product is equal to the sum of the number of decimal places in the multiplier and multiplicand.*

Ex: 3   *Multiply :*

       (*i*) **9.53 by 11**   (*ii*) **23.5 by 27**   (*iii*) **12.93 by 4.05**   (*iv*) **0.03 by 0.009**

Sol :   (*i*)   Multiplying both the numbers as whole numbers:

$$953 \times 11 = 10483$$

       ∵   Total number of decimal places in both numbers is 2

$$\therefore \quad 9.53 \times 11 = \mathbf{104.83.}$$

       (*ii*) We multiply 235 by 27

$$235 \times 27 = 6345$$

       ∵ Total no. of decimal places in the given number = 1

$$\therefore \quad\quad 23.5 \times 27 = \mathbf{634.5.}$$

```
      235
   ×   27
     1645
  +  470
     6345
```

   (*iii*) First we multiply 1293 and 405

$$1293 \times 405 = 523665$$

       ∵ Total no. of decimal places in the given number = 4

$$\therefore \quad\quad 12.93 \times 4.05 = \mathbf{52.3665.}$$

```
     1293
   ×  405
     6465
 + 51720
   523665
```

   (*iv*) Taking whole numbers 3 and 9 the product can be obtained mentally as 27

       Now the total number of decimal places in both the numbers = 5

$$\therefore \quad 0.03 \times 0.009 = \mathbf{0.00027.}$$

> We add zeros in front of the product to make number of decimal places 5.

EXERCISE 7 (b)

1. Find the product :

     (*i*) 13.03×10 (*ii*) 0.01563×100 (*iii*) 21.0103×10000

     (*iv*) 0.31×1000 (*v*) $12.\,12 \times 1000$ (*vi*) 0.001×10

     (*vii*) 0.4×1000 (*viii*) 10.111×10000 (*ix*) 0.065×1000

2. **Multiply :**
   (i) 2.96×14 (ii) 13.35×35 (iii) 0.093×16
   (iv) 0.00056×38 (v) 19.5×40

3. **Evaluate :**
   (i) 2.9×3.7 (ii) 37.5×0.8 (iii) 4.81×0.0074
   (iv) 75.6×67.5 (v) 0.00165×0.0036

4. **Write the products (do mentally) :**
   (i) 0.005×0.03 (ii) 0.04×30 (iii) 0.0016×0.002
   (iv) 0.007×80 (v) 90×0.08 (vi) 0.012×0.009

5. **Find the products :**
   (i) $2.3 \times 4.12 \times 12$ (ii) $3.8 \times 0.6 \times 5.31$ (iii) $0.23 \times 0.09 \times 1.11$
   (iv) $6.76 \times 0.01 \times 0.02$ (v) $0.3 \times 0.03 \times 0.003$ (vi) $1.2 \times 0.12 \times 0.012$

6. A fence is made of 10 bundles each 1.65 m long ; find its length.

7. From a piece of rope 20 m long, 100 pieces each of 7.5 cm long are cut off; how much of the rope remains ?

7.5   Division of Decimals

Type 1. **To divide a decimal number or a whole number by 10 or power of 10.**

Rule : *Move the decimal point as many places to the left as there are zeros in the divisor.*

Ex. 1   *Divide :*
   (i)   **$92.3 \div 10$**   (ii) **$49 \div 100$**   (iii)   **$1645.3 \div 1000$**

Sol :   (i) $92.3 \div 10 = 9.2\,3$ Shift one place.

   (ii) $49 \div 100 = 0.4\,9$ Shift two places.

   (iii) $1645.3 \div 1000 = 1.6\,4\,5\,3$ Shift three places.

> The arrow indicates the movement of decimal point from right to left.

Ex. 2   *Divide :*
   (i)   **$63 \div 1000$**   (ii) **$2.53 \div 100$**   (iii)   **$0.03 \div 10$**

Sol :
   (i) $63 \div 1000 = 0.0\,6\,3$

   (ii) $2.53 \div 100 = 0.0\,2\,5\,3$

   (iii) $0.03 \div 10 = 0.003$

> We add zeros or zeros to give the required number of decimal places.

Type 2. **To divide a decimal number by a whole number.**

Rule: *We proceed with division as in whole numbers but place the decimal point in the quotient directly above or below the decimal point in the dividend.*

Ex. 3 : *Divide 16.0518 by 3*

```
      5.3506
   3)16.0518
   − 15 ↓↓↓↓
      10
     − 9↓
      15
     − 15↓↓
      018
     − 18
       0
```
Or

Short Form

3	16.0518
	5.3506

Ex. 4 : *Divide 47.136 by 12*

```
       3.928
   12)47.136
    − 36 ↓↓↓
      111
    − 108↓
       33
      − 24↓
        96
       − 96
         0
```
Or

Short Form

12	47.136
	3.928

Ex. 5 : *Divide 0.562 by 200*

Sol :

2	0.562
	0.281

Then 0.562 ÷ 200 = 0.00281

(i.e. divide by 2 and then by the 100)

Ex. 6 : *Divide 6.5039 by 13*

Sol:
```
       0.5003
   13)6.5039
    − 65↓↓↓
      039
     − 39
       00
```

13	6.5039
	0.5003

Or

Type 3 : To divide a decimal by a decimal

> **Rule.** *Move the decimal point of the divisor to the right until it becomes a whole number (i.e. multiply by 10 or a power of 10). Next move the decimal point of the dividend the same number of places to the right, adding zeros if necessary. (Multiplying dividend and divisor by the same number does not affect the quotient)*

Ex. 7   Divide 4.86 by 0.6

Sol : $\dfrac{4.86}{0.6} = \dfrac{4.86 \times 10}{0.6 \times 10} = \dfrac{48.6}{6} = \textbf{8.1}$

Ex. 8 *Simplify : 14 ÷ 0.0028*

Sol :   The divisor has 4 places of decimal so we move 4 places to the right in both dividend and divisor,
i.e. = 140000 ÷ 28 = 5000.

Ex. 9   Divide 9.828 by 4.2

Sol: $\dfrac{9.828}{4.2} = \dfrac{9.828 \times 10}{4.2 \times 10} = \dfrac{98.28}{42}$

```
        2.34
   42 ) 98.28
     − 84 ↓
       142
     − 126 ↓
        168
      − 168
          0
```

Or

7	98.28
6	14.04
	2.34

```
    5000
   10000
  140000
    28
    2
     1
```

Ex. 10 *Divide 0.023328 by 3.6*

Sol : The divisor has one place of decimal so we move the decimal point to the right by one place in both dividend and divisor.

$$\therefore \frac{0.023328}{3.6} = \frac{0.23328}{36}$$

```
      0.  648
36 ) 0.23328
     − 216
     ───────
        172
     − 144
     ───────
        288
     − 288
     ───────
          0
```

Short Form

9	0.23328
4	0. 2592
	0. 648

Or

$$\therefore \ 0.023328 \div 3.6 = \textbf{0.648. Ans.}$$

EXERCISE 7 (c)

1. Divide :

(*i*) 156 by 10   (*ii*) 3.101 by 10   (*iii*) 0.0358 by 10   (*iv*) 13.9 by 100   (*v*) 13.001 by 100

(*vi*) 150 by 1000   (*vii*) 0.8 by 1000   (*viii*) 18.008 by 1000

2. Divide :

(*i*) 21.945 by 3   (*ii*) 42.9275 by 7   (*iii*) 120.3184 by 8   (*iv*) 11.00121 by 11   (*v*) 0.564 by 12

(*vi*) 87.138 by 9   (*vii*) 11.187 by 30   (*viii*) 0.6985 by 50   (*ix*) 0.2894 by 200   (*x*) 2.5 by 0.008

(*xi*) 6.3 by 0.0063   (*xii*) 0.308 by 28   (*xiii*) 0.00424 by 4000

3. Find :

(*i*) 1 ÷ 0.0625   (*ii*) 71.5 ÷ 5.5   (*iii*) 921.6÷0.0048   (*iv*) 0.0288 ÷ 2.4   (*v*) 0.0062 ÷ 2.5

(*vi*) 1326 ÷ 4.25   (*vii*) 352.872 ÷ 0.87   (*viii*) 55.5676÷17.3

Simplify :

4. $\dfrac{0.42}{0.03 \times 0.7}$ **5.** $\dfrac{0.81 \times 6.3}{2.1 \times 0.9}$ **6.** $\dfrac{0.46 \div 0.046}{0.0046 \div 46}$ **7.** $\dfrac{0.0016 \times 0.049}{0.07 \times 0.28}$

8. How many equal pieces of tape, each 1.4 cm long can be cut from a length of 29.4 cm.

9. A pile of 150 sheets is 5.4 cm. find the thickness of one sheet.

10. The product of two numbers is 29.75. If one number is 21.25, find the other.

11. The cost of 13 water bottles is Rs 163.02. What is the cost of one water bottle ?

Calculate :

12. 8.4 ÷ 0.07 − 12.5 of 3.4.   **13.** 0.64 of 500 ÷ 0.16.   **14.** 65.1 ÷ (1.25 + 3.4).

7.6 To Convert a Vulgar Fraction into a Decimal by Division Method.

Because all vulgar fractions can be written in the form $\dfrac{a}{b}$, *a given fraction* $\dfrac{a}{b}$ *can be expressed as a decimal by simply dividing a by b.* This is illustrated in the following examples.

Ex. 1 *Convert each of the following to a decimal :*

(i) $\dfrac{5}{8}$ (ii) $\dfrac{7}{11}$

Sol : (i) $\dfrac{5}{8} = 5 \div 8$

```
      0.625
  8 ) 5.000
    – 48
      20
    – 16
      40
    – 40
       0
```

$\therefore \dfrac{5}{8} = \mathbf{0.625.}$

(ii) $\dfrac{7}{11} = 7 \div 11$

```
        0.6363
  11 ) 7.0000
     – 6 6
        40
      – 33
        70
      – 66
        40
      – 33
         7
```

$\therefore \dfrac{7}{11} = \mathbf{0.6363....}$

(i) In the division of 5 by 8, the quotient 0.625 is called **terminating decimal** because the division process terminates when a final remainder 0 is reached.

(ii) In the division of 7 by 11, the quotient 0.6363 ... **is non-terminating** decimal. The division process never ends because the remainder **4** and **7** keep appearing and a remainder of 0 is never reached. The quotient is called a non-terminating repeating (recurring) decimal.

In case of a non-terminating repeating decimal a block of digits repeats without end. A repeating decimal is expressed by putting a bar over the block of digits that repeats. In the decimal for $\dfrac{7}{11} = 0.6363$ ... a block of two digits 63 is repeated $\therefore \dfrac{7}{11} = \mathbf{0.\overline{63}.}$

Ex. 3 *Express $\dfrac{2}{13}$ as a decimal.*

Sol:
```
       0.153846153846
  13 ) 2.000000000000
     – 13
        70
      – 65
        50
      – 39
       110
```

$$\frac{-104}{60}$$

$$\frac{-52}{80}$$

$$\frac{-78}{20}$$

$$\frac{-13}{70}$$

$$\frac{-65}{50}$$

$$\frac{-39}{110}$$

$$\frac{-104}{60}$$

$$\frac{-52}{80}$$

$$\frac{-78}{2}$$

$\therefore \quad \dfrac{2}{13} = 0.153846153846... = \mathbf{0.\overline{153846}}$

Another notation for repeating decimal is to put the dot over the first and the last digit of the repeating block of digits.

i.e., $\dfrac{7}{11} = 0.\overset{\cdot\cdot}{63}$; $\dfrac{2}{13} = 0.\overset{\cdot}{1}5384\overset{\cdot}{6}$

7.7 To Convert Decimal Number to a Vulgar Fraction

Case I : *When the decimals are terminating.*

You can write a terminating decimal as a fraction with a denominator that is a power of 10. Thus

(*i*) $0.5 = \dfrac{5}{10} = \dfrac{1}{2}$ ← Rewrite the fraction in the lowest terms.

(*ii*) $0.47 = \dfrac{47}{100}.$ (*iii*) $3.4 = 3\dfrac{4}{10} = 3\dfrac{2}{5}.$ (*iv*) $5.032 = \dfrac{5032}{1000} = \dfrac{629}{125}.$

> **Method : 1.** *Remove the decimal point and write the resulting number in the numerator.*
> **2.** *Write 1 in the denominator and annex as many zeros as the number of digits after the decimal point in the given decimal number.*

Ex. 1 *Convert the following decimals to vulgar fractions.*

  (*i*) **0.012**   (*ii*) **5.84**   (*iii*) **7.5655**   (*iv*) **0.000135**

Sol. (*i*) $0.012 = \dfrac{12}{1000} = \dfrac{3}{250}$ (*ii*) $5.84 = \dfrac{584}{100} = \dfrac{146}{25}$

3 digits after the decimal   3 zeros after 1   2 digits after the decimal   2 zeros after 1

(*iii*) $7.5655 = \dfrac{75655}{10000} = \dfrac{15131}{2000}$ (*iv*) $0.000135 = \dfrac{135}{1000000} = \dfrac{27}{200000}$

4 digits after the decimal   4 zeros after 1   6 digits after the decimal   6 zeros after 1

Case II : *When the decimals are repeating.*

Ex. 2. *Express each decimal as a fraction in simplest form.*

(i) $0.\overline{8}$ (ii) $1.\overline{27}$ (iii) $\overline{407}$

Sol.

(i) Let $n = 0.\overline{8} = 0.888 \ldots\ldots$ ...(i)

$10n = 10 \times 0.888 = 8.888 \ldots\ldots$ ...(ii)

Subtracting (i) from (ii), we get

$9n = 8$

or $9 \times 0.\overline{8} = 8$

$\therefore \ 0.\overline{8} = \dfrac{\mathbf{8}}{\mathbf{9}}.$

> **Think**
>
> Since there is one digit in the repetend 8 we multiply both members of $n = 0.\overline{8}$ by 10. This shifts the repeating digit one place to the left. The subtraction produces a terminating decimal numeral.

(ii) Let $n = 1.\overline{27} = 1.2727\ldots$

Multiply : $100n = 127.\overline{27}$

Subtract : $\underline{\quad n = \quad\ 1.\overline{27}\ }$

$99n = 126$

Divide : $n = \dfrac{126}{99} = \dfrac{\mathbf{14}}{\mathbf{11}}.$

> **Think**
>
> Since there are two digits in the repetend 27, we multiply both members, of $n = 1.\overline{27}$ by 10^2, or 100. This shifts the repeating block of digits two places to the left. The subtraction produces a terminating decimal numeral.

(iii) Let $n = 0.\overline{407}$

Multiply: $1000n = 407.\overline{407}$

Subtract : $\underline{\quad\quad n = 0.\overline{407}\ }$

$999n = 407$

> Since the block of repeating digits contains 3 digits, we multiply by 10^3, or 1000.

$\therefore \quad n = \dfrac{407}{999} = \dfrac{\mathbf{11}}{\mathbf{27}}.$

Rule: *Write the repeated figure only once in the numerator and write as many nines in the denominator as is the number of repeated digits.*

Applying this rule to the above examples, we get

$0.\overline{6} = \dfrac{6}{9} = \dfrac{2}{3}, \ 0.\overline{71} = \dfrac{71}{99}, \ 1.\overline{48} = 1 + \dfrac{48}{99} = 1 + \dfrac{16}{33} = \dfrac{49}{33}, \ 0.\overline{927} = \dfrac{927}{999} = \dfrac{103}{111}$

EXERCISE 7 (d)

I. **Express each of the following fractions as a decimal:**

1. $\dfrac{24}{1000}$ **2.** $\dfrac{62}{10}$ **3.** $\dfrac{1}{4}$ **4.** $\dfrac{4}{5}$ **5.** $\dfrac{5}{4}$ **6.** $\dfrac{26}{25}$ **7.** $\dfrac{9}{40}$ **8.** $\dfrac{35}{16}$

II. **Express each of the following fractions as a recurring decimal:**

1. $\dfrac{1}{3}$ **2.** $\dfrac{25}{6}$ **3.** $\dfrac{5}{9}$ **4.** $\dfrac{11}{18}$ **5.** $2\dfrac{4}{11}$ **6.** $4\dfrac{3}{7}$ **7.** $\dfrac{22}{7}$ **8.** $\dfrac{88}{9}$

III. **Convert each of the given decimals to a vulgar fraction.**

   1. 0.84   **2.** 0.015   **3.** 129.6   **4.** 0.0008   **5.** 52.54

IV. **Convert each of the following recurring decimals to a vulgar fraction.**

   1. 0.$\overline{4}$ **2.** 0.$\overline{25}$ **3.** 0.5$\overline{85}$ **4.** 5.$\overline{2}$ **5.** 2.3$\overline{1}$ **6.** 23.$\overline{43}$

7.8 Rounding-off Decimal Numbers

Sometimes we have decimal numbers with too many decimal places, which is not needed. So we round off the given numbers to the required number of decimal places with the help of the following sequence of steps:

(i) *We retain the digits up to one more than the required number of decimal places.*

(ii) *If the extra digit retained is 5 or more than five, then we add 1 to the digit just before it.*

(iii) *If the extra digit retained is less than 5, then we leave the digit just before it as such.*

(iv) *The extra digit is then omitted.*

Ex. 1 *Round off 64.3561 correct to 2 decimal places (2 d.p.)*

Sol :   ∵ We have to round off correct to 2 d.p so we retain 3 digits after the decimal point.

   ∴ Number = 64.356

   ∵ 3rd digit after decimal point. is 6 (i.e. more than 5)

   ∴ We add 1 to the 2nd digit i.e. 5

The digit in the 2nd place becomes 6 now. Then the 3rd digit is omitted.

   ∴ The number is **64.36** correct to 2 d.p.

Similarly :

   6.9215 = 6.92 correct to 2d.p.,   7.4157 = 7.416 correct to 3 d.p.,

   48.6258 = 48.6 correct to 1 d.p.,   7.048 = 7.0 correct to 1 d.p.,

   0.0637 = 0.1 correct to 1 d.p.,   6.4983 = 6.50 correct to 2 d.p.

EXERCISE 7 (e)

1. **Round off :**
   (*i*) 8.932 to the nearest hundredths .
   (*iii*) 4.7815 to the nearest thousandths.
   (*v*) 4.015 to the nearest tenths.
   (*ii*) 0.0063 to the nearest hundredths.
   (*iv*) 0.089 to the nearest tenths.
   [**Hint.** To the nearest tenth means to 1 dp, to the nearest hundredths means to 2 dp, to the nearest thousandths means to 3 dp and so on.]

2. **Round off to the nearest whole number :**
   (*i*) 7.89   (*ii*) 62.01   (*iii*) 4.5   (*iv*) 3.25   (*v*) 53.45   (*vi*) 20.69

3. **Round off :**
   (*i*) 26.335 correct to 1d.p.   (*ii*) 1.5618 correct to 2 d.p.   (*iii*) 0.07 × 1.23 correct to 3 d.p.
   (*iv*) 32.131 ÷ 11 correct to 2 d.p.   (*v*) 4.893 ÷ 7 correct to 1 d.p.   (*vi*) 7.89345 × 100 correct to 2 d.p.

4. Express 3/7 as a decimal correct to 3 decimal place.

7.9 Significant Digits

Significant digits are the total number of digits present in a number except the zeros preceding the first numeral. We should take the following points in account while counting the number of significant digits:

(i) *The position of decimal is not of any importance.*
(ii) *The zeros between numbers are counted.*
(iii) *The zeros after the last numeral are also counted.*
(iv) *The zeros before the first numeral are not counted.*

Illustrate

Ex. 2. (*i*) 6.203 has 4 significant digits.

(*ii*) 2.780 has 4 significant digits.

(*iii*) 0.049 has 2 significant digits.

(*iv*) 0.0048960 has 5 significant digits.

7.10 Rounding to Significant Sigits

It is done in the same way as followed for decimal places.

Ex. 3 (*i*) 2.4302   = 2.43 correct to 3 significant digits.

(*ii*) 0.05932   = 0.06 correct to 1 significant digit.

(*iii*) 64.6398   = 64.64 correct to 4 significant digits.

(*iv*) 27.83   = 28 correct to 2 significant figures.

(*v*) 0.003814 = 0.0038 correct to 2 significant figures.

EXERCISE 7 (i)

1. **Write the number of significant digits in the following numbers :**

   (*i*) 31.02   (*ii*) 0.00063890   (*iii*) 4.030   (*iv*) 78.9043   (*v*) 0.005

2. **Write :**

   (*i*) 41.3502 correct to 3 significant figures.   (*ii*) 0.0891 correct to one significant figure.

   (*iii*) 29.35 correct to 2 significant figures.   (*iv*) 600.05 correct to 4 significant figures.

   (*v*) 25.600 correct to 4 significant figures.

LOOKING BACK

Summary of Key Facts

1. The fractions whose denominators are 10, 100, 1000 etc. are called decimal fractions.

2. Numbers written in decimal form are called decimal numbers.

3. A decimal number has two parts, the whole number part and the decimal part.

4. The number of digits in the decimal part is the number of decimal places.

5. To add or subtract decimal numbers write the numbers one below the other so that the decimal points are in one vertical line. Then add or subtract.

6. **To multiply :**

   (*i*) **a decimal by 10 or powers of 10 :** shift the decimal point to the right by as many places as there are number of zeros, e.g., $3.596 \times 10 = 35.96$, $3.596 \times 100 = 359.6$, $3.596 \times 10^3 = 3.596 \times 1000 = 3596$, $3.596 \times 10^4 = 35960$ and so on.

   (*ii*) **a decimal by decimal :** Ignore the decimal point and multiply them as whole numbers. The number of decimal places in the product is the sum of the number of decimal places both in the multiplicand and multiplier e.g. to multiply 52.8 by 0.197, multiply 528 by 197 and counting from the right put decimal point after 4 digits in the product. Thus, $528 \times 197 = 104016$ ∴ $52.8 \times 0.197 = 10.4016$.

7. **To divide :**

   (*i*) **a decimal by 10 or powers of 10 :** Shift the decimal point to the right by as many places as there are number of zeros, e.g., $587.23 \div 10 = 58.723$, $587.23 \div 100 = 5.8723$, $587.23 \div 1000 = 0.58723$, $79 \div 1000 = 0.079$, $15 \div 10^4 = 0.0015$.

   (*ii*) **a decimal by a decimal :** Convert the divisor to a whole number by shifting the decimal point to the right by the same number of decimal places as there are in the divisor. Then shift the decimal point of the dividend also by the same number of places to the right. Now divide the new dividend by the whole number divisor e.g. $87.34 \div 2.5 \Rightarrow 873.4 \div 25$, $0.038 \div 1.97 \Rightarrow 3.8 \div 197$.

8. Recurring decimals are those in which a certain block of digits repeat again and again e.g. $2.3\overline{479}$ is a recurring decimal.

9. The process of expressing a number with too many decimal places, as a number with desired number of decimal places is called **rounding off or approximation.** To round off to n d.p. check the $(n+1)^{th}$ digit. If it is 5 or more than 5 add 1 to n, else leave it as such and omit the $(n+1)^{th}$ digit.

10. The total number of digits present in the numeral except the zeros preceding the first numeral are called **significant digits.**

MENTAL MATHS– 5

Work out :

1. $4.5 + 6.23$ **2.** $1.2 - 0.4$ **3.** 0.0016×0.05 **4.** $2 \times 7.56 \times 5$

5. $6450 \div 1000$ **6.** $90.15 \div 15$

7. Given $46 \times 93 = 4278$ without actually multiplying find (*i*) 0.46×0.93 (*ii*) 46×0.093

8. A plant is 1.17 m high. It grows by 18 cm, what is its height now?

9. Express 9/5 as a decimal.   **10.** Express 1.25 as a vulgar fraction.

11. Round off 6.0831 correct to 1 d.p.

12. 4 kg of sweets are shared equally among 5 children. How many kg of sweets does each child get ?

ANSWERS

EXERCISE 7 (a)

(*i*) 4.300, 0.430, 161.345, 2.302   (*ii*) 1.1000, 0.1100, 11.0110, 2.3589   (*iii*) 63.850, 5.000, 9.035, 101.300

(*i*) 13.963 (*ii*) 12.511 (*iii*) 42.485 (*iv*) 0.21749 (*v*) 96.436 (*vi*) 464.8872 (*vii*) 19.46382 (*viii*) 39.243

(*i*) 11.116 (*ii*) 342.868 (*iii*) 2.0197 (*iv*) 20.2693 (*v*) 6.3319 (*vi*) 0.0357 (*vii*) 0.624 (*viii*) 56.063

(*ix*) 1.089

(*i*) 1.275   (*ii*) 7.906   (*iii*) 6.172   (*iv*) 42.6641

5. Rs 165.24   6. Rs 12.35   7. 0.72 kg   8. 21.6353

EXERCISE 7 (b)

(*i*) 130.3 (*ii*) 1.563 (*iii*) 210103 (*iv*) 310 (*v*) 12120 (*vi*) 0.01 (*vii*) 400 (*viii*) 101110

(*ix*) 65

(*i*) 41.44 (*ii*) 467.25 (*iii*) 1.488 (*iv*) 0.02128 (*v*) 780

(*i*) 10.73 (*ii*) 30 (*iii*) 0.035594 (*iv*) 5103 (*v*) 0.00000594

(*i*) 0.00015 (*ii*) 1.2 (*iii*) 0.0000032 (*iv*) 0.56 (*v*) 7.2 (*vi*) 0.000108

(*i*) 113.712 (*ii*) 12.1068 (*iii*) 0.022977 (*iv*) 0.001352 (*v*) 0.000027 (*vi*) 0.001728

6. 16.5 m   7. 12.5 m.

EXERCISE 7 (c)

(*i*) 15.6 (*ii*) 0.3101 (*iii*) 0.00358 (*iv*) 0.139 (*v*) 0.13001 (*vi*) 0.15 (*vii*) 0.0008 (*viii*) 0.018008

(*i*) 7.315 (*ii*) 6.1325 (*iii*) 15.0398 (*iv*) 1.00011 (*v*) 0.047 (*vi*) 9.682 (*vii*) 0.3729 (*viii*) 0.01397

(*ix*) 0.001447 (*x*) 312.5 (*xi*) 1000 (*xii*) 0.011 (*xiii*) 0.00000106

(*i*) 16 (*ii*) 13 (*iii*) 192000 (*iv*) 0.012 (*v*) 0.00248 (*vi*) 312 (*vii*) 405.6 (*viii*) 3.212

4. 20 5. 2.7 6. 100000 7. 0.004 8. 21 9. 0.036 cm 10. 1.4

11. Rs 12.54 12. 77.5 13. 2000 14. 14

EXERCISE 7 (d)

1. 0.024 2. 6.2 3. 0.25 4. 0.8 5. 1.25 6. 1.04 7. 0.225 8. 2.1875

1. $0.\overline{3}$ 2. $4.1\overline{6}$ 3. $0.\overline{5}$ 4. $0.6\overline{1}$ 5. $2.3\overline{6}$ 6. $4.\overline{428571}$ 7. $3.\overline{142857}$ 8. $9.\overline{7}$

1. $\dfrac{21}{25}$ 2. $\dfrac{3}{200}$ 3. $\dfrac{648}{5}$ 4. $\dfrac{1}{1250}$ 5. $\dfrac{2627}{50}$

IV.   1. $\dfrac{4}{9}$ 2. $\dfrac{25}{99}$ 3. $\dfrac{585}{999}$ 4. $\dfrac{47}{9}$ 5. $\dfrac{229}{99}$ 6. $\dfrac{2320}{99}$

EXERCISE 7 (e)

1.   (*i*) 8.93   (*ii*) 0.01   (*iii*) 4.782   (*iv*) 0.1   (*v*) 4.0
2.   (*i*) 8   (*ii*) 62   (*iii*) 5   (*iv*) 3   (*v*) 53   (*vi*) 21
3.   (*i*) 26.3   (*ii*) 1.56   (*iii*) 0.086   (*iv*) 2.92   (*v*) 0.7   (*vi*) 789.35
4.   0.429

EXERCISE 7 (f)

1.   (*i*) 4   (*ii*) 5   (*iii*) 4   (*iv*) 6   (*v*) 1
2.   (*i*) 41.4   (*ii*) 0.09   (*iii*) 29   (*iv*) 600.1   (*v*) 25.60

MENTAL MATHS – 5

1. 10.73   2. 0.8   3. 0.00008   4. 75.6   5. 6.45   6. 6.01   7. (*i*) 0.4278 (*ii*) 4.278

8. 1.35 m   9. 1.8   10. $\dfrac{5}{4}$ 11. 6.1   12. 0.8 kg.

NUMBER WORLD

$111 = 3 \times 37 = 16 + 17 + 18 + 19 + 20 + 21$

In cricket, a score of 111 is called 'the **Nelson**' and is considered unlucky. A 'double Nelson is 222.

■ 111 is the ninth number that stays the same when written upside down. (Three two digit numerals are 69, 88, 11).

■ Numbers like 111 which are just written with one's are called **repunits.**

■ What happens when you square repunits ? Look at the following pattern :

1^2	=	1
11^2	=	121
111^2	=	12321
1111^2	=	1234321
11111^2	=	123454321
111111^2	=	12345654321
1111111^2	=	1234567654321
11111111^2	=	123456787654321
111111111^2	=	12345678987654321

Mathematicians have done a lot of research to discover which repunits are prime numbers. The first two prime repunits are 1 and 11, and the next is 19 digit long.

111

8. Powers and Roots

8.1 Introduction

You have learnt in class VI that if we multiply a number by itself again and again, then it can be written in a short form as under :

$$4 \times 4 \times 4 = 4^3 \ ; (-3) \times (-3) \times (-3) \times (-3) \times (-3) = (-3)^5$$

8.2 Power

In general, *for any non zero number a and a positive integer n, we define :*

$$a^n \ as \ a \times a \times a \times a \ldots\ldots\ldots\ldots \times a \ (n \ times)$$

a^n is called the **n^{th} power** of a and is also read as 'a raised to the power n'.

The non-zero number 'a' is called the **base** and 'n' is called the **exponent** or **power** or **index**.

8.3 Powers of (– 1)

Observe the pattern :

$(-1)^1 = -1, \ (-1)^2 = -1 \times -1 = +1, \ (-1)^3 = -1 \times -1 \times -1 = -1$

$(-1)^4 = -1 \times -1 \times -1 \times -1 = +1$ and so on.

Thus we have

(*i*) *When the power of – 1 is any even natural number, the product is always 1.*

(*ii*) *When the power of – 1 is any odd natural number, the product is always –1 .*

$$\boxed{\begin{array}{l} (-1)^{\text{ even natural number}} = 1 \\ (-1)^{\text{ odd natural number}} = -1 \end{array}}$$

Ex. 1 **Find the value of :**

(*i*) 9^3

(*ii*) $(-5)^4$

(*iii*) $(0.4)^4$

(*iv*) $\left(1\dfrac{1}{3}\right)^5$

(*v*) $\left(1\dfrac{6}{7}\right)^4$

(*vi*) $(2.3)^3$

Sol.

(*i*) $9^3 = 9 \times 9 \times 9 = \textbf{729}.$

(*ii*) $(-5)^4 = -5 \times -5 \times -5 \times -5 = \textbf{625}.$

(*iii*) $(0.4)^4 = 0.4 \times 0.4 \times 0.4 \times 0.4 = \textbf{0.0256}.$

(*iv*) $\left(1\dfrac{1}{3}\right)^5 = \left(\dfrac{4}{3}\right)^5 = \dfrac{4}{3} \times \dfrac{4}{3} \times \dfrac{4}{3} \times \dfrac{4}{3} \times \dfrac{4}{3} = \dfrac{1024}{243} = \textbf{4} \dfrac{\textbf{52}}{\textbf{243}}.$

(*v*) $\left(-\dfrac{6}{7}\right)^4 = \dfrac{-6}{7} \times \dfrac{-6}{7} \times \dfrac{-6}{7} \times \dfrac{-6}{7} = \dfrac{\textbf{1296}}{\textbf{2401}}.$

(*vi*) $(2.3)^3 = 2.3 \times 2.3 \times 2.3 = \textbf{12.167}.$

Ex. 2 **Evaluate :**

(*i*) $(-5)^3 \times (-1)^7 \times (-3)^2$

(*ii*) $\left(-\dfrac{3}{4}\right)^4 \times \left(\dfrac{1}{3}\right)^3$

(*iii*) $2^5 - 3^2.$

Sol. (i) $(-5)^3 \times (-1)^7 \times (-3)^2$ $\boxed{\because (-1)^7 = -1}$

      $= -5 \times -5 \times -5 \times -1 \times -3 \times -3 = \mathbf{1125}.$

(ii) $\left(-\dfrac{3}{4}\right)^4 \times \left(\dfrac{1}{3}\right)^3 = (-1)^4 \times \dfrac{3}{4} \times \dfrac{\cancel{3}}{4} \times \dfrac{\cancel{3}}{4} \times \dfrac{\cancel{3}}{4} \times \dfrac{1}{\cancel{3}} \times \dfrac{1}{\cancel{3}} \times \dfrac{1}{\cancel{3}} = \dfrac{3}{256}.$

(iii) $2^5 - 3^2 = 2 \times 2 \times 2 \times 2 \times 2 - 3 \times 3 = 32 - 9 = \mathbf{23}.$

EXERCISE 8 (a)

1. Find the value of

    (i) 2^5 (ii) $(-3)^3$ (iii) $(-3)^4$ (iv) $(-1)^{203}$ (v) $(-6)^4$ (vi) $(0.1)^2$ (vii) $(0.02)^3$

    (viii) $\left(-\dfrac{5}{9}\right)^3$ (ix) $\left(2\dfrac{1}{4}\right)^2$ (x) $(0.3)^4$ (xi) $(-1)^{90056}$ (xii) $(-0.2)^5$

2. Evaluate

    (i) $(-1)^{16} \times (-2)^3.$ (ii) $(-2)^3 \times (-3)^2 \times (-1)^{329}.$ (iii) $(0.1)^3 \times (-10)^4.$

    (iv) $(-2)^6 + 6(-1)^{31} + (-3)^3.$ (v) $(0.7)^2 \times 10^2 + (-5)^3.$

3. (i) $(3^3 - 2^4) \times \dfrac{1}{11}$ (ii) $(2)^7 + (-5)^3 + (6)^2 \times (-1)^7$

4. (i) $\left(\dfrac{5}{3}\right)^3 \times 9^2 \times \dfrac{2}{9}.$ (ii) $(8^2 - 3^3) \times \left(\dfrac{-2}{19}\right)^2 \times \dfrac{57}{4}.$

5. $\left[\left(\dfrac{1}{3}\right)^2 - \left(\dfrac{1}{4}\right)^2\right] \times \left(-\dfrac{2}{7}\right)^2 \times \left(-\dfrac{3}{5}\right)^2.$ **6.** $\left(4^5 - 6^3\right) \times \left(-\dfrac{1}{4}\right)^2.$

8.4 Square of a Number

> *If a number is multiplied by itself, the product so obtained is called the square of that number.*

For example :

    (i) $3 \times 3 = 3^2 = 9$ $\therefore$ 9 is the square of 3.

    (ii) $\left(\dfrac{4}{5}\right) \times \left(\dfrac{4}{5}\right) = \left(\dfrac{4}{5}\right)^2 = \dfrac{16}{25}$ $\therefore$ $\dfrac{16}{25}$ is the square of $\dfrac{4}{5}.$

    (iii) $0.7 \times 0.7 = 0.49$ $\therefore$ 0.49 is the square of 0.7.

    $\therefore$ If a is any number then $a \times a = a^2 = $ square of that number.

8.5 Perfect Square

> *A natural number is called a perfect square if it is the square of some natural number.*

1, 4, 9, 16, ... so on are the squares of the natural numbers 1, 2, 3, 4 .... and so on. They are call
perfect squares.

The first twenty perfect square natural numbers are :

Number	Square	Number	Square
1	1	11	121
2	4	12	144
3	9	13	169
4	16	14	196
5	25	15	225
6	36	16	256
7	49	17	289
8	64	18	324
9	81	19	361
10	100	20	400

8.6 Square Root

The square root of a positive integer n is an integer which when multiplied by itself gives n. The symbol $\sqrt{}$ _is used to indicate square root._

For example :

(i) $3 \times 3 = 9$ $\therefore$ $\sqrt{9} = 3$ (Square root of 9 is 3)

(ii) $6 \times 6 = 0.36$ $\therefore$ $\sqrt{0.36} = 0.6$

(iii) $\dfrac{3}{7} \times \dfrac{3}{7} = \dfrac{9}{49}$ $\therefore$ $\sqrt{\dfrac{9}{49}} = \dfrac{3}{7}$.

Square roots of the first twenty perfect squares is given below :

Number	Square Root	Number	Square Root
1	1	121	11
4	2	144	12
9	3	169	13
16	4	196	14
25	5	225	15
36	6	256	16
49	7	289	17
64	8	324	18
81	9	361	19
100	10	400	20

8.7 Method of Finding the Square Root of a given Number

> **Step 1** : _Split the given number into prime factors._
> **Step 2** : _Form pairs of like factors._
> **Step 3** : _From each pair, pick out one prime factor._
> **Step 4** : _Multiply the factors so picked._

Note: (i) We may also write the product of prime factors in exponential form and for finding the square root, we take half of the index value of each factor and then multiply.

(ii) **Square Root of a fraction** = $\dfrac{\text{Square root of the numerator}}{\text{Square root of the denominator}}$

(iii) **Square Root a decimal number :** convert to a decimal fraction and then work out as in (ii).

Ex. 1 *Find the square root of:*

(i) *7744*   (ii) *31.36*   (iii) *12 $\frac{1}{4}$.*

Sol. (i) $7744 = \underline{2 \times 2} \times \underline{2 \times 2} \times \underline{2 \times 2} \times \underline{11 \times 11} = 2^6 \times 11^2$

$\therefore \sqrt{7744} = 2 \times 2 \times 2 \times 11 = 88$

$\therefore \sqrt{7744} = 2^3 \times 11 = \mathbf{88}.$

2	7744
2	3872
2	1936
2	968
2	484
2	242
11	121
	11

> Taking half of the index values

(ii) $31.36 = \dfrac{3136}{100}$ $\therefore \sqrt{31.36} = \dfrac{\sqrt{3136}}{\sqrt{100}}$

$3136 = 2^6 \times 7^2$ $\therefore \sqrt{3136} = 2^3 \times 7$

$\therefore \sqrt{31.36} = \dfrac{2^3 \times 7}{10} = \dfrac{56}{10} = \mathbf{5.6.}$

2	3136
2	1568
2	784
2	392
2	196
2	98
7	49
	7

(iii) $\sqrt{12\dfrac{1}{4}} = \sqrt{\dfrac{49}{4}} = \dfrac{7}{2} = \mathbf{3\dfrac{1}{2}}.$

Ex. 2 *Find the square root of $23\dfrac{26}{121}$.*

Sol. $23\dfrac{26}{121} = \dfrac{2809}{121} = \dfrac{53 \times 53}{11 \times 11}$

> Try $50 \times 50; 51 \times 51;$
> $52 \times 52; 53 \times 53$

$\sqrt{23\dfrac{26}{21}} = \sqrt{\dfrac{2809}{121}} = \dfrac{\sqrt{2809}}{\sqrt{121}} = \dfrac{53}{11} = \mathbf{4\dfrac{9}{11}}.$

Ex. 3 *Find the least number by which 980 be multiplied to make it a perfect square. Find the perfec*
square so obtained and also its square root.

Sol. Resolving 980 into prime factors;

$980 = \underline{2 \times 2} \times 5 \times \underline{7 \times 7}$

2	980
2	490
5	245
7	49
	7

Making pairs of prime factors we can see that there is one factor namely 5 which does not exist in pair.

$\therefore$ To make the given number a perfect square we should complete the pair i.e. multiply the given number by 5

$\therefore$ Perfect Square obtained $= 980 \times 5 = 4900.$

$\sqrt{4900} = \sqrt{2^2 \times 5^2 \times 7^2} = 2 \times 5 \times 7 = \mathbf{70.}$

Ex. 4 *Find the least number by which 1200 must be divided to make it a perfect square. Find the perfec*
square number and also its square root.

Sol. Resolving 1200 into prime factors, we get

$1200 = \underline{2 \times 2} \times \underline{2 \times 2} \times \underline{5 \times 5} \times 3$

On making pairs we see that one factor, namely 3 does not exist in pair.

∴ To make 1200 a perfect square we divide it by 3.

∴ Perfect square number obtained $= 400 = 2^4 \times 5^2$

$$\sqrt{400} = \sqrt{2^4 \times 5^2} = 2^2 \times 5 = \mathbf{20}.$$

EXERCISE 8 (b)

1. Find the squares of the following numbers.

    (*i*) 15   (*ii*) 24   (*iii*) 60   (*iv*) 37   (*v*) 140   (*iv*) 0.05   (*vii*) $\dfrac{6}{11}$ (*viii*) $3\dfrac{1}{14}$

2. Find the square root of each of the following by factor method.

    (*i*)144   (*ii*) 400   (*iii*) 784   (*iv*) 1936   (*v*) 9025   (*iv*) 6084   (*vii*) 11664   (*viii*) 15876
    (*ix*) 5929   (*x*) 69696

    Find the square root of each of the following.

3. (*i*) $\dfrac{361}{225}$ (*ii*) $2\dfrac{14}{25}$ (*iii*) $3\dfrac{22}{49}$ (*iv*) $21\dfrac{51}{169}$

4. (*i*) 7.29   (*ii*) 0.0529   (*iii*) 72.25   (*iv*) 9.3025

5. For a class picnic, children collected Rs 3025. Each child gave as many rupees as there were children. How many children were there and how much money did each contribute ?

6. A cinema hall has 2304 seats in the form of rows, each rows containing as many seats as there are rows. How many seats are there in each row ?

7. Find the perimeter of a square whose area is 71824 m².

8. For each of the following, find the smallest number by which it should be multiplied so as to get a perfect square. Also find the square root of the square number so obtained.

    (*i*) 147   (*ii*) 1008   (*iii*) 2028

9. For each of the following number find the smallest number by which it should be divided so as to get a perfect square. Also find the square root of the square number so obtained.

    (*i*) 180   (*ii*) 3645   (*iii*) 450

8.8 Finding Square Root of a Perfect Square Number by Division Method

Sometimes it is not easy or convenient to write the factors of a number, as in solved Ex. 2. In such cases, we use the method of long division to find the square root.

Ex. 1. *Find the square root of 1849 by division method.*

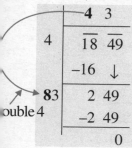

Solution steps :

1. Mark off the digits in pairs **from right to left. (←)**

2. Take the first pair of digits, find the nearest perfect square less than or equal to than the number. The largest perfect square less than 18 is 16 , the square of 4. Write 4 as the divisor and also as the quotient on top of 18. Subtract 4 × 4 = 16 from the first pair. Remainder is 2.

3. Bring down the next pair 49. **Double 4** (The quotient) and place its double i.e. 8 at the new divisor's place. Divide 24 by 8. It gives 3. Place 3 besides 8 as well as in the quotient, first above 49. Now multiply 83 by 3 and place under 249. Subtract. The remainder is 0 so the square root of 1849 is 43.

Ex. 2 *Find the square root of 15129 by division method.*

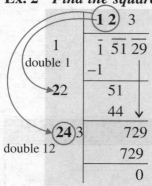

Solution steps :

1. Mark off the digits in pairs from right to left. Here we can see that **1 is unpaired.**
2. The largest square number less than or equal to 1 is 1. Write 1 as the divisor and also as the quotient above 1. Subtract $1 \times 1 = 1$ from 1. Remainder is 0.
3. Bring down the next pair 51. **Double 1** and place its double i.e. 2 at the new divisor's place. Now divide 5 by 2 to obtain 2. Place this 2 beside divisor 2 and also at the quotient's place above 51. Now $22 \times 2 = 44$, Place it below 51. Remainder is 7.
4. Bring down the next pair i.e. 29. Place if next to 7. **Double of 12 is 24.** Place it at the new divisor's place. Now $72 \div 24 = 3$. $\therefore$ Write 3 beside 24 and also at the quotient's place above 29. $243 \times 3 = 729$. Place it below 729. Subtract. Remainder is 0.

$$\therefore \sqrt{15129} = \textbf{123}.$$

EXERCISE 8 (c)

Find the square root of each of the following numbers by long division method :

1. 2209   **2.** 4761   **3.** 7396   **4.** 9409   **5.** 18225   **6.** 55696   **7.** 166464   **8.** 546121

9. 765625   **10.** 1085764

8.9 Cubes

The cube of a number is that number raised to the power 3. Thus, cube of $2 = 2^3 = 2 \times 2 \times 2 =$ cube of $5 = 5^3 = 5 \times 5 \times 5 = 125$.

8.10 Perfect Cube

We know that $2^3 = 8$, $3^3 = 27$, $6^3 = 216$, $7^3 = 343$, $10^3 = 1000$

The number 8, 27, 216, 343, 1000, ... are called perfect cubes. A natural number is said to be a perfect cube if it is the cube of some natural number.

The cubes of first 20 natural numbers are given below.

Number	Cube	Number	Cube	Number	Cube	Number	Cub
1	**1**	6	**216**	11	**1331**	16	409
2	**8**	7	**343**	12	**1728**	17	491
3	27	8	**512**	13	**2197**	18	583
4	64	9	**729**	14	**2744**	19	685
5	125	10	**1000**	15	**3375**	20	800

From the above table, you can observe the following properties of cubes of numbers.

1. Cubes of all odd natural numbers are odd.
2. Cubes of all even natural numbers are even.
3. The cube of a natural number which is a multiple of 3 is a multiple of 27.

For example :

(i) $6 \times 6 \times 6 = 216 \implies 6^3 = 216$ | 216 is the cube of 6.

(ii) $\frac{3}{4} \times \frac{3}{4} \times \frac{3}{4} = \frac{27}{64} \implies \left(\frac{3}{4}\right)^3 = \frac{27}{64}$ | $\frac{27}{64}$ is the cube of $\frac{3}{4}$.

(iii) $(0.5) \times (0.5) \times (0.5) = 0.125 \implies (0.5)^3 = 0.125$ | 0.125 is the cube of 0.5.

.11 Cube Root

We know that 8 is the cube of 2. We can state this fact in other form by saying that 2 is the cube root of 8.

Similarly,

We know that	*Therefore*
27 is the cube of 3	3 is the cube root of 27
64 is the cube of 4	4 is the cube root of 64
729 is the cube of 9	9 is the cube root of 729.

The cube root of a number is indicated by the sign $\sqrt[3]{}$. Thus,

$$\sqrt[3]{8} = 2, \quad \sqrt[3]{27} = 3, \quad \sqrt[3]{64} = 4, \quad \sqrt[3]{125} = 5, \quad \sqrt[3]{216} = 6, \quad \sqrt[3]{1331} = 11$$

.12 Cube Root of a Negative Number

We know that	**Therefore**
$(-1)^3 = -1 \times -1 \times -1$	cube root of $-1 = -1$
$(-2)^3 = -2 \times -2 \times -2 = -8$	cube root of $-8 = -2$
$(-5)^3 = -5 \times -5 \times -5 = -125$	cube root of $-125 = -5$
$(-9)^3 = -9 \times -9 \times -9 = -729$	cube root of $-729 = -9$

Thus we see that the cube root of a negative number exists.
Does the square root of a negative number exist ? **Ans.: No.**
Hence,

> *The cube root of a negative number exists but the square root of a negative number does not exist.*
> *The cube root of a negative number is negative.*

.13 Finding the Cube Root

The cube root of perfect cubes can be found by prime factorisation method. Cube roots of numbers which are not perfect cubes can be found by using tables of cube roots. We will not consider such numbers here.

x.1. *Find the cube root of 216.*

ol. **Step 1.** *Find the prime factors.*

Step 2. *Separate into groups of three similar factors each.*

Step 3. *Pick up one factor from each group and multiply.*

2	216
2	108
2	54
3	27
3	9
3	3
	1

$$\because 216 = 2 \times 2 \times 2 \times 3 \times 3 \times 3 \qquad 216 = 2^3 \times 3^3$$
$$\text{or}$$
$$\therefore \sqrt[3]{216} = 2 \times 3 = \mathbf{6}. \qquad \therefore \sqrt[3]{216} = 2 \times 3 = 6.$$

x.2. *Find the cube root of -74088.*

ol. The cube root of a negative number is negative. First find the cube root of the corresponding positive number and then put negative sign before it.

$$74088 = 2 \times 2 \times 2 \times 3 \times 3 \times 3 \times 7 \times 7 \times 7 = 2^3 \times 3^3 \times 7^3$$

$\therefore$ cube root of $74088 = 2 \times 3 \times 7 = \mathbf{42}$

$\therefore$ cube root of $-74088 = -\mathbf{42}$.

2	74088
2	37044
2	18522
3	9261
3	3087
3	1029
7	343
7	49
7	7
	1

Properties of Cube Roots

The two important properties of cube roots are

1. *If a and b are any two whole numbers, then*

$$\sqrt[3]{a \cdot b} = \sqrt[3]{a} \cdot \sqrt[3]{b}$$

i.e., cube root of the product of two whole numbers

= cube root of the first number × cube root of the second number.

Cube root of a fraction

2. *If a and b are any two whole numbers, i.e., integers (b ≠ 0), then*

$$\sqrt[3]{\frac{a}{b}} = \frac{\sqrt[3]{a}}{\sqrt[3]{b}}$$

3. We may also write the product of the prime factors in exponential form and then find the cube root. We divid each index (on power) by 3 and then multiply the new factors.

Ex. 3. *Find the cube root of :* (i) *8 × 729* (ii) *– 216.*

Sol. (i) $\sqrt[3]{8 \times 729} = \sqrt[3]{8} \times \sqrt[3]{729} = 2 \times 9 = $ **18.**

(ii) $\sqrt[3]{-216} = \sqrt[3]{(-1) \cdot 216} = \sqrt[3]{-1} \cdot \sqrt[3]{216} = (-1) \cdot 6 = $ **– 6.**

Ex.4 *Find the cube root of each of the following numbers:*

(i) $\dfrac{27}{125}$ (ii) $\dfrac{-216}{343}$

Sol. (i) $\dfrac{27}{125} = \dfrac{3 \times 3 \times 3}{5 \times 5 \times 5} = \dfrac{3^3}{5^3}$ ∴ Cube root of $\dfrac{27}{125} = \dfrac{\text{cube root of 27}}{\text{cube root of 125}} = \dfrac{3}{5}.$

(ii) $\dfrac{216}{343} = \dfrac{6 \times 6 \times 6}{7 \times 7 \times 7} = \dfrac{6^3}{7^3}$ ∴ Cube root of $\dfrac{216}{343} = \dfrac{\text{cube root of 216}}{\text{cube root of 343}} = \dfrac{6}{7}.$

∴ Cube root of $\dfrac{-216}{343} = -\dfrac{6}{7}.$

Ex.5 *Evaluate:* (i) $\sqrt[3]{0.064}$ (ii) $\sqrt[3]{0.000729}.$

Sol. (i) $0.064 = \dfrac{64}{1000}$ ∴ $\sqrt[3]{0.064} = $ cube root of $0.064 = $ cube root of $\dfrac{64}{1000}$

$= \dfrac{\text{cube root of 64}}{\text{cube root of 1000}} = \dfrac{4}{10} = 0.4.$

(ii) $0.000729 = \dfrac{729}{1000000}$ ∴ $\sqrt[3]{0.000729} = $ cube root of $\dfrac{729}{1000000}$

$= \dfrac{\text{cube root of 729}}{\text{cube root of 1000000}} = \dfrac{\text{cube root of } 3^6}{\text{cube root of } 10^6} = \dfrac{3^2}{10^2} = \dfrac{9}{100} = $ **0.09.**

Ex. 6 *What is the smallest number by which 243 should be multiplied to make the product a perfect cube Also find the cube root of the product.*

Sol. Resolving 243 into prime factors $243 = \underline{3 \times 3 \times 3} \times 3 \times 3$

Forming triplets we can see that, to complete the second triplet we have to multiply it by 3.

∴ Perfect cube = 243 × 3 = 729

729 $= \underline{3 \times 3 \times 3} \times \underline{3 \times 3 \times 3}$

cube root of = 729 = 3 × 3 = **9.**

3	243
3	81
3	27
3	9
	3

Ex.7 *What is the smallest number by which 8640 should be divided to make the quotient a perfect cube. Also find the cube root of the quotient.*

Sol.: Resolving 8640 into prime factors :

8640 = $\underline{2 \times 2 \times 2} \times \underline{2 \times 2 \times 2} \times \underline{3 \times 3 \times 3} \times 5$

Forming triplets we see that we have 5 as an extra factor so we divide 8640 by 5.

∴ Perfect cube = 1728 = $2^6 \times 3^3$

$\sqrt[3]{1728} = 2^2 \times 3 = \mathbf{12}.$ (Dividing index by 3)

5	8640
	1728

2	8640
2	4320
2	2160
2	1080
2	540
2	270
5	135
3	27
3	9
	3

EXERCISE 8 (d)

1. **Find the cube of each of the following numbers :**

   (i) 15 (ii) 40 (iii) $\dfrac{2}{3}$ (iv) $-\dfrac{6}{7}$ (v) $3\dfrac{4}{7}$

   (vi) $1\dfrac{6}{17}$ (vii) 0.3 (viii) 0.07 (ix) 2.4 (x) -3.8

2. **Which of the following numbers are perfect cubes ?**
   64, 125, 1331, 864, 4095
   (**Hint :** Resolve into prime factors and see if you can make triplets of like factors)

3. Write the cubes of multiples of 3 between 20 and 30.

4. **Find the cube root of each of the following numbers :**
   (i) 125 (ii) 512 (iii) 2197 (iv) 2744 (v) -1331 (vi) -6859
   Find the cube root of each of the following :

5. 27×64
6. -216×343
7. 125×1331
8. $27 \times (-2744)$
9. $\dfrac{64}{125}$

10. $\dfrac{-343}{4096}$
11. 0.008
12. 0.216
13. $5\dfrac{23}{64}$
14. $4\dfrac{17}{27}$

15. What is the smallest number by which 675 should be multiplied so that the product is a perfect cube ? Find the cube root of the perfect cube so obtained.

16. What is the smallest number by which 2916 should be divided so that the quotient is a perfect cube? Also find the cube root of the quotient.

17. Find the side of a cube whose volume is $\dfrac{343}{27}$ m^3.

LOOKING BACK

Summary of Key Facts

1. If *a* is a non-zero number and *n* is a natural number, then $a^n = a \times a \times a \times a$ _____ multiplied *n* times, where *a* is called the **base** and *n* is called **exponent**, power or **index** and a^n the **exponential form**.

2. If a is any non zero number then $a^2 = a \times a$ is the **square** of that number.

3. The square root of a number is that number which when multiplied by itself gives that number.

4. The symbol used for square root is $\sqrt{\ }$.

5. If *a* is any non-zero number then $a^3 = a \times a \times a$ is called the **cube** of that number.

6. The **cube root** of a given number is that number which when multiplied by itself 3 times gives the given number. It is denoted by $\sqrt[3]{\ }$.

7. If $\dfrac{a}{b}$ is a fraction then $\sqrt{\dfrac{a}{b}} = \dfrac{\sqrt{a}}{\sqrt{b}}$ and also $\sqrt[3]{\dfrac{a}{b}} = \dfrac{\sqrt[3]{a}}{\sqrt[3]{b}}$.

MENTAL MATHS – 6

1. Square root of 16 is ___

2. Square root of 121 is ___

3. Square root of 625 is ___

4. Square root of 900 is ___

5. $\sqrt{0.04}$ = ___   **6.** $\sqrt{0.49}$ = ___

7. Cube root of 125 is ___

8. Cube root of $\dfrac{8}{27}$ is ___

9. Cube root of 0.001 is ___

10. $\sqrt{0.343}$ = ___

11. $\sqrt[3]{0.008}$ = ___

12. The area of square field is 196 m². what is the length of one side?

13. The square root of a negative number does not exist. True or False ?

14. The cube root of 64 is ___

15. Evaluate $\sqrt[3]{125 \times 27}$.

16. $\sqrt[3]{\dfrac{729}{216}} \times \dfrac{6}{9}$ = ___

17. Find x if $4x^3 = 108$.

18. $\sqrt{49 \times 16} = 7 \times$ ___

19. A number must be odd if its square is odd. True or False !

20. Evaluate : $(3^2 + 4^2) \times \dfrac{1}{\sqrt[3]{125}} \times (-1)^{73}$.

UNIT REVIEW – 2

Simplify :

1. $-(-3|\ 5|) + (-|-7+2|) + |-20|$.

2. $2\dfrac{1}{3} - \dfrac{1}{3} \times 3\dfrac{1}{2} + 1\dfrac{7}{8} \div 1\dfrac{1}{4} - 3 \div \left(\dfrac{3}{4} \times 1\dfrac{1}{2}\right)$.

3. $\dfrac{7}{30}$ of $\left(\dfrac{1}{2} + \dfrac{7}{15}\right) \div \left(\dfrac{5}{6} - \dfrac{3}{5}\right)$.

4. $\dfrac{\dfrac{1}{4} - \dfrac{1}{9}}{\dfrac{1}{2} + \dfrac{1}{4} + \dfrac{1}{3}}$.

Evaluate :

5. $\dfrac{5.12 \times 4.2}{0.04}$.

6. $76.815 - 37.231 + 9.63 - 28.27$.

7. $0.018 \times 5.4 \times 1300$.

8. (a) $0.204 \div 0.006$ (b) $19.008 \div 0.0176$.

9. $(1.7 + 3.02 - 1.708) \times \dfrac{0.4}{0.16}$.

10. Find the reciprocal of $\left(\dfrac{2}{7} \div \dfrac{4}{21}\right) \div \dfrac{3}{5}$.

11. Arrange $2\dfrac{4}{5}, 5\dfrac{1}{3}, -2\dfrac{1}{2}, 3\dfrac{2}{3}$ in ascending order.

12. Find three fractions between $\dfrac{4}{11}$ and $\dfrac{3}{12}$.

13. Find the H.C.F of 1700, 255, 765 by division method.

14. Find the least number which when divided by 27, 36 or 63 leaves a remainder of 5.

15. Find the greatest number that will divide each of the numbers 380, 1232 and 478 leaving remainders 5, 7 and 3 respectively.

16. (i) What must be added to $5\dfrac{3}{5}$ to get $9\dfrac{1}{3}$?

(ii) By what number must $5\dfrac{3}{5}$ be multiplied to get $9\dfrac{1}{3}$?

17. Deepak spent Rs 84 on motor oil and Rs 240 on petrol. What fraction of the total amount did he spend on petrol?

18. How many jugs of lemonade each holding $1\frac{1}{2}$ litres can be filled from a can holding $3\frac{3}{8}$ litres of lemonade?

19. One tenth of a lamp post is painted red, $\frac{2}{3}$ of the remainder is painted white and the rest black. What fraction of the lamp post is black?

20. Reduce $\frac{343}{588}$ to the lowest terms.

21. Express 0.0325 as a vulgar fraction.

22. Convert $\frac{5}{13}$ to a recurring decimal.

23. Change each of the following recurring decimals to a vulgar fraction.
   (*a*) $0.4\overline{5}$ (*b*) $0.\overline{17}$ (*c*) $2.3\overline{48}$

24. Round off 6.371×9 correct to two decimal places.

25. Round off 0.007803 correct to 1 significant figure.

26. Ayushree is hosting a party. She buys :

45 balloons which cost Rs 1.30 each
12 party hats which cost Rs 2.60 each
24 burgers which cost Rs 12.50 each
25 soft drinks which cost Rs 9.40 each.
How much does she spend in all for the party ?

27. A lottery win of Rs 45450.90 is shared equally among 45 people. How much does each get?

28. Find the difference between $5\frac{3}{8}$ and 3.627?

29. Find the square root of : 1156

30. Find the cube root of (*a*) 0.001728   (*b*) $\frac{216}{2197}$.

31. Find the smallest number by which 1323 must be multiplied so that the product is a perfect cube?

32. Find the smallest number by which 3675 must be divided to get a perfect square number. Also find the square root of the perfect square number.

33. Evaluate : $\sqrt{169} + \sqrt{0.0169} - \sqrt{1.69}$.

34. Find the value $\sqrt{40 - \sqrt{\sqrt{400} - \sqrt{16}}}$.

ANSWERS

EXERCISE 8 (a)

1. (*i*) 32   (*ii*) -27 (*iii*) 81   (*iv*) -1 (*v*) 1296   (*vi*) 0.01   (*vii*) 0.000008
   (*viii*) $\frac{-125}{729}$ (*ix*) $5\frac{1}{16}$ (*x*) 0.0081   (*xi*) 1   (*xii*) -0.00032

2. (*i*) -8 (*ii*) 72   (*iii*) 10   (*iv*) 31   (*v*) -76 3. (*i*) 1   (*ii*) -33

4. (*i*) $\frac{250}{3}$ (*ii*) $\frac{111}{19}$ 5. $\frac{1}{700}$ 6. $\frac{101}{2}$

EXERCISE 8 (b)

1. (*i*) 225   (*ii*) 576   (*iii*) 3600   (*iv*) 1369   (*v*) 19600   (*vi*) 0.0025   (*vii*) $\frac{36}{121}$ (*viii*) $9\frac{85}{196}$

2. (*i*) 12   (*ii*) 20   (*iii*) 28   (*iv*) 44   (*v*) 95   (*vi*) 78   (*vii*) 108   (*viii*) 126
   (*ix*) 77   (*x*) 264

3. (*i*) $\frac{19}{15}$ (*ii*) $1\frac{3}{5}$ (*iii*) $1\frac{6}{7}$ (*iv*) $4\frac{8}{13}$

4. (*i*) 2.7   (*ii*) 0.23   (*iii*) 8.5   (*iv*) 3.05

5. 55 children contributed Rs 55 each.

6. 48 seats   7. 1072 m.   8. (*i*) 3, square root = 21 (*ii*) 7, square root = 84   (*iii*) 3, square root = 78

9. (*i*) 5, square root = 6   (*ii*) 5, square root = 27   (*iii*) 2, square root = 15.

EXERCISE 8 (c)

1. 47   2. 69   3. 86   4. 97   5. 135   6. 236   7. 408   8. 739   9. 875   10. 1042

EXERCISE 8 (d)

1. (*i*) 3375   (*ii*) 64000   (*iii*) $\frac{8}{27}$ (*iv*) $\frac{-216}{343}$ (*v*) $45\frac{190}{343}$ (*vi*) $2\frac{2341}{4913}$ (*vii*) 0.027   (*viii*) 0.000343
(*ix*) 13.824   (*x*) – 54.872

2. 64, 125, 1331   3. $21^3 = 9261, 24^3 = 13824, 27^3 = 19683$ 4. (*i*) 5   (*ii*) 8   (*iii*) 13   (*iv*) 14   (*v*) – 11   (*vi*) – 19

5. 12   6. – 42   7. 55   8. – 42   9. $\frac{4}{5}$ 10. $\frac{-7}{16}$ 11. 0.2   12. 0.6   13. $1\frac{3}{4}$ 14. $1\frac{2}{3}$

15. 5, cube root = 15   16. 4, cube root = 9   17. $2\frac{1}{3}$ m

MENTAL MATHS – 6

1. 4   2. 11   3. 25   4. 30   5. 0.2   6. 0.7   7. 5   8. $\frac{2}{3}$ 9. 0.1   10. 0.7
11. 0.2   12. 14 m   13. True   14. 4   15. 15   16. 1   17. 3   18. 4   19. True   20. – 5

UNIT REVIEW – 2

1. 30   2. 0   3. $\frac{29}{30}$ 4. $\frac{5}{39}$ 5. 537.6   6. 20.944   7. 126.36   8. (*a*) 34 (*b*) 1080   9. 7.53

10. $\frac{2}{5}$ 11. $-2\frac{1}{2}, 2\frac{4}{5}, 3\frac{2}{3}, 5\frac{1}{3}$ 12. $\frac{11}{34}, \frac{7}{23}, \frac{10}{35}$ 13. 85   14. 761   15. 25

16. (*i*) $3\frac{11}{15}$ (*ii*) $1\frac{2}{3}$ 17. $\frac{20}{27}$ 18. $2\frac{1}{4}$ jugs   19. $\frac{3}{10}$ 20. $\frac{7}{12}$ 21. $\frac{13}{400}$

22. $0.\overline{384615}$ 23. (*a*) $\frac{41}{90}$ (*b*) $\frac{17}{99}$ (*c*) $\frac{465}{198}$ 24. 57.34   25. 0.008   26. Rs 624.70   27. Rs 1010.02

28. 1.748   29. 34.   30. (*a*) 0.12 (*b*) $\frac{6}{13}$ 31. 7   32. 3, 35   33. 11.83   34. 6.

THE NUMBER WORLD

THE NUMBER 4

1. Car number plates ending in four have been banned in Beijing because they are said to be unlucky. The word for "four" sounds like the word for "dead" in Mandarin. Beijing is the first Chinese city to introduce such a measure although many buildings don't have 4th, 14th or 24th floors.
2. The word *four* has four letters. In the English language there is no other number whose number of letters is equal to its value.
3. On maps adjacent countries are usually shown is different colours. What is the smallest number of colours needed ? In 1852 a mathematician guessed that the answer is four colours for any map, no matter what shape the countries take. No one has ever found a map that needs more than four colours.

9. Ratio and Proportion

First we will revise the concepts already learnt by you in your previous class and then shall extend our study further.

9.1 Ratio

The picture shows three apples and five mangoes. We can compare their numbers in two ways as below :

(i) By saying that the number of mangoes is 2 more than the number of apples or by saying that the number of apples is 2 less than the number of mangoes. This is called the difference method.

(ii) By saying that $\dfrac{\text{Number of apples}}{\text{Number of mangoes}} = \dfrac{3}{5}$

or Number of apples $= \dfrac{3}{5}$ (Number of mangoes), i.e., *three fifth* of the number of mangoes.

The second way of comparing the quantities of two things is called the **ratio** method.

> A ratio is the *comparison of two or more quantities of the same kind using division* or we can define ratio of two quantities a and b of the same kind in the same units as a fraction $\dfrac{a}{b}$ which is written generally as **a : b** (read as a is to b).

In the ratio $\dfrac{a}{b}$, a is called the **first term** or antecedent and b is called the **second term** or **consequent**.

9.2 Important Points Relating to Ratios

While doing a study of ratios, we should keep in mind the following important points.

1. *In a ratio, the order of terms is very important.*

   i.e. The ratio 2 : 3 is different from the ratio 3 : 2.

2. **Since ratio is a fraction,** *the ratio will remain unchanged if each term of the ratio is multiplied or divided by the same non-zero number.*

   i.e. $4 : 7 = \dfrac{4}{7} = \dfrac{4 \times 3}{7 \times 3} = \dfrac{12}{21} \Rightarrow 4 : 7 = 12 : 21,\ \ 12 : 20 = \dfrac{12}{20} = \dfrac{12 \div 4}{20 \div 4} = \dfrac{3}{5} \Rightarrow 12 : 20 = 3 : 5.$

3. *Ratio exists between quantities of the same kind.*

   i.e.(i) There exists no ratio between the height of a child and the weight of a child.

   (ii) We cannot write a ratio between the age of a student and the marks obtained by the student.

4. *To find a ratio between quantities of the same kind, quantities should be expressed in the same units.*

i.e.   (*i*)   Ratio between 165 cm and 1m 87 cm

= Ratio between 165 cm and 187 cm = $\dfrac{165}{187} = \dfrac{15}{17}$ = **15 : 17.**

(*ii*)   Ratio between 45 minutes and 1 hour

= Ratio between 45 minutes and 60 minutes = $\dfrac{45}{60} = \dfrac{3}{4}$ = **3 : 4.**

5.   *Since ratio is a number, it has no units.*

6.   **To compare two ratios,** *we either convert them into equivalent like fractions* (*fractions with the same denominator*) **by finding the L.C.M. of the denominators or convert them to the decimal form.** i.e. To compare 3 : 5 and 2 : 3 we compare the fractions $\dfrac{3}{5}$ and $\dfrac{2}{3}$. Change to equivalent like fractions,

$\because$ L.C.M. of 5 and 3 = 15 $\therefore \dfrac{3}{5} = \dfrac{3 \times 3}{5 \times 3} = \dfrac{9}{15}$ and $\dfrac{2}{3} = \dfrac{2 \times 5}{3 \times 5} = \dfrac{10}{15}$

Since $\dfrac{10}{15} > \dfrac{9}{15} \Rightarrow \dfrac{2}{3} > \dfrac{3}{5}$ so **2 : 3 > 3 : 5.**

7.   *A ratio a : b =* $\dfrac{a}{b}$ *is in its lowest terms if the H.C.F. of a and b is 1.*

To convert a ratio to its lowest terms we divide both the terms of the ratio by their H.C.F. i.e. to conver 15 : 35 to the lowest terms, we find the H.C.F. of 15 and 35

$15 = 3 \times 5, 35 = 7 \times 5$ $\therefore$ H.C.F = 5

Dividing both the terms by the H.C.F.

$15 : 35 = \dfrac{15}{35} = \dfrac{15 \div 5}{35 \div 5} = \dfrac{3}{7}$ = **3 : 7.**

> *Alternatively, do as shown*
> $\dfrac{\overset{3}{\cancel{15}}}{\underset{7}{\cancel{35}}} = \dfrac{3}{7} = 3 : 7$

8.   *Increase or Decrease in a given ratio a : b.*

If a quantity increases or decreases in the ratio *a : b*, then *new quantity =* $\dfrac{b}{a}$ *of the original quantity.*

The fraction by which the original quantity is multiplied to get the new (increased) quantity is called the *multiplying ratio* (or factor), $\dfrac{\text{New (increased) quantity}}{\text{Original quantity}}$ = multiplying factor.

For example :

(*i*) To increase 54 kg in the ratio 2 : 3,

New weight after increase = $\dfrac{3}{2}$ of 54 = $\dfrac{3}{\cancel{2}} \times \overset{27}{\cancel{54}}$ = **81 kg.**

For example :

(*ii*) To decrease Rs 104 in the ratio 8 : 5

New amount after decrease = $\dfrac{5}{8}$ of 104 = $\dfrac{5}{\cancel{8}} \times \overset{13}{\cancel{104}}$ = **Rs 65.**

Ex. 1   *Express the ratio 36 : 81 in the simplest form.*
Sol.   H.C.F. of 36 and 81 is 9

$\therefore 36 : 81 = \dfrac{36}{81} = \dfrac{36 \div 9}{81 \div 9} = \dfrac{4}{9}$ = **4 : 9.**

Ex. 2   *Express the following ratios in the simplest form.*

      (i) $4\dfrac{1}{5} : 2\dfrac{1}{3}$ (ii) *0.4 : 0.6*   (iii) $\dfrac{1}{2} : \dfrac{1}{6} : \dfrac{1}{8}$.

Sol.   (*i*) Given ratio $= 4\dfrac{1}{5} : 2\dfrac{1}{3} = \dfrac{21}{5} : \dfrac{7}{3} = \dfrac{\frac{21}{5}}{\frac{7}{3}} = \dfrac{21}{5} \times \dfrac{3}{7} = \dfrac{9}{5} = \mathbf{9 : 5.}$

     (*ii*) $0.4 : 0.6 = \dfrac{4}{10} : \dfrac{6}{10} = 4 : 6 = \mathbf{2 : 3.}$

     (*iii*) Given ratio $= \dfrac{1}{2} : \dfrac{1}{6} : \dfrac{1}{8}$

> To convert fractional terms of a ratio to whole numbers we multiply each term by the L.C.M. of their denominators.

        L.C.M of 2, 6 and 8 = 24

        $\therefore \dfrac{1}{2} : \dfrac{1}{6} : \dfrac{1}{8} = \dfrac{1}{2} \times 24 : \dfrac{1}{6} \times 24 : \dfrac{1}{8} \times 24 = \mathbf{12 : 4 : 3.}$

Ex. 3   *Divide 84 toffees between two children in the ratio 5 : 7.*

Sol.   Sum of both the terms = 5 + 7 = 12

      $\therefore$ 1st child's share $= \dfrac{5}{12} \times \overset{7}{84} = \mathbf{35.}$

      2nd child's share $= \dfrac{7}{12} \times \overset{7}{84} = \mathbf{49.}$

Ex. 4   *Divide Rs 536 between A, B and C in the ratio $\dfrac{1}{5} : \dfrac{2}{3} : \dfrac{1}{4}$ respectively.*

Sol.   L.C.M. of 5, 3 and 4 = 60

          $\therefore \dfrac{1}{5} : \dfrac{2}{3} : \dfrac{1}{4} = \dfrac{1}{5} \times \overset{12}{60} : \dfrac{2}{3} \times \overset{20}{60} : \dfrac{1}{4} \times \overset{15}{60}$

                   $= 12 : 40 : 15$

      Sum of the terms of the ratios $= 12 + 40 + 15 = \mathbf{67}$

      $\therefore$ A's share $=$ Rs $\left(\dfrac{12}{67} \times \overset{8}{536} \right) = \mathbf{Rs\ 96.}$

      B's share $=$ Rs $\left(\dfrac{40}{67} \times \overset{8}{536} \right) = \mathbf{Rs\ 320.}$

      C's share $=$ Rs $\left(\dfrac{15}{67} \times \overset{8}{536} \right) = \mathbf{Rs\ 120.}$

Ex. 5   *If a : b = 3 : 4 and b : c = 16 : 27 , find a : c.*

Sol.   Since $a : b = 3 : 4$ and $b : c = 16 : 27$

      $\therefore \dfrac{a}{b} = \dfrac{3}{4}$ and $\dfrac{b}{c} = \dfrac{16}{27} \Rightarrow a : c = \dfrac{a}{c} = \dfrac{a}{b} \times \dfrac{b}{c} = \dfrac{3}{4} \times \dfrac{16}{27} = \dfrac{4}{9} = \mathbf{4 : 9.}$

Ex. 6   *If a : b = 3 : 5 and b : c = 6 : 7, find a : b : c.*

Sol. $a : b = 3 : 5 \Rightarrow \dfrac{a}{b} = \dfrac{3}{5}, b : c = 6 : 7 \Rightarrow \dfrac{b}{c} = \dfrac{6}{7}$

To find $a : b : c$ we have to make b equal in both the cases. L.C.M. of the two values of b i.e. 5 and 6 = 30

$$\therefore a : b = 3 : 5 = \frac{3}{5} = \frac{3 \times 6}{5 \times 6} = \frac{18}{30} = 18 : 30 \quad b : c = 6 : 7 = \frac{6}{7} = \frac{6 \times 5}{7 \times 5} = \frac{30}{35} = 30 : 35$$

$$\therefore a : b : c = \textbf{18 : 30 : 35.}$$

Ex. 7 *Students of a school have been divided into two groups in the ratio 6 : 11. If the first group has 870 students, how many students are there in all in the school ?*

Sol. Sum of the terms of the ratio = 6 + 11 = 17.

Let x be the total number of students in the school. $\therefore$ No. of students in the first group = $\frac{6}{17}$ of x

$$\Rightarrow \quad \frac{6}{17} \text{ of } x = 870 \quad \Rightarrow \quad x = 870 \times \frac{17}{6} = 2465.$$

The total number of students in the school = **2465.**

Ex. 8 *Divide Rs 414 into three parts such that first one is $\frac{2}{3}$ of the second and the ratio between second and third is 5 : 7.*

Sol. Let the ratio of the three parts be $x : y : z$.

$$x = \frac{2}{3} y \Rightarrow \frac{x}{y} = \frac{2}{3} \Rightarrow x : y = 2 : 3$$

Given : $y : z = 5 : 7$ $\therefore x : y = 2 : 3$ and $y : z = 5 : 7$

Now making y equal in both the cases, i.e., $3 \times 5 = 15$, we have, $x : y = 2 : 3 = 10 : 15$ and $y : z = 5 : 7 = 15 : 21$

$\Rightarrow x : y : z = \textbf{10 : 15 : 21.}$

Sum of the terms of the ratio = 10 + 15 + 21 = 46

$$\therefore \text{ 1st part = Rs } \left(\frac{10}{46} \times \overset{9}{414} \right) = \textbf{Rs 90.} \qquad \text{2nd part = Rs } \left(\frac{15}{46} \times \overset{9}{414} \right) = \textbf{Rs 135.}$$

$$\text{3rd part = Rs } \left(\frac{21}{46} \times \overset{9}{414} \right) = \textbf{Rs 189.}$$

Ex. 9 *The salary of Ravi increases in the ratio 3 : 5. His original salary was Rs 7500. Find his new salary.*

Sol. Original salary = Rs 7500

Increase in salary is in the ratio = 3 : 5

$$\therefore \text{ New salary = Rs } \left(\frac{5}{3} \text{ of } \overset{2500}{7500} \right) = \text{Rs } (5 \times 2500) = \textbf{Rs 12,500.}$$

Ex.10 *The temperature of a city after rains dropped in the ratio 7 : 6. What is the new temperature if the original temperature was 42°C ?*

Sol. Original temperature = 42°C

Decrease in temperature is in the ratio 7 : 6

$$\therefore \text{ New temperature = } \frac{6}{7} \times \overset{6}{42} = (6 \times 6)°C = \textbf{36°C.}$$

EXERCISE 9 (a)

Express each of the following ratios in the simplest form.

1. (i) 12 : 16   (ii) 28 : 63   (iii) 70 : 110

2. (i) 0.2 : 0.3   (ii) 0.25 : 0.45   (iii) 2.7 : 9   (iv) 4.2 : 6.3

3. (i) $\frac{1}{4} : \frac{1}{6}$ (ii) $3\frac{1}{2} : 2\frac{1}{4}$ (iii) $2\frac{1}{3} : 3\frac{2}{5}$ (iv) $\frac{1}{3} : \frac{1}{5} : \frac{1}{6}$ (v) $\frac{1}{4} : \frac{1}{8} : \frac{1}{10}$ (vi) $1\frac{3}{4} : 2\frac{2}{3} : 1\frac{5}{6}$

4. (i) 125 gm : 1 kg   (ii) 275 m : 3 km   (iii) 76 ml : 1 litre   (iv) 36 minutes : $1\frac{1}{2}$ hours

    (v) 4 days : 2 weeks   (vi) Rs 4.50 : 600 paise   (vii) 8 months : $1\frac{1}{2}$ years

5. There are 56 teachers in a school. Out of them, 42 are lady teachers and the rest are male teachers. **Find the ratio of:**
    (i) male teachers to the lady teachers   (ii) lady teachers to male teachers
    (iii) male teachers to total number of teachers.

6. Divide Rs 7400 among three peopole A, B and C in the ratio 3 : 5 : 12

7. Divide 104 pencils among three children in the ratio $\frac{1}{2} : \frac{1}{3} : \frac{1}{4}$.

8. A tree of height 4.5 m is broken into three pieces in the ratio 2 : 3 : 4. Find the length of each piece.

9. If $a : b = 5 : 7$ and $b : c = 14 : 15$ find $a : c$

10. If $l : m = 1\frac{1}{2} : 1\frac{3}{4}$ and $m : n = 2\frac{1}{3} : 4\frac{1}{5}$ find $l : n$. Also find $l : m : n$.

11. If $x : y = 2 : 7$ and $y : z = 9 : 11$ find $x : y : z$.

12. Divide 60 into three parts such that first will be $\frac{3}{4}$ of the second and the second will be $\frac{4}{5}$ of the third.

13. Divide Rs 1545 between three people A, B and C such that A gets three-fifths of what B gets and the ratio of the share of B to C is 6 : 11.

14. The ratio of the length to the breadth of a rectangle is 5 : 3. If the perimeter of the rectangle is 144 m, what is the length of the rectangle.

15. The ratio of the number of male operators to the number of female operators is 5 : 8. If there are 85 male operators, how many workers are there in the factory?

16. The sides of a triangle are in the ratio 2 : 3 : 4. If the shortest side measures 6 cm, what is the perimeter of the triangle?

17. The height of a child increases in the ratio 2 : 3. The height at present is 140 cm, what is the new height ?

18. Rina lost her weight in the ratio 5 : 3. Her original weight was 80 kg. What is her new weight?

19. **Which is the greater ratio :**
    (i) 4 : 7 or 9 : 11 ?   (ii) 13 : 40 or 5 : 8 ?

20. Two numbers are in the ratio 4 : 11 and their sum is 135. Find the numbers.

21. The ratio of the expenditure to the saving of a family is 7 : 3. Find the income if expenditure is Rs 6300.

9.3 Proportion

Let there be four numbers 4, 6, 16 and 24.
Ratio of the first two numbers = 4 : 6 = 2 : 3
Ratio of the third and fourth numbers = 16 : 24 = 2 : 3
We find that the two ratios are equal. We say that these four numbers are in **proportion**.

A proportion is an equation that states that two ratios are equal.

Four numbers are said to be in proportion if the ratio of the first two is equal to the ratio of the last two, i.e.. a, b, c and d are said to be in proportion if $a : b = c : d$.

This is expressed as $\boldsymbol{a : b : : c : d}$. It is read as '$\boldsymbol{a}$ is to $\boldsymbol{b}$ as $\boldsymbol{c}$ is to $\boldsymbol{d}$ '.

Here a, b, c and d are the first, second, third and fourth terms of the proportion respectively. The **first** and th **fourth** terms are called the **extremes** and the **second** and **third** terms are called the **means**.

In the proportion $a : b : : c : d$, d is called the **fourth proportional**.

Also, $a : b = c : d \Rightarrow \dfrac{a}{b} = \dfrac{c}{d} \Rightarrow ad = bc$.

Thus a, b, c and d are in proportion if $\boxed{\textbf{Product of extremes = Product of means.}}$

Three quantities a, b and c (of the same kind) are said to be in **continued proportion** if $\boldsymbol{a : b : : b : c}$ i.e.

$$\dfrac{a}{b} = \dfrac{b}{c} \Rightarrow b^2 = ac$$

Here b is called the **mean proportional** and a and c are known as the first proportional and third proportiona respectively.

$\boxed{\textbf{Mean proportion between } a \textbf{ and } c = \sqrt{ac}.}$

Note : In a ratio both the terms should be of the same kind, but in a proportion, the first two should be of the same kind and the last two should be of the same kind.

Ex. 1 *Determine whether the following numbers are in proportion or not :*

    (i) *1.2, 2.7, 0.4, 0.9*   **(ii)** $\dfrac{1}{3}, \dfrac{1}{8}, \dfrac{1}{5}, \dfrac{1}{9}.$

Sol.   **(i)**   Product of extremes $= 1.2 \times 0.9 = 1.08$ **(ii)** Product of extremes $= \dfrac{1}{3} \times \dfrac{1}{9} = \dfrac{1}{27}$

               Product of means $= 2.7 \times 0.4 = 1.08$ Product of means $= \dfrac{1}{8} \times \dfrac{1}{5} = \dfrac{1}{40}$

                  $\because$ Product of extremes = Product of means $\because$ Product of extremes $\neq$ Product of means

                  $\therefore$ 1.2, 2.7, 0.4 and 0.9 are in proportion. $\therefore$ $\dfrac{1}{3}, \dfrac{1}{8}, \dfrac{1}{5}, \dfrac{1}{9}$ are not in proportion.

Ex. 2 *Find the value of x in the proportion* $2\dfrac{1}{2} : x : : 3\dfrac{1}{2} : 4.$

Sol.   The proportion can be written as $\dfrac{5}{2} : x : : \dfrac{7}{2} : 4$

    $\because$ The four numbers are in proportion. $\therefore$ Product of extremes = product of means

    i.e., $\dfrac{5}{\cancel{2}} \times \cancel{4}^{\,2} = x \times \dfrac{7}{2} \Rightarrow 10 = \dfrac{7x}{2} \Rightarrow x = 10 \times \dfrac{2}{7} = \dfrac{20}{7} = 2\dfrac{6}{7}.$

Ex. 3 *Find the fourth proportional to 4.8, 1.6, 5.4.*

Sol.   Let the fourth proportional be x. Then 4.8, 1.6, 5.4, x are in proportion.

    $\therefore$ Product of extremes = product of means i.e., $4.8 \times x = 1.6 \times 5.4$

    $\Rightarrow x = \dfrac{1.6 \times 5.4}{4.8} = \dfrac{16 \times 54}{48 \times 10} = \dfrac{18}{10} = \textbf{1.8.}$

> There are 2 decimal places in the numerator and one decimal place in the denominator, so we remove the decimal points and multiply the denominater by 10

Ex. 4 *Find the mean proportional between* $\dfrac{1}{4}$ *and* $\dfrac{1}{25}$.

Sol. Let x be the mean proportional between $\dfrac{1}{4}$ and $\dfrac{1}{25}$. Then $\dfrac{1}{4} : x :: x : \dfrac{1}{25}$.

$$x^2 = \frac{1}{4} \times \frac{1}{25} = \frac{1}{100} \Rightarrow x = \sqrt{\frac{1}{100}} = \frac{1}{\sqrt{100}} = \frac{1}{10}.$$

$\therefore \dfrac{1}{10}$ is the mean proportional between $\dfrac{1}{4}$ and $\dfrac{1}{25}$.

Ex. 5 *Find the third proportional to* (i) 3.6, 1.8 (ii) $4\dfrac{1}{6}$, 25

Sol. (i) Let the third proportional to 3.6 and 1.8 be x.

Then 3.6, 1.8 and x are in continued proportion $\therefore$ 3.6 : 1.8 :: 1.8 : x.

$$\therefore \frac{3.6}{1.8} = \frac{1.8}{x} \Rightarrow 3.6\,x = 1.8 \times 1.8 \Rightarrow x = \frac{1.8 \times 1.8}{3.6} = \frac{18}{36} \times \frac{18}{10} = \frac{9}{10} = \mathbf{0.9}.$$

(ii) Let the third proportional to $4\dfrac{1}{6}$ and 5 be x. Then $\dfrac{25}{6}$, 5 and x are in continued proportion, i.e., $\dfrac{25}{6} : 5 :: 5 : x$.

$$\Rightarrow \frac{25}{6}\,x = 5 \times 5 \Rightarrow x = 5 \times 5 \times \frac{6}{25} = \mathbf{6}.$$

Ex. 6 *An aeroplane flies 3000 km in 5 hrs. How much distance will be covered if it travels for 7 hours ?*

Sol. Ratio of the distance travelled should be equal to the ratio of the times taken.

Let the distance travelled in 7 hrs be x. Then, 3000 : x = 5 : 7

$$\Rightarrow \frac{3000}{x} = \frac{5}{7} \Rightarrow x = \frac{3000 \times 7}{5} = 4200.$$

$\therefore$ The distance covered in 7 hrs is **4200 km.**

Ex. 7 *At a particular time, the shadow of a pole and tower are respectively 20 m and 30m. If the height of the tower is 48m, find the height of the pole.*

Sol. Ratio of the shadows = Ratio of heights.

Let x be the height of the pole. Then, 20 : 30 = x : 48 $\Rightarrow \dfrac{20}{30} = \dfrac{x}{48} \Rightarrow x = \dfrac{20 \times 48}{30} = 32$

$\therefore$ The height of the pole is **32 m.**

EXERCISE 9 (b)

1. Determine whether the following numbers are in proportion or not.

(i) $\dfrac{1}{2}, \dfrac{1}{4}, \dfrac{1}{7}, \dfrac{1}{14}$ (ii) 12, 15, 4, 5 (iii) 2, $3\dfrac{1}{2}$, 3, $4\dfrac{1}{2}$ (iv) 1.2, 1.6, 0.9, 1.2 (v) $\dfrac{1}{3}, \dfrac{1}{4}, \dfrac{1}{6}, \dfrac{1}{7}$

2. Find the value of x in each of the given proportions :

(i) 0.9 : 0.6 :: x : 3 (ii) x : 5 :: 28 : 35 (iii) 1.6 : x :: 0.12 : 0.24 (iv) $\dfrac{1}{15} : \dfrac{1}{4} :: x : \dfrac{1}{5}$ (v) 16 : x :: x : 25

3. Find the fourth proportional to :

(i) 8, 32, 17 (ii) 8.1, 1.2, 2.7, (iii) 3 kg, 7 kg, 15 kg (iv) $\dfrac{1}{3}, \dfrac{1}{5}, \dfrac{1}{7}$

4. **Find the mean proportional between**

    (*i*) 144 and 225   (*ii*) 0.32 and 0.08   (*iii*) $\dfrac{1}{36}$ and $\dfrac{1}{9}$

5. **Find the third proportional to :**

    (*i*) 32, 16   (*ii*) $4\dfrac{1}{6}$, 5   (*iii*) 4.2, 0.7   (*iv*) 240 paise, 480 paise.

6. Show that 6, 36, 216 are in continued proportion.

7. If 25 persons can dig a trench 36 m long in one day, then find the number of persons required to dig a trench 108 m long in one day.

8. Rajat can type 3200 words in one hour. How many words can he type in 15 minutes?

9. 8 boys eat 5.6 kg of butter in a week. How much butter will 14 boys eat in a week, quantity remaining the same in each case.

10. In a proportion, the extremes are 11 and 35. If one of the mean is 7, find the other.

LOOKING BACK

Summary of Key Facts

   1.   A **ratio** is formed when two quantities are compared by division i.e. $a : b$ or $\dfrac{a}{b}$.

   2.   Usually a ratio is written in its simplest form.

   3.   A ratio has no unit.

   4.   If a quantity increases (or decreases) in the ratio $a : b$, then new quantity is $\dfrac{b}{a}$ of the

       original quantity. $\dfrac{b}{a}$ is called the multiplying factor.

   5.   An equality of two ratios is called a proportion.

   6.   The first and fourth terms of a proportion are called **extremes** and second and third terms are called **means**.

   7.   Four quantities a, b, c and d are said to be in proportion

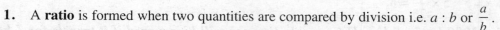

       if $\boldsymbol{a : b = c : d} \Rightarrow \dfrac{a}{b} = \dfrac{c}{d} \Rightarrow ad = bc$ i.e. **Product of extremes = Product of means.**

   8.   In a proportion $a : b : : c : d$, d is called the **fourth proportional.**

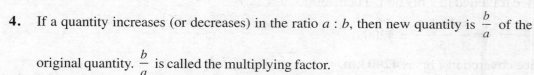

   9.   Three quantities a, b, c are said to be in continued proportion if $a : b = b : c$ or $\dfrac{a}{b} = \dfrac{b}{c}$ i.e., $\boldsymbol{b^2 = ac}$.

  10.   In a continued proportion $a : b : : b : c$, b is called the **mean proportional** between a and c is, and c called the **third proportional.**

MENTAL MATHS – 7

1. Express the ratio 12 : 18 in its simplest form.
2. Divide 25 chocolates among two children in the ratio $\frac{1}{2} : \frac{1}{3}$.
3. There are 'b' boys and 'g' girls in a class. Find the ratio of the number of boys to the total number of students in the class.

4. Are 5, 6, 15, 18 in proportion ?
5. Are 4.8, 2.4, 0.2, 0.1 in proportion ?
6. The product of means in a proportion is $\frac{1}{48}$, one of the extremes is $\frac{1}{6}$. Find the other extreme.

ANSWERS

EXERCISE 9 (a)

1. (i) 3 : 4   (ii) 4 : 9   (iii) 7 : 11
2. (i) 2 : 3   (ii) 5 : 9   (iii) 3 : 10   (iv) 2 : 3
3. (i) 3 : 2   (ii) 14 : 9   (iii) 35 : 51   (iv) 10 : 6 : 5   (v) 10 : 5 : 4   (vi) 21 : 32 : 22
4. (i) 1 : 8   (ii) 11 : 120   (iii) 19 : 250   (iv) 2 : 5   (v) 2 : 7   (vi) 3 : 4   (vii) 4 : 9
5. (i) 1 : 3   (ii) 3 : 1   (iii) 1 : 4   6. A gets Rs 1110, B gets Rs 1850 and C gets Rs 4440.
7. 48, 32, 24   8. 1m, 1.5m, 2m   9. 2 : 3   10. 10 : 21 ; 30 : 35 : 63   11. 18 : 63 : 77   12. Rs 15, Rs 20, Rs. 25
13. A = Rs 270, B = Rs 450, C = Rs 825   14. 45 m   15. 221 workers   16. 27 cm   17. 210 cm
18. 48 kg   19. (i) $\frac{9}{11}$ (ii) $\frac{5}{8}$ 20. 36, 99   21. Rs 9000.

EXERCISE 9 (b)

1. (i) Yes   (ii) Yes   (iii) No   (iv) Yes   (v) No.
2. (i) 4.5   (ii) 4   (iii) 3.2   (iv) 4/75   (v) 20.
3. (i) 68   (ii) 0.4   (iii) 35 kg   (iv) $\frac{3}{35}$
4. (i) 180   (ii) 0.16   (iii) $\frac{1}{18}$
5. (i) 8   (ii) 6   (iii) $\frac{7}{60}$ (iv) 960 paise   7. 75 persons   8. 800 words   9. 9.8 kg.   10. 55

MENTAL MATHS-7

1. 2 : 3   3. 15, 10   3. $\frac{b}{b+g}$ 4. Yes   5. Yes   6. $\frac{1}{8}$

ENRICHMENT
MATHEMATICS AND ART

The **golden rectangle** is a shape which has appeared in art and architecture through the years. The ratio of the lengths of the sides of a golden rectangle is approximately **1 : 1.6.** This ratio is called the golden ratio. A golden rectangle is pleasing to the eye.

The golden ratio was discovered by the Greeks about the middle of the fifth century B.C.

1. A rectangle measures 10.5 cm by 16.8 cm. Is it a golden rectangle ?

2. What are the dimensions of two Golden rectangles that can be constructed with sides of 3.2 cm ?

3. The golden ratio is more precisely expressed as 1 : 1.618. Some people use $1 : 1\frac{5}{8}$. Are these two ratios exactly equivalent ?

ANSWERS

1. Yes   2. 3.2 cm by 5.12 cm ; 3.2 cm by 2 cm   3. No., $1 : 1\frac{5}{8} = 1 : 1.625$.

10. Unitary Method

You have already solved problems based on unitary method in class 6. In this chapter we shall introduce two more methods i.e. variation method and multiplying ratio method to solve these types of problems.

10.1 Unitary Method

The method of finding the value of the required number of quantity by first finding the value of the unit quantity is called **unitary method.**

While solving problems by unitary method, we come across two types of variations or proportions.

(*i*) **Direct Variation**   (*ii*) **Inverse Variation**

10.2 Direct Variation

A direct variation is indicated when two quantities are so related that (i) *an increase in one causes a corresponding increase in the other or when a decrease in one causes a corresponding decrease in the other* (*ii*) *They increase or decrease in the same ratio.*

Examples of Direct Variation are:

(*i*) The cost of articles varies directly as the number of articles. The more the number of articles, more the cost; the less the number of articles, less the cost.

(*ii*) The speed varies directly as the distance covered, provided the time remains the same.

(*iii*) Work done varies directly as the number of men employed.

10.3 Inverse Variation

An inverse variation is indicated when two quantities are so related that (*i*) *an increase in one causes a corresponding decrease in the other and vice versa* (*ii*) *the ratio of any two values of one quantity is the inverse of the ratio of the corresponding values of the other.*

Examples of Inverse variations are:

(*i*)   Speed varies inversely as time; more speed, less time; less speed, more time.

(*ii*) Volume varies inversely as density.

(*iii*) Number of men, required at work varies inversely as time taken. More men, less time; less men, more time.

Remark : Whatever value we have to find out we always place it on the right and the given quantity on the left.

10.4 Examples based on Direct Variation

Ex. 1   *12 bags of wheat weigh 90 kg. How much will 20 bags weigh ?*

Sol.   12 bags of wheat weigh 90 kg.

$\therefore$ 1 bag of wheat weighs $90 \times \dfrac{1}{12}$ kg. $\left[12 = \dfrac{12}{1} \right]$ Less no. of bags weigh less, so divide

$\therefore$ 20 bags of wheat weigh $\dfrac{90}{12} \times \dfrac{20}{1} = \mathbf{150 \ kg.}$ more no. of bags weigh more.

Alternate Method

Ratio of the number of bags = Ratio of the weights.

Let x be the required weight, then $12 : 20 = 90 : x$ $\left[20 = \dfrac{20}{1} \right]$

$$\Rightarrow \frac{12}{20} = \frac{90}{x} \Rightarrow x = \frac{90 \times 20}{12} = \textbf{150 kg.}$$

Ex.2 *A scooter consumes 28 litres of petrol in covering a distance of 2100 km. How much petrol will be needed to cover a distance of 3600 km ?*

Sol. 2100 km can be covered in = 28 litres of petrol

$\therefore$ 1 km can be covered in $28 \times \dfrac{1}{2100}$ litres

less distance, less petrol

$\therefore$ 3600 km can be covered in $\dfrac{28}{2100} \times \dfrac{3600}{1}$

More distance More petrol

= **48 litres.**

Alternate Method

Ratio of the distances covered = Ratio of petrol consumed.

Let x litres be the required quantity of petrol, then, $2100 : 3600 = 28 : x$

$$\Rightarrow \frac{2100}{3600} = \frac{28}{x} \Rightarrow x = \frac{28 \times 3600}{2100} = \textbf{48 litres.}$$

Ex.3 $22\dfrac{1}{2}$ *m of silk costs Rs 214.20. What is the cost of* $6\dfrac{3}{4}$ *m?*

Sol. The cost of $22\dfrac{1}{2}$ m $\left(\dfrac{45}{2} \text{ m} \right)$ of silk = Rs 214.20

$\therefore$ cost of 1 m of silk = Rs $\dfrac{214.20 \times 2}{45}$

less length, less cost

$\therefore$ cost of $6\dfrac{3}{4}$ m of silk = Rs $\dfrac{214.20 \times 2}{45} \times \dfrac{27}{4} = \textbf{Rs 64.26.}$

more length, more cost

Alternate Method

Ratio of the lengths of the cloth = Ratio of costs

Let x rupees be the required cost. Then, $\dfrac{45}{2} : \dfrac{27}{4} = 214.20 : x$

$$\Rightarrow \frac{\dfrac{45}{2}}{\dfrac{27}{4}} = \frac{214.20}{x} \Rightarrow \frac{45 \times 4}{2 \times 27} = \frac{214.20}{x}$$

$$\Rightarrow x = \frac{214.20 \times 2 \times 27}{45 \times 4} = \textbf{Rs 64.26.}$$

10.5 Examples based on Inverse Variation

Ex.4 *If 20 men consume a certain quantity of rice in 14 days, in how may days will 8 men consume the same quantity of rice.*

Sol. 20 men consume a certain quantity in 14 days

∴ 1 man will consume that quantity in $14 \times \dfrac{20}{1}$ days   less number, more days

∴ 8 men will consume that quantity in $14 \times \dfrac{20}{1} \times \dfrac{1}{8}$ days **= 35 days.**   more number, less days

Alternate Method

Ratio of the number of men = Inverse ratio of number of days.

Let x be the required number of days. Then, $20 : 8 = x : 14$

$$\Rightarrow \frac{20}{8} = \frac{x}{14} \Rightarrow x = \frac{20 \times 14}{8} = \textbf{35 days.}$$

Ex.5 *Seema cycles to her school at an average speed of 12 km / hr. It takes her 20 minutes to reach th*
school. If she wants to reach her school in 15 minutes, what will be her average speed.

Sol. 20 minutes are taken at a speed of 12 km/hr.

∴ 1 minute is taken at a speed of $12 \times \dfrac{20}{1}$ km/hr.   less time, more speed so multiply

∴ 15 minutes are taken at a speed of $12 \times \dfrac{20}{1} \times \dfrac{1}{15}$ km/hr **= 16 km/hr.**   more time, less speed

Alternate Method

Ratio of the times taken = Inverse ratio of the speeds.

Let x be the required speed. Then, $20 : 15 = x : 12$

$$\Rightarrow \frac{20}{15} = \frac{x}{12} \Rightarrow x = \frac{20 \times 12}{15} = 16 \text{ km/hr.}$$

Hence the average speed required is **16 km/hr.**

Ex.7 *A fort had provisions for 150 men for 45 days. After 10 days, 25 men left the fort. How long will th*
food last at the same rate ?

Sol. The remaining food would last $(45 - 10)$ or 35 days for 150 men. But 25 men have left.

∴ Number of remaining men =125. For 150 men the food will last 35 days

∴ For 1 man the food will last $35 \times \dfrac{50}{1}$ days   less number of men more no. of days

∴ For 125 men the food will last $35 \times \dfrac{150}{1} \times \dfrac{1}{125} = \textbf{42 days.}$ more men, less no of days

Alternate Method

Ratio of the number of men = Inverse ratio of the number of days.

Let the required number of days be x.   Then, $150 : 125 = x : 35$

$$\Rightarrow \frac{150}{125} = \frac{x}{35} \Rightarrow x = \frac{150 \times 35}{125} = 42 \text{ days.}$$

Hence the food will last **42 days.**

EXERCISE – 10 (a)

1. 16 articles cost Rs 72. What will be the cost of 30 articles?

2. A journey of 552 km takes 6 days. How long will a journey of 1012 km take, if it is done at the same rate?

3. 45 baskets are required to carry 2835 mangoes. How many baskets will be required to carry 6615 mangoes?

4. Two and a half litres of paint are used to cover 725 sq m of area. How much will be required to paint 2001 sq m of area.

5. $5\frac{1}{4}$ m³ of a copper sheet weighs 1563 kg. What will be the weight of $3\frac{1}{2}$ m³ of sheet.

6. Harsh takes 150 steps in walking a distance of 125 metres. What distance would he cover in 360 steps ?

7. At a party 8 bottles of soft drink are served for every batch of 5 children. How many bottles would be served if 40 children were present in the party.

8. The amount of extension in an elastic spring varies directly as the weight hung on it. If a weight of 150g produces an extension of 2.9 cm, then what weight would produce an extension of 17.4 cm.

9. Fifteen chairs can be bought for Rs 3532.50. How many chairs can be bought for Rs 5416.50.

10. $23\frac{2}{11}$ ares of land is rented for Rs 8670. For what amount should $4\frac{1}{4}$ ares of land be rented?

11. A person at a speed of 72 km/hr travels from Dehradun to Lucknow in 10 hours. What should be the average speed of the car so that the person can complete the journey in 8 hours.

12. 28 pumps can empty a reservoir in 18 hours. In how many hours can 42 such pumps do the same work ?

13. A contractor who had a work force of 630 persons undertook to complete a portion of a stadium in 14 months. He was asked to complete the job in 9 months. How many extra persons had he to employ ?

14. Working 4 hours a day, Savita can type a manuscript in 15 days. How many hours a day should she work so as to finish the work in 10 days ?

15. A hostel had rations for 60 days for 500 students. After 12 days, 300 more students join the hostel. How long will the remaining ration last ?

16. If it would take 4 people, 15 hours to clear the trees from some land, how many people will be needed to complete the job in 6 hours ?

17. A man travels a certain distance by train in 4 hours and 12 minutes at the speed of 44.8 km per hour. How much time will it take to cover the same distance if the speed of the train is increased to 58.8 km per hour.

18. A besieged town has provisions to last for 3 weeks. Its population is 22400. How many people must be sent away in order that the provisions may last for 7 weeks.

19. It is found that a book will contain 350 pages if 32 lines are allowed in a page. How many lines should be allowed in a page, if the book is to contain 280 pages.

20. Twenty articles can be bought for a certain sum when the price of each article is Re 0.81. How many articles can be bought for the same sum if the price rises to Re 0.90 p.

TIME AND WORK

10.6 Introduction

In solving problems on time and work, the following points should be remembered :

1. If a man finishes total work in d days, then in 1 day he does $\frac{1}{d}$ of the total work.

   For example : if a man finishes work in 4 days, then in 1 day he does $\frac{1}{4}$ of the work.

2. Conversely ; if the work in 1 day, that a man does, is given, then the total number of days taken to finish the work.

$$= \frac{1}{\text{One day's work}}$$

For example : if a man does $\frac{1}{10}$ of the work in 1 day, then the total number of days required to finish the

work $= \frac{1}{\frac{1}{10}}$, i.e. $1 \div \frac{1}{10} = 1 \times \frac{10}{1} = 10$ days.

In other words, the total number of days is the reciprocal of the amount of work done in 1 day.

Ex. 1 *A can do a piece of work in 3 days, B can do it in 6 days. How long will A and B take, working together ?*

Sol. In 1 day A can do $\frac{1}{3}$ of the work.

In 1 day B can do $\frac{1}{6}$ of the work.

$\boxed{\dfrac{1}{3} + \dfrac{1}{6} = \dfrac{2+1}{6} = \dfrac{3}{6} = \dfrac{1}{2}}$

∴ A and B together do $\left\{\frac{1}{3} + \frac{1}{6}\right\}$, i.e. $\frac{1}{2}$ of the work in 1 day.

∴ A and B together do the whole work in $\left(1 \div \frac{1}{2}\right)$ days, i.e. in **2 days.**

Ex. 2. *A and B together can do a piece of work in 8 days, but A alone can do it in 12 days. How many days would B alone take to do the same work ?*

Sol. In 1 day A and B together can do $\frac{1}{8}$ of the work.

In 1 day A alone can do $\frac{1}{12}$ of the work.

∴ In 1 day B alone can do $\left(\frac{1}{8} - \frac{1}{12}\right)$ of the work, i.e. $\frac{1}{24}$ of the work.

∴ B alone will take $\left(1 \div \frac{1}{24}\right)$, i.e. **24 days** to do the work.

Ex. 3 *A and B can do a piece of work in 12 days, B and C in 15 days; C and A in 20 days. In how many days will they finish it together and separately?*

Sol. (A + B)'s 1 day's work $= \frac{1}{12}$; (B + C)'s 1 day's work $= \frac{1}{15}$; (C + A)'s 1 day's work $= \frac{1}{20}$

∴ 2 (A + B + C)'s 1 day's work $= \frac{1}{12} + \frac{1}{15} + \frac{1}{20} = \frac{5+4+3}{60} = \frac{12}{60} = \frac{1}{5}$

or (A + B + C)'s 1 day's work $= \frac{1}{2} \times \frac{1}{5} = \frac{1}{10}$

Thus, A, B and C can finish the work together in **10 days.**

Now, C's 1 day's work

$= [(A + B + C)\text{'s is 1 day's work}] - [(A + B)\text{'s 1 day's work}] = \left(\frac{1}{10} - \frac{1}{12}\right) = \frac{6-5}{60} = \frac{1}{60}$

∴ C alone can finish the work in **60 days.**

Similarly, A's 1 day's work $= \left(\frac{1}{10} - \frac{1}{15}\right) = \frac{3-2}{30} = \frac{1}{30}$

∴ A alone can finish the work in **30 days,**

B's 1 day's work $= \frac{1}{10} - \frac{1}{20} = \frac{2-1}{20} = \frac{1}{20}$

$\therefore$ B alone can finish the work in **20 days.**

10.7 Problems on Pipes and Cisterns

A cistern or a water tank is connected with two types of pipes. One which fills it up is called an **inlet** and the other which empties it out is called an **outlet.**

(*i*) If a pipe fills a water tank in 10 hours then in one hour it fills $\frac{1}{10}$th part of it. In other words, we can say that the work done by the pipe in 1 hour is $\frac{1}{10}$.

(*ii*) Similarly, if an outlet empties a tank in 8 hours, then in one hour it empties $\frac{1}{8}$th part of the tank. We can say that the work done by the outlet in one hour is $\left(-\frac{1}{8}\right)$.

> **Remark :** The work done by the inlet is always positive whereas the work done by the outlet is always negative.

Ex. 1. *A cistern can be filled by one tap in 4 hours and another tap in 6 hours. How long will it take to fill the cistern if both taps are opened together ?*

Sol. One tap fills the cistern is 4 hours. The other tap fills the cistern in 6 hours

$\therefore$ Work done by one tap in 1 hour $= \frac{1}{4}$

Work done by the other tap in 1 hour $= \frac{1}{6}$

The work done by both taps in 1 hour $= \left(\frac{1}{4} + \frac{1}{6}\right) = \frac{3+2}{12} = \frac{5}{12}$.

$\therefore$ Both the taps when opened together will fill the cistern in $\frac{12}{5}$ **hours.**

Ex. 2. *A water tank can be filled by a tap in 8 hours and emptied by an outlet pipe in 12 hours. How long will it take to fill the cistern if both the tap and the pipe are opened together ?*

Sol. The time taken by the tap to fill the tank = 8 hours

The time taken by the pipe to empty the tank = 12 hours

$\therefore$ The work done by the tap in 1 hour $= \frac{1}{8}$

The work done by the pipe in 1 hour $= -\frac{1}{12}$

thus, when opened together the work done by the tap and the pipe

$= \frac{1}{8} + \left(-\frac{1}{12}\right) = \frac{1}{8} - \frac{1}{12} = \frac{3-2}{24} = \frac{1}{24}$

$\therefore$ When both are opened together the tank can be filled in **24 hours.**

1. Two men can do a piece of work in 3 days and 4 days respectively. If they work together, in how many days will they finish the work ?

2. One man can do a piece of work in 3 hours; another can do the same piece of work in 2 hours. How long will they take if they work together ?

3. A and B together can do a piece of work in 10 days, but A alone can do it in 15 days. How many days would B alone take to do the same work ?

4. Two motor cycle mechanics, Vinod and Preetam, working together, can overhaul a motor cycle in 3 days. Vinod working alone can do the job in 5 days. If Preetam works alone, how long will he take to do the same job ?

5. Three men A, B, C , can do a piece of work in 9 hours, 18 hours, and 12 hours respectively. How long will they take if they work together ?

6. A and B can do a piece of work in 10 hours, B and C in 12 hours and C and A in 15 hours. How long will they take if they work together ? How long will each take to complete the work independently ?

7. A cistern can be filled by one tap in 4 hours and by another in 3 hours. How long will it take to fill if both taps are opened together ?

8. A cistern can be filled by one tap in $2\frac{1}{2}$ hours and by another in $3\frac{3}{4}$ hours. How long will the cistern take to fill, if they are opened together ?

9. A cistern can be filled by a tap in 4 hours and emptied by an outlet pipe in 6 hours. How long will it take to fill the cistern if both the tap and the pipe are opened together ?

10. One tap fills a bath in 12 min. and another tap fills it in 15 min. The waste-pipe can empty the both in 10 min. In what time will the bath be filled if both are turned on and if the waste pipe has been left open accidentally ?

11. A pipe can fill a cistern in 6 hours. Due to a leak in the bottom it is filled in 7 hours. When the cistern is full, in how much time will it be emptied by the leak ?

LOOKING BACK

Summary of Key Facts

1. The method in which the value of a unit quantity is first calculated to find the value of any required quantity is called unitary method.

2. **In direct variation.**
   (i) The increase (or decrease) in one quantity causes an increase or decrease in the other quantity as well.
   (ii) The ratio of one kind of terms = ratio of the second kind of terms.

3. **In inverse variation.**
   (i) The increase or decrease in one quantity causes a decrease or increase in the other quantity.
   (ii) The ratio of one kind of terms = Inverse ratio of the second kind of terms.

4. If a person can finish a piece of work in n days, then the work done by the person in 1 day $= \frac{1}{n}$.

5. If a person completes $\frac{1}{n}$ th part of a work in 1 day, their the time taken by the person to finish the work is n days

6. A cistern is fitted with two pipes – One pipe to fill it which is called an **inlet** and the other pipe to empty it which is called an **outlet.**

7. If an inlet fills a tank in n hours, then it will fill $\frac{1}{n}$ th part of the tank in 1 hour, i.e. the work done by it in 1 hour is $\frac{1}{n}$

8. If an outlet empties a full tank in m hours then it will empty $\frac{1}{m}$ th part of the tank in 1 hour, i.e. the work done by it in 1 hour is $-\frac{1}{m}$. (Note that the work done by the outlet is negative)

MENTAL MATHS- 8

1. 5 men do a work in 10 days. In how many days will one man complete the work ?
2. 7 Pens cost Rs 56. What is the cost 21 Pens ?
3. Cost of 3 geometry boxes is Rs 31.50. What is the cost of 10 geometry boxes ?
4. **Classify as cases of Direct variation and Indiret variation.**

(i) Number of articles x and their price y.
(ii) Distance and time, speed remaining the same.
(iii) Weights of articles and their cost.
(iv) Wages and hours of work.
(v) The number of men to do a work and the time taken to finish the job.

ANSWERS

EXERCISE 10 (a)

1. Rs 135   2. 11 days   3. 105 baskets   4. 6.9 litres   5. 1042 kg   6. 300 m   7. 64 bottles
8. 900 gm   9. 23 chairs   10. Rs 1589.50   11. 90 km/hr   12. 12 hrs   13. 350 persons   14. 6 hrs
15. 30 days   16. 10 people   17. $3\frac{1}{5}$ hrs.   18. 12800 people   19. 40 lines   20. 18 articles.

EXERCISE 10 (b)

1. $\frac{12}{7}$ days   2. $1\frac{1}{5}$ hours.   3. 30 days   4. $7\frac{1}{2}$ days.   5. 4 hours.

6. 8 hrs; A, 24 hours; B, $17\frac{1}{7}$ hours;   C, 40 hours   7. $1\frac{5}{7}$ hours   8. 1 hr. 30 min.   9. 12 hours   10. 20 min

11. 42 hours $\left[\textbf{Hint.} \frac{1}{6} - \frac{1}{x} = \frac{1}{7} \right]$.

MENTAL MATHS - 8

1. 50 days   2. Rs 168   3. Rs 105   4. (i) Direct   (ii) Direct   (iii) Direct   (iv) Direct   (v) Indirect.

FUN WITH MATHS

The Importance of Number 14

■ Trishala mother of **Mahavira** had 14 divine dreams. On enquiring with the astrologers she was told that the dreams portended the birth of a great son, a Tirthankara.

■ There are 14 finger bones in each hand. The face also contains 14 bones.

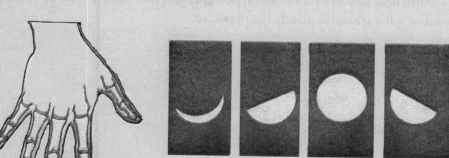

■ The moon undergoes a 14-day cycle of waxing and waning when it grows from a narrow crescent to a full, round, shining disc and then back to a narrow crescent again.

■ Lord Rama went into exile for 14 years in accordance with the wishes of his father, king Dashratha.

11. Percentange, Profit and Loss and Discount

11.1 Introduction

In class 6 you have studied in detail the idea of Percentage. The words per cent (denoted by %) mean " per 100" or "divided by 100".

Thus, 7% is another way of writing $\frac{7}{100}$ or 0.07. Any per cent can be expressed as a fraction or a decimal.

For example :

$$25\% = \frac{25}{100} = \frac{1}{4} \; ; \qquad \frac{2}{3}\% = \frac{2}{3} \div 100 = \frac{1}{150}$$

$$150\% = \frac{150}{100} = 1.5 \; ; \qquad 0.2\% = \frac{0.2}{100} = 0.002$$

Any rational number can be expressed as a per cent by transforming it so that its denominator becomes 100

For example :

$$\frac{1}{2} = \frac{1 \times 50}{2 \times 50} = \frac{50}{100} = 50\% \; ; \qquad\qquad \frac{3}{4} = \frac{3 \times 25}{4 \times 25} = \frac{75}{100} = 75\%$$

$$0.375 = \frac{0.375 \times 100}{100} = \frac{37.5}{100} = 37.5\% ; \qquad \frac{2}{3} = \frac{2 \times \frac{100}{3}}{3 \times \frac{100}{3}} = \frac{66\frac{2}{3}}{100} = 66\frac{2}{3}\%$$

Rule. *To change a fraction to percentage, multiply by 100, and to change percentage to a fraction, multiply by $\frac{1}{100}$.*

11.2 Problems on Percentage

In class VI, you have already learnt how to solve problems on percentage. Here we will take up some more problems to revise and consolidate what you have aleady learnt before.

Ex. 1 *Find $12\frac{1}{2}\%$ of 7200 kg.*

Sol. $12\frac{1}{2}\%$ of 7200 kg $= \frac{25}{2} \times \frac{1}{100} \times 7200 = \textbf{900 kg.}$

Ex. 2 *What percentage is Rs 18.75 of Rs 25 ?*

Sol. The required percentage $= \frac{18.75}{25} \times 100 = 75.00$ i.e. **75%.**

Ex. 3 *On a certain day, 15% of the boys were absent and 34 were present. How many boys were there in the class ?*

Sol. If 15% of the boys were absent, then $(100 - 15)\%$, i.e. 85% of the boys were present.

If 85 boys are present, then the total number of boys = 100.

If 34 boys are present, then the total number of boys $= 100 \times \dfrac{1}{85} \times 34 =$ **40 boys.**

Alternatively, you may work out as under :

85% of total strength of the class = 34

i.e., $\dfrac{85}{100}$ of total strength $= 34 \Rightarrow$ Total strength $= 34 \times \dfrac{100}{85} = 40.$

Ex. 4 *A man, whose salary is Rs 7500 a year, receives an increase of 8 per cent. Find his new salary.*

Sol. The increase $= \dfrac{8}{100}$ of Rs 7500 a year = Rs 600 a year

Therefore the new annual salary is Rs 7500 + Rs 600 = **Rs 8100.**

Ex. 5 *If the price of an article is raised from Rs 200 to Rs 250 a year, find the increase per cent.*

Sol. On a price of Rs 200 the increase is Rs 50 a year.

$\therefore$ The increase on a price of Rs $100 = \dfrac{50}{200} \times 100 =$ Rs 25

Therefore, the increase per cent = **25%.**

Ex. 6 *40% of a certain number is 320, find the number.*

Sol. If the number is x, then 40% of $x = 320$

i.e. $\dfrac{40}{100} x = 320$ $\qquad \therefore x = \dfrac{100}{40} \times 320 =$ **800.**

Ex. 7 *The population of a town increases by 5% annually. If the population is now 1, 85 220, what was it an year ago ?*

Sol. Suppose an year ago the population was = 100

$\therefore$ Population increases every year by 5%

$\therefore$ Present population = 105

If this present population is 105, then an year ago it was = 100

If the present population is 1, then an year ago it was $= \dfrac{100}{105}$

If the present population is 1,85,220 then an year ago it was $= \dfrac{100}{105} \times 185220 =$ **1,76,400.**

Ex. 8 *Gun-powder contains 75% nitre and 10% sulphur. The rest of it is charcoal. Find the amount of charcoal in 9 kg of gun-powder.*

Sol. Amount of nitre in 9 kg of gun-powder

$$= 75\% \text{ of } 9 \text{ kg} = \dfrac{75}{100} \times 9 \text{ kg} = \dfrac{27}{4} \text{ kg} = \textbf{6.75 kg}$$

Amount of sulphur in 9 kg of gun-powder

$$= 10\% \text{ of } 9 \text{ kg} = \dfrac{10}{100} \times 9 \text{ kg} = \dfrac{9}{10} \text{ kg} = \textbf{0.9 kg}$$

Since the rest is charcoal, therefore

Amount of charcoal in 9 kg of gun-powder = 9 kg – (6.75 + 0.90) kg = 9 kg – 7.65 kg = **1.35 kg**

Alternatively : Amount of charcoal $= 15\%$ of 9 kg $= \dfrac{15}{100} \times 9$ kg = 1.35 kg.

Ex. 9 *An alloy of tin and copper consists of 15 parts of tin and 105 parts of copper. Find the percentage of copper in the alloy.*

Sol. Since the alloy contains 15 parts of tin and 105 parts of copper

$\therefore$ Percentage of tin $= \dfrac{15}{15 + 105} \times 100\% = \dfrac{15}{120} \times 100\% = \dfrac{25}{2} \% = \textbf{12.5\%.}$

Percentage of copper $= \dfrac{105}{120} \times 100\% = \dfrac{175}{2}\% =$ **87.5%.**

Alternatively : percentage of copper $= (100 - 12.5)\% =$ **87.5%.**

EXERCISE 11 (a)

1. **Fill in the blanks :**

    (i) 16% of 150 =...   (ii) $10\dfrac{1}{2}\%$ of 400=...   (iii) ...% of 64=16   (iv) ...% of 300 = 225

    (v) 25% of... = 13   (vi) 120% of...= 60   (vii) 0.7% of 1000 =...   (viii) $\dfrac{2}{3}\%$ of .... = 30

2. **Express the following fractions as a percentage.**

    (i) $\dfrac{3}{4}$ (ii) $\dfrac{5}{16}$ (iii) $\dfrac{7}{18}$ (iv) 0.75   (v) 0.7   (vi) 0.128

3. **Express the following percentages as fractions :**

    (i) 5%   (ii) $12\dfrac{1}{2}\%$ (iii) 150%   (iv) $33\dfrac{1}{3}\%$ (v) $9\dfrac{3}{8}\%$

4. **What is**

    (i) 45% of 1600 ?   (ii) $15\dfrac{3}{4}\%$ of Rs 86.56 ?

5. (i) Find $166\dfrac{2}{3}\%$ of 3 metres.   (ii) Express 48 cm as a percentage of 1 metre.

6. What percentage is Rs 6 of Rs 450 ?

7. A man whose income is Rs 576 a year, spends Rs 426 a year. What percentage of his income does he save ?

8. A girl obtained 85% marks out of a total of 500 marks. How many marks did she get ?

9. An alloy consists of 13 parts of copper to 7 parts of zinc and 5 parts of nickel. What is percentage composition of the alloy?

10. A man loses 20% of his money. After spending 25% of the remainder, he has Rs 480 left. How much money did he originally have ?

11. The population of a town increases by 10% annually. If the present population is 22000, find its population a year ago.

12. In an examination, Piyush scored 490 marks. If he secured 70% marks, find the maximum marks.

13. Chalk contains 10% calcium, 3% carbon, and 12% oxygen. Find the amount (in grams) of each of these compounds in 1 kg of chalk.

14. There are 120 girls and 57 boys in a school. If 5% of the girls leave and no new pupils are admitted, what percentage of the whole school will be boys ?

15. A man received 5% increase in his salary. His new salary is Rs 252. What was his original salary ?

16. A boy obtained 60 marks out of 70 in English, 50 out of 60 in Mathematics, and 40 out of 50 in History. What were his percentage marks in each of the three subjects ? In which subject did he perform the best ? What were his percentage marks on the whole ?

17. In an election a candidate got 65% of the total valid votes. 8% of the total votes was declared invalid. If the total number of votes were 600000, find the number of valid votes polled in favour, of the candidate.

18. A boy spends 20% of his pocket money on oranges, one quarter of it on apples and 5% in paying fines, what fractional part of the whole has he left ?

11.3 Percentage Change

Percentage increase $= \left(\dfrac{\text{Increase in value}}{\text{Original value}} \times 100 \right)\%$

Percentage decrease $= \left(\dfrac{\text{Decrease in value}}{\text{Original value}} \times 100 \right)\%$

Percentage error $= \left(\dfrac{\text{Error}}{\text{Actual value}} \times 100 \right)\%$

Ex. 1 *Increase 80 by 35%.*

Sol. Increase $= 35\%$ of $80 = \dfrac{35}{100} \times 80 = 28$ $\therefore$ Increased value $= (80 + 28) = \mathbf{108}$.

Ex. 2 *What sum of money when decreased by 20% becomes Rs 108 ?*

Sol. Let the sum of money be Rs. 100

Decrease $= 20\%$ $\therefore$ Decreased amount $= 80\%$

Then, 80% of the original amount $=$ Rs 108

i.e., $\dfrac{80}{100}$ of the original amount $=$ Rs. 108

$\therefore$ Original amount $=$ Rs $\dfrac{108 \times 100}{80} = \mathbf{Rs.135}$.

Ex. 3 *The price of an article was Rs 175 and 1 year later the price reduced to Rs 105. By how much per cent has the value decreased ?*

Sol. Original Price $=$ Rs 175

Decrease in Price $=$ Rs $(175 - 105) =$ Rs 70

$\therefore \%$ decrease in price $= \left(\dfrac{\text{Decrease in price}}{\text{Original price}} \times 100 \right)\% = \left(\dfrac{70}{175} \times 100 \right)\% = 40\%$.

$\therefore$ The price has decreased by **40%**.

Ex. 4 *My bank deposit has increased by 40% during the past year. It is now Rs 50400; What was it a year ago ?*

Sol. Let the bank deposit during the past year be Rs 100.

Increase $= 40\%$ $\therefore$ Increased amount $=$ Rs 140

$\therefore 140\%$ of last year's deposit $=$ Rs 50400

i.e., $\dfrac{140}{100}$ of last year's deposit $=$ Rs 50400

Last year's deposit $=$ Rs $50400 \times \dfrac{100}{140} = \mathbf{Rs\ 36000}$.

Ex. 5 *By what must a number be multiplied so as to increase it by 17% ?*

Sol. Let the original number be x.

Increase in value $= 17\%$ of $x = \left(\dfrac{17}{100} \cdot x \right)$, $\therefore$ Increased value $= x + \dfrac{17x}{100}$

$= \dfrac{100x + 17x}{100} = \dfrac{117x}{100}$ $\therefore$ The number should be multiplied by $\dfrac{117}{100}$.

Ex. 6 *The weight of a 10 year old girl was 32 kg. But it was misread as 36 kg. Find the error percentag*

Sol. Actual weight of the girl = 32 kg;

$$\text{error} = 36 \text{ kg} - 32 \text{ kg} = 4 \text{ kg}.$$

$$\therefore \text{ Percentage error} = \left(\frac{\text{Error}}{\text{Actual weight}} \times 100 \right)\%$$

$$= \left(\frac{4}{32} \times 100 \right)\% = 12\frac{1}{2}\%.$$

EXERCISE 11 (b)

1. (*a*) Increase 80 by 10%. (*b*) Increase 125 by 60%.
   (*c*) Decrease 540 by 25%. (*d*) Decrease 75 by 40%.

2. What sum of money when decreased by 17% becomes Rs 498.

3. What number when increased by 27% becomes 508 ?

4. The Price of a refrigerator has increased by 12%. 6 months back the price was 9600. What is the pric now ?

5. The number of people working for a particular organisation increased by 15% during an year. Find th number at the beginning of the year if there were 230 at the end of the year.

6. A ream of paper which 2 years back cost Rs 120 now costs Rs 150. What is the percentage increase ?

7. The weight of a liquid was 3.75 gm, before heating and 3.50 gm after heating, find the loss % (% decrease)

8. Prakash got 30% marks, in an examination and failed by 6 marks. Sudhir got 40% marks which are 6 mor than the minimum marks, required to pass. Find the maximum marks and minimum percentage of mark required to pass.

9. Find the error percent in taking the area of a field which is 50m wide and 70 m long as 3800m².

PROFIT AND LOSS

11.4 Review

You have studied the concept of profit and loss in class 6 and also solved simple problems. We will now he you to revise and strengthen your understanding of *this topic by* reviewing briefly what you have already lear and taking up more problems relating to the concept of profit and loss.

1. The price at which an article is purchased is called the cost price of the article. It is abbreviated as C.P.

2. The price at which an article is sold, is called the selling price of the article. It is abbreviated as S.P.

3. When S.P. > C. P. then there is profit and **profit = S.P − C.P.**

4. When S. P. < C.P. then there is loss and **loss = C.P. − S.P.**

   Also (*i*) **C.P = S.P − Profit**   (*ii*) **C.P. = S.P. + loss**

5. **Profit or loss per cent** = $\dfrac{\text{Total profit or loss}}{\text{Cost price}} \times 100.$

6. $\text{S.P} = \left(\dfrac{100 + \text{gain}\%}{100} \right) \times \text{C.P}$ or $\text{S.P} = \left(\dfrac{100 - \text{loss}\%}{100} \right) \times \text{C.P}$

7. $\text{C.P} = \left(\dfrac{100}{100 + \text{gain}\%} \right) \times \text{S.P}$ or $\text{C.P} = \left(\dfrac{100}{100 - \text{loss}\%} \right) \times \text{S.P}$

11.5 Solved Examples

Type 1. To Find profit and loss percent

Ex. 1 *Ravinder buys a used watch for Rs 225 and spends Rs 15 on its repairs. If he sells the same for Rs 300, find his profit per cent.*

Sol. Purchase price of wrist watch = Rs 225

Amount spent on repairs = Rs 15

$\therefore$ C.P. of the watch = Purchase price + repair expenses

= Rs 225 + Rs 15 = Rs 240; S.P. of the watch = Rs 300

Since S. P. > C.P., profit = Rs 300 – Rs 240 = Rs 60

$$\therefore \text{Profit \%} = \left(\frac{\text{Total profit}}{\text{C.P}} \times 100\right)\% = \left(\frac{60}{240} \times 100\right)\% = \mathbf{25\%}.$$

Ex.2 *I bought a washing machine for Rs 8000 and was compelled by circumstances to sell it for Rs 6000, find my loss per cent.*

Sol. C. P. = Rs 8000;   S.P. = Rs 6000

$\therefore$ Total loss = Rs 8000 – Rs 6000 = Rs 2000

$$\therefore \text{Loss per cent} = \left(\frac{\text{Total loss}}{\text{C.P}} \times 100\right)\% = \left(\frac{2000}{8000} \times 100\right)\% = \mathbf{25\%}.$$

Ex. 3 *(i)   If the cost price of 18 cycles be equal to selling price of 16 cycles, find the gain or loss per cent.*

(ii)   If the cost price of 10 chairs be equal to selling price of 16 chairs, find the gain or loss per cent.

Sol. *(i)* Let C.P. of 1 cycle = Re 1. Then C.P. of 18 cycles = Rs 18

$\therefore$ S.P of 16 cycles = C.P. of 18 cycles = Rs 18

$\therefore$ S.P. of 18 cycles = Rs $\dfrac{18}{16} \times 18$ = Rs $\dfrac{81}{4}$

Since S.P. > C. P. so gain = S.P. – C. P. = Rs $\dfrac{81}{4}$ – Rs 18 = Rs $\dfrac{9}{4}$

$$\therefore \text{ gain \%} = \left(\frac{\text{gain} \times 100}{\text{C.P.}}\right)\% = \left(\frac{\frac{9}{4} \times 100}{18}\right)\% = \left(\frac{9 \times \overset{25}{\cancel{100}}}{\underset{1}{\cancel{4}} \times \underset{2}{\cancel{18}}}\right)\% = \frac{25}{2}\% = \mathbf{12\frac{1}{2}\%}.$$

(ii) Let C.P of each chair be Re 1, then C.P. of 16 chairs = Rs 16

S.P. of 16 chairs = C.P. of 10 chairs = Rs 10

Here C. P. > S.P. so there is loss = C.P. – S.P = Rs 16 – Rs 10 = Rs 6

$$\therefore \text{ loss \%} = \left(\frac{\text{loss} \times 100}{\text{C.P.}}\right)\% = \left(\frac{6 \times 100}{16}\right)\% = \frac{75}{2}\% = \mathbf{37.5\%}.$$

Ex. 4 *Anil bought a second hand scooter for Rs 7500 and spent Rs 500 on its repairs. He then sold it to Deepak at a loss of 12%. What is Anil's loss ?*

Sol. Total C.P. = Purchase price + Repair expenses = Rs 7500 + Rs 500 = Rs 8000.

Let the C.P. be Rs 100, then S.P. = Rs (100 – 12) = Rs 88

$\because$ When the C.P. is Rs 100 then S.P. = Rs 88

$\therefore$ When the C.P. is Rs 8000, then S.P. = Rs $\dfrac{88}{100} \times 8000$ = Rs 7040

$\therefore$ Loss = C.P. – S.P. = Rs 8000 – Rs 7040 = **Rs 960.**

Alternative method : Loss % = $\dfrac{\text{Loss}}{\text{C.P.}} \times 100 \Rightarrow$ Loss = $\dfrac{\text{Loss\% } \times \text{C.P.}}{100}$

Here, loss% = 12%, C.P. = Rs 8000 $\therefore$ Loss = Rs $\dfrac{12 \times 8000}{100}$ = **Rs 960.**

Ex. 5 *Rahul bought a motorcycle for Rs 45000 and paid Rs 200 for its cartage. He sold it at a gain of 10%. What is Rahul's profit ?*

Sol. C.P. of motor cycle = Purchase price + cartage = Rs 45000 + Rs 200 = Rs 45,200.

Gain of 10% means for a C.P. of Rs 100, S.P. = Rs 110

$\therefore$ For a C.P. of Rs 45, 200, S.P. = Rs $\dfrac{110}{100} \times 45\ 200$ = Rs 49720

$\therefore$ Rahul's profit = S.P. – C.P. = Rs 49720 – Rs 45200 = **Rs 4520.**

Alternative method : Profit% = $\dfrac{\text{Profit}}{\text{C.P.}} \times 100 \Rightarrow$ Profit = $\dfrac{\text{Profit \% } \times \text{C.P}}{100}$

Here, Profit% = 10% $\therefore$ Profit = Rs $\dfrac{10 \times 45200}{100}$ = **Rs 4520.**

Ex. 6 *A man buys balloons 3 for a rupee and sells them at 2 for a rupee; find his gain per cent.*

Sol. Suppose the man buys (2×3), i.e. 6 balloons

C.P. of 6 balloons = Rs 2; S.P. of 6 balloons = Rs 3 $\qquad \therefore$ Total gain = Rs 3 – Rs 2 = Re 1

$\therefore$ Gain per cent = $\dfrac{\text{Total gain}}{\text{C.P.}} \times 100 = \dfrac{1}{2} \times 100 =$ **50%.**

Ex. 7 *Anwar sold two washing machines at Rs 12000 each. On one he gains 25% and on another he loses 25%. How much does he gain or lose in the whole transaction ?*

Sol. **First washing machine :**

S.P. = Rs 12000, gain = 25% $\therefore$ C.P. = $\dfrac{100}{100 + \text{Profit \%}} \times$ S.P. = Rs $\left(\dfrac{100}{125} \times 12000 \right)$ = Rs 9600

Second washing machine :

S.P. = Rs 12000, Loss = 25% $\therefore$ C.P. = $\dfrac{100}{100 - \text{loss \%}} \times$ S.P. = Rs $\left(\dfrac{100}{75} \times 12000 \right)$ = Rs 16000

Total C.P. of both the washing machines = Rs (9600 + 16000) = Rs 25600

Total S.P. of both the washing machines = Rs (12000 × 2) = Rs 24000

$\therefore$ loss in the whole transaction = Rs (25600 – 24000) = Rs 1600

$\therefore$ loss % = $\left(\dfrac{\text{Loss}}{\text{C.P.}} \times 100 \right)\% = \left(\dfrac{1600}{25600} \times 100 \right)\% = \dfrac{25}{4}\% = 6\dfrac{1}{4}\%.$

EXERCISE 11 (c)

1. An article was bought for Rs 5000 and sold for Rs 6500. Find the gain and gain%.
2. A cycle was purchased for Rs 2000 and sold for Rs1800. Find the loss and loss per cent.
3. A man buys 50 balloons at Rs 3 each, and sells them at Rs 4 each. What is his total gain and also his gain per cent ?
4. A bookseller buys 500 ball pens at Rs 4 each. He sells 300 of them at Rs 5 each and the rest at Rs 6 each. Find his gain per cent.

5. A person buys a cooler for Rs 1400 and spends Rs 100 on its repairs. If he sells the same for Rs 1800, find his profit per cent.

6. (i) If the C.P. of 6 articles is equal to the S.P of 4 articles, find the gain per cent.

    (ii) If the C.P. of 15 tables be equal to the S.P. of 20 tables, find the loss per cent.

7. If a person sells an article for Rs 650, gaining $\frac{1}{8}$ th of its C.P., find his gain per cent.

    [**Hint.** Gain% = $\frac{Gain}{C.P} \times 100 = \frac{x/8}{x} \times 100$]

8. A man buys toffees at 10 for Rs 3 and sells them at 8 for Rs 3 ; find his gain per cent.

9. Sunil bought an article for Rs 650 and sold it at a loss of 13% Find the loss.

10. A shopkeeper bought a T.V. for Rs 20,000 and paid Rs 100 for its cartage. He sold it at a gain of 12%, what is the shopkeeper's profit ?

11. If oranges are bought at the rate of 11 for Rs 10 and sold at 10 for Rs 11, find the gain or loss per cent.

12. If the selling price of 10 articles is equal to the cost price of 11 articles, find the gain per cent,

    [**Hint.** Let C.P of each article be Re 1 Then C. P. of 10 articles = Rs 10 and S.P. of 10 articles = C. P. of 11 articles = Rs 11]

13. A man sold two paintings at Rs 924 each. On one he gains 20% and on another he loses 20%. How much does he gain or lose in the whole transaction ?

14. Kamal sold two articles at Rs 840 each. On one he gains 20% and on the other he loses 20%. How much does he gain or lose in the whole transaction ? Also find his gain or loss per cent in the whole transaction.

Type 2. Finding C.P. and S.P.

Ex. 8 *Find the cost price of an article that is sold for Rs 1200 at a profit of 20%.*

Sol. If S.P. is Rs 120, then C.P. = Rs 100

If S.P. is Re 1, then C.P. = Re $\frac{100}{120}$

If S.P. is Rs 1200, then C.P. = Rs $\frac{100}{120} \times 1200$ = **Rs 1000.**

Ex. 9 *A television set was bought for Rs 3760 and sold at a gain of $12\frac{1}{2}$%. How much did the seller receive ?*

Sol. If C.P. is Rs 100, then S.P. = Rs $\frac{225}{2}$

If C.P. is Re 1, then S.P. = Rs $\frac{225}{2} \times \frac{1}{100}$

If C.P is Rs 3760, then S.P. = $\frac{225}{2} \times \frac{1}{100} \times$ Rs $\frac{3760}{1}$ = **Rs 4230.**

Alternative Method :

S.P. = $\left(\frac{100 + gain\%}{100}\right) \times$ C.P. = Rs $\frac{100 + 12\frac{1}{2}}{100} \times 3760$

= Rs. $\frac{100 + \frac{25}{2}}{100} \times 3760$ = Rs $\frac{\cancel{225}^{9}}{2 \times \cancel{100}_{4}} \times 3760$ = **Rs 4230.**

Ex. 10 *A man sold a computer for Rs 51, 000 at a loss of 15%. What was the cost of the computer?*

Sol. S.P. of the computer = Rs 51,000. Let C.P. be Rs 100. Loss = 15%; so S.P. = Rs 85.

If S.P. is Rs 85, then C.P. = Rs 100

If S.P. is Re 1, then C.P. = Rs $\dfrac{100}{85}$

If S.P. is Rs 51000 then C.P. = Rs $\dfrac{100}{85} \times 51000$ = **Rs 60000**

Alternative Method : C.P. = $\dfrac{100 \times S.P}{100 - \text{loss}\%}$ = Rs $\dfrac{100 \times 51000}{100 - 15}$ = Rs $\dfrac{100 \times 51000}{85}$ = **Rs 60,000.**

Ex. 11 *A man lost 5% by selling a piece of land for Rs 2337. What would he have gained or lost had he sold it for Rs 2644.50 ? Find the gain or loss per cent also.*

Sol. In the first case, C.P. = $\dfrac{100 \times S.P}{100 - \text{loss}\%}$ = $\dfrac{100}{95} \times$ Rs 2337 = Rs 2460

Now C.P. = Rs 2460.00, S.P. = Rs 2644.50
Total profit = Rs 2644.50 – Rs 2460.00 = Rs 184.50

Profit percent = $\dfrac{\text{Profit}}{\text{C.P.}} \times 100$ = $\dfrac{184.50}{2460} \times 100 = 7\dfrac{1}{2}\%.$

Type 3. Transaction through more than two persons.

Ex. 12 *A sells an article to B at a profit of 5%. B sells the same to C for Rs 1071 thereby making a profit of 2 %. What did A pay for it?*

Sol. S.P. of *B* = Rs 1071, Profit = 2 %

∴ C.P. of *B* = $\dfrac{100}{100 + \text{Profit}\%} \times$ S.P. = $\dfrac{100}{102} \times$ Rs 1071 = Rs 1050

∴ S. P. of *A* = C.P. of *B* = Rs 1050, Profit = 5%

∴ C.P. of *A* = $\dfrac{100}{100 + \text{Profit}\%} \times$ S.P. = $\dfrac{100}{105} \times$ Rs 1050 = **Rs 1000.**

Ex. 13 *Harish bought a cycle of Rs 480 and sold it to Satish at a profit of $6\dfrac{1}{4}$%. Satish sold the same to Girish at a profit of 10%. Find how much did Girish pay for it.*

Sol. **Harish :** If C.P. of cycle is Rs 100, its S.P. is Rs $106\dfrac{1}{4}$ = Rs $\dfrac{425}{4}$

If C.P. of cycle is Rs 480, its S.P. is Rs $\dfrac{425}{4} \times \dfrac{1}{100} \times 480$ = Rs 510

∴ Harish sells the cycle to Satish at Rs 510, i.e., C.P. of Satish = Rs 510
Now Satish sells it to Girish at a profit of 10%.
Satish :
If C.P. is Rs 100, S.P. is Rs 110

If C.P. is Rs 510, S.P. is Rs $\dfrac{110}{100} \times 510$ = Rs 561.

Satish sells the cycle to Girish at Rs 561 ∴ Girish pays **Rs 561** for the cycle.

EXERCISE 11 (d)

1. For what price should I sell an article which cost me Rs 8, so as to gain 15 per cent ?

2. I buy a fan for Rs 1550, and sell it in such a way that I lose 10% in the transaction. For how much do I sell the fan?

3. Find the cost price of an article which is sold at a profit of 8%, for Rs 2160.

4. By selling a parrot for Rs 250 Karim gains 25%; Find the C.P. of the parrot.

5. John sold his black and white television set for Rs 1280 losing thereby 20%. Find the amount he paid for purchasing the set.

6. A shopkeeper buys paper at Rs 50 per ream. At what price per quire should he sell it so as to gain 20%?
   [**Hint.** 1 ream = 20 quires]

7. If by selling goods for Rs 3432, 10% of their cost is gained, at what price should they have been sold so as to gain 20 % ?

8. Vivek purchased a refrigerator for Rs 18000 and a micro wave for Rs 10,500. On the refrigerator he lost 5% and on the microwave he gained 17%. Find his total gain or loss per cent.

9. By selling 144 hens, Kamal lost the S.P. of 6 hens. Find his loss per cent. Had he purchased them for Rs 7200, what would have been the S.P. of one hen ?
   [**Hint.** Let the S.P. of one hen be Re 1, then S.P. of 144 hens = Rs 144,
   C.P. of 144 hens = S.P. + loss = S.P. of 144 hens + S.P. of 6 hens]

10. A sells an article, which cost him Rs 400 to B at a profit of 20%. B then sells it to C making a profit of 10% on the price he paid to A. What does C pay to B ?

11. A buys an article for Rs 65 and sells it to B at a profit of 20%. B sells to C at a loss of 20%. What does C pay for it?

12. A buys an article and sells it to B at a profit of 12%. B sells it back to A at the price which A previously paid for it. What is B's percentage loss ?

13. A shopkeeper sold a sofa set at 8% gain. Had he purchased it for 5% less and sold it for Rs 36 less than what he actually sold it for, he would have gained $12\frac{1}{2}\%$. For how much did the man purchase the sofa set ?

DISCOUNT

1.6 Introduction

It is a custom of shopkeepers in certain cases to deduct a certain percentage from the marked prices of their goods for cash payment. Thus, many dealers of ready-made garments allow a discount of 10% off the quoted or marked price of the garments to those who pay cash on the counter. *For example,* suppose a shirt is quoted at Rs 85 to a customer whom he does not expect will pay him a year or so after the shirt is delivered to him, but he is willing to deduct 10% of Rs 85, i.e. Rs 8.50, from the price if the customer pays at once. The cash price of the shirt is therefore, Rs 76.50, and the amount deducted, here Rs 8.50, is called the **cash discount.** In transactions, as above, **cash discounts are always calculated as fractions or percentages of the marked prices (M.P.);** a discount of 20 p in the rupee is equivalent to a deduction of $\frac{20}{100}$ of the marked price, that is 20% of the marked price.

When a retailer buys goods from a wholesale merchant, the prices in the trade catalogue issued by the wholesaler are usually subject to a trade discount, which is a percentage of the catalogued prices; this percentage varies from time to time according to the costs of raw materials, manufacture, taxation, and so on.

11.7 Solved Examples

Ex. 1 *A manufacturer's catalogued price of a car is Rs 42000, but he allows the retailer 20% discoun What does the retailer pay for the car ?*

Sol. The discount = Rs $\frac{20}{100} \times 42000$ = Rs 8400

∴ The retailer pays = Rs 42000 – Rs 8400 = **Rs 33600.**

Ex. 2. *Find the S.P. when M.P. = Rs 64 and discount = 12.5%.*

Sol. Marked price = Rs 64, Discount 12.5%, S.P. = ?

Discount on Rs 64 = 12.5% of Rs 64 = Rs $\frac{12.5}{100} \times 64$ = Rs $\frac{125}{1000} \times 64$ = Rs 8

S.P. = M.P. – discount = Rs 64 – Rs 8 = **Rs 56.**

Ex. 3 *Find the M.P. when S.P. = Rs 1920 and discount = 4%.*

Sol. Let the marked price be Rs 100. Discount rate = 4%

∴ Discount on Rs 100 = Rs 4 ∴ S.P. = Rs 100 – Rs 4 = Rs 96

If the S.P. is Rs 96 then M.P. = Rs 100

If the S.P. is Re 1 then M.P. = Rs $\frac{100}{96}$

If the S.P. is Rs 1920 then M.P. = Rs $\frac{100}{96} \times 1920$ = Rs 2000

Hence, the required M.P. is **Rs 2000.**

Ex. 4 *The wholesaler allows the retailer a trade discount of 25% on an article listed Rs 54. The retail gives a cash discount of 5% on the listed price; what profit does now retailer make ? Find his prof per cent also.*

Sol. The listed price = Rs 54, the trade discount = Rs $\frac{25}{100} \times 54$ = Rs 13.50

The cost price of the retailer = Rs 54 – Rs 13.50 = Rs 40.50

The cash discount = Rs $\frac{5}{100} \times 54$ = Rs 2.70

The selling price of the retailer = Rs 54 – Rs 2.70 = Rs 51.30

Profit of the retailer = Rs 51.30 – Rs 40. 50 = Rs 10. 80

Profit % = $\frac{10.80}{40.50} \times 100 = \frac{80}{3} = 26\frac{2}{3}$ %.

EXERCISE 11 (e)

1. **A shopkeeper marks the price of an article at Rs 80.00. Find the selling price if**
   (*i*) he allows a discount of 10%;
   (*ii*) he allows two successive discounts of 5% each.
2. Find the S.P. when M.P. = Rs 990 and discount = 10%.
3. Find the M.P. when S.P. = Rs 990 and discount = 1 %.
4. **Find discount when**
   (*i*) M.P. = Rs 25 and S.P. = Rs 23.50   (*ii*) M.P. = Rs 1880 and S.P. = Rs 1504.

5. A shopkeeper gives a discount of 5 paise in the rupee on a commodity whose marked price is Rs 16. What is the selling price and what percentage is represented by the discount?

6. A manufacturer's catalogued price of a machine is Rs 240, but he allows the retailer 30% discount. What does the retailer pay for the machine?

7. A shopkeeper gives a discount of 10% for cash payment. At what price is an article marked if its cash price is Rs 13.50?

8. A carpet is quoted at Rs 2400 in a wholesaler's catalogue, but the retailer only pays Rs 2000 for it. Express the trade discount allowed as a percentage.

9. The catalogue price of an article is Rs 16, but the retailer is allowed a trade discount of 25%. At what price must the retailer sell it to gain 25% of what he pays for it.

LOOKING BACK
Summary of Key Facts

1. (*i*) Per cent means per hundred or for every hundred. The symbol % is used to denote per cent. e.g. 78 marks out of 100 is 78%.

(*ii*) A fraction with denominator 100 such as $\frac{19}{100}$ is called a per cent. The numerator tells the precentage. It is 19% here.

2. **To convert :**

(*i*) A fraction into a per cent, multiply the fraction by 100, e.g. $\frac{3}{4} = \frac{3}{4} \times 100\% = 75\%$.

(*ii*) A ratio into a per cent, write it as a fraction and multiply the fraction by 100,

e.g. $17 : 25 = \left(\frac{17}{25} \times 100\right)\% = 68\%$

(*iii*) A decimal into a per cent. multiply by 100, i.e. shift the decimal point two places to the right, e.g. $0.075 = 7.5\%$, $0.3957 = 39.57\%$.

(*iv*) A per cent into a fraction, drop per cent symbol % and divide by 100, e.g., $40\% = \frac{40}{100} = \frac{2}{5}$.

(*v*) A per cent into a ratio, drop per cent symbol and form a ratio with the number obtained after dropping the symbol as the first term and 100 as the second term,

e.g. $76\% = \frac{76}{100} = 76 : 100 = 19 : 25$.

(*vi*) A per cent into a decimal, drop per cent symbol and shift the decimal point two places to the left, e.g. $89\% = 0.89$, $12.75\% = 0.1275$.

3. $\text{Increase\%} = \frac{\text{Increase}}{\text{Original value}} \times 100$; $\text{Decrease\%} = \frac{\text{Decrease}}{\text{Original value}} \times 100$; $\text{Error \%} = \frac{\text{Error}}{\text{Actual value}} \times 100$

4. (*i*) Profit = S.P. – C.P. (if S.P. > C.P.)   (*ii*) Loss = C.P. – S.P. (if S.P. < C.P.)

(*iii*) Overhead charges such as transportation, toll-tax, repairs etc., are included in the cost price.

5. (*i*) $\text{Profit\%} = \frac{\text{Profit}}{\text{C.P.}} \times 100 \Rightarrow \text{Profit} = \frac{\text{Profit\%} \times \text{C.P.}}{100}$, $\text{C.P.} = \frac{\text{Profit}}{\text{Profit\%}} \times 100$

(*ii*) $\text{Loss\%} = \frac{\text{Loss}}{\text{C.P.}} \times 100 \Rightarrow \text{Loss} = \frac{\text{Loss\%} \times \text{C.P.}}{100}$, $\text{C.P.} = \frac{\text{Loss}}{\text{Loss\%}} \times 100$

6. (i) S.P. $= \dfrac{(100 + \text{profit\%})}{100} \times$ C.P.   (ii) S.P. $= \dfrac{100 - \text{loss\%}}{100} \times$ C.P.

7. (i) C.P. $= \dfrac{100 \times \text{S.P.}}{(100 + \text{profit\%})}$ (ii) C.P. $= \dfrac{100 \times \text{S.P.}}{(100 - \text{loss\%})}$.

8. (i) Discount is allowed on the marked price
    (ii) S.P. = Marked price – Discount

MENTAL MATHS – 9

1. Find 10% of 70 ?
2. What is the number whose 7% is 28 ?
3. Convert 35% into a simple fraction.
4. Write $\dfrac{2}{5}$ as a per cent.
5. Convert 9% into a decimal.
6. What percentage of 50 is 8 ?
7. 50 % of a length is 30 cm. What is the whole length?
8. Sameer saves 15% of his monthly income of Rs 10000. How much does he save every month ?
9. An article was purchased for Rs 80 and sold for Rs 100. What is the gain?
10. A book was bought for Rs 60 and sold for Rs 50. What is the loss?
11. Suyash bought an article for Rs 800 and sold for Rs 1000. Find his gain per cent.
12. By selling a cycle for Rs 2000, a person gains $\dfrac{1}{5}$ th of the selling price. Find the cost price.
13. Find the C.P. when S.P. = Rs 850 and loss = 15%
14. Find the C.P. when S.P. = Rs 2200 and gain = 10%?
15. Toffees are bought at the rate of 5 for a rupee and sold at 4 for a rupee. Find the gain per cent.
    [**Hint: Think mentally** C.P. of 20 toffees = ... S.P. of 20 toffees = ... *etc.*]
16. By selling 8 dozens of pencils, a shopkeeper gains the selling price of one dozen pencils. Find his gain per cent.
17. Find the S.P. when M.P. = Rs 500, discount = 20%.
18. Find the discount in per cent when M.P. = Rs 400 and S.P. = Rs 360.

ANSWERS

EXERCISE 11 (a)

1. (i) 24   (ii) 42   (iii) 25   (iv) 75   (v) 52   (vi) 50   (vii) 7   (viii) 4500

2. (i) 75%   (ii) 31.25%   (iii) $38\dfrac{8}{9}$%   (iv) 75%   (v) 70%   (vi) 12.8%

3. (i) $\dfrac{1}{20}$ (ii) $\dfrac{1}{8}$ (iii) $\dfrac{3}{2}$ (iv) $\dfrac{1}{3}$ (v) $\dfrac{3}{32}$

4. (i) 720   (ii) Rs 13.63 to nearest paisa.

5. (i) 5 metres   (ii) 48 %   6. $1\dfrac{1}{3}$%

7. $26\dfrac{1}{24}$%   8. 425 marks   9. copper 52%, zinc 28%, nickel 20%   10. Rs 800   11. 20,000   12. 700

13. Calcium 100 g, Carbon 30g, Oxygen 120 g`   14. $33\dfrac{1}{3}$%   15. Rs 240

16. $85\dfrac{5}{7}$% in English, $83\dfrac{1}{3}$% in Mathematics, 80% in History; He did best in English; Total percentage marks = $83\dfrac{1}{3}$%

17. 3, 58, 800   18. $\dfrac{1}{2}$

EXERCISE 11 (b)

1. (*a*) 88   (*b*) 200   (*c*) 405   (*d*) 45   2. Rs 600   3. 400   4. Rs 10752   5. 200 people

6. 25%   7. $6\frac{2}{3}\%$ 8. Max. Marks = 120, Minimum Pass Marks = 35%   9. $8\frac{4}{7}\%$

EXERCISE 11 (c)

1. Rs 1500, 30%   2. Rs 200, 10%   3. Rs 50, $33\frac{1}{3}\%$ 4. 35%   5. 20%   6. (i) 50%   (ii) 25%

7. $12\frac{1}{2}\%$ 8. 25%   9. Rs 84.50   10. Rs 2412   11. 21%   12. 10%   13. Loss Rs 77

14. Loss Rs 70, Loss %=4%

EXERCISE 11 (d)

1. Rs 9.20   2. Rs 1395   3. Rs 2000   4. Rs 200   5. Rs 1600   6. Rs 3   7. Rs 3744

8. gains $3\frac{2}{19}\%$ 9. Loss 4%, S.P. = Rs 48   10. Rs 528   11. Rs 62.40   12. $10\frac{5}{7}\%$ loss   13. Rs 3200

EXERCISE 11 (e)

1. (i) 72 (ii) Rs 72.20   2. Rs 891   3. Rs 1000   4. (i) Rs, 1.50   (ii) Rs 376   5. Rs. 15.20; 5 %   6. Rs 168

7. Rs 15   8. $16\frac{2}{3}\%$ 9. Rs 15

MENTAL MATHS – 9

1. 7   2. 400   3. $\frac{7}{20}$ 4. 40%   5. 0.09   6. 16%   7. 60 cm

8. Rs 1500   9. Rs 20   10. Rs 10   11. 25 %   12. Rs 1600   13. Rs 1000   14. Rs 2000

15. 25%   16. $14\frac{2}{7}\%$ 17. Rs 400   18. 10%

JUST FOR FUN

Among the many legends which history preserves for us is the legend about a Maharaja of India, who wished to reward one of his subjects for inventing the game of chess. The Maharaja told his subject, "Make your request. Whatever you ask will be granted." The inventor of chess, being a clever man, said, "Your Majesty, give me one grain of wheat to cover the first square of the chess-board, two grains of wheat to cover the second square, four grains to cover the third, and so on. So your Majesty, double the number of grains to put on each succeeding square and give me enough grain to cover all 64 squares of the chess-board." The Maharaja thought the request sounded reasonable and agreed.

What the inventor had asked for was

$$1 + 2^1 + 2^2 + 2^3 + ... + 2^{62} + 2^{63} + 2^{64}.$$

number of grains of wheat. This totals to 18 446 744 073 709 551 615 grains. If we assume a bushel of grain contains about 5000000 grains, then 4 000 billion bushels would be needed. This amounts to the world's wheat production for a 2000 years period.

12. Simple Interest

12.1 Introduction

Let us revise in brief what you have studied in your previous class.

Interest is the money which the lender of a sum receives from the borrower, in consideration of the borrower using the sum.

The sum lent is called the **Principal.** The **rate of interest per cent** means that the sum mentioned as the rate is the interest for 100. Thus, 8% means that Rs 8 is the interest for Rs 100. Generally this rate is given for one year, and is then called *rate per cent per annum.*

The sum of the principal and the interest on it for any period is called the **amount** for that period.

Questions on interest involve four quantities: *the principal, the rate of interest* (given generally per cent per annum), the *period* and the *total Interest* for that period. Sometimes the amount is given instead of the principal or the interest (not the rate of interest, but the total interest). Any three of these quantities being given, we have to find the fourth. The questions are thus, solved by proportion, or the unitary method, or applying the formula given below.

If P denotes the principal, R the rate of interest per cent per annum, T the number of years, and $S.I.$ the total interest, then

$$S.I. = \frac{P \times R \times T}{100} \qquad \dots (1)$$

If A denotes the amount, then

$$A = P + S.I. = P + \frac{PRT}{100} = P\left(I + \frac{RT}{100}\right) \qquad \dots (2)$$

12.2 Solved Examples

Ex. 1 *A invested Rs 600 at 6 per cent and B invested Rs 950 at 8 per cent. Who received more interest annually and by how much?*

Sol. Interest received by A $= Rs \dfrac{600 \times 6 \times 1}{100} = Rs\ 36$ Interest received by B $= Rs \dfrac{950 \times 8 \times 1}{100} = Rs\ 76$

$\therefore$ B received **more** interest by **Rs 40.**

Ex. 2 *At what rate will Rs 6250 amount to Rs 7000 in 4 years ?*

Sol. Amount = Rs 7000, Principal = Rs 6250   Interest = Rs 7000 – Rs 6250 = Rs 750, Time = 4 years

Now $S.I. = \dfrac{P \times R \times T}{100}$ $\therefore\ 750 = \dfrac{6250 \times R \times 4}{100}$

or $R = \dfrac{750 \times 100}{6250 \times 4} = 3$ $\therefore$ **Rate is 3% per annum.**

Ex. 3 *Find the sum which will amount to Rs 364.80 at $3\frac{1}{2}$ % p. a. in 8 years at simple interest.*

Sol. Let us take the principal equal to Rs 100. Simple interest on Rs 100 at $3\frac{1}{2}$ % p.a. in 8 years

$$= \text{Rs } 100 \times \frac{7}{2} \times \frac{8}{100} = \text{Rs } 28$$

∴ Amount = Rs 100 + Rs 28 = Rs 128

If the amount is Rs 128, then principal = Rs 100

If the amount is Re 1, then principal = Rs $\frac{100}{128}$

If the amount is Rs 364.80, then principal = Rs $\frac{100}{128} \times 364.80 = $ **Rs 285.**

Ex. 4 *A man has Rs 7000 to invest. He invests Rs 4000 at 3% p.a. At what rate of interest must he invest the remainder in order to obtain a 4% interest on the total sum?*

Sol. Annual interest on Rs 4000 at 3% p.a. = Rs $\frac{4000 \times 3 \times 1}{100} = $ Rs120

Annual interest on Rs 7000 at 4% p.a. = Rs $\frac{7000 \times 4 \times 1}{100} = $ Rs 280

Interest he should get on the remainder Rs 3000 = Rs 280 – Rs 120 = Rs160

$$S.I. = \frac{P \times R \times T}{100}, \qquad \therefore 160 = \frac{3000 \times R \times 1}{100} \Rightarrow R = \frac{16}{3} = 5\frac{1}{3} \text{ % p.a.}$$

Ex. 5 *Find the simple interest on Rs 720 from April 5 to June 17 at $4\frac{1}{2}$ % p.a.*

Sol. Number of days

April 25 ←—— Omit April 5
May 31
June 17 ←—— Include June 17
——————
73 days

$\left. \right\}$ See note below

∴ T = 73 days = $\frac{73}{365}$ year = $\frac{1}{5}$ year $S.I. = \frac{P \times R \times T}{100} = $ Rs $\frac{720}{100} \times \frac{9}{2} \times \frac{1}{5} = $ **Rs 6.30.**

> **Note :** While calculating the number of days, omit the day the money was invested but count the day when it was withdrawn. In the above example April 5 is omitted but June 17 is counted. The number of days in a year is to be always taken as 365.

EXERCISE 12 (a)

1. Find the Simple Interest on Rs 112.50 for 4 years at $1\frac{1}{2}$ % per annum (p.a.)

2. **Find the simple interest and amount when**
    (*i*) Principal = Rs 500, Rate = 8% p.a., Time = 3 years
    (*ii*) Principal = Rs 750, Rate = 9% p.a., Time = 6 years
    (*iii*) Principal = Rs 800, Rate = 1.5% p.m., Time =1.3 years
    　　　　[**Hint :** Rate = 1.5% per month = (1.5 × 12)% p.a. = 18% p.a.]
    (*iv*) Principal = Rs 400, Rate = 20 paise per rupee per annum, Time = 6 months

[**Hint :** Rate= 20 paise per rupee per annum = (20 × 100) paise per 100 rupees p.a = Rs 20 pe

100 rupee p.a. = 20% p.a   Time = 6 months = $\frac{6}{12}$ year = $\frac{1}{2}$ year]

(v) Principal = Rs 300, Rate = 12% p.a., Time = 8 months.

3. At what rate will the principal of Rs 2000 yield an interest of Rs 112.50 in 15 months ?

4. In what time will Rs 7850 amount to Rs 8635 at 4% per annum ?

5. Find the principal that will yield an interest of Rs 367.50 in $4\frac{1}{2}$ years at $3\frac{1}{3}$% per annum.

6. Find the sum which will amount to Rs. 165.75 in $3\frac{1}{2}$ years at 3% per annum simple interest.

7. Find the simple interest on Rs 450 at 6% per annum from July 4 to September 15.

8. If the rate of interest is reduced from 5% p.a. to $3\frac{1}{2}$% p.a., find the decrease in a half-year's interest o
Rs 540.

9. If Rs 160 amounts to Rs 166 in 8 months, find to what it will amount in 1 year at the same rate of interest

10. At what rate will Rs 100 double itself in 7 years at simple interest ?

11. How long will it take Rs 100 to double itself at 5% simple interest ?

12. Rs 7000 left in a bank for 10 years at simple interest amounts to Rs 9800. What would it amount to afte
another 5 years at the same rate ?

12.3 Miscellaneous Problems

Type 1

Ex. 1   *Rs 450 amounts to Rs 504 in 3 years, how much will Rs 615 amount to in $2\frac{1}{2}$ years at the same rat*
of interest.

Sol.   From the first part of the question
Amount = Rs 504, Principal = Rs 450   ∴ Interest = Rs 504 – Rs 450 = Rs 54

Rate (R) = $\frac{S.I. \times 100}{P \times T} = \frac{54 \times 100}{450 \times 3}$ = 4% p.a

From the second part of the question, Principal = Rs 615, Rate (R) = 4%, Time = $2\frac{1}{2} = \frac{5}{2}$ years

∴ Interest = $\frac{P \times R \times T}{100}$ = Rs $\frac{615 \times 4 \times \frac{5}{2}}{100}$ = **Rs 61.50.**

Ex. 2   *Rs 890 becomes Rs 1068 in 4 years at simple interest. What amount will become Rs 1620 in 7 year*
at the same rate of interest ?

Sol.   From the first part of the question, we calculate the rate of interest.

Principal = Rs 890, Amount = Rs 1068, Interest = Rs 1068 – Rs 890 = Rs 178, Time = 4 years

∴ Rate = $\frac{S.I. \times 100}{P \times T} = \frac{178 \times 100}{890 \times 4}$ = 5 %,

Let the principal be Rs 100

Interest on Rs 100 for 7 years at 5% = Rs 35, Amount = Rs 100 + Rs 35 = Rs 135

When the amount is Rs 135, principal = Rs 100

∴ When the amount is Rs 1620, principal = Rs $\frac{100}{135} \times 1620$ = **Rs 1200.**

Type 2

Ex. 3 *A sum lent on simple interest becomes Rs 2520 in 2 years and Rs 2700 in 5 years. Find the sum and the rate of interest.*

Sol. Amount in 5 years = Rs 2700, Amount in 2 years = Rs 2520

∴ Interest of 3 years = Rs 2700 – Rs 2520 = Rs 180

Interest for 1 year = Rs $\frac{180}{3}$ = Rs 60.

Interest for 2 years = Rs (2 × 60) = Rs 120

Principal = Rs 2520 – Rs 120 = **Rs 2400**

∴ Rate = $\frac{S.I. \times 100}{P \times T} = \frac{120 \times 100}{2400 \times 2} = \frac{5}{2}\% = 2\frac{1}{2}\%$ **p.a.**

Type 3

Ex. 4. *I lent Rs 3000 to Shahid for 4 years and Rs 200 to Salman for 2 years. Find the rate of interest if I get an interest of Rs 480 in the end.*

Sol.: Interest on Rs 3000 for 4 years = Interest on Rs 12000 for 1 year

Interest on Rs 2000 for 2 years = Interest on Rs 4000 for 1 year

∴ Interest on Rs. (12000 + 4000), i.e., Rs. 16000 for 1 year = Rs 480

∴ Interest on Rs 100 for 1 year Rs $\frac{480}{1600} \times 100$ = Rs 3

∴ Interest rate = **3% per annum.**

Type 4

Ex. 5. *Shishir and Vinay borrowed Rs 2500 and Rs 300 respectively at the same rate of simple interest for $2\frac{1}{2}$ years. If Vinay paid Rs 175 more interest than Shishir, find the rate of interest per annum .*

Sol. Sum borrowed by Vinay = Rs 3000; Sum borrowed by Shishir = Rs 2500

∴ Difference of sums borrowed by the two persons = Rs 3000 – Rs 2500 = Rs 500

It is given that Vinay paid Rs 175 more interest than Shishir

Therefore, S.I. on Rs 500 for $2\frac{1}{2}$ years is Rs 175

∴ Rate = $\frac{100 \times S.I.}{P \times T} = \frac{100 \times 175}{500 \times \frac{5}{2}}\% = \mathbf{14\%}$ **per annum.**

EXERCISE 12 (b)

1. If Rs 450 amounts to Rs 540 in 4 years at simple interest, find the sum that will amount to Rs 637.50 is 5 years at the same rate of interest.

2. A sum amounts to Rs 1326 in 6 years at 5% p.a. simple interest. In what time will this sum double itself at the same rate of interest ?

3. A man lent equal sums of money at $5\frac{1}{2}$ per cent and 4 per cent per annum respectively for a period of 3 years. If he earned Rs 72 more for the money lent out at $5\frac{1}{2}$ %, find the sum of money lent at 4%

4. Two equal sums were lent out at 7% and 5% interest respectively. The interests earned on the two loans add up to Rs 960 for 4 years. Find the total sum lent out.

5. A sum lent out at simple interest becomes Rs 4480 in 3 years and Rs 4800 in 5 years. Find the sum and th rate of interest.

6. Divide Rs 2500 into two parts such that the simple interest on one at 4% for 5 years is double that of th other at 5% for 3 years.

7. A sum of money lent out at simple interest amounts to Rs. 2880 in 2 years and to Rs. 3600 in 5 years. Fin the sum of money and rate of interest.

8. Shekhar and Arvind borrowed Rs 2250 and Rs 2500 respectively at the same rate of simple interest for $3\frac{1}{2}$ years

   If Arvind paid Rs 140 more interest than Shekhar, find the rate of interest per annum.

9 The simple interest. on a certain sum for 4 years at 9% per annum is Rs 216 less than the simple interest on th same sum for 3 years at 18% per annum. Find the sum.

LOOKING BACK
Summary of Key Facts

1. The money borrowed by a borrower is called **principal.**

2. The additional money paid by the borrower to the lender for having used the borrowed money is called the **interest**

3. **Amount = Principal + Interest.**

4. Interest on Rs 100 for 1 year is called the **rate per cent per annum.**

5. If the principal remains the same throughout the loan period and interest is reckoned uniformly on it, then it is called **simple interest** and is abbreviated as S.I.

6. If P = Principal, R = Rate per cent per annum, T = Time in years and S. I = Simple interest then

   (i) S. I. $= \dfrac{P \times R \times T}{100} \Rightarrow$ (ii) $P = \dfrac{100 \times S.I.}{R \times T}$ (iii) $R = \dfrac{100 \times S.I.}{P \times T}$ (iv) $T = \dfrac{100 \times S. I.}{P \times R}$.

MENTAL MATHS - 10

Find the simple interest on :

1. Rs 900 for one year at 8% per annum.
2. Rs 1000 for 6 months at 10% per annum.
3. Rs 2000 for 5 years at 7% per annum.
4. Rs 500 for 6 years at 8% per annum.
5. How much will Rs 1000 become when it is invested at 20% per annum for 1 year.
6. How much will Rs 10,000 become when it is invested at 5% for one year ?

Find the principal

7. When S.I. = Rs 50; Rate = 5% per annum Time = 2 years.
8. When S.I. = Rs 70, Rate = 14%. p.a., Time = 2 years.

Find the time when

9. Principal = Rs 800, Rate = 5% per annum, S.I = Rs 160.
10. Principal = Rs 1500, S.I. =Rs 300, Rate = 4% p.a.

ANSWERS

EXERCISE 12 (a)

1. Rs 6.75

2.

	(i)	(ii)	(iii)	(iv)	(v)
Interest	Rs 120	Rs 405	Rs 187.20	Rs 40	Rs 24
Amount	Rs 620	Rs 1155	Rs 987.20	Rs 440	Rs 324

3. $4\frac{1}{2}$ % p.a.   4. $2\frac{1}{2}$ years   5. Rs 2450   6. Rs 150   7. Rs 5.40   8. Rs 4.05   9. Rs 169   10. $14\frac{2}{7}$ % p.a.

11. 20 years   12. Rs 11760

EXERCISE 12 (b)

1. Rs 510   2. 20 years   3. Rs 1600   4. Rs 4000   5. Rs 4000, 4% p.a.   6. Rs 1500, Rs 1000

7. Rs 2400, 10% p.a.   8. 16% p.a.,   9. Rs. 1200

MENTAL MATHS—10

1. Rs 72   2. Rs 50   3. Rs 700   4. Rs 240   5. Rs 1200   6. Rs 10,500   7. Rs 500

8. Rs 250   9. 4 years   10. 5 Years

13. Distance, Time and Speed

13.1 Introduction

Suppose a train travels 60 kilometres in 1 hour, 120 kilometres in 2 hours, 180 kilometres in 3 hours and so on, then we say that it is moving with a uniform **speed** or an average speed of 60 kilometres per hour. It is abbreviated as 60 km/h. 180 kilometres is the **distance** covered by it in 3 hours. 2 hours is the **time** taken to cover 120 kilometres.

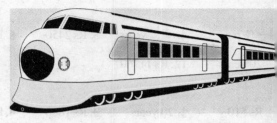

13.2 Formulas

The following formulas express the relationship between three quantities, **"Distance, Speed, and Time**. Two of these quantities being known, the third quantity can be determined with the help of these formulas.

1. **Distance = Time × Speed**

2. **Speed =** $\dfrac{\text{Distance}}{\text{Time}}$

3. **Time =** $\dfrac{\text{Distance}}{\text{Speed}}$

Aid to Memory
(*i*) To find speed, cover S so that $S = \dfrac{D}{T}$
(*ii*) To find distance, cover D so that $D = S \times T$
(*iii*) To find time, cover T so that $T = \dfrac{D}{S}$

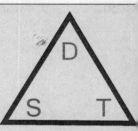

13.3 Solved Examples

Ex. 1 *Convert a speed of 1 km/h to a speed in metres per second.*

Sol. Using 1 km = 1000m, and 1 hour = 3600 seconds, we have

$$1 \text{ km/h} = \frac{1 \text{ km}}{1 \text{ hour}} = \frac{1000 \text{ m}}{3600 \text{ s}} = \frac{5 \text{ m}}{18 \text{ s}} = \frac{5}{18} \text{ m/s}.$$

If follows, therefore, that

> *To change* a speed in km/h to a speed in m/s, multiply by $\dfrac{5}{18}$.
>
> *Conversely*, to change a speed in m/s to a speed in km/h, multiply by $\dfrac{18}{5}$.

Ex. 2 *Convert a speed of 54 km/h to a speed in m/s.*
Method I

Sol. $54 \text{ km/h} = 54 \times \dfrac{5}{18} \text{ m/s} = \textbf{15 m/s}.$

Method II

$$54 \text{ km/h} = \frac{54 \times 1000 \text{m}}{1 \text{h}} = \frac{54 \times 1000 \text{m}}{3600 \text{ s}} = \frac{15 \text{ m}}{1 \text{ s}} = 15 \text{ m/s}.$$

Ex. 3. *At an average speed of 65 km/h, Jayanti Janta Express reaches Agra Cantt from New Delhi in hours. What is the distance between Agra Cantt and New Delhi?*

Sol. Speed = 65 km/h, Time taken = 3 h

∴ Distance covered = speed × time = (65 × 3) km = 195 km

Hence, the distance between Agra Cantt and New Delhi = **195 km.**

Ex. 4. *The Grand Trunk Express covers a distance of 2192 km between New Delhi and Chennai in 36 hours 15 min. Find whether its average speed is more than 60 km/h.*

Sol. Distance covered = 2192 km,

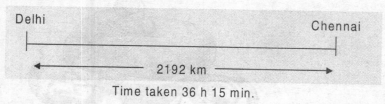

Time taken 36 h 15 min.

Time taken = 36 h 15 min = $36\dfrac{15}{60}$ h = $36\dfrac{1}{4}$ h = $\dfrac{145}{4}$ h

∴ Average speed = $\dfrac{\text{Distance}}{\text{Time}} = \dfrac{2192}{\dfrac{145}{4}}$ km/h

$$= 2192 \times \dfrac{4}{145} \text{ km/h} = \dfrac{8768}{145} \text{ km/h} = \textbf{60.47 km/h (correct to 2 dp)}$$

Hence, the average speed of the train is more than 60 km/h.

Ex. 5. *In a journey of 80 km, a train covers the first 60 km at 40 km/h and the remaining distance at 20 km/h. Calculate the average speed for the whole journey.*

Sol. Time taken to cover 60 km at 40 km/h = $\dfrac{60}{40}$ hrs = $\dfrac{3}{2}$ hrs

Time taken to cover 20 km at 20 km/h = $\dfrac{20}{20}$ hr = 1 hr.

∴ Total time taken = $\left(\dfrac{3}{2} + 1\right)$ hrs. = $2\dfrac{1}{2}$ hrs.

∴ Average speed = $\dfrac{\text{Total distance}}{\text{Total time}} = \dfrac{80 \text{ km}}{5/2 \text{ h}} = \dfrac{80 \times 2}{5}$ km/h = **32 km/h.**

Ex. 6. *Two men start from the same place, walk at the rate of 4 km per hour and 4.5 km per hour respectively. How many kilometres will they be apart at the end of $3\dfrac{1}{2}$ hours, if they walk*

(i) *In the same direction ;* (ii) *In the opposite directions?*

Sol. (i) If they walk in the same direction, then in 1 hour, they are apart by (4.5 – 4), i.e., 0.5 km.

∴ In $3\dfrac{1}{2}$ hours, they are apart by $\left(0.5 \times \dfrac{7}{2}\right)$ = **1.75 km.**

(ii) If they walk in opposite directions, then in one hour, they are apart by (4.5 + 4), i.e., 8.5 km.

$\therefore$ In $3\frac{1}{2}$ hours, they are apart by $\left(8.5 \times \frac{7}{2}\right) = $ **29.75 km.**

Ex. 7. *Distance between two towns X and Y is 110 km. A motor cycle rider starts from X towards Y at 7 a.m. at a speed of 20 km per hour. Another motor cycle rider starts from Y towards X at 8 a.m. at a speed of 25 km per hour. Find, when they will cross each other.*

Sol. Suppose they meet at P after x hours from the start of the first rider. Then the first rider covers the distance XP in x hours and second rider covers the distance YP in $(x-1)$ hours (since he starts 1 hour later at 8 a.m.

First rider :

Speed = 20 km/h, Time = x hours

$\therefore$ Distance covered = $XP = 20x$ km

Second rider :

Speed = 15 km/h, Time = $(x-1)$ hours

$\therefore$ Distance covered = $YP = 25(x-1)$ km

$XP + YP = 110$ km

$20x + 25(x-1) = 110 \Rightarrow 20x + 25x - 25 = 110$

$\Rightarrow \quad 45x = 110 + 25 = 135 \Rightarrow x = \frac{135}{45} = $ **3**

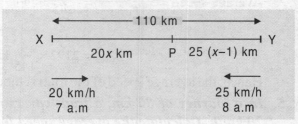

Hence, they meet 3 hours after the start of the journey, i.e., at **10 a.m.**

EXERCISE 13 (a)

1. **Express each of the following speeds in m/s.**
   (*i*) 36 km/h   (*ii*) 72 km/h   (*iii*) 90 km/h   (*iv*) 270 km/h

2. **Express each of the following speeds in km/h :**
   (*i*) 15 m/s   (*ii*) 35 m/s   (*iii*) 16 m/s   (*iv*) 62 m/s

3. The speed of a Maruti car is 54 km/h. What is the speed in m/s ?

4. The speed of a goods train is 8 m/s. What is its speed in km/h ?

5. Ravi runs 15.6 km per hour. How many metres does he run in 2 minutes ?

6. If the speed of a train be 92.4 km per hour, how many metres would it cover in 20 minutes ?

7. If you can cycle at an average speed of 12 km per hour, how many km can you cycle in 2 hours 45 minutes ?

8. How long will an express train travelling at 50 km/h take to cover a distance of 5 km between two stations ?

9. A train runs at 45 km/h. How far does it go in 6 seconds ?

10. A train is running at a speed or 48 km/h. How long will it take to reach a signal at a distance of 80 metres from the starting platform ?

11. A car passes through a street 200 metres long in 18 seconds. How many km/h is it travelling ?

12. A train covers the distance between two stations which are 11 km apart in 12 minutes. At what rate per hour is it travelling ?

13. Lamp-posts are placed 30 metres apart along a road. How long will a car travelling at 45 km an hour take to pass 6 lamp-posts, not counting the first of them.

14. A train passes the telegraph posts which are placed 76 metres apart alongside a railway track at intervals of 4 seconds. At what rate is the train travelling in km per hour ?

15. How long will a boy take to run round a square field of side 35 metres. if he runs at the rate of 9 km/h ?

16. Sound travels at 335 metres per second in air. Find its speed in km per hour.

17. Tamil Nadu Express takes 21 hrs and 48 min in reaching Warangal from New Delhi at an average speed of 72 km/hr. How far is Warangal from New Delhi?

18. A gun is fixed at a distance 1.7 km away from Saurabh. Saurabh hears the sound 5 seconds later. Find the speed at which sound travels.

19. Which is greater, a speed of 36 km per hour or 8 metres per second? What is the difference in the distances travelled in 1 second?

20. A train is booked to do the run between two places, 55 km apart, in 1 hr 20 min. If it travels for the first 30 km at 36 km an hour, at what speed must it travel for the rest of the distance in order to complete the journey in time?

21. A man walks from his home to a town 6 km away at 4 km per hour and returns again to his home at 12 km per hour using a tonga. What is the man's average speed for the double journey?

22. A car can travel the distance between the station and the post-office, which are 1.2 km apart, in 1.8 minutes. How much faster must it travel to do the distance in 1.5 minutes?

23. A man goes uphill with an average speed of 45 km/h and comes down with an average speed of 35 km/h. The distance travelled in both the cases being the same. Find the average speed for the entire journey.

24. A train covers a distance in 50 minutes if it runs at a speed of 48 km per hour on an average. The speed at which the train must run to reduce the time of journey to 40 minutes, will be

   (*i*) 50 km/h   (*ii*) 55 km/h   (*iii*) 60 km/h   (*iv*) 70 km/h.

25. Suresh started cycling along the boundaries of a square field from corner point A. After half an hour he reached the corner point C, diagonally opposite to A. If his speed was 8 km per hour, what is the area of the field in square km?

13.4 Problems on Trains

Note that :

1. While passing a stationary object such as a signal post or a telegraph pole or a standing man, a train travels a distance equal to its length.

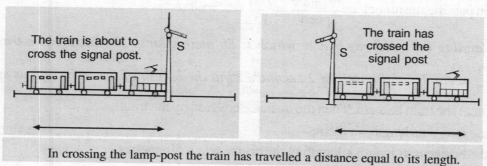

In crossing the lamp-post the train has travelled a distance equal to its length.

2. While passing a bridge or a tunnel or a train at rest or a platform, a train travels a distance equal to the sum o its length and the object which it crosses.

Before crossing the bridge

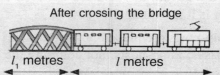

After crossing the bridge

l metres l_1 metres l_1 metres l metres

In crossing the bridge the train travels a distance equal to the sum of the lengths of the train and the bridge.

Ex. 1. *A 270 m long goods train is running at 40.5 km/hr. How much time will it take to cross a tree?*

Sol.   Distance covered by the train in crossing the tree

$$= \text{length of the train} = 270 \text{ m} = \frac{270}{1000} \text{ km} = 0.27 \text{ km}.$$

Speed of the train = 40.5 km/hr.

∴   Time taken in crossing the tree $= \dfrac{\text{distance}}{\text{speed}} = \dfrac{0.27}{40.5} \text{ h}$

$$= \frac{27}{4050} \text{ h} = \frac{1}{150} \text{ h} = \frac{1}{150} \times 3600 \text{ sec} = \textbf{24 sec.}$$

Ex.2. *A train, 450 m long, crosses a pole in $22\frac{1}{2}$ sec. What is the speed of the train in km/h ?*

Sol.   Distance covered by the train in crossing the pole

$$= \text{length of the train} = 450 \text{ m}$$

Time taken in crossing the pole $= 22\dfrac{1}{2} \text{ sec} = \dfrac{45}{2} \text{ sec}$

> Recall that $1 \text{ m/s} = \dfrac{18}{5} \text{ km/h}$

∴   Speed of the train $= \dfrac{\text{distance}}{\text{time}} = \dfrac{450}{45/2} \text{ m/s} = 20 \text{ m/s}$

$$= 20 \times \frac{18}{5} \text{ km/h} = \textbf{72 km/h}$$

Ex. 3. *A train, 540 metres long, is running with a speed of 54 km/h. In how much time will it pass a tunne 180 metres long ?*

Sol.   Speed of the train = 54 km/h $= 54 \times \dfrac{5}{18} \text{ m/s} = 15 \text{ m/s}$

Distance covered in passing the tunnel

$$= \text{length of the train} + \text{length of the tunnel} = 540 \text{ m} + 180 \text{ m} = 720 \text{ m}$$

∴   Time taken in passing the tunnel $= \dfrac{\text{distance}}{\text{speed}} = \dfrac{720}{15} \text{ sec.} = \textbf{48 sec.}$

Ex. 4. *A man is standing on a railway bridge which is 50 metres long. He finds that a train crosses the bridge in $4\frac{1}{2}$ seconds but himself in 2 seconds. Find the length of the train and its speed.*

Sol.   Let the length of the train be x cm. Then the distance covered by the train

(i) in crossing the man = its length = x metres

(ii) in crossing the bridge = its length + length of the bridge = $(x + 50)$ metres

∴   The train covers x metres in 2 seconds and $(x + 50)$ metres in $(9/2)$ seconds.

∴ Speed of the train = $\dfrac{\text{Distance}}{\text{Time}} = \dfrac{x}{2}$ or $\dfrac{x+50}{\dfrac{9}{2}}$, *i.e.*, $\dfrac{2(x+50)}{9}$

∴ $\dfrac{x}{2} = \dfrac{2(x+50)}{9}$

$\Rightarrow 9x = 4(x+50) \Rightarrow 9x = 4x + 200 \Rightarrow 5x = 200$ or $x = 40$

∴ Length of the train = **40 metres.**

Also, speed = $\dfrac{x}{2} = \dfrac{40}{2} = 20$ m/s $= 20 \times \dfrac{18}{5}$ km/h = **72 km/h.**

EXERCISE 13 (b)

1. A train 150 metres long is running with a speed of 36 km/h. In what time will it pass a telegraph post ?
2. A train 200 metres long is running with a speed of 36 km/h. How much time will it take to pass a standing man ?
3. A train 80 metres long is running at a rate of 45 km/h. How much time will it take to cross a platform 220 metres long ?
4. A train 120 metres long passes a telegraph pole in 5 seconds. How long will it take to cross a railway platform 180 metres long ?
5. A train running at the rate of 36 km/h passes a standing man in 8 seconds. What is the length of the train?
6. A train 80 metres long takes half a minute in crossing a tunnel 420 metres long. Find the speed of the train?
7. A train 100 metres long running at 36 km/h takes 25 seconds to pass a bridge. Find the length of the bridge.
8. A train 50 metres long passes a platform 100 metres long in 10 seconds. What is the speed of the train in metres per second?
9. A 225 metres long train crosses a 275 metres long tunnel in one minute. Find the speed of the train in km/hr.

LOOKING BACK
Summary of Key Facts

1. (*i*) Speed = $\dfrac{\text{distance}}{\text{time}}$ $\left(S = \dfrac{D}{T}\right)$ (*ii*) Time = $\dfrac{\text{distance}}{\text{speed}}$ $\left(T = \dfrac{D}{S}\right)$

   (*iii*) Distance = Speed × Time (D = S × T)

2. (*i*) 1 km/hr = $\dfrac{5}{18}$ m/s   (*ii*) 1m/s = $\dfrac{18}{5}$ km/h.

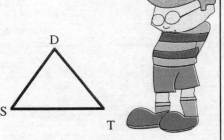

3. (*i*) While passing an object like a signal post or a telegraph pole or a standing man, a train travels a distance equal to its length.

   (*ii*) In crossing an object like a bridge or a tunnel or a platform, a train travels a distance equal to the sum of its length and the object which it crosses.

MENTAL MATHS – 11

1. Convert 36 km/hr into m/ sec.
2. Convert 50 m/sec into km/hr.
3. The speed of car is 70 km/hr. It takes 3 hrs to cover a certain distance. Find the distance covered in metres.
4. Which speed is greater: 54 km/hr or 15 m/sec ?
5. A train crosses a flag post in 11 secs. If the length of the train is 220 m, find the speed of the train ?
6. A train having a length of 140 m crosses a railway platform of length 130 m in 30 sec., calculate the speed of the train.

ANSWERS

EXERCISE 13 (a)

1. (*i*) 10 m/s   (*ii*) 20 m/s   (*iii*) 25 m/s   (*iv*) 75 m/s
2. (*i*) 54 km/h   (*ii*) 126 km/h   (*iii*) 57.6 km/h   (*iv*) 223.2 km/h
3. 15 m/s   4. 28.8 km/h   5. 520 m   6. 30,800 m   7. 33 km   8. 6 min   9. 75 m
10. 6 sec   11. 40 km/h   12. 55 km/h   13. 12 sec.   14. 68.4 km/h   15. 56 sec.   16. 1206 km/h
17. 1569.6 km   18. 340 m/s   19. 36 km/h ; 2m   20. 50 km/h   21. 6 km/h   22. 8 km/h faster

23. $39 \frac{3}{8}$ km/h [**Hint.** Let each of the distances travelled by x km. Then,

$$t_1 = \frac{x}{45} h, \quad t_2 = \frac{x}{35} h \quad \therefore \text{Average speed} = \frac{\text{Total distance}}{\text{Total time}} = \frac{2x}{\frac{x}{45} + \frac{x}{35}} \text{km/h} = \frac{2}{\frac{35+45}{45 \times 35}} = \frac{2 \times 45 \times 35}{80} \text{km/h}]$$

24. 60 km/h   25. 4 sq km

EXERCISE 13 (b)

1. 15 sec   2. 20 sec   3. 24 sec   4. $12 \frac{1}{2}$ sec   5. 80 m   6. 60 km/h   7. 150 m

8. 15 m/s   9. 30 km/h

MENTAL MATHS – 11

1. 10 m/sec   2. 180 km/hr   3. 210000 m   4. Both are equal   5. 20 m/sec.   6. 9 m/sec.

14. Averages

14.1 Introduction

In our daily working, we come across the *word average* quite often. We read in newspapers or magzines about the average rainfall, average score in a particular test match, the average temperature of a particular city, average speed of a new car launched, average number of people travelling by metro rail on a particular day and so on. The list is endless.

So now we shall tell you what is meant by average and how you can find it.

Another name for average is **Mean**.

Definition : *If several quantities of the same kind are added together and the sum is divided by the number of quantities concerned, the quotient is called the mean or average of the numbers :*

$$\text{Average} = \frac{\text{Sum of quantities}}{\text{Number of quantities}}$$

∴ **Sum of quantities = Average × Number of quantities**

TYPE 1. To find the Average

Ex.1. *Find the average of the following numbers :*

(*a*) *48, 26, 37, 51, 73, 29*

(*b*) *3.4, 8.1, 1.9, 0.4*

Sol. (*a*) Sum of the given numbers = 48 + 26 + 37 + 51 + 73 + 29 = 264

Number of numbers = 6

∴ Average = $\dfrac{\text{Sum of numbers}}{\text{Number of numbers}} = \dfrac{264}{6} = $ **44.**

(*b*) Sum of the given numbers = 3.4 + 8.1 + 1.9 + 0.4 = 13.8,

Number of numbers = 4

∴ Average = $\dfrac{\text{Sum of numbers}}{\text{Number of numbers}} = \dfrac{13.8}{4} = $ **3.45.**

Ex. 2. *The following are the heights of a sampling of plants of the same kind in a certain nursery: 40.7 ; 38.3 ; 43.6 ; 45.1 ; 33.6 ; 35.8 ; 42.8 ; 49.3 ; 38.2 ; 41.5 cm. By how many centimetres does the height of the tallest plant exceed the average?*

Sol. Sum of the heights = (40.7 + 38.3 + 43.6 + 45.1 + 33.6 + 35.8 + 42.8 + 49.3 + 38.2 + 41.5) cm
= 408.9 cm.

Number of plants = 10

∴ Average height = $\dfrac{\text{Sum of the heights}}{\text{Number of plants}} = \dfrac{408.9}{10} = $ **40.89 cm.**

The height of the tallest plant is 45.1 cm. It exceeds the average height by (45.1 – 40.89) *i.e.*, by **4.21 cm.**

TYPE 2. Average Being Given, to Find the Sum

Ex. 3. *The batting average of a player for 15 innings was 21. Find the total number of runs scored by him.*

Sol. Total number of runs scored = Average × Number of innings

$$= 21 \times 15 = \textbf{315 runs.}$$

Ex. 4. *The average age of 5 children of a family is 12 years. If four of them are respectively 6, 11, 13 and 16 years old, find the age of the fifth child.*

Sol. Let the age of the fifth child be x years.

∴ Sum of the ages of the five children = $(6 + 11 + 13 + 16 + x)$ years.

Number of children = 5, Average age = 12 years.

Now applying the formula : Average = $\dfrac{\text{Sum of quantities}}{\text{Number of quantities}}$

We have, $12 = \dfrac{6 + 11 + 13 + 16 + x}{5}$

$\Rightarrow \dfrac{46 + x}{5} = 12 \Rightarrow 46 + x = 12 \times 5 \Rightarrow 46 + x = 60 \Rightarrow x = 60 - 46 = 14$

∴ The age of the fifth child is **14 years.**

Alternative Method :

Average age of 5 children = 12 years

∴ Total age of 5 children = (12×5) year = 60 years

Sum of the ages of 4 children = $(6 + 11 + 13 + 16)$ years = 46 years

∴ Age of the fifth child = $(60 - 46)$ years = 14 years.

Ex. 5. *Given that the average of five numbers is 27. If one of the numbers is excluded, the average becomes 25. Determine the excluded number.*

Sol. Average of 5 numbers = 27 ∴ Sum of 5 numbers = 27 × 5 = 135

Given one number is excluded and average of remaining 4 numbers = 25

∴ Sum of remaining 4 numbers = 25 × 4 = 100

∴ Excluded Number = 135 − 100 = **35.**

Ex. 6. *What is the average cost per book of 80 books, 50 of which cost Rs 30 each and the rest Rs 40 each ?*

Sol. Total cost of 50 books costing Rs 30 each = Rs (50 × 30) = Rs 1500

Total cost of 30 books costing Rs 40 each = Rs (30 × 40) = Rs 1200

∴ Total cost of 80 books = Rs (1500 + 1200) = Rs 2700

∴ Average cost per book = $\dfrac{\text{Total cost of 80 books}}{80}$ = Rs $\dfrac{2700}{80}$ = **Rs 33.75.**

Ex. 7. *A cricketer had an average score of 58 runs in 9 innings. Find out how many runs are to be scored in the tenth inning so that the average score becomes 61.*

Sol. Average score in 9 innings = 58

∴ Total score in 9 innings = 58 × 9 = 522 runs.

Average score in 10 innings = 61

∴ Total score in 10 innings = 61 × 10 = 610 runs.

∴ Runs scored in the 10th inning = 610 − 522 = **88 runs.**

Ex. 8. *The average weight of class of 20 students is 48 kg. Two more students weighing 60 kg and 58 kg respectively join the class. What is the average weight of the class now?*

Sol.   Average weight of 20 students = 48 kg

$\therefore$ Total weight of 20 students = (48 × 20) kg = 960 kg

Now 2 students of weights 60 kg and 58 kg join the class

$\therefore$ Total weight of 22 students = (960 + 60 + 58) kg = 1078 kg.

$\therefore$ New average weight of the class = $\dfrac{1078}{22}$ = **49 kg.**

EXERCISE 14

1. **Find the average of the following numbers :**

   (a) 4, 7, 9, 12, 8   (b) 1, 0, –1, –3, 8   (c) First 4 prime numbers   (d) 2.2, 5.7, 4.8, 9.1, 6.7, 12.3

   (e) 21, 48, 35, 60, 49, 18, 23   (f) $\dfrac{3}{5}$; $\dfrac{1}{2}$; $\dfrac{2}{3}$; $\dfrac{1}{4}$

2. A child scores 48 in English, 63 in Hindi, 75 in Mathematics, 72 in Science and 79 in Social Studies. Find the child's average score.

3. In one week, a fast food joint sold 145 burgers on Monday, 107 on Tuesday, 160 on Wednesday, 154 on Thursday, 175 on Friday, 185 on Saturday and 250 on Sunday. Find the average number of burgers sold in the week.

4. **The rainfall in a certain town is as under :**

Months	Jan.	Feb.	March	April	May	June	July	August
Rainfall (in cm)	3.25	2.5	2.75	2.65	1.05	3.5	4.25	4.55

   Find the average rainfall during this period.

5. The average height of 6 persons is 164 cm. What is their total height?

6. The average expenditure per day of a man during the month of July is Rs 350. What is his total expenditure during the month?

7. The average distance travelled by a person in 4 days is 250 km. The distances travelled by him in first three days are 225 km, 180 km, 230 km respectively. What is the distance travelled by him on the fourth day?

8. Sahil bought 12 pens at Rs 8.25 each and 8 more at Rs 7.50 each. What is the average cost of each pen?

9. The average score of 11 students in a class is 80.6. One of the students having a average score of 92 leaves the school. What is the average score of the remaining students?

10. The average monthly salary of 15 workers in a factory is Rs 1285. If the salary of the manager is included, the average becomes Rs 1355. What is the manager's salary ?

11. Find the combined average age of a group of 150 people, if the average age of 50 people is 30 and that of the other 100 people is 60.

12. In a class of 20 boys and 15 girls, the average weight of the class is 42 kg. The average weight of the girls is 41.5 kg. What is the average weight of the boys?

13. The mean of 10 observations is 3.5. If two observations namely 3.5 and 2.5 are deleted, find the new mean?

14. The average attendance of a school for the first four days of the week was 780 and for the first five days it was 840. How many were present on Friday?

15. Find the unknown number if average of 6 numbers is 45, and the other five numbers are 35, 38, 46, 39, 50.

16. The average number of icecream cones sold on Monday, Tuesday and Wednesday, in a school were 43. The average for Tuesday, Wednesday and Thursday was 45. For Thursday the sale was 42. Find the sale on Monday.

LOOKING BACK

Summary of Key Facts

$$\text{Average} = \frac{\text{Sum of quantities}}{\text{Number of quantities}}$$

Sum of quantities = Average × Number of quantities

MENTAL MATHS-12

Find the average of :

1. 1, 2, 3

2. –5, –3, –1, 0, 19

3. First 3 odd numbes.

4. Prime numbers between 4 and 10.

5. 1.5, 2.1 and 2.4

6. The averge age of 30 pupils is 11 years. Find the total age of the pupils.

7. The average earning of a labourer for 7 days is Rs 80. Find his total income during these days.

8. The average height of 5 pupils in a class is 140 cm. If the total height of 4 pupils is 590 cm, find the height of the fifth pupil.

UNIT REVIEW – 3

1. Express $62\frac{1}{4}\%$ as (a) decimal (b) fraction.

2. Express (a) $\frac{17}{60}$ (b) 1.07 as a per cent.

3. **Work out :** (a) 30 % of 400 gm. (b) $37\frac{1}{2}\%$ of 42 m. (c) $10\frac{1}{4}\%$ of Rs 80.

4. A school raises Rs 28000 during a summer fete. The school gives 42 % of the money to charity. How much mone is left?

5. Sanjana works in a software company. Her monthly salary of Rs 22,800 is increased by $7\frac{1}{2}\%$. Find her new salary?

6. A man weighs 209 kg after having lost 5% of his original weight. Calculate the original weight.

7. Find x if 40 % of x is 384.

8. If A : B = 3 : 4 and B : C = 5 : 7, find A : B : C.

9. Divide 390 in the ratio $\frac{1}{2} : \frac{1}{3} : \frac{1}{4}$.

10. Find the fourth proportional to 1.2, 0.8, 4.2.

11. Find the mean proportional between $\frac{1}{7}$ and $\frac{1}{28}$.

12. Two lengths of wood are in the ratio 4 : 7. The longer length is 35 cm. What is the total length of wood?

13. In what time will Rs 1000 amount to Rs 1200 at 8 % per annum S.I. ?

14. At what rate of interest will the sum of Rs 4000 amount to Rs 4292 for the period 10th April 2005 to 3rd Septembe 2005 ?

15. A sum amounts to Rs 576 after a period of $3\frac{1}{2}$ years at the rate of 8% per annum S.I. Find the sum.

16. The cost price of 16 pens is equal to the selling price of 12 pens. Is there a gain or a loss ? Find the gain or loss%.
17. What will be the marked price of an article if it is sold for Rs 228 after allowing a discount of 5% ?
18. A cycle dealer offers a discount of 10 % and still makes a profit of 26 %. What is the actual cost of the cycle if M.P is Rs 840 ?
19. A shopkeeper buys eggs at Rs 75 per 100. For how much should he sell each egg so as to make a gain of 20% ?
20. A shopkeeper sold two pairs of jeans at Rs 720 each. On one he gains 20% and on the other he loses 20%. Find his gain or loss in the whole transaction.
21. 58 boxes of a certain commodity require a shelf length of 17.4 m. How many boxes of the same commodity would occupy a shelf length of 20.4 m. ?
22. A school has food for 650 pupils to last for 30 days. How long will it last if 50 pupils leave the school?
23. A bullock cart covers a distance of 18 km in $4\frac{1}{2}$ hrs. What is the average speed of the cart?
24. Sound travels in air at 335 m/s. Express its speed in km/hr.
25. In a journeyof 120 km, a car covers the first 80 km at a speed of 40 km/hr and the rest of the distance at a speed of 20km/hr. Calculate the average speed for the whole journey.
26. If a train 90 m long takes 12 sec to pass a platform 110 m long, what is the speed of the train?
27. *A* and *B* together can do a piece of work in 15 days. B alone can do it in 20 days. How many days would A alone take to complete the work?
28. Two taps can fill a cistern in 10 hours and 12 hours respectively and a third can empty it, if full, in 15 hours. If all the three taps are opened together when the cistern is empty, how long will it take to fill it?
29. If the average of 16, 14, *x*, 23, 20 is 18, find the value of *x*.
30. The average monthly salary of 19 members of a group is Rs 1600. One more member whose monthly salary is Rs 2000 per month has joined the group. Find the new average monthly salary of the group.

ANSWERS

EXERCISE 14

1. (*a*) 8   (*b*) 1   (*c*) 4.25   (*d*) 6.8   (*e*) 36.28   (*f*) $\frac{121}{240}$

2. 67.4 marks   3. 168   4. 3.0625 cm   5. 984 cm   6. Rs 10850   7. 365 km   8. Rs 7.95

9. 79.46   10. Rs 2405   11. 50   12. 42.375 kg   13. 3.625   14. 1080   15. 62

16. 36 cones

MENTAL MATHS-12

1. 2   2. 2   3. 3   4. 6   5. 2   6. 330 years   7. Rs 560

8. 110 cm

UNIT REVIEW - 3

1. (*a*) 0.6225   (*b*) $\frac{249}{400}$ 2. (*a*) $28\frac{1}{3}$%   (*b*) 107%   3. (*a*) 120 gm   (*b*) $15\frac{3}{4}$ m   (*c*) Rs 8.20

4. Rs 16240   5. Rs 24510   6. 220 kg   7. 960   8. 15 : 20 : 28   9. 180, 120, 90   10. 2.8

11. $\frac{1}{14}$ 12. 55 cm   13. $2\frac{1}{2}$ years   14. $18\frac{1}{4}$%   15. Rs 450   16. Gain, $33\frac{1}{3}$%   17. Rs 240

18. Rs 600   19. Re 0.9   20. Loss : 4%   21. 68 boxes   22. $32\frac{1}{2}$ days   23. 4 km/hr   24. 1206 km/hr

25. 30 km/hr   26. $16\frac{2}{3}$ m/sec.   27. 60 days   28. $8\frac{4}{7}$ hours   29. 17   30. Rs 1620.

15. Algebraic Expressions

15.1 Review

Let us recall the important and basic definitions of algebra which you have studied in Class 6.

1. **Constants and Variables :** *A symbol in algebra having a fixed value is called a constant, whereas a symbol which can be given or assigned a varied number of values is called a variable.*

$4, 0.35, \dfrac{5}{7}, -\dfrac{6}{9}$ are all fixed values and hence are constants.

Variables are generally represented by letters of the English alphabet, x, y, z etc. They can be assigned any value.

By convention, the unknown constants are represented by the letters a, b, c, etc.

2. **Algebraic Expression :** *A combination of constants and variables connected by the basic mathematical operators, i.e., $+, -, \div, \times$ is called an algebraic expression.*

For example : $4xy, 2x^2 - y, 4x - 2y + 3z, \dfrac{p}{q}, a^2 + b^2$ etc. are all algebraic expressions.

3. **Term :** *The various parts of an algebraic expression connected by $+$ or $-$ sign are called terms of the expression.*

For example : $2x + 4y^2 - 3z$ has three terms namely $+2x, +4y^2, -3z$; $2xy - 4y^2$ has two terms namely $+2xy$ and $-4y^2$.

4. **Like terms and Unlike terms :** *The terms having the same literal factors are called like terms and those having different literal factors are called unlike terms.*

For example : $-6x^2y$ and $4yx^2$ are like terms whereas

$2xy, -3x^2y, 4xy^2$ are unlike terms.

5. **Coefficients :** The numerical part is called the **numerical coefficient** and literal part or the variable part is called the **literal coefficient**.

For example : In $24xy$, 24 is the numerical coefficient and xy is the literal coefficient.

15.2 Types of Algebraic Expressions

(i) **Monomials :** Expressions with a single term are called monomials.

For example : $-3xy, 4y^2, 2z$ are all monomials.

(ii) **Binomials :** Expressions with two terms are called binomials.

For example : $4x + 3y, 2x^2y - 4y, a + \dfrac{1}{a}$ etc. are binomials.

(iii) **Trinomials :** Expressions with three terms are called trinomials.

For example : $2x + 4y - 3z, 4x^2y + 6xy - \dfrac{7y}{x}$ are trinomials.

(iv) **Multinomials :** Expressions with two or more terms are called multinomials.

15.3 Polynomials

1. **Polynomial in one variable :** An algebraic expression of the form $a + bx + cx^2 + dx^3$, where a, b, c and d are constants and x is a variable is called a polynomial. **The powers of the variable involved are non-negative integers.**

   The degree of the polynomial is the greatest power of the variable present in the polynomial.

For example : $6 + 8a$ is a polynomial of degree 1 and $4x^3 - 2x + 3$ is a polynomial of degree 3.

2. **Polynomial in two or more variables :** It is an algebraic expression involving two or more variables with non-negative integral powers :

   In such a polynomial, the degree of any term is the sum of the powers of the variables in that term. The greatest sum is the degree of the polynomial.

For example : (i) $4x + 4y^2 + 4xy$ is a polynomial in x and y and its degree is 2.

(ii) $11x^2y^2 + 4xy - 2xy^2$ is a polynomial in x and y of degree 4.

Note : Terms where the powers of the variable are negative, i.e., x^{-1} or $\dfrac{1}{x}, \dfrac{1}{y^2}, \dfrac{x}{y}, \dfrac{x^2}{y}$ do not make a polynomial.

EXERCISE 15 (a)

1. **State the coefficient and degree of each expression if it is a monomial.**

   (a) 37   (**Ans.** a constant monomial of degree 0)

   (b) $\dfrac{2x^2}{y}$ (**Ans.** not a monomial because of division by a variable)

   (c) 23   (d) $8y$ (e) $\dfrac{1}{5}pq$ (f) $-7m^2n$ (g) $\dfrac{5}{t^2}$ (h) c^2+13 (i) $\sqrt{7}d^3$

2. **Select like monomials in each polynomial, if any :**

   (a) $7 - 3x + 5$ (b) $x + y + 2x - z$ (c) $a+2b - c+b$ (d) $2xy-5xz+4yz-yz,$

   (e) $5pqr + 2qrs + 7pqr - 3prs$ (f) $mn^2 + m^2n^2 - 2m^2n + 6m^2n,$

   (g) $2ab^2c^2-7a^2bc+9a^2b^2c^2+8a^2bc^2$ (h) $8(e + f) - 3(e + f) + 5(e - f)$

3. **State the degree of each polynomial.**

   (a) $x^2 + x^3 - 5x +2$ (b) $5 + 2y + y^2$ (c) $2a^2 + 4b^8$ (d) $7x^2y^6 + x^5$ (e) $2x^7 + 11 + x - 2x^{10}$

4. **Tell whether the given polynomial is a monomial, binomial, trinomial, or one of these. Then state the degree and the coefficients of the polynomial.**

   (i) $5c^2d$ (ii) $5c^2 + d$ (iii) $8p^2 - 2p + 4$ (iv) $3q + 7q^3 - 5q^2$ (v) $6abc - 5a^2b^2c^2$

   (vi) $- 6a^3 + 2a^2b - ab^2 + 9b^3$

5. **Arrange the given polynomial in order of decreasing degree in x.**

   (i) $3x + x^2 - 7$ (ii) $9x^2-2x^4+8-5x^3$ (iii) $x^2y - 3y^3 + 4x^3 - 2xy^2$ (iv) $3x^2y^2 - 8xy^3 + x^4 - y^4 + 2x^3y$

6. **Evaluate if $a =2, b = 1$ and $c = 10$.**

   (i) a^3 (ii) $(3b)^2$ (iii) $(a + b)^2,$ (iv) $(c - 3)^2$ (v) $\left(\dfrac{1}{2}c\right)^3$

   (vi) $\dfrac{4a^3}{b}$ (vii) $7(a^2 - b^2)$ (viii) $3b(a^3 - c^2)$ (ix) $a^2 + b^2 + c^2$ (x) $(a + b + c)^2$

OPERATIONS ON DECIMAL NUMBERS

15.4 Addition and Subtraction of Monomials (Like Terms)

Method : 1. *To add like monomials, add the numerical coefficients and retain the common literal coefficient.*

2. *To subtract like monomials, subtract the numerical coefficients and retain common literal coefficient.*

Examples : 1. $3x + 4x = (3 + 4)x = 7x.$

2. $5ab + 7ab + 12ab = 24ab.$

3. $3x^2y - 2x^2y + 4x^2y = (3 - 2 + 4) x^2y = 5x^2y.$

4. $\dfrac{1}{3} abc + \dfrac{2}{5} abc = \left(\dfrac{1}{3} + \dfrac{2}{5}\right) abc = \left(\dfrac{5 + 6}{15}\right) abc = \dfrac{11}{15} abc.$

After some practice, students should be able to add or subtract the numerical coefficients mentally.

5. $7y^2z - 5y^2z = 2y^2z.$

15.5 Addition of Polynomials

Ex. 1. *Add : 5a – 3b and 2a + 7b.*

Method : **Step1 :** *Arrange polynomials in order under one another placing like terms in the same column.*

Step 2 : *Add like terms.*

Sol.
$$5a - 3b$$
$$\underline{2a + 7b}$$
The sum is : $\qquad$ $7a + 4b$

Ex. 2. *Add : 4x – 7x² + 8 and 5 + 8x² – 13x.*

Sol. Re-arrange the terms of each polynomial in order of decreasing powers of x and line up like terms in a vertical column.

$$-7x^2 + 4x + 8$$
$$\underline{8x^2 - 13x + 5}$$
The sum is : $\qquad$ $x^2 - 9x + 13$

Ex. 3. *Add 4a – 7c + 5b,   3a + 13c, – 9b + 5c.*

Sol. Re-arrange in alphabetical order and line up like terms vertically. Notice that places for terms which are missing are left blank.

$$4a + 5b - 7c$$
$$3a \qquad\quad + 13c$$
$$\underline{\qquad - 9b + 5c}$$
The sum is : $\qquad$ $7a - 4b + 11c$

Instead of adding vertically, we may add polynomials horizontally also. This is shown below.

Ex. 4. *Add : – 5x² + 6xy – 18y², 2xy + 7x² + y², 10y² – x² + 1.*

Sol. The sum is

$(-5x^2 + 6xy - 18y^2) + (2xy + 7x^2 + y^2) + (10y^2 - x^2 + 1)$

$= (-5x^2 + 7x^2 - x^2) + (6xy + 2xy) + (-18y^2 + y^2 + 10y^2) + 1$ $\qquad$ Collecting like terms together

$= x^2 + 8xy - 7y^2 + 1.$

15.6 Subtraction of Polynomials

Method : Step 1. *Arrange polynomials in order in columns, placing like terms in the same column and the minuend above the subtrahend.*

     Step 2. *Subtract like terms. To do this, change the sign of each term of the subtrahend polynomial and add.*

Ex. 5. *Subtract $4a - 3b$ from $3a + 8b$.*

Sol.

$$3a + 8b \quad\quad \textbf{Minuend}$$
$$4a - 3b \quad\quad \textbf{Subtrahend}$$
$$\underline{\quad -\ \ +\quad}$$

Place the new signs below the old signs of the terms of the subtrahend.

The difference is $-a + 11b$

Ex. 6. *Find the difference of $3x^2 + 8 - 5x$ and $-2x^2 + 3x - 13$.*

Sol.

$$3x^2 - 5x + \ 8$$
$$-\ 2x^2 + 3x - 13$$
$$\underline{+\quad -\quad +\quad\quad}$$
$$5x^2 - 8x\ + 21$$

The difference is

■ **Horizontal Method :**

$3x^2 + 8 - 5x - (-2x^2 + 3x - 13)$

$= 3x^2 + 8 - 5x + 2x^2 - 3x + 13.$

$= 3x^2 + 2x^2 - 5x - 3x + 8 + 13$

$= 5x^2 - 8x + 21.$

1. *Enclose the subtrahend in brackets and put a '−' sign before it outside the bracket.*

2. *Remove the bracket. You know that signs of all the terms inside the bracket will change.*

3. *Put like terms together.*

   Remark : After sufficient practice. You should be able to do step 3 mentally.

EXERCISE 15 (b)

(A)

Add :

1. $7xy, 2xy, 9xy$ **2.** $4a, 5a, -3a, -2a$ **3.** $-70mn, -30mn, 12mn$ **4.** $4.3x^2y, -2.4x^2y, 5.4x^2y$

5. $\dfrac{4}{5}y^3z, \dfrac{-2}{3}y^3z, \dfrac{1}{2}y^3z, \dfrac{1}{4}y^3z$

Subtract :

6. $3x$ from $7x$ **7.** $\dfrac{4}{5}x^2y$ from $\dfrac{7}{5}x^2y$ **8.** $-6xy$ from $11xy$ **9.** $-2a$ from $-9a$ **10.** $-9m^2n^2$ from $-6m^2n^2$.

(B)

Add :

1. $4a - 5b$ **12.** $p^2 + 2pq$ **13.** $4a^2 + 6a - 7$
    $\underline{4a + 7b}$ $\underline{3p^2 - 5pq}$ $-a^2 \quad\quad +11$
                                                                     $\underline{5a^2 - 3a + 2}$

4. $a^2 - 6ab + 8b^2, 2a^2 - 4ab + b^2, -5a^2 + 13ab - 10b^2$

5. $x^4 + 4x^3 - 2x - 1, 6x^3 - 4x^2 + 5x + 6, 3 + 7x^2 - 9x$

16. $5x^2 + 8x - 4$, $11 - 4x + 3x^2$, $-3x + 6 - 4x^2$

Try to add without writing in colums. Simplify.

17. $8x^2 - 4x + 6 - 4x^3 - 6x + 11 - 2x^2 - 9x^3$

18. $4xy - \dfrac{2}{3}x + \dfrac{4}{5}y - \dfrac{1}{3}x + 6xy - 4x + 2y - 6xy$

Subtract :

19.	$8x + 9$	**20.**	$6r - 11s$	**21.**	$5a + 3b$	**22.**	$4x^2 + 7x - 18$
	$\underline{5x + 4}$		$\underline{-2r + 3s}$		$\underline{6a - b}$		$\underline{2x^2 - 4x - 15}$

23. $a - b + c$ from $2a + b - c$.　　　　**24.** $x^2 - 2xy + y^2$ from $x^2 + 2xy + y^2$.

25. $x^2 - 3x - 3$ from $x - 3 - x^2 + x^3$.

26. Subtract the sum of $3a - 4b + 5c$ and $-5a + 7b - 9c$ from $a - b - c$.

27. The perimeter of a triangle is $6a + 5b - 2c$. If two sides are $a - b + 6c$ and $3a + 6b - 10c$, find the thir
side.

Simplify :

28. (i) $(5x - 2y) - (-3x - y)$.　　　　(ii) $-(-3m - 2) - (-8m - 7)$.

29. $\{(5x^2 - 8xy - 11y^2) - (7x^2 - 2xy + 5y^2)\} + (2x^2 - 23xy - 10y^2)$.

30. What must be added to $2a^3 - 4a + 5$ to get $7a^3 - 4a^2 + 11a - 6$?

15.7 Multiplication

Recollect the following rules for the multiplication of positive and negative numbers.

Rule	Illustration	
$(+x) \times (+y) = (+xy)$	$(+5) \times (+3) = +15$	Product is positive
$(-x) \times (-y) = (+xy)$	$(-5) \times (-3) = +15$	
$(+x) \times (-y) = (-xy)$	$(+5) \times (-3) = -15$	Product is negative
$(-x) \times (+y) = (-xy)$	$(-5) \times (+3) = -15$	

Remember that $x^m \times x^n = x^{m+n}$ where x is a literal and m & n are positive integers.

15.8 Multiplication of Monomials

* To multiply monomials (i) *Multiply numerical coefficients* (ii) *Multiply literal coefficien*
(iii) *Multiply the results.*

For example :

1. $4a^2b \times -6a^3b^2c$　　　　$= (4 \times -6) \times (a^2b \times a^3b^2c)$
　　　　　　　　　　　　　　$= -24a^5b^3c$

Method :
Think
$a^2 \times a^3 = a^{2+3} = a^5$
$b \times b^2 = b^{1+2} = b^3$

2. $\dfrac{-6}{8}x^4yz \times 24x^2y^2z^3 = \left(\dfrac{-6}{8} \times 24\right) \times \left(x^4yz \times x^2y^2z^3\right)$
　　　　　　　　　　　　　　　　$= -18x^6y^3z^4$.

Think
$x^4 \times x^2 = x^{4+2} = x^6$
$y \times y^2 = y^{1+2} = y^3$
$z \times z^3 = z^{1+3} = z^4$

15.9 Multiplication of a Polynomial by a Binomial

Method : *Multiply each term of the polynomial by the monomial, and then add the products to get the resul*

For example :

(i) $-4x^2 \times (2x + 3y)$ $= (-4x^2 \times 2x) + (-4x^2 \times 3y) = -8x^3 - 12x^2y.$

(ii) $6a^2b^2 (a^2 - b^2 + ab)$ $= (6a^2b^2 \times a^2) + (6a^2b^2 \times -b^2) + (6a^2b^2 \times ab)$
$= 6a^4b^2 - 6a^2b^4 + 6a^3b^3.$

15.10 Multiplication of Two Polynomials

Method : _To multiply any two polynomials, multiply each term of one polynomial by each term of the other. Finally add the products combining like terms together._

Ex. 1. _Multiply $(4x - 9y)$ and $(3x + 11y)$._

Sol. Horizontal Method :

$(4x - 9y)(3x + 11y) = 4x(3x + 11y) - 9y(3x + 11y)$
$= 12x^2 + 44xy - 27xy - 99y^2$
$= 12x^2 + 17xy - 99y^2.$

Column Method :

$$
\begin{array}{r}
4x - 9y \\
3x + 11y \\
\hline
12x^2 - 27xy \\
44xy - 99y^2 \\
\hline
12x^2 + 17xy - 99y^2
\end{array}
$$

> First, multiply $4x - 9y$ by $3x$
> Next, multiply $4x - 9y$ by $11y$
> Finally, add like terms.

Ex. 2. _Find the product $(a - 2b)(a^2 + 4ab - b^2)$._

Sol.   Horizontal Method :

$(a - 2b)(a^2 + 4ab - b^2)$
$= a(a^2 + 4ab - b^2) - 2b(a^2 + 4ab - b^2)$
$= a^3 + 4a^2b - ab^2 - 2a^2b - 8ab^2 + 2b^3$
$= a^3 + 4a^2b - 2a^2b - ab^2 - 8ab^2 + 2b^3$
$= a^3 + 2a^2b - 9ab^2 + 2b^3.$

> Combining like terms together

Column Method :

$$
\begin{array}{r}
a^2 + 4ab - b^2 \\
a - 2b \\
\hline
a^3 + 4a^2b - ab^2 \\
- 2a^2b - 8ab^2 + 2b^3 \\
\hline
a^3 + 2a^2b - 9ab^2 + 2b^3
\end{array}
$$

> 1. Multiply by a
> 2. Multiply by $-2b$
> 3. Add.

Note : Students should now try to attempt multiplication problems by horizontal method.

Ex. 3. _Simplify : $(x^2 - 4xy - 4y^2)(2x^2 + 8xy + 2y^2)$._

Sol. $(x^2 - 4xy - 4y^2)(2x^2 + 8xy + 2y^2)$
$= x^2(2x^2 + 8xy + 2y^2) - 4xy(2x^2 + 8xy + 2y^2) - 4y^2(2x^2 + 8xy + 2y^2)$
$= 2x^4 + 8x^3y + 2x^2y^2 - 8x^3y - 32x^2y^2 - 8xy^3 - 8x^2y^2 - 32xy^3 - 8y^4$
$= 2x^4 - 38x^2y^2 - 40xy^3 - 8y^4.$

Ex. 4. _Simplify : $(a + 1)(a + 2)(a + 3)$._

Sol. $(a + 1)(a + 2)(a + 3) = (a + 1)\{(a + 2)(a + 3)\}$

$$= (a + 1) \{a (a + 3) + 2 (a + 3)\} = (a + 1) \{a^2 + 3a + 2a + 6\}$$
$$= (a + 1) \{a^2 + 5a + 6\}$$
$$= a (a^2 + 5a + 6) + 1 (a^2 + 5a + 6)$$
$$= a^3 + 5a^2 + 6a + a^2 + 5a + 6$$
$$= a^3 + 6a^2 + 11a + 6.$$

EXERCISE 15 (c)

1. **Find the product of :**

   (i) $- 6x^2y$ and $7x^3y^3$.

   (ii) $- 4\, abc, - 6\, a^2bc^3$ and $2a^3b^4c^3$.

   (iii) $4a, 5b, - 6ab$.

   (iv) $\dfrac{-3}{5}x^2, \dfrac{15}{6}y^2x^2$ and $\dfrac{4}{7}x^2y^2z^2$.

2. **Multiply :**

   (i) $(3x - 6y)$ by $7a^2b$.

   (ii) $(4a^2 - 7b^3)$ by $- 6a^2b$.

   (iii) $\left(\dfrac{2}{5}x^2y^2 - \dfrac{3}{7}x^3 + 4y^3\right)$ by $35x^2y^2z^2$.

   (iv) $(6x^3 - 4x^2 + 2x - 8)$ by $- 3x^4$.

   Find the following products :

3. (i) $(2x + 3y)(4x - 9y)$.

   (ii) $(- 11x^2 + 2xy + 9y^2)(6x + 3y)$.

   (iii) $(5a^2 - 6ab - 7b^2)(- 2a^2 + 3b^2)$.

   (iv) $\left(\dfrac{1}{5}x^2 - \dfrac{1}{6}y^2\right)(5x^2 + 6y^2)$.

4. (i) $(x^2 - 2xy - 9y^2)(x^2 + 9xy - 11y^2)$.

   (ii) $(6 + 3x - x^2)(2x^2 - 5)$.

   (iii) $\left(\dfrac{4}{5}x^2 + y\right)\left(\dfrac{4}{5}x^2 + y\right)$.

   (iv) $\left(p - \dfrac{2}{3}q\right)\left(p + \dfrac{2}{3}q\right)$.

5. Find the product of $(3a^2b + 4a)$ and $(ab + a^2)$ and verify the result for $a = 2$ and $b = 1$.

6. **Find the product :**

   (i) $4x^2 \times (2x - 3y) \times 4xy \times (x + 4y)$.

   (ii) $3a^2b^2 \times (3a^2 - b) \times 4b \times (4a^2 + 2b)$.

Simplify :

7. (i) $6a^2 + 2a(4a + 3b) - 12ab$

   (ii) $4x^3y + 7x^2y \times (3x - 4y) + 2xy (-3x^2 + 2y$

8. $(4a - 3b + 11c)(a + b) - (16b - 13c + 2a)(a - c)$.   9. $(x^2 - 1)(x + 1)(x + 2)(x - 4)$.

10. $(3x - 4)(2x^2 - 5x + 1) - (2x - 1)(3x^2 + 7x - 5)$.

15.11 Division of Algebraic Expressions

For a variable x

$x^m \div x^n = x^{m-n}$ where m, n are positive integers and $m > n$.

Also, $x^0 \times \dfrac{x^n}{x^n} = \dfrac{x^{0+n}}{x^n} = \dfrac{x^n}{x^n} = 1 \Rightarrow x^0 = 1.$

15.12 Division of a Monomial by a Monomial

To divide a monomial by a monomial :

(i) *Divide the numerical coefficients,*   (ii) *Divide the literal coefficients,*   (iii) *Multiply the result.*

Ex. 1. *Divide* $-42x^4y^3z$ *by* $6x^2y^2z$.

Sol. $(-42x^4y^3z) \div 6x^2y^2z = \dfrac{-42x^4y^3z}{6x^2y^2z}$

$$= \left(\dfrac{-42}{6}\right) \times \left(\dfrac{x^4y^3z}{x^2y^2z}\right)$$

$$= -7x^{4-2}\,y^{3-2}\,z^{1-1}$$

$$= -7x^2yz^0 = -7xy^2. \quad \boxed{\text{Since } z^0 = 1}$$

Ex. 2. *Divide* $-28a^3b^2c^2$ *by* $-16a^4b^3c$.

Sol. $(-28a^3b^2c^2) \div (-16a^4b^3c)$

$$= \dfrac{-28a^3b^2c^2}{-16a^4b^3c} = \left(\dfrac{-28}{-16}\right) \times \left(\dfrac{a^3b^2c^2}{a^4b^3c}\right)$$

$$= \dfrac{7}{4} \times \dfrac{c^{2-1}}{a^{4-3}b^{3-2}} = \dfrac{7}{4} \times \dfrac{c}{ab} = \dfrac{7c}{4ab}.$$

15.13 Division of a Polynomial by a Monomial

Method : *Divide each term of the polynomial by the monomial.*

Ex. 1. *Divide* $3a^3 - 4a^2 + 5a$ *by* $3a$.

Sol. $(3a^3 - 4a^2 + 5a) \div 3a = \dfrac{3a^3}{3a} - \dfrac{4a^2}{3a} + \dfrac{5a}{3a} = a^2 - \dfrac{4}{3}a + \dfrac{5}{3}.$

Ex. 2. *Divide* $-12x^2y^2 + 4x^3y + 5xy - 9xy^3$ *by* $-4x$.

Sol. $(-12x^2y^2 + 4x^3y + 5xy - 9xy^3) \div (-4x) = \dfrac{-12x^2y^2}{-4x} + \dfrac{4x^3y}{-4x} + \dfrac{5xy}{-4x} - \dfrac{9xy^3}{-4x}$

$$= 3xy^2 - x^2y - \dfrac{5}{4}y + \dfrac{9}{4}y^3.$$

15.14 Division of Polynomials

Ex.1. *Divide* $2x^2 - 11x + 12$ *by* $x - 4$.

Method :

1. Set up as a form of long division in which the polynomials are arranged in descending order, leaving space for missing terms.

2. Divide the first term of the dividend $(2x^2)$ by the first term of the divisior (x) and write the quotient above the line.

3. Multiply the first term of the quotient $(2x)$ by each term of the divisor $(x - 4)$ and write the product below the dividend.

4. Subtract like terms and bring down one or more terms as needed.

5. Now use the remainder $-3x + 12$ as the new dividend and repeat steps 2 to 4.

6. Stop when the remainder becomes zero or when there is no term in the remainder into which the first term of the divisor will divide evenly.

Sol. *(By Steps)*

Step 1. $x - 4\overline{)2x^2 - 11x + 12}$

Step 2. $x - 4\overline{)2x^2 - 11x + 12}^{\;2x}$

Step 3.
$$x - 4\overline{)2x^2 - 11x + 12}^{\;2x}$$
$$2x^2 - 8x$$

Step 4.
$$\underline{-\quad\quad +}$$
$$-3x + 12$$

Step 5.
$$x - 4\overline{)-3x + 12}^{\;-3}$$
$$\underline{-3x + 12}$$
$$\underline{+\quad\quad -}$$
$$0$$

Step 6. No further steps are needed.

Full Solution

$$\begin{array}{r} 2x - 3 \\ x - 4 \overline{)\,2x^2 - 11x + 12} \\ 2x^2 - 8x \\ \underline{-\quad +\qquad} \\ -3x + 12 \\ -3x + 12 \\ \underline{\qquad\qquad} \\ 0 \end{array}$$

Verification :
Divisor × quotient + remainder
$= (x-4)\,(2x-3) + 0$
$= 2x^2 - 11x + 12 = $ Dividend
Hence, our solution is correct.

Remark: You know that if a number is divided by another number, then

Dividend = Divisor × Quotient + Remainder

Similarly, if a polynomial is divided by another polynomial, then

Dividend = Divisor × Quotient + Remainder

You can use the above relation to check the result of division.

Ex.2. *Divide $6x^3 - x + 19x^2 - 29$ by $2x + 3$ and verify the result.*

Sol. First arrange the dividend in descending powers of x.

$$\begin{array}{r} 3x^2 + 5x - 8 \\ 2x + 3 \overline{)\,6x^3 + 19x^2 - x - 29} \\ 6x^3 + 9x^2 \\ \underline{-\qquad -\qquad\qquad} \\ 10x^2 - x \\ 10x^2 + 15x \\ \underline{-\qquad -\qquad\qquad} \\ -16x - 29 \\ -16x - 24 \\ \underline{+\qquad +\qquad} \\ -5 \end{array}$$

Verification :
Divisor × quotient + remainder
$= (2x + 3)\,(3x^2 + 5x - 8) + (-5)$
$= 2x\,(3x^2 + 5x - 8) + 3\,(3x^2 + 5x - 8) - 5$
$= 6x^3 + 10x^2 - 16x + 9x^2 + 15x - 24 - 5$
$= 6x^3 + (10x^2 + 9x^2) + (-16x + 15x) - 29$
$= 6x^3 + 19x^2 - x - 29 = $ Dividend
Hence, the result is correct.

The quotient is $3x^2 + 5x - 8$ with a remainder of -5.

Ex. 3. *Divide $x^3 - 8$ by $x - 2$, $x \neq 2$.*

Sol.
$$\begin{array}{r} x - 2 \overline{)\,x^3 \qquad\qquad - 8}\,(\,x^2 + 2x + 4 \\ x^3 - 2x^2 \\ \underline{-\quad +\qquad} \\ 2x^2 \\ 2x^2 - 4x \\ \underline{-\quad +\qquad} \\ 4x - 8 \\ 4x - 8 \\ \underline{-\quad +\qquad} \\ 0 \end{array}$$

$\therefore$ Quotient $= \boldsymbol{x^2 + 2x + 4}$

Remarks : If one or more terms are missing in the dividend, be sure to leave a blank space for each such term.

$x \neq 2$, because $x - 2 = 0$ for $x = 2$ and division by zero is not allowed.

EXERCISE 15 (d)

(A)

Divide :

1. (i) $6x^2$ by $3x$.   (ii) $-9a^3$ by a^2.   (iii) $-48x^2yz$ by $-60xy^2z^3$.   (iv) $a^2b^3c^4$ by $-9a^4b^5c$.

2. (i) $\dfrac{2}{3}x^2$ by x.   (ii) $\left(\dfrac{3}{5}a^3b^2\right)$ by $\dfrac{-9}{10}ab$.   (iii) $\dfrac{-8}{9}x^4y^3$ by $-\dfrac{4}{27}x^3y^2$.

(B)

Divide :

3. $(a + 2a^3 + 3a^4)$ by $2a$.   **4.** $25x^3y + 15x^2y^2 - 10xy$ by $5xy$.   **5.** $(y^4 - 3y^3 + \dfrac{1}{2}y^2)$ by $3y$.

6. $(14x^2yz - 28x^2y^2z^3 + 32y^2z^2)$ by $-4xy$.   **7.** $(20a^3 - 16a^2b + 4b^2)$ by $4a^2b^2$.

(C)

Divide :

8. $a^2 + 6a + 5$ by $a + 1$ **9.** $x^2 + 7x + 6$ by $x + 6$ **10.** $x^2 - 3x + 2$ by $x - 1$

11. $x^2 + 4x - 21$ by $x + 7$ **12.** $13x^2 + 22x - 8$ by $x + 2$ **13.** $14 - 17x + 5x^2$ by $2 - x$

Divide and verify the result in each case.

14. $x^3 + 3 - 4x + 2x^2$ by $x - 2$.   **15.** $x^4 + 4x - 2x^2 + x^3 - 10$ by $x - 2$.

16. $x^3 - 4x^2 - 25x + 70$ by $x - 6$.   **17.** $8x^2 + 21x + x^3 + 18$ by $6 + 5x + x^2$.

15.15 Removal of Brackets

You have learnt how to insert a bracket. Just as $a + b - c$ can be written as $a + (b - c)$, similarly $a + (b - c)$ can be written as $a + b - c$. And just as $a - b + c$ can be written as $a - (b - c)$; similarly, $a - (b - c)$ can be written as $a - b + c$.

> **Rule 1.** _A bracket with a + sign before it may be removed without changing the sign of any term within it._

Thus, $5a + (+ 2a - 8) = 5a + 2a - 8 = 7a - 8.$

> **Rule 2.** _A bracket with a '–' sign before it may be removed by changing the sign of every term within the bracket._

Thus, $5x - (2x - 9) = 5x - 2x + 9 = 3x + 9.$

     $7a^2 - (-a^2 - 2a + 3) = 7a^2 + a^2 + 2a - 3 = 8a^2 + 2a - 3.$

> **Rule 3.** _A bracket with a term before it may be removed by multiplying each term in the bracket by the term before it._

Thus, $2x + 3(x - 7) = 2x + 3x - 21 = 5x - 21$

> **Rule 4.** _When different types of brackets are used in a single expression, remove one type at a time beginning with the innermost one._

Ex. 1 Simplify : $3x + 2 - [2x - \{x - 3(5x - 4)\}].$

Sol.   Given expression $= 3x + 2 - [2x - \{x - 15x + 12\}]$

                        $= 3x + 2 - [2x - x + 15x - 12]$

                        $= 3x + 2 - 2x + x - 15x + 12 = -\mathbf{13x + 14.}$

EXERCISE 15 (e)

Remove brackets and simplify if possible, by collecting like terms :

1. $7 + (a - 2)$ **2.** $5 + 2(a - 1)$ **3.** $6a - (8a + 3)$

4. $3x - 4(x + 7)$ **5.** $p - 3 (p - q)$ **6.** $-(x-3)-2(x + 6)$

7. $3a - (b+5) + 2(a-b)$ **8.** $m - 2(m + 3) + 5(m - 1)$ **9.** $a(a - b) - b(b - a)$

10. $2x - \{7 - 3(x + 10) + x\}$ **11.** $(b^2 - c^2) - [b^2 - b(5b + c) + c^2]$

LOOKING BACK
Summary of Key Facts

1. A symbol having a fixed value is called a constant.
2. A symbol which takes different values is called a variable, also called a literal.
3. An algebraic expression is a combination of literals and variables connected by $+, -. \times, \div$.
4. Several parts of an algebraic expression connected by + or – sign are called **terms** of the expression.
5. Terms having same literal factors are called **like terms**, otherwise they are called **unlike terms.**
6. An algebraic expression with a single term is called a monomial, with two terms a **binomial** and with three terms a **trinomal.**
7. A **polynomial** is an algebraic expression where the powers of the variable involved are non-negative.
8. The highest power of the variable in a polynomial is called its degree.
9. For addition or subtraction of two or more algebraic expressions first we collect like terms and then find the sum or difference of the numerical coefficients of these terms.
10. For multiplication of:
    (a) **Monomial by monomial:** multiply the numercial coefficients and multiply the literal factors and then find the product.
    (b) **Polynomial by monomial:** multiply each term of the polynomial by the monomial and then simplify.
    (c) **Polynomial by polynomial:** multiply each term of one polynomial with each term of the other polynomid and simplify.
11. **For division of:**
    (a) Two monomials = (Quotient of their numercial coefficients) × (Quotient of their literal coefficients)
    (b) Polynomial by a monomial : Divide each term of the polynomial by the monomial.
    The result of division of a polynomial by polynomial can be checked using the formula.

dividend = divisor × quotient + remainder.

MENTAL MATHS - 13

Simplify:

1. $7a + 5a$ **2.** $-6m - 15m$

3. $4x - 10y + 7x + 3y$

4. $-3abc - 5cab - 7bca$

5. $5t - 2(t - 4)$

Find the product :

6. $3a^3$ and $5a^2$

7. $11ab$ and $-5abc$

8. $(a^{1000}) (b^{9999}) (abc) (0)$

9. $(x^3) (x^{20}) (x^{17}) (x^{60}) (x^0)$

10. $7a(2a + 3)$

11. $5x(2x^2 - 7xy^2)$

Simplify :

12. $(x + 5) (x + 6)$

13. $b^2 r^3 \div br^2$

14. $(12a^2b^2c + 16abc) \div 4ab$.

15. $18a^3b^3c^3 \div 9a^3c^4$.

ANSWERS

EXERCISE 15 (a)

1. (a) Degree 0; no coefficient as there is no variable.   (c) Degree 0; no coefficient .   (d) Degee 1, coefficient 8,

(e) Coefficient $\frac{1}{5}$, degree 2   (f) Coefficient— 7, degree 3   (g) Not a monomial as division by t^2 is involved.

(h) Not a monomial as there are 2 terms. It is a binomial.   (i) Coefficient $\sqrt{7}$, degree 3.

2. (a) 7, 5   (b) $x, 2x$ (c) $2b, b$ (d) $4yz, -yz$ (e) 5 pqr, 7 pqr (f) $-2\,m^2n, 6m^2n$ (g) None

(h) $8e, -3e, 5e$, and $8f, -3f, -5f$

3. (a) 3   (b) 2   (c) 8   (d) 8   (e) 10.

4. (i) Monomial of degree 3; coeffeient 5,   (ii) Binomial of degree 2; coefficients 5 and 1,

(iii) Trinomal of degree 2; coefficients 8, –2 and 4   (iv) Trinomial of degree 3; coefficient3, 7 and –5

(v) Binomial of degree 6; coefficients 6 and –5

(vi) None of these. Polynomial of a degree 3; coefficients are –6, 2, –1, and 9.

5. (i) $x^2 + 3x - 7$ (ii) $-2x^4 - 5x^3 + 9x^2 + 8.$ (iii) $4x^3 + x^2y - 2xy^2 - 3y^3.$

(iv) $x^4 + 2x^3y + 3x^2y^2 - 8xy^3 - y^4.$

6. (i) 8   (ii) 9   (iii) 9   (iv) 49   (v) 125   (vi) 32   (vii) 21   (viii) –276   (ix) 105   (x) 169.

EXERCISE 15 (b)

(A)

1. $18xy$ 2. $4a$ 3. $-88\,mn$ 4. $7.3x^2y$ 5. $\frac{53}{60}y^3z$ 6. $4x$ 7. $\frac{3}{5}x^2y$ 8. $17xy$ 9. $-7a$ 10. $3m^2n^2$

(B)

11. $8a + 2b$ 12. $4p^2 - 3pq$ 13. $8a^2 + 3a + 6$ 14. $-2a^2 + 3ab - b^2$ 15. $x^4 + 10x^3 + 3x^2 - 6x + 8$ 16. $4x^2 + x + 13$

17. $-13x^3 + 6x^2 - 10x + 17$ 18. $4xy - 5x + \frac{14}{5}y$

(C)

19. $3x + 5$ 20. $8r - 14s$ 21. $-a + 4b$ 22. $2x^2 + 11x - 3$ 23. $a + 2b - 2c$ 24. $4xy$ 25. $x^3 - 2x^2 + 4x$

26. $3a - 4b + 3c$ 27. $2a + 2c$ 28. (i) $8x - y$ (ii) $11m + 9$ 29. $-29xy - 26y^2$ 30. $5a^3 - 4a^2 + 15a - 11$

EXERCISE 15 (c)

1. (i) $-42x^5y^4$ (ii) $+48\,a^6b^6c^7$ (iii) $-120a^2b^2$ (iv) $\frac{-6}{7}x^6y^4z^2$

2. (i) $21a^2bx - 42a^2by$ (ii) $-24a^4b + 42a^2b^4$ (iii) $14x^4y^4z^2 - 15x^5y^2z^2 + 140x^2y^5z^2$ (iv) $-18x^7 + 12x^6 - 6x^5 + 24x^4$

3. (i) $8x^2 - 6xy - 27y^2$ (ii) $-66x^3 - 21x^2y + 60xy^2 + 27y^3$ (iii) $-10a^4 + 12a^3b + 29a^2b^2 - 18ab^3 - 21b^4$ (iv) $x^4 + \frac{11}{30}x^2y^2 - y^4$

4. (i) $x^4 + 7x^3y - 38x^2y^2 - 59xy^3 + 99y^4$ (ii) $-2x^4 + 6x^3 + 17x^2 - 15x - 30$ (iii) $\frac{16}{25}x^4 + \frac{8}{5}x^2y + y^2$ (iv) $p^2 - \frac{4}{9}q^2$

5. $3a^3b^2 + 4a^2b + 3a^4b + 4a^3$ 6. (i) $32x^5y + 80x^4y^2 - 192x^3y^3$ (ii) $144a^6b^3 + 24a^4b^4 - 24a^2b^5$

7. (i) $14a^2 - 6ab$ (ii) $19x^3y - 28x^2y^2 + 4xy^2$ 8. $2a^2 - 3b^2 - 13c^2 - 15ab + 26ac + 27bc$ 9. $x^5 - x^4 - 11x^3 - 7x^2 + 10x + 8$

10. $-34x^2 + 40x - 9$

EXERCISE 15 (d)

(A)

1. (i) $2x$ (ii) $-9a$ (iii) $\frac{4x}{5yz^2}$ (iv) $\frac{-c^3}{9a^2b^2}$ 2. (i) $\frac{2}{3}x$ (ii) $\frac{-2}{3}a^2b$ (iii) $6xy$

(B)

3. $\frac{1}{2} + a^2 + \frac{3}{2}a^3$ 4. $5x^2 + 3xy - 2$ 5. $\frac{y^3}{3} - y^2 + \frac{1}{6}y$ 6. $-\frac{7}{2}xz + 7xyz^3 - \frac{8yz^2}{x}$ 7. $\frac{5a}{b^2} - \frac{4}{b} + \frac{1}{a^2}$ 8. $a + 5$

9. $x + 1$ 10. $x - 2$ 11. $x - 3$ 12. $13x - 4$ 13. $7 - 5x$ 14. $x^2 + 4x + 4$; R 11

15. $x^3 + 3x^2 + 4x + 12$; R 14   16. $x^2 + 2x - 13$; R (–8)   17. $x + 3$

EXERCISE 15 (e)

1. $a + 5$ 2. $2a + 3$ 3. $-2a - 3$ 4. $-x - 28$ 5. $-2p + 3q$ 6. $-3x - 9$ 7. $5a - 3b - 5$

8. $4m - 11$ 9. $a^2 - b^2$ 10. $4x + 23$ 11. $5b^2 + bc - 2c^2$

MENTAL MATHS–13

1. $12a$ 2. $-21m$ 3. $11x - 7y$ 4. $-15abc$ 5. $3t + 8$ 6. $15a^5$ 7. $-55a^2b^2c$

8. 0 9. x^{100} 10. $14a^2 + 21a$ 11. $10x^3 - 35x^2y^2$ 12. $x^2 + 11x + 30$ 13. br 14. $3\,abc + 4c$

15. $\frac{2b^3}{c}$

FUN WITH MATHS

PUZZLERS

1. Seven rupee coins have been placed on a paper as shown. By drawing only three straight lines, separate all the coins.

2. Write down the longest possible number using only two digits.

Fig. Q. 1

ANSWERS

1.

2. $9^9 = (9 \times 9 \times 9 \times 9 \times 9 \times 9 \times 9 \times 9 \times 9)$

Fig. Ans- 1

16. Formula

16.1 Introduction

If the length of a rectangle is l cm and its breadth is b cm then its area which we call as A sq cm is $l \times b$ sq cm. In the language of algebra we write it as:

$$A = lb.$$

We call this statement $A = lb$ a formula. A formula expresses very briefly what it might take a whole paragraph to express in words.

> **Formula :** *A formula is an algebraic rule for calculating. It is written in the form of an equation by using variables and mathematical symbols:*

Some common examples are :

	Formula	Meaning of letters
Area of a square	$A = s^2$	A is the area, s is one side.
Perimeter of a rectangle	$P = 2l + 2b$	P is the perimeter, l is the length and b is the breadth.
Simple Interest	$I = \dfrac{PRT}{100}$	I is the interest, P is the principal, R is rate and T is time.
Volume of a cube	$V = a^3$	V is the volume, a is the length of one edge of the cube.
Motion or travel	$d = st$	d is the distance, s is the speed and t is the time.

16.2 Framing a Formula

To translate a statement of words into an equation using literals and symbols is called framing the formula.

Illustrations :

1. A number x increased by 7 equals 15.　　　　　　　　　　**Formula :** $x + 7 = 15$
2. The sum of two numbers x and y is z.　　　　　　　　　　**Formula :** $x + y = z$
3. Five times a number x decreased by 7 is equal to 11.　　　**Formula :** $5x - 7 = 11$
4. Area A of a triangle is one half the product of its base b and height h.　　**Formula :** $A = \dfrac{1}{2} bh.$

EXERCISE 16 (a)

Frame a formula for each of the following statements :

1. A is equal to a times the sum of b and c.
2. Twice s is equal to the sum of x and y, multiplied by t.
3. The volume V of a cuboid is the product of its length l, breadth b and height h.
4. The sum of x and y is 5 more than 7 times their difference. Take x greater than y.
5. Twice the sum (S) of the first n numbers in order (1, 2, 3, ... etc) is equal to the product of n and $n + 1$.
6. Area of a rhombus (A) is equal to one half the product of its diagonals d_1 and d_2.

157

7. Four-fifths of a number x decreased by two-thirds of itself is equal to 13.
8. Circumference C of a circle is equal to the product of π and its diameter d.
9. The speed S of a vehicle is equal to distance D divided by time T.
10. Sahil earns Rs x a week. He spends Rs y a month. Make a formula to show his saving Rs z in a year.
11. The mass M of a solid equals the product of its volume V and density D.
12. Work done W equals the product of force applied F and distance moved S.
13. Area of a circle A equals the product of π and square of its radius r.
14. **Derive a formula for each relationship :**
     (i) the number of seconds (s) in m minutes.
     (ii) the number of hours (h) in d days.
     (iii) the number of seconds (s) in h hours.
     (iv) the number of hours (h) in m minutes.
     (v) the number of hours (h) in w weeks
     (vi) the number of days (d) in M months of 30 days.
     (vii) the number of minutes m in h hours and 30 seconds.
    (viii) the number of days d in M months of 30 days, w weeks and
          5 days.

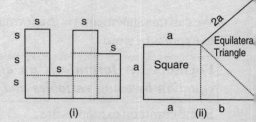

Fig : Q. 16

15. A plane flies x kilometres north then y kilometres east. Total distance it flies is d kilometers.
16. State the formula for the perimeter P of each figure:

16.3 Changing the Subject of a Formula

The **subject of a formula** is the variable that is expressed in terms of the other variables. Thus, in $p = 4s$, p is the subject of the formula. The subject can be changed.

Thus $p = 4s$ becomes $\frac{p}{4} = s$ or, $s = \frac{p}{4}$ when both sides are divided by 4. As you can see, by doing so, the subject has changed from p to s.

We solve a formula for a variable by transforming the formula so that the variable becomes the subject.

Consider the following examples:

1. $V = \dfrac{1}{3}Bh$ Gives V directly

   $\Rightarrow 3V = Bh$

   $\Rightarrow \dfrac{3V}{h} = B$ Solve for B

   $\dfrac{3V}{B} = h$ Solve for h

2. $2s = a + b + c$

   $\Rightarrow s = \dfrac{a+b+c}{2}$ Solve for s

   $\Rightarrow 2s - b - c = a$ Solve for a

   $2s - a - c = b$ Solve for b

   $2s - a - b = c$ Solve for c

3. $i = prt$

   $r = \dfrac{i}{pt}$ Solve for r

4. $p = 2l + 2w$

   $p - 2w = 2l$

   $\dfrac{p-2w}{2} = l$ Solve for l

   $p - 2l = 2w$

   $\Rightarrow \dfrac{p-2l}{2} = w$ Solve for w

EXERCISE 16 (b)

Solve for the variable indicated:

1. $S = C + p$ for p

2. $S = r - e$ for r

3. $D = RT$ for R

4. $A = \dfrac{h}{b}$ for h

5. $A = \dfrac{h}{b}$ for b

6. $\dfrac{V}{lw} = h$ for V

7. $Y = \dfrac{f}{3}$ for f

8. $a - b - 30 = c$ for a

9. $P = 2a + b$ for a

10. $F = \dfrac{9}{5}C + 32$ for C

11. $\dfrac{a}{b} = \dfrac{c}{6d}$ for c

12. $S = \dfrac{1}{2}gt^2$ for g

13. $t = \sqrt{l}$ for l

14. $S = \dfrac{1}{2}gt^2$ for t

15. $A = \dfrac{h}{2}(x + y)$ for h

16. $\dfrac{1}{f} = \dfrac{1}{u} - \dfrac{1}{v}$ for v.

16.4 Finding the Value of a Variable in a Formula.

Case (*i*) *To find the value of a variable that is the subject of a formula.*

The value of a variable in a formula may be found if values are given for other variables. By substitution, replace the other variables by their given values, and then solve for the subject, that is, evaluate the numerical expression that results.

Ex.1. *Find the value of s in $2s = a + b + c$ when $a = 6$, $b = 8$ and $c = 12$.*

Sol. $$2s = a + b + c = 6 + 8 + 12$$
$$\Rightarrow \quad 2s = 26 \quad \therefore s = \frac{26}{2} = \mathbf{13}.$$

Ex.2. *Find A if $A = p + prt$ and $p = 500$, $r = 0.03$, $t = 4$.*

Sol. $$A = p + prt = 500 + 500(0.03) \times 4 = 500 + 60 = \mathbf{560}.$$

Case (*ii*) *To find the value of a variable that is not the subject of a formula.*

You may use either of the following two methods in such cases.

Method 1. *Substitute first, then solve.*

Method 2. *Transform the formula first* to make the variable to be found the subject of the formula, then substitute, and then solve.

Ex.3. *Find the value of t in $s = \dfrac{1}{2}gt^2$ if $s = 40$ and $g = 9.8$.*

Sol. **Method 1 :** $40 = \dfrac{1}{2} \times 9.8 \times t^2 = 4.9t^2$

$$\Rightarrow \quad t^2 = \frac{40}{4.9} = \frac{400}{49} \quad \therefore \quad t = \sqrt{\frac{400}{49}} = \frac{20}{7} = 2\frac{6}{7}.$$

Method 2 : $s = \dfrac{1}{2}gt^2 \Rightarrow 2s = gt^2 \Rightarrow \dfrac{2s}{g} = t^2$

$$\Rightarrow t^2 = \frac{2s}{g} = \frac{2 \times 40}{9.8} = \frac{40}{4.9} = \frac{400}{49} \quad \therefore \quad t = \sqrt{\frac{400}{49}} = \frac{20}{7} = 2\frac{6}{7}.$$

Ex.4. *In the formula $F = \dfrac{9}{5}C + 32$, find C if $F = 59$.*

Sol. $$F = \frac{9}{5}C + 32$$
$$\Rightarrow \quad 5F = 9C + 160 \Rightarrow 5F - 160 = 9C \Rightarrow 9C = 5F - 160$$
$$\Rightarrow \quad 9C = 5 \times 59 - 160 = 295 - 160 = 135 \quad \therefore \quad C = \frac{135}{9} = \mathbf{15}.$$

EXERCISE 16 (c)

1. $A = lw$ Find A if $l = 13$ and $w = 9$, find w if A $= 150$ and $l = 15$.

2. $V = lwh$ Find V if $l = 8$, w $= 7$ and $h = 4$, find h if V $= 1470$, $l = 15$, and $w = 7$.

3. $C = 2\pi r$ Find C if $\pi = 3.14$ and $r = 6$, find r if $\pi = 3.14$ and $C = 18.84$.

4. $i = prt$ Find i if $p =$ Rs 700, $r = 0.05$, and $t = 3$yrs. find p if $i =$ Rs 135, $r = 0.03$, and $t = 9$yrs

5. $F = \dfrac{9}{5}C + 32$ Find F if $C = 55$, find C if $F = 212$.

6. $s = \dfrac{1}{2}gt^2$ Find s if $g = 32$, $t = 8$, find g if $s = 800$, $t = 10$.

7. $a^2 = b^2 + s^2$ Find a if $b = 15$, $s = 20$, find b if $a = 15$, $s = 12$.

8. $2A=h\,(x+y)$ Find A if $h = 5.4$, $x = 3.7$, $y = 2.2$, find h if A $= 70$, $x = 3.3$, $y = 6.7$.

LOOKING BACK

Summary of Key Facts

1. A **formula** is a mathematical rule expressing relationship between quantities in the form of an equation.

2. The **subject of a formula is** that variable that is expressed in terms of other variables.

ANSWERS

EXERCISE 16 (a)

1. $A = a(b + c)$ 2. $2s = (x + y) \times t$ 3. $V = lbh$ 4. $(x + y) = 5 + 7 (x - y)$ 5. $2S = n(n + 1)$ 6. $A = \dfrac{1}{2}d_1d_2$

7. $\dfrac{4}{5}x - \dfrac{2}{3}x = 13$ 8. $C = \pi d$ 9. $S = \dfrac{D}{T}$ 10. $z = 52x - 12y$ 11. $M = V \times D$ 12. $W = FS$ 13. $A = \pi r^2$

14. (i) $s = 60m$ (ii) $h = 24d$ (iii) $s = 3600h$ (iv) $h = \dfrac{m}{60}$ (v) $h = 168 w$ (vi) $d = 30$M (vii) $m = 60h + \dfrac{1}{2}$.

(viii) $d = 30m + 7w + 5$ 15. $d = x + y$ 16. (a) $P = 18s$ (b) $P = 7a + b$

EXERCISE 16 (b)

1. $p = S - C$ 2. $r = S + e$ 3. $R = \dfrac{D}{T}$ 4. $h = bA$ 5. $b = \dfrac{h}{A}$ 6. $V = lwh$ 7. $f = 3Y$

8. $a = b + c + 30$ 9. $a = \dfrac{P-b}{2}$ 10. $C = \dfrac{5}{9}(F - 32)$ 11. $c = \dfrac{6ad}{b}$ 12. $g = \dfrac{2s}{t^2}$ 13. $l = t^2$

14. $t = \pm \sqrt{\dfrac{2s}{g}}$ 15. $h = \dfrac{2A}{x + y}$ 16. $v = \dfrac{uf}{f - u}$

EXERCISE 16 (c)

1. $A = 117; w = 10$ 2. $V = 224; h = 14.$ 3. $C = 37.68; r = 3$ 4. $i =$ Rs. 105; $p =$ Rs. 500 5. $F = 131; C = 100$

6. $S = 1024, g = 16$ 7. $a = 25; b = 9$ 8. $A = 15.93; h = 14.$

FIGURES CAN BE FUN

1. There is a way of writing 1 by using all ten digits at once: $\dfrac{148}{296} + \dfrac{35}{70} = 1$

2. The number 3 which cannot be wholly divided by any number (except 1 and itself) has the property that it will wholly divide 111, 222, 333, 444, 555, 666, 777, 888, 999.

17. Exponents

17.1 Introduction

You have learnt in class VI that if we multiply a number by itself again and again, then it can be written in a short form called **exponential or power notation.**

For example :

$$4 \times 4 \times 4 = 4^3 \qquad (-3) \times (-3) \times (-3) \times (-3) = (-3)^4$$

In the same manner, we can write

$$\frac{1}{2} \times \frac{1}{2} \times \frac{1}{2} \times \frac{1}{2} \times \frac{1}{2} \times \frac{1}{2} \times \frac{1}{2} = \left(\frac{1}{2}\right)^7$$

$$\frac{-5}{7} \times \frac{-5}{7} \times \frac{-5}{7} \times \frac{-5}{7} = \left(\frac{-5}{7}\right)^4$$

A numeral such as $\left(\frac{1}{2}\right)^7$ is called an exponential expression.

In $\left(\frac{1}{2}\right)^7$, $\frac{1}{2}$ is called the base and 7 the exponent.

We read $\left(\frac{1}{2}\right)^7$ as "$\frac{1}{2}$ raised to the power 7".

EXPONENT

$$\left(\frac{-5}{7}\right)^4 \text{ means } \frac{-5}{7} \times \frac{-5}{7} \times \frac{-5}{7} \times \frac{-5}{7}$$

BASE

$\left(\frac{-5}{7}\right)$ raised to the power 4.

In general, *for any number **a** and a positive integer **n** we define.*

$a^n = a \times a \times a \times a \text{ --- } \times a \text{ (n times)}$

a^n *is called the **n^{th} power of a** and is also read as 'a raised to the power n.'*

The number 'a' is called the **base** and n is called the **exponent** or **power** or **index**.

Now look at the following illustrations.

$(-1)^2 = -1 \times -1 = 1$, $(-1)^3 = 1 \times -1 \times -1 = -\textbf{1}.$

$(-2)^6 = -2 \times -2 \times -2 \times -2 \times -2 \times -2 = \textbf{64}$

$(-2)^7 = -2 \times -2 \times -2 \times -2 \times -2 \times -2 \times -2 = -\textbf{128}.$

$$\left(\frac{-1}{3}\right)^4 = \frac{-1}{3} \times \frac{-1}{3} \times \frac{-1}{3} \times \frac{-1}{3} = \frac{1}{81}, \quad \left(-\frac{1}{3}\right)^5 = \frac{-1}{3} \times \frac{-1}{3} \times \frac{-1}{3} \times \frac{-1}{3} \times \frac{-1}{3} = \frac{-1}{243}.$$

Also we have

$$\left(\frac{5}{6}\right)^3 = \frac{5}{6} \times \frac{5}{6} \times \frac{5}{6} = \frac{5 \times 5 \times 5}{6 \times 6 \times 6} = \frac{5^3}{6^3} = \frac{125}{216}.$$

$$\left(-\frac{3}{2}\right)^5 = \frac{-3}{2} \times \frac{-3}{2} \times \frac{-3}{2} \times \frac{-3}{2} \times \frac{-3}{2} = \frac{-3 \times -3 \times -3 \times -3 \times -3}{2 \times 2 \times 2 \times 2 \times 2} = \frac{(-3)^5}{2^5} = -\frac{243}{32}.$$

Do you observe that :

I. 1. A negative rational number raised to an even power is positive.

2. A negative rational number raised to an odd power in negative.

3. $(-1)^{\text{odd natural number}} = -1$

4. $(-1)^{\text{even natural number}} = 1$

Thus $(-1)^{47} = -1$, $(-1)^{192} = 1$, $(-1)^{51} = -1$, $(-1)^{376} = 1$

II. If $\dfrac{p}{q}$ is any rational number and n is any integer, than $\left(\dfrac{p}{q}\right)^n = \dfrac{p^n}{q^n}$.

Ex.1. *Express each of the following powers of rational numbers as a rational number.*

(i) $\left(\dfrac{2}{5}\right)^4$ (ii) $\left(\dfrac{-3}{7}\right)^3$ (iii) $\left(\dfrac{-3}{4}\right)^4$

Sol. (i) $\left(\dfrac{2}{5}\right)^4 = \dfrac{2}{5} \times \dfrac{2}{5} \times \dfrac{2}{5} \times \dfrac{2}{5} = \dfrac{2 \times 2 \times 2 \times 2}{5 \times 5 \times 5 \times 5} = \dfrac{16}{625}$.

(ii) $\left(\dfrac{-3}{7}\right)^3 = \dfrac{-3}{7} \times \dfrac{-3}{7} \times \dfrac{-3}{7} = \dfrac{-3 \times -3 \times -3}{7 \times 7 \times 7} = \dfrac{-27}{343}$.

(iii) $\left(\dfrac{-3}{4}\right)^4 = \dfrac{-3}{4} \times \dfrac{-3}{4} \times \dfrac{-3}{4} \times \dfrac{-3}{4} = \dfrac{-3 \times -3 \times -3 \times -3}{4 \times 4 \times 4 \times 4} = \dfrac{81}{256}$.

Ex.2. *Express in power notation.*

(i) $\dfrac{16}{81}$ (ii) $\dfrac{-27}{343}$ (iii) $-\dfrac{1}{243}$

Sol. (i) $\dfrac{16}{81} = \dfrac{2 \times 2 \times 2 \times 2}{3 \times 3 \times 3 \times 3} = \dfrac{2^4}{3^4} = \left(\dfrac{2}{3}\right)^4$.

(ii) $\dfrac{-27}{343} = \dfrac{-3 \times -3 \times -3}{7 \times 7 \times 7} = \dfrac{(-3)^3}{7^3} = \left(\dfrac{-3}{7}\right)^3$.

(iii) $-\dfrac{1}{243} = -\dfrac{1}{243} = \dfrac{-1}{3 \times 3 \times 3 \times 3 \times 3} = \dfrac{(-1)^5}{3^5} = \left(\dfrac{-1}{3}\right)^5$.

> **Result used**
>
> $\dfrac{p^n}{q^n} = \left(\dfrac{p}{q}\right)^n$

Ex.3. *Find the value of:*

(a) $\left(\dfrac{-3}{5}\right)^4 \times \left(\dfrac{1}{3}\right)^3$ (b) $(-2)^5 \div \left(-\dfrac{1}{3}\right)^4$.

Sol. (a) $\left(\dfrac{-3}{5}\right)^4 \times \left(\dfrac{1}{3}\right)^3 = \dfrac{-3}{5} \times \dfrac{-3}{5} \times \dfrac{-3}{5} \times \dfrac{-3}{5} \times \dfrac{1}{3} \times \dfrac{1}{3} \times \dfrac{1}{3}$

$= \dfrac{-1}{5} \times \dfrac{-1}{5} \times \dfrac{-1}{5} \times \dfrac{-3}{5} = \dfrac{3}{625}$.

(b) $(-2)^5 \div \left(\dfrac{-1}{3}\right)^4 = \dfrac{(-2)^5}{\left(\dfrac{-1}{3}\right)^4} = \dfrac{-2 \times -2 \times -2 \times -2 \times -2}{\left(-\dfrac{1}{3}\right) \times \left(-\dfrac{1}{3}\right) \times \left(-\dfrac{1}{3}\right) \times \left(-\dfrac{1}{3}\right)}$

$= \dfrac{-32}{\dfrac{1}{81}} = -32 \times 81 = -2592$.

Ex.4. *Simplify :*

(a) $\left[\left(\dfrac{1}{2}\right)^2 - \left(\dfrac{1}{4}\right)^3\right] \times 2^3$

(b) $\left(3^2 - 2^2\right) \div \left(\dfrac{1}{5}\right)^2$

Sol. (a) $\left[\left(\dfrac{1}{2} \times \dfrac{1}{2}\right) - \left(\dfrac{1}{4} \times \dfrac{1}{4} \times \dfrac{1}{4}\right)\right] \times (2 \times 2 \times 2) = \left[\dfrac{1}{4} - \dfrac{1}{64}\right] \times 8$

$$= \left(\dfrac{16-1}{64}\right) \times 8 = \dfrac{15}{64} \times 8 = \dfrac{15}{8}.$$

(b) $\left(3^2 - 2^2\right) \div \left(\dfrac{1}{5}\right)^2 = (9-4) \div \left(\dfrac{1}{5} \times \dfrac{1}{5}\right) = 5 \div \dfrac{1}{25} = 5 \times 25 = \mathbf{125.}$

Ex.5. *Find the reciprocal of :*

(i) $(-2)^4$ (ii) $\left(-\dfrac{3}{8}\right)^3$ (iii) $\left(\dfrac{-7}{11}\right)^{105}$

Sol. (i) Reciprocal of $(-2)^4 = \dfrac{1}{(-2)^4} = \dfrac{1^4}{(-2)^4} = \left(\dfrac{1}{-2}\right)^4 = \left(-\dfrac{1}{2}\right)^4.$

$\boxed{\dfrac{1}{-2} = -\dfrac{1}{2}}$

(ii) $\left(-\dfrac{3}{8}\right)^3 = \dfrac{(-3)^3}{8^3}$ ∴ Reciprocal of $\left(-\dfrac{3}{8}\right)^3 = \dfrac{8^3}{-3^3} = \left(\dfrac{8}{-3}\right)^3 = \left(-\dfrac{8}{3}\right)^3.$

$\boxed{\because \dfrac{8}{-3} = -\dfrac{8}{3}}$

(iii) $\left(\dfrac{-7}{11}\right)^{105} = \dfrac{(-7)^{105}}{11^{105}}$ ∴ Reciprocal of $\dfrac{(-7)^{105}}{11^{105}} = \dfrac{11^{105}}{(-7)^{105}} = \left(\dfrac{11}{-7}\right)^{105} = \left(\dfrac{-11}{7}\right)^{105}$

EXERCISE 17 (a)

1. **Express each of the following in exponential form :**

(i) $\dfrac{2}{3} \times \dfrac{2}{3} \times \dfrac{2}{3} \times \dfrac{2}{3}$

(ii) $\dfrac{3}{8} \times \dfrac{3}{8} \times \dfrac{3}{8} \times \dfrac{3}{8} \times \dfrac{3}{8}$

(iii) $\dfrac{-5}{7} \times \dfrac{-5}{7} \times \dfrac{-5}{7} \times \dfrac{-5}{7} \times \dfrac{-5}{7} \times \dfrac{-5}{7}$

(iv) $\dfrac{-11}{8} \times \dfrac{-11}{8} \times \dfrac{-11}{8} \times \dfrac{-11}{8} \times \dfrac{-11}{8} \times \dfrac{-11}{8} \times \dfrac{-11}{8} \times \dfrac{-11}{8} \times \dfrac{-11}{8}$

2. **Express each of the following as a number of the form** p/q **:**

(i) $\left(\dfrac{5}{9}\right)^2$ (ii) $\left(\dfrac{4}{7}\right)^3$ (iii) $\left(-\dfrac{2}{3}\right)^7$ (iv) $\left(\dfrac{-5}{2}\right)^3$ (v) $\left(-\dfrac{1}{2}\right)^8$

3. **Express each of these rational numbers in power notation :**

(i) $\dfrac{9}{64}$ (ii) $\dfrac{49}{25}$ (iii) $\dfrac{-8}{27}$ (iv) $-\dfrac{1}{216}$ (v) $\dfrac{-32}{243}$

4. **Find the value of :**

(i) $\left(\dfrac{1}{3}\right)^3 \times \left(\dfrac{3}{2}\right)^2$ (ii) $\left(\dfrac{-2}{3}\right)^4 \times \left(\dfrac{-3}{4}\right)^3$ (iii) $\left(\dfrac{-1}{5}\right)^3 \times \left(\dfrac{-1}{5}\right)^2$ (iv) $\left(\dfrac{4}{-5}\right)^2 \times (-5)^3$ (v) $\left(\dfrac{-1}{3}\right)^5 \div \left(\dfrac{2}{3}\right)^3$

(vi) $\left(\dfrac{-1}{2}\right)^3 \times (-1)^{85} \times \left(\dfrac{2}{5}\right)^2$ (vii) $\left(\dfrac{1}{2}\right)^4 \div \left(\dfrac{1}{3}\right)^4 + \left(\dfrac{-1}{2}\right)^3$ (viii) $\left(\left(\dfrac{-3}{5}\right)^3 + \dfrac{7}{25}\right) \times \left(\dfrac{5}{2}\right)^3$

(ix) $(12^2 - 5^3) \times \dfrac{(-1)^{40}}{19}$

5. **Find the reciprocal of :**

    (i) $\left(\dfrac{2}{5}\right)^4$ (ii) $\left(\dfrac{-3}{4}\right)^3$ (iii) $(-2)^4$ (iv) $\left(\dfrac{-3}{7}\right)^2$ (v) $\left(\dfrac{-11}{4}\right)^3$

    (vi) $\left(\dfrac{-7}{4}\right)^{208}$ (vii) $\left(-\dfrac{1}{10}\right)^{47}$ (viii) $\left(\dfrac{-3}{17}\right)^{89}$

6. **Find the absolute value of :**

    (i) $\left(\dfrac{3}{4}\right)^3$ (ii) $-\left(\dfrac{7}{8}\right)^2$ (iii) $\left(\dfrac{-2}{3}\right)^4$ (iv) $\left(\dfrac{-3}{2}\right)^5$

7. **Evaluate** $b^2 - 9\,(b-1)^2$ if $b = 1.1$ $\left\{ \text{Hint. Put } b = 1.1 = \dfrac{11}{10} \right\}$

LAWS OF EXPONENTS

Case (i) *Positive integral Exponents*

17.2 Law 1. Finding the Product of Powers of the Same Number.

Let us consider the product

(i) $3^5 \times 3^2 = (3 \times 3 \times 3 \times 3 \times 3) \times (3 \times 3)$

           $= 3 \times 3 \times 3 \times 3 \times 3 \times 3 \times 3 = 3^7 = 2187.$

(ii) $\left(\dfrac{-3}{4}\right)^2 \times \left(\dfrac{-3}{4}\right)^3 = \left(\dfrac{-3}{4} \times \dfrac{-3}{4}\right) \times \left(\dfrac{-3}{4} \times \dfrac{-3}{4} \times \dfrac{-3}{4}\right)$

           $= \dfrac{-3}{4} \times \dfrac{-3}{4} \times \dfrac{-3}{4} \times \dfrac{-3}{4} \times \dfrac{-3}{4} = \left(\dfrac{-3}{4}\right)^5$

From these examples we conclude that

$3^5 \times 3^7$ 3^{5+7} Add the Exponents $= 3^{12}$

In general,

> Let x be any number and m, n be positive integers, then $x^m \times x^n = x^{m+n}$

Ex.1. *Simplify and express the result in power notation :*

(a) $\left(\dfrac{3}{5}\right)^8 \times \left(\dfrac{3}{5}\right)^5$ (b) $\left(\dfrac{7}{3}\right)^5 \times \left(\dfrac{7}{3}\right)^6 \times \left(\dfrac{7}{3}\right)^{20}$

Sol. (a) $\left(\dfrac{3}{5}\right)^8 \times \left(\dfrac{3}{5}\right)^5 = \left(\dfrac{3}{5}\right)^{8+5} = \left(\dfrac{3}{5}\right)^{13}.$

(b) $\left(\dfrac{7}{3}\right)^5 \times \left(\dfrac{7}{3}\right)^6 \times \left(\dfrac{7}{3}\right)^{20} = \left(\dfrac{7}{3}\right)^{5+6+20} = \left(\dfrac{7}{3}\right)^{31}.$

Ex.2. *Express the result in power notation :*

(i) $3^x \cdot 3^2$ (ii) $2^{4a} \cdot 2^{3a}$

Sol. (i) $3^x \cdot 3^2 = 3^{x+2}$ (ii) $2^{4a} \cdot 2^{3a} = 2^{4a+3a} = 2^{7a}.$

17.3 Law 2. Find a Power of a Power of a Number

Consider the expression $(2^5)^3$.

If you apply the definition of power and law 1 to this expression, you obtain the following:

$$(2^5)^3 = 2^5 . 2^5 . 2^5 = 2^{5+5+5} = 2^{15} = 2^{5\times3}$$

> *In general, if x is any number and m, n are positive* integers :
> $$(x^m)^n = x^{mn}$$
>
> Multiply m by n
> $(x^m)^n$

Ex.1. *Simplify* $\left(\dfrac{1}{2^3}\right)^2$.

Sol. $\left(\dfrac{1}{2^3}\right)^2 = \dfrac{1}{2^{3\times2}} = \dfrac{1}{2^6} = \dfrac{1}{64}$.

Ex.2. *Simplify and express the result in power notation :*

(i) $\left[\left(\dfrac{2}{3}\right)^4\right]^2$

(ii) $\left[\left(\dfrac{-3}{4}\right)^3\right]^4$

Sol. **(i)** $\left[\left(\dfrac{2}{3}\right)^4\right]^2 = \left(\dfrac{2}{3}\right)^{4\times2} = \left(\dfrac{2}{3}\right)^8$.

(ii) $\left[\left(\dfrac{-3}{4}\right)^3\right]^4 = \left(\dfrac{-3}{4}\right)^{3\times4} = \left(-\dfrac{3}{4}\right)^{12}$.

Ex.3. *Express the following with a single exponent :*

(i) $(2^3)^5 \times (2^7)^2$

(ii) $\left(\left(\dfrac{-3}{5}\right)^2 \times \left(-\dfrac{3}{5}\right)^4\right)^3$.

Sol. **(i)** $(2^3)^5 \times (2^7)^2 = 2^{15} \times 2^{14}$ using $(a^m)^n = a^{m\times n}$

$= 2^{15+14} = \mathbf{2^{29}}$.   using $a^m \times a^n = a^{m+n}$

(ii) $\left(\left(\dfrac{-3}{5}\right)^2 \times \left(-\dfrac{3}{5}\right)^4\right)^3 = \left(\left(-\dfrac{3}{5}\right)^{2+4}\right)^3$ using $a^m \times a^n = a^{m+n}$

$= \left(\left(-\dfrac{3}{5}\right)^6\right)^3 = \left(-\dfrac{3}{5}\right)^{18}$.   using $(a^m)^n = a^{m\times n}$

7.4 Law 3. Finding the Power of a product of rational numbers

Using the definition of power, we have:

$(2 \times 3)^4 = (2 \times 3) . (2 \times 3) . (2 \times 3) . (2 \times 3)$

$\qquad\qquad = (2 \times 2 \times 2 \times 2) . (3 \times 3 \times 3 \times 3) = 2^4 . 3^4$

$(xy)^3 \quad = (x\,y) . (x\,y) . (x\,y) = (x . x . x) (y . y . y)$

$\qquad\quad = x^3 . y^3$

Thus,

> *In general, for all numbers x and y, if m is a positive integer* $(x\,y)^m = x^m . y^m$.

Ex. 4. *Find the value of*

(i) $(5x)^3$ when $x = -\dfrac{2}{5}$ (ii) $(-2ab)^4$ when $a = \dfrac{3}{5}$, $b = \dfrac{-1}{2}$.

Sol.   (i) Given $x = \dfrac{-2}{5}$

$$(5x)^3 = 5^3 \cdot x^3 = 5^3 \cdot \left(\dfrac{-2}{5}\right)^3 = 5^3 \, (-1)^3 \left(\dfrac{2}{5}\right)^3$$

$$= -5 \times 5 \times 5 \times \dfrac{2 \times 2 \times 2}{5 \times 5 \times 5} = -2 \times 2 \times 2 = -8.$$

(ii) Given $a = \dfrac{3}{5}$, $b = -\dfrac{1}{2}$

$$(-2ab)^4 = (-2)^4 \times a^4 \times b^4 = (-1)^4 \times 2^4 \times a^4 \times b^4 = 2^4 \times \left(\dfrac{3}{5}\right)^4 \times \left(\dfrac{-1}{2}\right)^4$$

$$= 2 \times 2 \times 2 \times 2 \times \dfrac{3 \times 3 \times 3 \times 3}{5 \times 5 \times 5 \times 5} \times (-1)^4 \times \dfrac{1}{2 \times 2 \times 2 \times 2} = \dfrac{81}{625}.$$

17.5 Law 4. Finding Quotients of Powers of the Same Number

Quotients involving power can be simplified as shown in the following examples.

$$\dfrac{5^4}{5^4} = \dfrac{5 \times 5 \times 5 \times 5}{5 \times 5 \times 5 \times 5} = 1 \qquad\qquad \dfrac{5^7}{5^4} = \dfrac{(5 \times 5 \times 5)(5 \times 5 \times 5 \times 5)}{5 \times 5 \times 5 \times 5} \begin{matrix} \rightarrow 7 \text{ factors} \\ \rightarrow 4 \text{ factors} \end{matrix}$$

$$= 5 \times 5 \times 5 \rightarrow (7-4) \text{ factors}$$

$$= 5^{7-4} = 5^3$$

$$\dfrac{5^4}{5^7} = \dfrac{5 \times 5 \times 5 \times 5}{(5 \times 5 \times 5)(5 \times 5 \times 5 \times 5)} \begin{matrix} \rightarrow 4 \text{ factors} \\ \rightarrow 7 \text{ factors} \end{matrix}$$

$$= \dfrac{1}{5 \times 5 \times 5} \rightarrow (7-4) \text{ factors}$$

$$= \dfrac{1}{5^{7-4}} = \dfrac{1}{5^3}.$$

The examples above suggest the following properties for division of powers.

For all non-zero rational numbers x and all positive integers m and n		
If m = n, *then* $\dfrac{x^m}{x^n} = 1$	*If m > n* *then* $\dfrac{x^m}{x^n} = x^{m-n}$	*If m < n* *then* $\dfrac{x^m}{x^n} = \dfrac{1}{x^{n-m}}$

Notice that x cannot be 0 in the fractions above since division by 0 is not defined.

Ex. 1 *Simplify each expression :*

(i) $\dfrac{4^6}{4^4}$ (ii) $\dfrac{(-2)^7}{(-2)^{12}}$ (iii) $\left(\dfrac{-3}{4}\right)^4 \div \left(\dfrac{-3}{4}\right)^2$ (iv) $(-4)^6 \div (-4)^8$.

Sol.   (i) $\dfrac{4^6}{4^4} = 4^{6-4} = 4^2 = \mathbf{16.}$

(ii) $\dfrac{(-2)^7}{(-2)^{12}} = \dfrac{1}{(-2)^{12-7}} = \dfrac{1}{(-2)^5} = \dfrac{1}{-32} = -\dfrac{1}{32}.$

(iii) $\left(\dfrac{-3}{4}\right)^4 \div \left(\dfrac{-3}{4}\right)^2 = \left(\dfrac{-3}{4}\right)^{4-2} = \left(\dfrac{-3}{4}\right)^2 = \dfrac{(-3)^2}{4^2} = \dfrac{9}{16}.$

(iv) $(-4)^6 \div (-4)^8 = \dfrac{(-4)^6}{(-4)^8} = \dfrac{1}{(-4)^{8-6}} = \dfrac{1}{(-4)^2} = \dfrac{1}{16}.$

Ex.2. *Simplify and express the result in power notation :*

(i) $\left(\dfrac{3}{4}\right)^{17} \div \left(\dfrac{3}{4}\right)^4$ (ii) $\left(\dfrac{4}{5}\right)^{23} \div \left(\dfrac{4}{5}\right)^{37}$

Sol. (i) $\left(\dfrac{3}{4}\right)^{17} \div \left(\dfrac{3}{4}\right)^4 = \left(\dfrac{3}{4}\right)^{17-4} = \left(\dfrac{3}{4}\right)^{13}.$

(ii) $\left(\dfrac{4}{5}\right)^{23} \div \left(\dfrac{4}{5}\right)^{37} = \dfrac{1}{\left(\dfrac{4}{5}\right)^{37-23}} = \dfrac{1}{\left(\dfrac{4}{5}\right)^{14}} = 1 \div \left(\dfrac{4}{5}\right)^{14} = 1 \times \left(\dfrac{5}{4}\right)^{14} = \left(\dfrac{5}{4}\right)^{14}.$

EXERCISE 17 (b)

Express the following products as an exponent of single number :

1. (i) $5^7 \times 5^2$ (ii) $7^3 \times 7^4$ (iii) $2^{10} \times 2^4$ (iv) $6(6)^5$ (v) $5^2(5^2)(5^3)$ (vi) $4^5 \times 4^4 \times 4^7$

2. (i) $\left(\dfrac{1}{3}\right)^5 \times \left(\dfrac{1}{3}\right)^2$ (ii) $\left(\dfrac{3}{4}\right)^7 \times \left(\dfrac{3}{4}\right)^{20}$ (iii) $\left(\dfrac{-5}{6}\right)^5 \cdot \left(\dfrac{-5}{6}\right)^6$ (iv) $\left(\dfrac{-5}{9}\right)^4 \times \left(\dfrac{-5}{9}\right)^{12}$ (v) $\left(\dfrac{4}{7}\right)^3 \times \left(\dfrac{4}{7}\right)^6 \times \left(\dfrac{4}{7}\right)^{11}$

3. Simplify and express the result in exponential form :

(i) $(3^2)^3$ (ii) $(2^2)^3$ (iii) $(10^3)^2$ (iv) $((-2)^3)^4$ (v) $\left(\left(\dfrac{1}{10}\right)^5\right)^2$ (vi) $\left(\left(-\dfrac{1}{3}\right)^7\right)^2$

(vii) $(3^2)^6$ (viii) $\left(\left(\dfrac{1}{5}\right)^4\right)^5$ (ix) $\left(\left(-\dfrac{6}{7}\right)^3\right)^6$ (x) $\left(\left(\dfrac{5}{9}\right)^7\right)^3$

4. Express each of the following with a single exponent :

(i) $(3^5)^2 \times (3^4)^9$ (ii) $\left(\left(-\dfrac{1}{3}\right)^2\right)^3 \times \left(\left(-\dfrac{1}{3}\right)^4\right)^5$ (iii) $(-7^2)^5 \times (-7^4)^2$

5. Simplify :

(i) $(3 \times 2^3)^2$ (ii) $(-2 \times 10^3)^2$ (iii) $\left(-\dfrac{1}{2} \times 5\right)^2$ (iv) $3^7 \times \left(\dfrac{1}{3}\right)^7$ (v) $\left(\dfrac{21}{19}\right)^4 \times \left(\dfrac{19}{7}\right)^4$

6. Simpify :

(i) $\dfrac{5^4}{5^3}$ (ii) $\dfrac{2^8}{2^5}$ (iii) $\dfrac{7^8}{7^6}$ (iv) $\dfrac{(-2)^4}{(-2)}$ (v) $\dfrac{(-3)^{10}}{(-3)^6}$

7. (i) $\dfrac{8^5}{8^7}$ (ii) $\dfrac{9^{10}}{9^{12}}$ (iii) $\dfrac{5^7}{5^{10}}$ (iv) $\dfrac{(-4)^5}{(-4)^8}$

8. (i) $\left(\dfrac{3}{5}\right)^7 \div \left(\dfrac{3}{5}\right)^5$ (ii) $\left(\dfrac{7}{8}\right)^{20} \div \left(\dfrac{7}{8}\right)^{18}$ (iii) $\left(\dfrac{-4}{5}\right)^9 \div \left(\dfrac{-4}{5}\right)^{10}$

Case 2: Zero and Negative Exponents

	We have	But we already know that	This suggests that we should define
(i)	$\dfrac{a^9}{a^9} = a^{9-9} = a^0$	$\dfrac{a^9}{a^9} = 1$	a^0 as 1
(ii)	$\dfrac{a^3}{a^9} = a^{3-9} = a^{-6}$	$\dfrac{a^3}{a^9} = \dfrac{1}{a^{9-3}} = \dfrac{1}{a^6}$	a^{-6} as $\dfrac{1}{a^6}$

Therefore, to make $\dfrac{a^m}{a^n} = a^{m-n}$, true for all cases, we state the following definitions of *zero exponent* and *negative integer exponent.*

Let a be any non-zero rational number, and let n be any positive integer.

a^0 means 1 $\longleftarrow$ zero exponent, e.g., $5^0 = 1$, $\left(\dfrac{3}{7}\right)^0 = 1$, $\left(\dfrac{-5}{9}\right)^0 = 1$

a^{-n} means $\dfrac{1}{a^n}$ $\longleftarrow$ negative integer exponent e.g., $5^{-1} = \dfrac{1}{5}$, $\left(\dfrac{4}{5}\right)^{-1} = \dfrac{5}{4}$.

Ex.1. **Find the value of**

(i) 4^0 (ii) 3^{8-8} (iii) $3^0 + 4^0 + 5^0$ (iv) $(9^0 - 7^0) \times (9 + 7)$

Sol. (i) $4^0 = 1$ (ii) $3^{8-8} = 3^0 = 1$ (iii) $3^0 + 4^0 + 5^0 = 1 + 1 + 1 = 3$.

(iv) $(9^0 - 7^0) \times (9 + 7) = (1 - 1) \times 16 = 0 \times 16 = 0$.

Ex.2. **Simplify :** $\left[\left(\dfrac{-2}{3}\right)^3 \times \left(\dfrac{-2}{3}\right)\right] \div \left(\dfrac{4}{9}\right)^2$ **and express the result as a power of 2.**

Sol. $\left[\left(\dfrac{-2}{3}\right)^3 \times \left(\dfrac{-2}{3}\right)\right] \div \left(\dfrac{4}{9}\right)^2 = \left[\left(\dfrac{-2}{3}\right)^{3+1}\right] \div \left[\left(\dfrac{2}{3}\right)^2\right]^2$

$$= \left(\dfrac{-2}{3}\right)^4 \div \left(\dfrac{2}{3}\right)^4 = \left(\dfrac{2}{3}\right)^4 \div \left(\dfrac{2}{3}\right)^4 = \left(\dfrac{2}{3}\right)^{4-4} = \left(\dfrac{2}{3}\right)^0 = 1 = 2^0.$$

Using $\left(\dfrac{a}{b}\right)^m \times \left(\dfrac{a}{b}\right)^n = \left(\dfrac{a}{b}\right)^{m+n}$

$\left(\left(\dfrac{a}{b}\right)^m\right)^n = \left(\dfrac{a}{b}\right)^{mn}$

$\because (-1)^4 = +1$

Ex.3. **Simplify :**

(i) $\left(\dfrac{5}{7}\right)^{-1} \times \left(\dfrac{7}{3}\right)^{-1}$ (ii) $(5^{-1} \times 3^{-1}) \div 6^{-1}$

Sol. (i) $\left(\dfrac{5}{7}\right)^{-1} \times \left(\dfrac{7}{3}\right)^{-1} = \dfrac{7}{5} \times \dfrac{3}{7} = \dfrac{3}{5}$.

Using $\left(\dfrac{a}{b}\right)^{-1} = \dfrac{b}{a}$

(ii) $(5^{-1} \times 3^{-1})^{-1} \div 6^{-1} = \left(\dfrac{1}{5} \times \dfrac{1}{3}\right)^{-1} \div \dfrac{1}{6}$

Using $a^{-1} = \dfrac{1}{a}$

$$= \left(\dfrac{1}{15}\right)^{-1} \div \dfrac{1}{6} = 15 \times 6 = 90.$$

Using $\left(\dfrac{a}{b}\right)^{-1} = \dfrac{b}{a}$

Ex.4. (i) $(-5)(-5)^{-3} = (-5)^{1+(-3)} = (-5)^{-2} = \dfrac{1}{(-5)^2} = \dfrac{1}{25}$.

(ii) $2^{-3} \cdot 2^{-4} = 2^{-3+(-4)} = 2^{-7} = \dfrac{1}{2^7} = \dfrac{1}{128}$.

(iii) $3^8 \div 3^{-2} = 3^{8-(-2)} = 3^{8+2} = \mathbf{3^{10}}$.

(iv) $\left[(2)^{-3}\right]^{-1} = 2^{-3 \times -1} = 2^3 = \mathbf{8}$.

Ex.5. *Find the reciprocal of the rational number* $\left(\dfrac{1}{2}\right)^{-2} \div \left(\dfrac{2}{3}\right)^{-3}$.

Sol. $\left(\dfrac{1}{2}\right)^{-2} \div \left(\dfrac{2}{3}\right)^{-3} = \left(\dfrac{2}{1}\right)^2 \div \left(\dfrac{3}{2}\right)^3 = 4 \div \dfrac{27}{8} = 4 \times \dfrac{8}{27} = \dfrac{32}{27}$

Reciprocal of $\dfrac{32}{27} = \dfrac{27}{32}$ $\therefore$ reciprocal of $\left(\dfrac{1}{2}\right)^{-2} \div \left(\dfrac{1}{3}\right)^{-3}$ is $\dfrac{27}{32}$.

EXERCISE 17 (c)

Give the meaning of each of the following, and if possible simplify :

1. (i) 3^0 (ii) 8^0 (iii) $(419)^0$ (iv) 5^{-1} (v) 5^{-3} (vi) 7^{-2} (vii) $\left(\dfrac{1}{3}\right)^{-1}$

2. (i) $\left(\dfrac{1}{x}\right)^{-1}$ (ii) $\left(\dfrac{2}{3}\right)^{-1}$ (iii) $(-2)^{-1}$ (iv) $(-3)^{-1}$ (v) $(-4)^{-1}$ (vi) $\left(-\dfrac{1}{2}\right)^{-1}$

Find the value of :

3. (i) $7^0 + 8^0 + 9^0$ (ii) $(20^0 - 23^0) \times 18^0$ (iii) $3^0 \times 3^{-1}$ (iv) $2^{-1} \times 2^{-3}$ (v) $(3^{-1} \div 4^{-1})^2$

4. $(4^{-1} + 8^{-1}) \div \left(\dfrac{2}{3}\right)^{-1}$ **5.** $\left(\dfrac{2}{3}\right)^{-2} \times \left(\dfrac{3}{4}\right)^{-3} \times \left(\dfrac{7}{8}\right)^0$ **6.** $\left(\dfrac{4}{9}\right)^{-2} \times \left(\dfrac{1}{4}\right)^{-2} \times \dfrac{1}{3^{-2}} \times \left(\dfrac{17}{18}\right)^0$

Simplify :

7. (i) $2^4\, 2^{-2}$ (ii) $(5a)^0$ (iii) $\dfrac{3^{-5}}{3^{-5}}$ (iv) $\dfrac{7^{-6}}{7^{-6}}$ (v) $3^{-5} \cdot 3^8$ (vi) $\left(\dfrac{-2}{3}\right)^{-2} \left(\dfrac{-2}{3}\right)$

8. (i) $(-5)\,(-5)^{-3}$ (ii) $(-2)^{-1} \div (-2)^{-4}$ (iii) $(-3)^{-6} \div (-3)^{-3}$ **9.** (i) $\left[\left(\dfrac{2}{3}\right)^{-3}\right]^{-1}$ (ii) $\left[\left(\dfrac{1}{2}\right)^{-2}\right]^3$

(iii) $\left(\left(\dfrac{15}{19}\right)^{-4}\right)^{-20}$ **10.** (i) $\left(\dfrac{10}{3}\right)^{-7} \div \left(\dfrac{5}{3}\right)^{-4}$ (ii) $\left(\dfrac{7}{9}\right)^{-11} \times \left(\dfrac{9}{14}\right)^{-9}$

11. If $x = \left[\left(\dfrac{2}{3}\right)^2\right]^3 \times \left(\dfrac{1}{3}\right)^{-2} \times 3^{-1} \times \dfrac{1}{6}$, find the reciprocal of x

12. Find the reciprocal of the following numbers : (i) $\left(\left(\dfrac{8}{11}\right)^2\right)^{-5} \times \left(\dfrac{11}{8}\right)^{-12}$ (ii) $\left(-\dfrac{3}{7}\right)^{-3} \div \left(-\dfrac{3}{7}\right)^{-4}$

Simplify :

13. $\left[\left(-\dfrac{1}{3}\right)^8 \div \left(-\dfrac{1}{3}\right)^5\right] - \left[\left(-\dfrac{1}{3}\right)^5 \div \left(-\dfrac{1}{3}\right)^3\right]$ **14.** $(2^{-1} \div 5^{-1})^2 \times \left(\dfrac{-5}{8}\right)^{-2}$ **15.** $\left[\left(\dfrac{1}{3}\right)^{-3} - \left(\dfrac{1}{2}\right)^{-3}\right] \div \left(\dfrac{1}{4}\right)^{-3}$

LOOKING BACK

Summary of Key Facts

1. For any number a and a positive integer n, we define

   $a^n = a \times a \times a \times a \,.......... \times a$ (n times)

2. **Laws of exponents :**

   Let x and y be any non–zero numbers and let m and n be any integers then

   (i) $x^m \cdot x^n = x^{m+n}$ (ii) $(xy)^m = x^m \cdot y^m$ (iii) $(x^m)^n = x^{mn}$

   (iv) $\dfrac{x^m}{x^n} = x^{m-n}$ (v) $\left(\dfrac{x}{y}\right)^n = \dfrac{x^n}{y^n}$ (vi) $x^0 = 1$ (zero exponent)

   (vii) $x^{-n} = \dfrac{1}{x^n}$ (viii) $\left(\dfrac{x}{y}\right)^{-n} = \left(\dfrac{y}{x}\right)^n$ (ix) 0^{-n} and 0^0 are not defined.

MENTAL MATHS – 14

1. Express in exponential notation :

   (i) $\dfrac{7}{8} \times \dfrac{7}{8} \times \dfrac{7}{8} \times \dfrac{7}{8} \times \dfrac{7}{8}$ (ii) $\dfrac{-5}{9} \times \dfrac{-5}{9} \times \dfrac{-5}{9} \times \dfrac{-5}{9} \times \dfrac{-5}{9} \times \dfrac{-5}{9} \times \dfrac{-5}{9}$

2. Express as a rational number : (i) $\left(\dfrac{5}{4}\right)^3$ (ii) $\left(-\dfrac{2}{3}\right)^4$

3. Express as an exponent of a rational number : (i) $\dfrac{16}{81}$ (ii) $-\dfrac{1}{216}$ (iii) $\dfrac{1}{1000000}$

   Find the value of the following in the exponential from :

4. $\left(\dfrac{2}{5}\right)^7 \times \left(\dfrac{3}{5}\right)^4$ 5. $\left(\left(-\dfrac{1}{3}\right)^5\right)^2$ 6. $\left(\dfrac{7}{11}\right)^{30} \div \left(\dfrac{7}{11}\right)^{10}$ 7. $\left(\dfrac{5}{16}\right)^{12} \div \left(\dfrac{5}{16}\right)^{12}$ 8. $\left(\dfrac{4}{-3}\right)^{-3}$

9. Find the value of :   (i) $\left(\dfrac{5}{7}\right)^{-2}$ (ii) $(-5)^{-1}$

10. Express $\left(-\dfrac{3}{4}\right)^{-2}$ as a rational number.   11. Simplify : $\left(\dfrac{2}{3}\right)^{-2} \times \left(\dfrac{7}{8}\right)^0$

12. By what number should $(-3)^7$ be divided so that the quotient is (i) $(-3)^2$ (ii) $(-3)^{-2}$

13. Find the reciprocal of $\left(\dfrac{2}{5}\right)^{-3}$.

ANSWERS

EXERCISE 17 (a)

1. (i) $\left(\dfrac{2}{3}\right)^4$ (ii) $\left(\dfrac{3}{8}\right)^5$ (iii) $\left(\dfrac{-5}{7}\right)^6$ (iv) $\left(\dfrac{-11}{8}\right)^9$

2. (i) $\dfrac{25}{81}$ (ii) $\dfrac{64}{243}$ (iii) $\dfrac{-128}{2187}$ (iv) $\dfrac{-125}{8}$ (v) $\dfrac{1}{256}$

3. (i) $\left(\dfrac{3}{8}\right)^2$ (ii) $\left(\dfrac{7}{5}\right)^2$ (iii) $\left(-\dfrac{2}{3}\right)^3$ (iv) $\left(-\dfrac{1}{6}\right)^3$ (v) $\left(\dfrac{-2}{3}\right)^5$

4. (i) $\dfrac{1}{12}$ (ii) $\dfrac{-1}{12}$ (iii) $\dfrac{-1}{3125}$ (iv) -80 (v) $-\dfrac{1}{72}$ (vi) $\dfrac{1}{50}$

   (vii) $\dfrac{79}{16}$ (viii) 1   (ix) 1

5. (i) $\left(\dfrac{5}{2}\right)^4$ (ii) $\left(\dfrac{4}{-3}\right)^3$ (iii) $\left(-\dfrac{1}{2}\right)^4$ (iv) $\left(\dfrac{7}{-3}\right)^2$ (v) $\left(\dfrac{4}{-11}\right)^3$ (vi) $\left(\dfrac{4}{-7}\right)^{208}$

   (vii) $\left(\dfrac{10}{-1}\right)^{47}$ (viii) $\left(\dfrac{17}{-3}\right)^{89}$

6. (i) $\dfrac{27}{64}$ (ii) $\dfrac{49}{64}$ (iii) $\dfrac{16}{81}$ (iv) $\dfrac{243}{32}$ 7. 1.12

EXERCISE 17 (b)

1. (i) 5^9 (ii) 7^7 (iii) 2^{14} (iv) 6^6 (v) 5^7 (vi) 4^{16}

2. (i) $\left(\dfrac{1}{3}\right)^7$ (ii) $\left(\dfrac{3}{4}\right)^{27}$ (iii) $\left(\dfrac{-5}{6}\right)^{11}$ (iv) $\left(\dfrac{-5}{9}\right)^{16}$ (v) $\left(\dfrac{4}{7}\right)^{20}$

3. (i) 3^6 (ii) 2^6 (iii) 10^6 (iv) $(-2)^{12}$ (v) $\left(\dfrac{1}{10}\right)^{10}$ (vi) $\left(-\dfrac{1}{3}\right)^{14}$

   (vii) 3^{12} (viii) $\left(\dfrac{1}{5}\right)^{20}$ (ix) $\left(\dfrac{-6}{7}\right)^{18}$ (x) $\left(\dfrac{5}{9}\right)^{21}$

4. (i) 3^{46} (ii) $\left(-\dfrac{1}{3}\right)^{26}$ (iii) $(-7)^{18}$

5. (i) 576   (ii) 4000000   (iii) $\dfrac{25}{4}$ (iv) 1   (v) 81

6. (i) 5   (ii) 8   (iii) 49   (iv) -8 (v) 81

7. (i) $\dfrac{1}{64}$ (ii) $\dfrac{1}{81}$ (iii) $\dfrac{1}{125}$ (iv) $-\dfrac{1}{64}$

8. (i) $\dfrac{9}{25}$ (ii) $\dfrac{49}{64}$ (iii) $\dfrac{-5}{4}$.

EXERCISE 17 (c)

1. (i) 1   (ii) 1   (iii) 1   (iv) $\dfrac{1}{5}$ (v) $\dfrac{1}{5^3}=\dfrac{1}{125}$ (vi) $\dfrac{1}{7^2}=\dfrac{1}{49}$ (vii) 3

2. (i) x (ii) $\dfrac{3}{2}$ (iii) $-\dfrac{1}{2}$ (iv) $-\dfrac{1}{3}$ (v) $-\dfrac{1}{4}$ (vi) -2

3. (i) 3   (ii) 0   (iii) $\dfrac{1}{3}$ (iv) $\dfrac{1}{16}$ (v) $\dfrac{16}{9}$

4. $\dfrac{1}{4}$ 5. $\dfrac{16}{3}$ 6. 729

7.   (i) 4   (ii) 1   (iii) 1   (iv) 1   (v) 27   (vi) $\dfrac{-3}{2}$

8.   (i) $\dfrac{1}{25}$ (ii) -8 (iii) $-\dfrac{1}{27}$ 9.   (i) $\dfrac{8}{27}$ (ii) 64   (iii) $\left(\dfrac{15}{19}\right)^{80}$

10. (i) $\dfrac{27}{16000}$ (ii) $\dfrac{41472}{49}$ 11. $\dfrac{729}{32}$ 12. (i) $\left(\dfrac{11}{8}\right)^{2}$ (ii) $\left(\dfrac{-7}{3}\right)$ 13. $\dfrac{-4}{27}$ 14. 16   15. $\dfrac{19}{64}$

MENTAL MATHS–14

1.   (i) $\left(\dfrac{7}{8}\right)^{5}$ (ii) $\left(\dfrac{-5}{9}\right)^{7}$ 2. (i) $\dfrac{125}{64}$ (ii) $\dfrac{16}{81}$ 3. (i) $\left(\dfrac{4}{9}\right)^{2}$ (ii) $\left(-\dfrac{1}{6}\right)^{3}$ (iii) $\left(\dfrac{1}{10}\right)^{6}$ 4. $\dfrac{2^{7} \times 3^{4}}{5^{11}}$

5. $\left(-\dfrac{1}{3}\right)^{10}$ 6. $\left(\dfrac{7}{11}\right)^{20}$ 7. 1   8. $\left(\dfrac{-3}{4}\right)^{3}$ 9. (i) $\dfrac{49}{25}$ (ii) $\dfrac{1}{-5}$ 10. $\dfrac{16}{9}$ 11. $\dfrac{9}{4}$

12. (i) $(-3)^{5}$ (ii) $(-3)^{9}$ 13. $\left(\dfrac{2}{5}\right)^{3}$

FUN WITH NUMBERS

A Curious Number

If you split the number 3025 into two parts like this 30   25

And add the two parts together:

30 + 25 = 55

And square the result : 55^{2}

you get 55 × 55 = 3025

The original number!

There are two other four digits numbers that you can play with in this way.

Which are the two numbers?

ANSWERS

The two numbers are 2025 and 9801.

18. Special Products (Some Special Identities)

18.1 Introduction

In order to save time when multiplying binomials, special formulas are framed so that the products may be found mentally. These formulas are called *special products*. Here we shall study a few *special products* or *identities*.

18.2 The Identity

$(x + a)(x + b) = x^2 + (a + b)x + ab.$

$$\begin{aligned}
\text{LHS} &= (x + a)(x + b) \\
&= x(x + b) + a(x + b) = x^2 + bx + ax + ab \\
&= x^2 + (ax + bx) + ab = x^2 + (a + b)x + ab = \text{RHS}.
\end{aligned}$$

Ex. 1. *Using the identity $(x + a)(x + b) = x^2 + (a + b)x + ab$, find the products of :*

    (a) $(x + 2)(x + 7)$ (b) $(x - 3)(x + 6)$

    (c) $(x + 7)(x - 10)$ (d) $(x - 1)(x - 8)$

Sol.

$$\begin{aligned}
\text{(a)}\quad (x + 2)(x + 7) &= x^2 + (2 + 7)x + 2 \times 7 \\
&= x^2 + 9x + 14.
\end{aligned}$$

$$\begin{aligned}
\text{(b)}\quad (x - 3)(x + 6) &= x^2 + (-3 + 6)x + (-3 \times 6) \\
&= x^2 + 3x - 18.
\end{aligned}$$

$$\begin{aligned}
\text{(c)}\quad (x + 7)(x - 10) &= x^2 + (7 + (-10))x + (7 \times -10) \\
&= x^2 - 3x - 70.
\end{aligned}$$

$$\begin{aligned}
\text{(d)}\quad (x - 1)(x - 8) &= x^2 + (-1 + (-8))x + (-1 \times -8) \\
&= x^2 - 9x + 8.
\end{aligned}$$

All these products can be verified by long method also.

Thus, $(x + 2)(x + 7) = x(x + 7) + 2(x + 7) = x^2 + 7x + 2x + 14 = x^2 + 9x + 14.$

EXERCISE 18 (a)

Find the following products using the identity:

$(x + a)(x + b) = x^2 + (a + b)x + ab$

1. $(x + 5)(x + 7)$ 2. $(x - 11)(x + 9)$

3. $(x + 12)(x - 5)$ 4. $(x + 6)(x + 13)$

5. $(x - 10)(x - 9)$ 6. $(x - 3)(x + 7)$

7. $(x + 3)(x - 1)$ 8. $(x + 3)(x + 1)$

9. $(x - 3)(x + 1)$ 10. $\left(x + \dfrac{1}{3}\right)(x + 3)$

11. $\left(x + \dfrac{2}{5}\right)\left(x + \dfrac{3}{5}\right)$ 12. $(x - 4)(x - 8)$

18.3 Square of a Binomial

Two simple binomials are $a + b$ and $a - b$. The first two identities relate to finding the square of these binomials, i.e, $(a + b)^2$ and $(a - b)^2$

$$\begin{aligned}
(a + b)^2 &= (a + b)(a + b) = a(a + b) + b(a + b) = a^2 + ab + ab + b^2 \\
&= a^2 + 2ab + b^2 \quad [\text{Since } ba = ab]
\end{aligned}$$

Thus, we have the following identity.

Identity 1 : $(a + b)^2 = a^2 + 2ab + b^2$

Aid to memory :

$$(a + b)^2 = a^2 + 2ab + b^2$$

1. Square the first term of the binomial.
2. Double the product of the two terms.
3. Square the second term of the binomial.

Also, $(a - b)^2 = (a - b)(a - b) = a(a - b) - b(a - b)$

$$= a^2 - ab - ba + b^2$$

$$= a^2 - 2ab + b^2. \quad \text{[Since } ba = ab\text{]}$$

Thus, we have the second identity as under :

Identity 2 : $(a - b)^2 = a^2 - 2ab + b^2$

Note that the signs of the square term, i.e., a^2 and b^2 are always plus. The sign of the term containing twice t product ab is the same as the sign between the two terms of the binomial.

Remark : Because each of the expressions $a^2 + 2ab + b^2$ and $a^2 - 2ab + b^2$ is a trinomial that can obtained by squaring a binomial, a polynomial that can be written in one of these forms is called a **trinomi square**. For example, since

$$m^2 + 6m + 9 = m^2 + 2(3)m + 3^2 = (m + 3)^2,$$

The trinomial $m^2 + 6m + 9$ is a trinomial square. It is also called a **perfect square trinomial.**

Ex. 1. *Find the following products* :

    (i)   **(x + 3) (x + 3)**   **(ii)**   **(2x + 3y) (2x + 3y)**   **(iii) (3x² + 5y²) (3x² + 5y²)**

Sol.   (i) $(x + 3)(x + 3) = (x + 3)^2$

         $= (x)^2 + 2 \times x \times 3 + (3)^2 = x^2 + 6x + 9.$

                                    (Ist term)² + 2 (Ist term) (2nd term) + (2nd term)²

     (ii) $(2x + 3y)(2x + 3y) = (2x + 3y)^2$

         $= (2x)^2 + 2 \times 2x \times 3y + (3y)^2 = 4x^2 + 12xy + 9y^2.$

     (iii) $(3x^2 + 5y^2)(3x^2 + 5y^2) = (3x^2 + 5y^2)^2$

         $= (3x)^2 + 2 \times 3x^2 \times 5y^2 + (5y^2)^2$

         $= 9x^4 + 30x^2y^2 + 25y^4.$

Ex. 2. *Find the following products* :

    (i)   **(3x − 5) (3x − 5)**   **(ii)** $\left(5x - \dfrac{1}{10}y\right)\left(5x - \dfrac{1}{10}y\right)$ **(iii)** $\left(\dfrac{1}{2}x^2 - \dfrac{7}{3}y^3\right)\left(\dfrac{1}{2}x^2 - \dfrac{7}{3}y^3\right)$

Sol.   (i) $(3x - 5)(3x - 5) = (3x - 5)^2$

         $= (3x)^2 - 2 \times (3x) \times 5 + (5)^2$

                                    (1st term)² − 2×1st term ×2nd term +(2nd term

         $= 9x^2 - 30x + 25$

(ii) $\left(5x - \dfrac{1}{10}y\right)\left(5x - \dfrac{1}{10}y\right) = \left(5x - \dfrac{1}{10}y\right)^2$

$$= (5x)^2 - 2 \times 5x \times \dfrac{1}{10}y + \left(\dfrac{1}{10}y\right)^2 = 25x^2 - xy + \dfrac{1}{100}y^2$$

(iii) $\left(\dfrac{1}{2}x^2 - \dfrac{7}{3}y^3\right)\left(\dfrac{1}{2}x^2 - \dfrac{7}{3}y^3\right) = \left(\dfrac{1}{2}x^2 - \dfrac{7}{3}y^3\right)^2$

$$= \left(\dfrac{1}{2}x^2\right)^2 - 2 \times \dfrac{1}{2}x^2 \times \dfrac{7}{3}y^3 + \left(\dfrac{7}{3}y^3\right)^2 = \dfrac{1}{4}x^4 - \dfrac{7}{3}x^2y^3 + \dfrac{49}{9}y^6.$$

Ex. 3. *Simplify :*

(i) $\left(4z + \dfrac{5}{2}\right)^2$ (ii) $\left(16a - \dfrac{1}{4}\right)^2$ (iii) $\left(4z^7 + \dfrac{1}{z^7}\right)^2$ (iv) $\left(5m - \dfrac{1}{5m}\right)^2.$

Sol. (i) $\left(4z + \dfrac{5}{2}\right)^2 = (4z)^2 + 2 \times 4z \times \dfrac{5}{2} + \left(\dfrac{5}{2}\right)^2 = 16z^2 + 20z + \dfrac{25}{4}.$

     (ii) $\left(16a - \dfrac{1}{4}\right)^2 = (16a)^2 - 2 \times 16a \times \dfrac{1}{4} + \left(\dfrac{1}{4}\right)^2 = 256a^2 - 8a + \dfrac{1}{16}.$

     (iii) $\left(4z^7 + \dfrac{1}{z^7}\right)^2 = (4z^7)^2 + 2 \times 4z^7 \times \dfrac{1}{z^7} + \left(\dfrac{1}{z^7}\right)^2 = 16z^{14} + 8 + \dfrac{1}{z^{14}}.$

     (iv) $\left(5m - \dfrac{1}{5m}\right)^2 = (5m)^2 - 2 \times 5m \times \dfrac{1}{5m} + \left(\dfrac{1}{5m}\right)^2 = 25m^2 - 2 + \dfrac{1}{25m^2}.$

Ex. 4. *Evaluate the following, using identities:*

     (i) $(103)^2$ (ii) 98^2

Sol. (i) $(103)^2 = (100 + 3)^2$

$$= (100)^2 + 2 \times 100 \times 3 + (3)^2$$

$$= 10000 + 600 + 9 = \mathbf{10,609.}$$

     (ii) $(98)^2 = (100 - 2)^2$

$$= (100)^2 - 2 \times 100 \times 2 + (2)^2$$

$$= 10000 - 400 + 4 = \mathbf{9,604.}$$

> Using $(a + b)^2 = a^2 + 2ab + b^2$

> Using $(a - b)^2 = a^2 - 2ab + b^2$

Ex. 5. *Find the value of the expression $25x^2 - 30xy + 9y^2$ when $x = 2$ and $y = -3$.*

Sol. $25x^2 - 30xy + 9y^2 = (5x)^2 - 2 \times 5x \times 3y + (3y)^2$

$$= (5x - 3y)^2 = [5 \times 2 - 3 \times (-3)]^2$$

$$= (10 + 9)^2 = 19^2 = \mathbf{171.}$$

> Putting $x = 2$ and $y = -3$

Ex. 6. *If* $x + \dfrac{1}{x} = 3$, *find the value of* :

    (i) $x^2 + \dfrac{1}{x^2}$ *(ii)* $x^4 + \dfrac{1}{x^4}$

Sol.   Given : $x + \dfrac{1}{x} = 3$

    (i) $\left(x + \dfrac{1}{x} \right)^2 = 3^2$ (Squaring both sides)

$$\Rightarrow \quad x^2 + 2 \times x \times \dfrac{1}{x} + \dfrac{1}{x^2} = 9$$

$$\Rightarrow \quad x^2 + 2 + \dfrac{1}{x^2} = 9 \quad \Rightarrow \quad x^2 + \dfrac{1}{x^2} = 9 - 2 = \mathbf{7.}$$

(ii) Now, squaring again both sides, we get.

$$\left(x^2 + \dfrac{1}{x^2} \right)^2 = 7^2$$

$$\Rightarrow \quad x^4 + 2 \times x^2 \times \dfrac{1}{x^2} + \dfrac{1}{x^4} = 49$$

$$\Rightarrow \quad x^4 + 2 + \dfrac{1}{x^4} = 49 \quad \Rightarrow \quad x^4 + \dfrac{1}{x^4} = 49 - 2 = \mathbf{47.}$$

EXERCISE 18 (b)

Find the following products :

1. *(i)* $(x + 2)(x + 2)$ *(ii)* $(3x + 5)(3x + 5)$ *(iii)* $\left(\dfrac{3}{4}x^2 + 5 \right)\left(\dfrac{3}{4}x^2 + 5 \right)$

2. *(i)* $(y - 9)(y - 9)$ *(ii)* $\left(7t - \dfrac{1}{2}u \right)\left(7t - \dfrac{1}{2}u \right)$ *(iii)* $(5x^2 - 4y^2)(5x^2 - 4y^2)$

Write down the squares of :

3. *(i)* $p + 5$ *(ii)* $2t + 9$ *(iii)* $5c + 2d$ *(iv)* $9m + \dfrac{1}{4}$ *(v)* $3x + \dfrac{1}{3x}$

    (vi) $(2y^2 + 5z^2)$ *(vii)* $\left(7x^3 + \dfrac{1}{7}y^3 \right)$ *(viii)* $\left(\dfrac{1}{2}a^4 + \dfrac{1}{3}b^7 \right)$

4. *(i)* $t - 3$ *(ii)* $9t - 11$ *(iii)* $7p - 8q$ *(iv)* $8m - \dfrac{1}{2}$ *(v)* $12x - \dfrac{1}{5x}$

    (vi) $3m^3 - 7n^4$ *(vii)* $x^3 - \dfrac{1}{x^3}$ *(viii)* $\dfrac{1}{5}p^5 - \dfrac{1}{2}q^6$

5. Simplify :

    (i) $(a + 8)^2$ *(ii)* $(x + 1)^2$ *(iii)* $(d - 6)^2$ *(iv)* $(7 - y)^2$ *(v)* $(a^2 + b^2)^2$

    (vi) $(m^2 - n^2)^2$ *(vii)* $(mx - ny)^2$ *(viii)* $(2ax + 9y)^2$ *(ix)* $(a^3b - xy^3)^2$ *(x)* $(0.3x + 4)^2$

    (xi) $\left(\dfrac{1}{4}x^3 + 2 \right)^2$ *(xii)* $\left(\dfrac{3}{5}a - 10b \right)^2$ *(xiii)* $\left(\dfrac{1}{3}b^2 - 3c^2 \right)^2$ *(xiv)* $\left(2x^2 + \dfrac{1}{3x^2} \right)^2$ *(xv)* $\left(5m^3 - \dfrac{1}{5m^3} \right)^2$

6. Using the identity of square of a binomial, evaluate the following :

    (i) $(102)^2$ *(ii)* $(53)^2$ *(iii)* $(501)^2$ *(iv)* $(807)^2$ *(v)* $(59)^2$

    (vi) $(48)^2$ *(vii)* $(698)^2$ *(viii)* $(999)^2$

7. **Find the value of the expression:**

    (i) $25x^2 + 70x + 49$ if $x = -1$ *(ii)* $49x^2 - 84xy + 36y^2$ if $x = 2$, $y = 3$

8. If $\left(x + \dfrac{1}{x}\right) = 12$, find the value of $\left(x^2 + \dfrac{1}{x^2}\right)$.

9. If $\left(x + \dfrac{1}{x}\right) = 5$, find the values of *(i)* $\left(x^2 + \dfrac{1}{x^2}\right)$ and *(ii)* $\left(x^4 + \dfrac{1}{x^4}\right)$.

10. If $x - \dfrac{1}{x} = 7$, find the value of $\left(x^2 + \dfrac{1}{x^2}\right)$.

11. If $x - \dfrac{1}{x} = 8$, find the values of *(i)* $\left(x^2 + \dfrac{1}{x^2}\right)$ and *(ii)* $\left(x^4 + \dfrac{1}{x^4}\right)$.

18.4 The Product of the Sum and the Difference of the Same two Terms.

The multiplication at the right shows the steps used to find the product of the binomials $a + b$ and $a - b$. Notice that two terms of the product, ab and $-ab$, are opposites, and so their sum is zero.

$$(a + b)(a - b)$$
$$= a(a - b) + b(a - b)$$
$$= a^2 - ab + ba - b^2$$
$$= a^2 \quad - \quad b^2$$

1. Square the first term.

2. Square the second term.

3. Subtract the second square from the first by placing a minus sign between the two squares.

Thus we have

$$(a + b)(a - b) = a^2 - b^2.$$

Note that there are only two terms in the product.

Remark : You can mentally find the product of two numbers if you recognize that one factor is the sum of two particular numbers and the other factor is the difference of these numbers.

Ex. 1. *Find the products* :

    (i) $(x + 6)(x - 6)$ *(ii)* $(4 - x)(4 + x)$

    (iii) $(2b + 3c)(2b - 3c)$ *(iv)* $\left(\dfrac{1}{2}ab - x^2\right)\left(\dfrac{1}{2}ab + x^2\right)$

    (v) $(5x^2 - 7y^2)(5x^2 + 7y^2)$ *(vi)* $\left(x^3 + \dfrac{1}{x^3}\right)\left(x^3 - \dfrac{1}{x^3}\right)$

ol. *(i)* $(x + 6)(x - 6) = x^2 - 6^2 = \mathbf{x^2 - 36}$.

    (ii) $(4 - x)(4 + x) = (4)^2 - x^2 = \mathbf{16 - x^2}$.

    (iii) $(2b + 3c)(2b - 3c) = (2b)^2 - (3c)^2 = \mathbf{4b^2 - 9c^2}$.

    (iv) $\left(\dfrac{1}{2}ab - x^2\right)\left(\dfrac{1}{2}ab + x^2\right) = \left(\dfrac{1}{2}ab\right)^2 - (x^2)^2 = \mathbf{\dfrac{1}{4}a^2b^2 - x^4}$.

    (v) $(5x^2 - 7y^2)(5x^2 + 7y^2) = (5x^2)^2 - (7y^2)^2 = \mathbf{25x^4 - 49y^4}$.

    (vi) $\left(x^3 + \dfrac{1}{x^3}\right)\left(x^3 - \dfrac{1}{x^3}\right) = (x^3)^2 - \left(\dfrac{1}{x^3}\right)^2 = \mathbf{x^6 - \dfrac{1}{x^6}}$.

Ex. 2. *Find the continued product* $(x+3)(x-3)(x^2+9)$.

Sol. $(x+3)(x-3)(x^2+9)$

$= [(x+3)(x-3)](x^2+9)$ $\boxed{\text{Associative Law}}$

$= (x^2-9)(x^2+9) = (x^2)^2 - (9)^2 = x^4 - 81$.

Ex. 3. *Using the identity for difference of two squares, find the product* 51×49.

Sol. $51 \times 49 = (50+1)(50-1) = (50)^2 - (1)^2 = 2500 - 1 = 2499$.

Ex. 4. *Simplify :* $279 \times 279 - 21 \times 21$.

Sol. $279 \times 279 - 21 \times 21 = (279)^2 - (21)^2$

$= (279+21)(279-21) = 300 \times 258 = 77400$.

EXERCISE 18 (c)

Find the following products :

1. (i) $(x+2)(x-2)$ (ii) $(d-8)(d+8)$ (iii) $(7-p)(7+p)$ (iv) $(4a-3b)(4a+3b)$ (v) $(5+9m)(5-9m)$

   (vi) $(ab+9)(ab-9)$ (vii) $(x^2-y^2)(x^2+y^2)$ (viii) $\left(\dfrac{2}{5}ab - c\right)\left(\dfrac{2}{5}ab + c\right)$ (ix) $\left(\dfrac{2}{b} - \dfrac{5}{c}\right)\left(\dfrac{2}{b} + \dfrac{5}{c}\right)$

2. (i) $(a+1)(a-1)(a^2+1)$ (ii) $(a+x)(a-x)(a^2+x^2)$ (iii) $\left(x - \dfrac{1}{x}\right)\left(x + \dfrac{1}{x}\right)\left(x^2 + \dfrac{1}{x^2}\right)$

   (iv) $\left(x^3 - \dfrac{1}{x^3}\right)\left(x^3 + \dfrac{1}{x^3}\right)\left(x^6 + \dfrac{1}{x^6}\right)$.

3. Using the identity for difference of two squares, find the values of :

   (i) 18×22 (ii) 71×69 (iii) 101×99 (iv) 53×47 (v) $(86)^2 - (76)^2$

   (vi) $(203)^2 - (197)^2$ (vii) $(121)^2 - (119)^2$ (viii) $(169)^2 - (131)^2$

4. Find the value of x, if :

   (i) $13x = (58)^2 - (45)^2$ (ii) $24x = (99)^2 - (87)^2$

5. Simplify :

   (i) $179 \times 179 - 21 \times 21$ (ii) $1.62 \times 1.62 - 0.38 \times 0.38$

   (iii) $\dfrac{297 \times 297 - 203 \times 203}{94}$ (iv) $\dfrac{23.71 \times 23.71 - 16.29 \times 16.29}{0.742}$

LOOKING BACK
Summary of Key Facts

1. An algebraic expression containing a single term is called a **monomial**,

     e.g. $7x$, $5x^2y$, $\dfrac{3x^2y^{-2}}{z}$ etc.

2. An algebraic expression containing two or more terms connected by '+' or '−' signs is called a **polynomial**.

3. A polynomial containing two terms is given the special name '**binomial**' and a polynomial containing three terms is called a **trinomial**, e.g. $5x - 7y$ is a binomial while $3x^2 - 6x + 7$ is a trinomial.

No special names are given to algebraic expressions containing more than three terms. They are first referred to as 'Polynomials'.

4. In a monomial like $5x^2z$, 5 is called the **numerical coefficient** of x^2z and x^2z is called the **literal coefficient** of 5.

5. Monomials like $3x, 5x$; $3x^2y, -7x^2y$ are called **like monomials** while monomials like $5x^3, -2x^2y, 7xy^2, y^3$ are called **unlike monomials**.

6. The **product of two monomials** is the product of their numerical coefficients and literals in the two monomials, the exponent of each literal being the sum of its exponents in the given monomials.

   e.g. $5a^3b^4c^7 \times -8a^5b^{25}c^{30} = (5 \times -8) \times a^{3+5}b^{4+25}c^{7+30} = -40a^8b^{29}c^{37}$.

7. **The product of a monomial and a binomial** is obtained on multiplying each term of the binomial by the monomial and adding up the two products.

   e.g. $-5x^2y(3x^2 + 5y^2) = (-5 \times 3)x^2yx^2 + (-5 \times 5)x^2yy^2 = -15x^4y - 25x^2y^3$.

8. **The product of two binomials** is obtained on multiplying each term of one binomial by each term of the other binomial and adding up the products.

   e.g. $(5x + 7y)(3x - 2y) = 5x(3x - 2y) + 7y(3x - 2y)$
   $= 15x^2 - 10xy + 21xy - 14y^2 = 15x^2 + 11xy - 14y^2$.

9. The product of a binomial and a polynomial (trinomial, expression containing 4 or more terms) is obtained on multiplying each term of the binomial with each term of the polynomial and adding up.

   e.g. $(2m - 3n)(2m^2 - 5mn + 7n^3)$
   $= (2m)(2m^2 - 5mn + 7n^2) - 3n(2m^2 - 5mn + 7n^2)$
   $= 4m^3 - 10m^2n + 14mn^2 - 6m^2n + 15mn^2 - 21n^3$
   $= 4m^3 - 16m^2n + 29mn^2 - 21n^3$.

10. **Important Identities :** For all values of a and b,

   $(a + b)^2 = a^2 + 2ab + b^2 = [$ (Ist term)^2 + 2(Ist term) (2nd term) + (2nd term)$^2]$
   $(a - b)^2 = a^2 - 2ab + b^2$
   $a^2 - b^2 = (a + b)(a - b)$

MENTAL MATHS–15

Expand using suitable identity.

1. $(x + 3)^2$ 2. $(2x - 3y)^2$

Multiply by using a suitable identity.

3. $\left(3a - \dfrac{1}{3}\right)\left(3a - \dfrac{1}{3}\right)$ 4. $(x^2 + y^2)(x^2 + y^2)$

5. $(4a - 6b)(4a + 6b)$

6. $\left(x - \dfrac{1}{x}\right)\left(x + \dfrac{1}{x}\right)$

Evaluate using identity :

7. $135^2 - 125^2$ 8. 99×101

ANSWERS

EXERCISE 18 (a)

1. $x^2 + 12x + 35$ 2. $x^2 - 2x - 99$ 3. $x^2 + 7x - 60$ 4. $x^2 + 19x + 78$ 5. $x^2 - 19x + 90$

6. $x^2 + 4x - 21$ 7. $x^2 + 2x - 3$ 8. $x^2 + 4x + 3$ 9. $x^2 - 2x - 3$ 10. $x^2 + \dfrac{10}{3}x + 1$

11. $x^2 + x + \dfrac{6}{25}$ 12. $x^2 - 12x + 32$

EXERCISE 18 (b)

1. (i) $x^2 + 4x + 4$ (ii) $9x^2 + 30x + 25$ (iii) $\dfrac{9}{16}x^4 + \dfrac{15}{2}x^2 + 25$

2. (i) $y^2 - 18y + 81$ (ii) $49t^2 - 7ut + \dfrac{1}{4}u^2$ (iii) $25x^4 - 40x^2y^2 + 16y^4$

3. (i) $p^2 + 10p + 25$ (ii) $4t^2 + 36t + 81$ (iii) $25c^2 + 20cd + 4d^2$ (iv) $81m^2 + \dfrac{9}{2}m + \dfrac{1}{16}$ (v) $9x^2 + 2 + \dfrac{1}{9x^2}$

(vi) $4y^4 + 20y^2z^2 + 25z^4$ (vii) $49x^6 + 2x^3y^3 + \frac{1}{49}y^6$ (viii) $\frac{1}{4}a^8 + \frac{1}{3}a^4b^7 + \frac{1}{9}b^{14}$

4. (i) $t^2 - 6t + 9$ (ii) $8t^2 - 198t + 121$ (iii) $49p^2 - 112pq + 64q^2$ (iv) $64m^2 - 8m + \frac{1}{4}$ (v) $144x^2 - \frac{24}{5} + \frac{1}{25x}$

(vi) $9m^6 - 42m^3n^4 + 49n^8$ (vii) $x^6 - 2 + \frac{1}{x^6}$ (viii) $\frac{1}{25}p^{10} - \frac{1}{5}p^5q^6 + \frac{1}{4}q^{12}$

5. (i) $(a^2 + 16a + 64)$ (ii) $x^2 + 2x + 1$ (iii) $d^2 - 12d + 36$ (iv) $49 - 14y + y^2$ (v) $a^4 + 2a^2b^2 +$

(vi) $m^4 - 2m^2n^2 + n^4$ (vii) $m^2x^2 - 2mnxy + n^2y^2$ (viii) $4a^2x^2 + 36axy + 81y^2$ (ix) $a^6b^2 - 2a^3bxy^3 + x^2y^6$ (x) $0.09x^2 + 2.4x + 1$

(xi) $\frac{1}{16}x^6 + x^3 + 4$ (xii) $\frac{9}{25}a^2 - 12ab + 100b^2$ (xiii) $\frac{1}{9}b^4 - 2b^2c^2 + 9c^4$ (xiv) $4x^4 + \frac{4}{3} + \frac{1}{9x^4}$ (xv) $25m^6 - 2 + \frac{1}{25m^6}$

6. (i) 10404 (ii) 2809 (iii) 251001 (iv) 651249 (v) 3481
(vi) 2304 (vii) 487204 (viii) 998001

7. (i) 4 (ii) 16 8. 142 9. (i) 23; (ii) 527 10. 51 11. (i) 66; (ii) 4354

EXERCISE 18 (c)

1. (i) $x^2 - 4$ (ii) $d^2 - 64$ (iii) $49 - p^2$ (iv) $16a^2 - 9b^2$ (v) $25 - 81m^2$

(vi) $a^2b^2 - 81$ (vii) $x^4 - y^4$ (viii) $\frac{4}{25}a^2b^2 - c^2$ (ix) $\frac{4}{b^2} - \frac{25}{c^2}$

2. (i) $a^4 - 1$ (ii) $a^4 - x^4$ (iii) $x^4 - \frac{1}{x^4}$ (iv) $x^{12} - \frac{1}{x^{12}}$

3. (i) 396 (ii) 4899 (iii) 9999 (iv) 2491 (v) 1620
(vi) 2400 (vii) 480 (viii) 11400

4. (i) 103 (ii) 93

5. (i) 31600 (ii) 2.48 (iii) 500 (iv) 400

MENTAL MATHS–15

1. $x^2 + 6x + 9$ 2. $4x^2 - 12xy + 9y^2$ 3. $9a^2 - 2a + \frac{1}{9}$ 4. $x^4 + 2x^2y^2 + y^4$ 5. $16a^2 - 36b^2$ 6. $x^2 - \frac{1}{x^2}$
7. 2600 8. 9999

INTERESTING NUMBER FACTS

1. 3,4 and 5 are the only consecutive positive integers, the sum of whose cubes is itself a perfect cube.

2. 1729 is the smallest positive integer that can be expressed as the sum of two cubes in different ways as $12^3 + 1^3$ and $10^3 + 9^3$.

3. The product of four consecutive positive integers can never be equal to a perfect square.

4. $1^2 + 2^2 + 3^2 + ... + 24^2 = 49,00 = 70^2$.

For no other value of n is true that the sum of the first n perfect squares is itself a perfect square.

19. Factorisation of Algebraic Expressions

19.1 Introduction

You know that two or more numbers that are multiplied to form a product are called factors. For example, since $15 = 3 \times 5$, therefore, 3 is a factor of 15 and also 5 is a factor of 15. In Algebra, since $a(b + c) = ab + ac$, therefore, the polynomial $ab + ac$ has the factors a and $b + c$. A factor such as a is a **common monomial factor** in the terms ab and ac. Look at these examples :

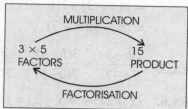

Finding products

$$a(b + c) = ab + ac$$
$$3(x + y) = 3x + 3y$$
$$a(b + c + d) = ab + ac + ad$$
$$3x(4x^2 - 2x - 7) = 12x^3 - 6x^2 - 21x$$

Finding factors

$$ab + ac = a(b + c)$$
$$3x + 3y = 3(x + y)$$
$$ab + ac + ad = a(b + c + d)$$
$$12x^3 - 6x^2 - 21x = 3x(4x^2 - 2x - 7)$$

In $3x + 3y$, 3 is the common monomial factor, and $x + y$ is the other factor. Notice that you usually do not factorise the number when you are factorising a polynomial. You do not need to write $10x + 10y$ as $2 \times 5 \times (x + y)$.

19.2 Type 1. To factorise a polynomial whose terms have a common monomial factor.

Sample solutions :

Ex. 1. $7x - 7y = 7(x - y)$ — Take out the common factor 7.
Ex. 2. $ac - bc + c = c(a - b + 1)$ — Take out the common factor c.
Ex. 3. $6x^4 - 15x^3 + 3x^2 = 3x^2(2x^2 - 5x + 1)$ — Take out the greatest common factor $3x^2$.
Ex. 4. $4m^3n - 7m^2n^2 = m^2n(4m - 7n)$ — Take out the greatest common factor m^2n.

EXERCISE 19 (a)

Factorise the following polynomials:

1. $3x - 12$
2. $80 + 16y$
3. $8x - 8y$
4. $7x + 14$
5. $a^2 + 7a$
6. $5y - 7y^2$
7. $8c^2 - 24c$
8. $5m^2 - 6m.$
9. $12u - 20uv$
10. $10pq - 12p^2q$
11. $24d + 32d^3$
12. $30g + 54gh$
13. $28c^2d^2 - 21c^2d$
14. $36y^3z + 48y^2z^2$
15. $6p + 8p^2 - 4p^3$
16. $12a^3 - 15a^2 - 7a$
17. $15y^2z^3 - 20y^3z^4 + 35y^2z^2$
18. $14m^5n^4p^2 - 42m^7n^3p^7 - 70m^6n^5p^3$

19.3 Type 2. When the given algebraic expression contains common binomial factors.

Sample Solutions :

Ex. 1. $b(b + d) - d(b + d) = (b + d)(b - d)$ — The common binomial factor is $(b + d)$

Ex. 2. $y(y - 3) + 7(y - 3) = (y - 3)(y + 7)$ — The common binomial factor is $(y - 3)$.

Ex. 3. $a(z^2 + 5) - (z^2 + 5)$
$= a(z^2 + 5) - 1(z^2 + 5)$
$= (z^2 + 5)(a - 1)$ — The common binomial factor is $(z^2 + 5)$
$-(z^2 + 5)$ means $-1(z^2 + 5)$ **[Note]**

In working with common binomial factors, you should learn to recognize factors that are opposites of each other.

For example :

$$x - y = x + (-y) = -y + x = -(y - x)$$

$$\boxed{x - y = -(y - x)}$$

Ex.4. $n(n - 3) - 7(3 - n)$

Notice that $n - 3$ and $3 - n$ are opposites.

$= n(n - 3) - 7[-(n - 3)]$ **[Step 1]**

After some parctice you should be able

$= n(n - 3) + 7(n - 3)$ **[Step 2]**

to omit step 2 and write step 3 directly.

$= (n - 3)(n + 7).$ **[Step 3]**

Ex.5. $\dfrac{3b - 3a}{7a - 7b} = \dfrac{3(b - a)}{7(a - b)} = \dfrac{-3(a - b)}{7(a - b)} = -\dfrac{3}{7}.$

Ex.6. $(x - 2)^2 + 9(x - 2) = (x - 2)[(x - 2) + 9] = (x - 2)(x + 7).$

EXERCISE 19 (b)

Factorise the following polynomials :

1.	$z(z - 1) + 2(z - 1)$	**2.**	$6(3 + x) + x(3 + x)$
3.	$2y(y + 5) - 3(y + 5)$	**4.**	$5t(t - 4) - 6(t - 4)$
5.	$5(2 + b) - 6b(2 + b)$	**6.**	$x(x + 11) + (x + 11)$
7.	$p(6 - p) - (6 - p)$	**8.**	$d(d - 5) + 7(5 - d)$
9.	$(x + 2)^2 + 5(x + 2)$	**10.**	$(y - 2)^2 - 3(y - 2)$
11.	$14(3y - 5z)^3 + 7(3y - 5z)^2$	**12.**	$(n - 10)^2 + (10 - n)$
13.	$5x + 10y - 7(x + 2y)^2$	**14.**	$(x + y)(3x - 7) - (x + y)(2x - 11)$
15.	$(3a - 1)^2 - 6a + 2$	**16.**	$x(x - 2z) + y(x - 2z) + (2z - x)$

19.4 Type 3. Grouping Suitable Terms.

Sometimes the terms of the given polynomial need to be arranged in suitalbe groups so that each group has common factor.

Ex.7. **Factorise :**

     (i) $a^2 + bc + ab + ac$ **(ii)** $p^2q - pr^2 - pq + r^2$

Sol.   **(i)** $a^2 + bc + ab + ac$

     $= a^2 + ab + ac + bc$ [Shift bc as shown]

     $= a(a + b) + c(a + b)$

     $= (a + b)(a + c).$

For suitably re-arranging the terms, work out mentally what arrangement would give common binomial factor. Here we have shifted bc to a new position.

     (ii) $p^2q - pr^2 - pq + r^2$

     $= p^2q - pq - pr^2 + r^2$

     $= pq(p - 1) - r^2(p - 1)$

     $= (p - 1)(pq - r^2).$

Here we have interchanged the positions of $-pq$ and $-pr^2$

EXERCISE 19 (c)

Factorise :

1.	$ax^2 + by^2 + bx^2 + ay^2$	**2.**	$a^2 + 2b + ab + 2a$	**3.**	$px + qx + py + qy$
4.	$x^3 + 3x^2 + 6x + 18$	**5.**	$x^2 - ax - bx + ab$	**6.**	$3ac + 2bc + 3ad + 2bd$
7.	$8pr + 4qr + 6ps + 3qs$	**8.**	$7ab + 9cb + 7ad + 9cd$	**9.**	$3mn + 2pn + 3mq + 2pq$
10.	$10pq - 3rq - 10ps + 3rs$	**11.**	$ab^2 - bc^2 - ab + c^2$	**12.**	$2b^2 + 8ab + 4ac + bc$
13.	$6pm + 9mq + 8pn + 12qn$	**14.**	$2axy^2 + 10x + 3ay^2 + 15$		

19.5 Factorising Difference of two Squares

Formula : $a^2 - b^2 = (a + b)(a - b)$

Method

1. *Find the square roots of the two square terms.*
2. *Write the sum of the two square roots as one of the factors.*
3. *Write the difference of the two square roots as the other factor.*

Caution. Two square terms with a plus sign between them (for example, $a^2 + b^2$) is the sum of two squares and cannot be factorised by the above method.

Ex.1. *Factorise*:

    (i) $x^2 - 16$ *(ii)* $9 - x^2$ *(iii)* $\dfrac{16}{81}m^2 - 121$ *(iv)* $64a^6 - 49b^2c^4$

    (v) $49(2x + y)^2 - 64(x - 3y)^2$ *(vi)* $5 - 20x^2$

Sol. *(i)* $x^2 - 16 = (x)^2 - 4^2 = (x + 4)(x - 4)$.

    (ii) $9 - x^2 = (3)^2 - x^2 = (3 + x)(3 - x)$.

    (iii) $\dfrac{16}{81}m^2 - 121 = \left(\dfrac{4}{9}m\right)^2 - (11)^2 = \left(\dfrac{4}{9}m + 11\right)\left(\dfrac{4}{9}m - 11\right)$.

    (iv) $64a^6 - 49b^2c^4 = (8a^3)^2 - (7bc^2)^2 = (8a^3 + 7bc^2)(8a^3 - 7bc^2)$.

    (v) $49(2x + y)^2 - 64(x - 3y)^2$ $= [7(2x + y)]^2 - [8(x - 3y)]^2$

                                 $= (14x + 7y)^2 - (8x - 24y)^2$

                                 $= (14x + 7y + 8x - 24y)(14x + 7y - 8x + 24y)$

> Note, that because of the '–' sign before the bracket –24y beomes + 24y.

                                 $= (22x - 17y)(6x + 31y)$.

    (vi) $5 - 20x^2 = 5(1 - 4x^2)$

                   $= 5[(1)^2 - (2x)^2]$

                   $= 5(1 + 2x)(1 - 2x)$.

> Always look for the common factor first. Here the common factor is 5.

Ex.2. **Factorise:**

    (i) $b^4 - x^4$ *(ii)* $81x^4 - y^4$ *(iii)* $2x^4 - 32$.

Sol. *(i)* $b^4 - x^4 = (b^2)^2 - (x^2)^2$

                   $= (b^2 + x^2)(b^2 - x^2)$

                   $= (b^2 + x^2)(b + x)(b - x)$.

    (ii) $81x^4 - y^4 = (9x^2)^2 - (y^2)^2$

                     $= (9x^2 + y^2)(9x^2 - y^2) = (9x^2 + y^2)[(3x)^2 - y^2]$

                     $= (9x^2 + y^2)(3x + y)(3x - y)$.

> **Caution**
>
> Note that the second expression, (viz. $b^2 - x^2$ is also a difference of two squares. Do not forget to factorise it)

    (iii) $2x^4 - 32 = 2(x^4 - 16) = 2[(x^2)^2 - 4^2]$

                   $= 2(x^2 + 4)(x^2 - 4) = 2(x^2 + 4)(x + 2)(x - 2)$.

> First take out the common factor 2

EXERCISE 19 (d)

Factorise the following binomials :

1. $a^2 - 4$ 2. $25 - x^2$ 3. $9b^2 - 16$ 4. $49p^2 - 16$

5. $a^2 - b^2$ 6. $a^2x^2 - y^2$ 7. $49c^2 - 25d^2$ 8. $100 - r^2$

9. $49a^2 - 1$ 10. $100b^2 - 81$ 11. $x^2y^2 - 4$ 12. $1 - d^2$

13. $b^4 - 100$ 14. $25 - a^2x^2$ 15. $144 - a^6$ 16. $b^4 - a^2$

17. $a^2b^2 - y^2$ **18.** $\frac{1}{4}b^2 - 49$ **19.** $c^2 - 0.36$ **20.** $x^2 - \frac{1}{9}$

21. $\frac{4}{25}m^2 - 64$ **22.** $\frac{x^2}{9} - \frac{y^2}{4}$ **23.** $\frac{36}{a^2} - \frac{25}{b^2}$ **24.** $x^2 - 0.01$

25. $25(x + y)^2 - 36(x - 2y)^2$ [**Hint :** given expression $= (5x + 5y)^2 - (6x - 12y)^2$]

26. $81 - (x - 7)^2$ **27.** $x^3 - x$ **28.** $18a^2x^2 - 32$ **29.** $3x^3y - 243xy^3$

30. $a^4 - 81$ **31.** $x^4 - y^4$ **32.** $a^4 - 16x^4$

LOOKING BACK

Summary of Key Facts

1. When an expression is the product of two or more expressions then each of the these expressions is called a **factor** of the given expression.

   e.g. (*i*) 5, *x*, *y*, 5*x*, 5*y*, *xy* are all factors of 5*xy*.

   (*ii*) *x* and *a* + *b* are factors of *x* (*a* + *b*).

2. The process of writing a given algebraic expession as the product of two or more factors is called factorisation.

   e.g. factorising $x^2 + ax$ means, writing it in the form $x(x + a)$.

3. The greatest common factor of two or more monomials is the product of the greatest common factors of the numerical coefficients and the common letters with smallest powers.

   e.g. greatest common factor of $16x^4y^9$ and $24x^7y^5$ is $8x^4y^5$.

4. A binomial may be factorised by taking out the greatest common factor of the two terms of the binomial.

   e.g. $16x^4y^9 + 24x^7y^5 = 8x^4y^5(2y^4 + 3x^3)$.

5. When a binomial is a common factor, we factorise by writing the given expression as the product of this binomial and the quotient of the given expression by the binomial.

   e.g. $x(a + b) + y(a + b) = (a + b)(x + y)$

6. If the given expression is the difference of two squares, we use the formula $a^2 - b^2 = (a + b)(a - b)$

       e.g. $16x^2 - 25y^2 = (4x)^2 - (5y)^2 = (4x + 5y)(4x - 5y)$.

MENTAL MATHS 16

Factorise :

1. $x^2 + x$ **2.** $6x^2 + 12x$ **3.** $x^2y - xy^2$ **4.** $5x + 35$ **5.** $5(p + q) - 7q(p + q$

6. $(x + 3)y + (x + 3)x$ **7.** $2p(y - x) + q(x - y)$ **8.** $9a^2 - 16b^2$ **9.** $100 - \frac{49}{16a^2}$ **10.** $3a^3 - 48a$.

ANSWERS

EXERCISE 19 (a)

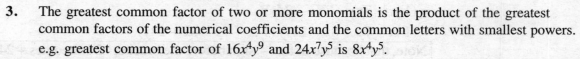

1. $3(x - 4)$ **2.** $16(5 + y)$ **3.** $8(x - y)$ **4.** $7(x + 2)$ **5.** $a(a + 7)$ **6.** $y(5 - 7y)$ **7.** $8c(c - 3)$

8. $m(5m - 6)$ **9.** $4u(3 - 5v)$ **10.** $2pq(5 - 6p)$ **11.** $8d(3 + 4d^2)$ **12.** $6g(5 + 9h)$ **13.** $7c^2d(4d - 3)$

14. $12y^2z(3y + 4z)$ **15.** $2p(3 + 4p - 2p^2)$ **16.** $a(12a^2 - 15a - 7)$ **17.** $5y^2z^2(3z - 4yz^2 + 7)$

18. $14m^5n^3p^2(n - 3m^2p^5 - 5mn^2p)$

EXERCISE 19 (b)

1. $(z-1)(z+2)$ 2. $(3+x)(6+x)$ 3. $(y+5)(2y-3)$ 4. $(t-4)(5t-6)$ 5. $(2+b)(5-6b)$ 6. $(x+11)(x+1)$ 7. $(6-p)(p-1)$

8. $(d-5)(d-7)$ 9. $(x+2)(x+7)$ 10. $(y-2)(y-5)$ 11. $7(3y-5z)^2(6y-10z+1)$ 12. $(n-10)(n-11)$

13. $(x+2y)(5-7x-14y)$ 14. $(x+y)(x+4)$ 15. $3(3a-1)(a-1)$ 16. $(x-2z)(x+y-1)$

EXERCISE 19 (c)

1. $(a+b)(x^2+y^2)$ 2. $(a+2)(a+b)$ 3. $(p+q)(x+y)$ 4. $(x^2+6)(x+3)$ 5. $(x-a)(x-b)$ 6. $(3a+2b)(c+d)$

7. $(4r+3s)(2p+q)$ 8. $(7a+9c)(b+d)$ 9. $(3m+2p)(n+q)$ 10. $(10p-3r)(q-s)$ 11. $(ab-c^2)(b-1)$

12. $(2b+c)(b+4a)$ 13. $(3m+4n)(2p+3q)$ 14. $(2x+3)(ay^2+5)$

EXERCISE 19 (d)

1. $(a+2)(a-2)$ 2. $(5+x)(5-x)$ 3. $(3b+4)(3b-4)$ 4. $(7p+4)(7p-4)$ 5. $(a+b)(a-b)$ 6. $(ax+y)(ax-y)$ 7. $(7c+5d)(7c-5d)$

8. $(10+r)(10-r)$ 9. $(7a+1)(7a-1)$ 10. $(10b+9)(10b-9)$ 11. $(xy+2)(xy-2)$ 12. $(1+d)(1-d)$ 13. $(b^2+10)(b^2-10)$

14. $(5+ax)(5-ax)$ 15. $(12+a^3)(12-a^3)$ 16. $(b^2+a)(b^2-a)$ 17. $(ab+y)(ab-y)$ 18. $\left(\dfrac{1}{2}b+7\right)\left(\dfrac{1}{2}b-7\right)$

19. $(c+0.6)(c-0.6)$ 20. $\left(x+\dfrac{1}{3}\right)\left(x-\dfrac{1}{3}\right)$ 21. $\left(\dfrac{2}{5}m+8\right)\left(\dfrac{2}{5}m-8\right)$ 22. $\left(\dfrac{x}{3}+\dfrac{y}{2}\right)\left(\dfrac{x}{3}-\dfrac{y}{2}\right)$ 23. $\left(\dfrac{6}{a}+\dfrac{5}{b}\right)\left(\dfrac{6}{a}-\dfrac{5}{b}\right)$

24. $(x+0.1)(x-0.1)$ 25. $(11x-7y)(-x+17y)$ 26. $(x+2)(-x+16)$ 27. $x(x+1)(x-1)$ 28. $2(3ax+4)(3ax-4)$

29. $3xy(x-9y)(x+9y)$ 30. $(a-3)(a+3)(a^2+9)$ 31. $(x-y)(x+y)(x^2+y^2)$ 32. $(a-2x)(a+2x)(a^2+4x^2)$

MENTAL MATHS - 16

1. $x(x+1)$ 2. $6x(x+2)$ 3. $xy(x-y)$ 4. $5(x+7)$ 5. $(5-7q)(p+q)$ 6. $(x+3)(y+x)$ 7. $(x-y)(-2p+q)$

8. $(3a+4b)(3a-4b)$ 9. $\left(10+\dfrac{7}{4a}\right)\left(10-\dfrac{7}{4a}\right)$ 10. $3a(a+4)(a-4)$

THINK ABOUT IT

1. A famous mathematician named Lagrange stated a theorem that all whole numbers could always be split into square numbers.

Thus $24 = 16 + 4 + 4$; $35 = 25 + 9 + 1$

Now try yourself

Split the following numbers into square numbers.

(i) 29   (ii) 37   (iii) 47   (iv) 52   (v) 59

2. Lagrange also stated that there are no numbers which need more than four square numbers. Try to contradict this statement if you can. A new theorem will then be named after you.

PUZZLE

What two perfect squares when subtracted equal another perfect square ?   **Ans. 25, 16.**

20. Simplification of Algebraic Fractions

20.1 Introduction

You have already studied about fractions in Pure Arithmetic. In this chapter, you will study about algebraic fractions and their simplifications.

20.2 Algebraic Fraction

Fractions like $\dfrac{x}{5}$, $\dfrac{y-3}{7}$, $\dfrac{5x}{2x^2-1}$, $\dfrac{x^3+1}{2x^2+x-1}$ having polynomials in the numerator or denominator or both are called **algebraic fractions.**

An algebraic fraction is in its simplest form when the polynomials in the numerator and denominator do not have a common factor (except1).

Ex.1 *Reduce the following algebraic fractions to lowest terms :*

(i) $\dfrac{3b}{6ab}$ (ii) $\dfrac{5x^2}{10xy}$ (iii) $\dfrac{15\,m^2p^3}{18\,n^4p}$

Sol.   (i) $\dfrac{3b}{6ab}=\dfrac{\cancel{3}\times\cancel{b}}{2\times\cancel{3}\times a\times\cancel{b}}=\dfrac{1}{2a}$.   (ii) $\dfrac{5x^2}{10xy}=\dfrac{\cancel{5}\times\cancel{x}\times x}{2\times\cancel{5}\times\cancel{x}\times y}=\dfrac{x}{2y}$.

(iii) $\dfrac{15m^2p^3}{18n^4p}=\dfrac{5m^2p^2}{6n^4}$.

> Think: $\dfrac{15}{18}=\dfrac{5}{6}$, $\dfrac{p^3}{p}=p^{3-1}=p^2$

20.3 Operations on Algebraic Fractions :

■ *To multiply algebraic fractions, multiply together all the numerators to form a new numerator and all the denominators to form a new denominator.*

For example : $\dfrac{12a^2b}{8ab^3}\times\dfrac{24ab^2}{36bc^2}=\dfrac{\overset{1}{\cancel{12}}a^2b\times\overset{\overset{1}{\cancel{3}}}{\cancel{24}}ab^2}{\underset{\underset{3}{\cancel{8}}}{}ab^3\times\underset{3}{\cancel{36}}bc^2}=\dfrac{a^2b\times ab^2}{ab^3\times bc^2}=\dfrac{a^3b^3}{ab^4c^2}=\dfrac{a^2}{bc^2}$.

> Think: $\dfrac{a^3}{a}=a^{3-1}=a^2$, $\dfrac{b^3}{b^4}=\dfrac{1}{b^{4-3}}=\dfrac{1}{b}$

■ *To divide one algebraic fraction by another, multiply the dividend by the reciprocal of the divisor.*

For example : $\dfrac{5x^2}{2a^2b}\div\dfrac{3b^2}{2x}=\dfrac{5x^2}{2a^2b}\times\underset{\text{Reciprocal}}{\underset{\uparrow}{\dfrac{2x}{3b^2}}}=\dfrac{5x^2\times2x}{2a^2b\times3b^2}=\dfrac{5x^3}{3a^2b^3}$.

> Think: $x^2\times x=x^{2+1}=x^3$, $b\times b^2=b^{1+2}=b^3$

■ *To add or subtract algebraic fractions, express all the fractions with their lowest common denominator. Now, form the algebraic sum of the numerators and retain the common denominator. Now, simplify.*

For example : $\dfrac{4a}{7}+\dfrac{2a}{3}=\dfrac{3\times4a+7\times2a}{21}=\dfrac{12a+14a}{21}=\dfrac{26a}{21}$.

> LCM = 21

Ex.2. *Simplify the following algebraic expressions :*

$(i)\ \dfrac{8m^2n^3}{5x^2yz} \times \dfrac{15xyz^3}{16mn^2}$

$(ii)\ \dfrac{15b^2}{40c} \times \dfrac{27c^2}{81d^3} \div \dfrac{abc}{8d^3}$

Sol. $(i)\ \dfrac{8m^2n^3}{5x^2yz} \times \dfrac{15xyz^3}{16mn^2} = \dfrac{\overset{1}{\cancel{8}}\times\overset{3}{\cancel{15}}}{\underset{1}{\cancel{5}}\times\underset{2}{\cancel{16}}}\times\dfrac{m^2}{m}\times\dfrac{n^3}{n^2}\times\dfrac{x}{x^2}\times\dfrac{y}{y}\times\dfrac{z^3}{z} = \dfrac{3mnz^2}{2x}$.

$(ii)\ \dfrac{15b^2}{40c}\times\dfrac{27c^2}{81d^3} \div \dfrac{abc}{8d^3} = \dfrac{15b^2}{40c}\times\dfrac{27c^2}{81d^3}\times\dfrac{8d^3}{abc} = \dfrac{15\times27\times8}{40\times81}\times\dfrac{b^2}{c}\times\dfrac{c^2}{d^3}\times\dfrac{d^3}{abc} = \dfrac{b}{a}$.

Ex.3. *Simplify the following algebraic expressions :*

$(i)\ \dfrac{2x}{3} + \dfrac{x}{4} - \dfrac{5x}{6}$

$(ii)\ \dfrac{2(x-5)}{10} + \dfrac{3x}{5}$

$(iii)\ \dfrac{3(x-2)}{7} + \dfrac{2(2x+1)}{14} + x$

Sol. $(i)\ \dfrac{2x}{3} + \dfrac{x}{4} - \dfrac{5x}{6} = \dfrac{4\times2x + 3\times x - 2\times5x}{12} = \dfrac{8x+3x-10x}{12} = \dfrac{x}{12}$.
$\boxed{LCM = 12}$

$(ii)\ \dfrac{2(x+5)}{10} - \dfrac{3x}{5} = \dfrac{2(x+5)-2\times3x}{10} = \dfrac{2x+10-6x}{10} = \dfrac{10-4x}{10} = \dfrac{\overset{1}{\cancel{2}}(5-2x)}{\underset{5}{\cancel{10}}} = \dfrac{5-2x}{5}$.

$(iii)\ \dfrac{3(x-2)}{7} + \dfrac{2(2x+1)}{14} + x = \dfrac{2\times3(x-2)+2(2x+1)+14\times x}{14}$
$\boxed{LCM = 14}$

$= \dfrac{6x-12+4x+2+14x}{14} = \dfrac{24x-10}{14} = \dfrac{\overset{1}{\cancel{2}}(12x-5)}{\underset{7}{\cancel{14}}} = \dfrac{12x-5}{7}$.

Ex.4. *Simplify the following algebraic expressions :*

$(i)\ \dfrac{5a}{4}$ **of** $\left(\dfrac{5a}{4} - \dfrac{4a}{5}\right)$

$(ii)\ \left(\dfrac{2x}{3} + \dfrac{4x}{5}\right) \div \left(\dfrac{5x^2}{6} - \dfrac{7x^2}{12}\right)$

Sol. $(i)\ \dfrac{5a}{4}$ **of** $\left(\dfrac{5a}{4} - \dfrac{4a}{5}\right) = \dfrac{5a}{4}$ of $\left(\dfrac{25a-16a}{20}\right) = \dfrac{5a}{4}$ of $\dfrac{9a}{20} = \dfrac{5a}{4}\times\dfrac{9a}{20} = \dfrac{9a^2}{16}$.

$(ii)\ \left(\dfrac{2x}{3} + \dfrac{4x}{5}\right) \div \left(\dfrac{5x^2}{6} - \dfrac{7x^2}{12}\right) = \left(\dfrac{10x+12x}{15}\right) \div \left(\dfrac{10x^2-7x^2}{12}\right) = \dfrac{22x}{15} \div \dfrac{3x^2}{12} = \dfrac{22x}{\underset{5}{\cancel{15}}}\times\dfrac{\overset{4}{\cancel{12}}}{3x^2} = \dfrac{88}{15x}$.

EXERCISE 20

1. Reduce the following algebraic fractions to lowest terms.

$(i)\ \dfrac{14a^2b}{56ab}$

$(ii)\ \dfrac{21x^2y^2}{28y^2z^2}$

$(iii)\ \dfrac{8abc^2}{20a^3b^2c}$

$(iv)\ \dfrac{18a^5xy^2}{16a^2xy^5}$

2. Multiply and express the result in lowest terms :

$(i)\ \dfrac{4x^2}{5y} \times \dfrac{3y}{16x}$

$(ii)\ \dfrac{16x^2y^3}{9a^3} \times \dfrac{27a^2}{8xy}$

$(iii)\ \dfrac{2x}{5a} \times \dfrac{3a^2}{4x} \times \dfrac{5}{6ax}$

$(iv)\ \dfrac{16a^2b^3}{3ac^4} \times \dfrac{25c^2}{32ab^4} \times \dfrac{9ab^3}{5c}$

$(v)\ 3x^2y \times \dfrac{(4x-y)}{3x}$

3. Divide :

$(i)\ \dfrac{2ab^2}{3c^3} \div \dfrac{4a^3b}{9c^2}$

$(ii)\ \dfrac{5x^2y}{6ad} \div \dfrac{10xy^2}{3a^2d}$

$(iii)\ \dfrac{3a^2c^4}{4b^2} \div 6ac^2$

$(iv)\ 4abc \div \dfrac{2a^2b}{3d^2}$.

4. **Simplify the following algebraic expressions :**

(i) $\dfrac{4x}{9}+\dfrac{5x}{6}$
(ii) $\dfrac{2a}{13}-\dfrac{4a}{39}$
(iii) $\dfrac{x}{4}-\dfrac{x}{8}+\dfrac{x}{12}$
(iv) $\dfrac{2x}{3}-\dfrac{x}{6}+\dfrac{3x}{4}$
(v) $\dfrac{3(3x+2)}{4}-\dfrac{2(4x+5)}{5}$

(vi) $c-\dfrac{c-1}{3}-\dfrac{c+2}{6}$
(vii) $\dfrac{1+3b}{6}-\dfrac{b}{2}$
(viii) $\dfrac{1}{2}\left(\dfrac{4x}{5}-\dfrac{1}{3}\right)-\dfrac{2}{3}\left(\dfrac{x}{4}+\dfrac{1}{5}\right)$

5. **Subtract :** $\dfrac{a}{10}+\dfrac{b}{4}-\dfrac{2c}{3}$ from $\dfrac{3a}{5}-\dfrac{3b}{4}+\dfrac{5c}{6}$

6. **Simplify :**

(i) $\dfrac{2a}{5}$ of $\left(\dfrac{(a+b)}{4}-\dfrac{(a-b)}{12}\right)$
(ii) $\left(\dfrac{x}{4}-\dfrac{x}{6}+\dfrac{x}{12}\right)\div\left(\dfrac{x}{6}-\dfrac{x}{3}+\dfrac{2x}{9}\right)$
(iii) $\left(\dfrac{5c}{3}-c\right)\left(\dfrac{c}{2}-\dfrac{c}{5}\right)\left(c+\dfrac{2c}{4}\right)$

(iv) $\left(1-\dfrac{2c-1}{15}+\dfrac{2-c}{6}\right)\div\dfrac{2}{5c}$

LOOKING BACK

A Summary of Key Facts

1. A fraction having polynomials in the numerator and denominator is called an algebraic fraction.
2. An algebraic fraction is in its simplest form, when the numerator and denominator do not have a common factor except 1.
3. The rules for addition, subtraction, multiplication and division of algebraic fractions are the same as those for arithmetical fractions.

ANSWERS

EXERCISE 20

1. (i) $\dfrac{a}{4}$
(ii) $\dfrac{3x^2}{4z^2}$
(iii) $\dfrac{2c}{5a^2b}$
(iv) $\dfrac{9a^3}{8y^3}$

2. (i) $\dfrac{3x}{20}$
(ii) $\dfrac{6xy^2}{a}$
(iii) $\dfrac{1}{4x}$
(iv) $\dfrac{15ab^2}{2c^3}$
(v) $xy(4x-y)$

3. (i) $\dfrac{3b}{2a^2c}$
(ii) $\dfrac{xa}{4y}$
(iii) $\dfrac{ac^2}{8b^2}$
(iv) $\dfrac{6cd^2}{a}$

4. (i) $\dfrac{23x}{18}$
(ii) $\dfrac{2a}{39}$
(iii) $\dfrac{5x}{24}$
(iv) $\dfrac{5x}{4}$
(v) $\dfrac{13x-10}{20}$
(vi) $\dfrac{1}{2}c$
(vii) $\dfrac{1}{6}$
(viii) $\dfrac{7x-9}{30}$

5. $\dfrac{1}{2}(a-2b+3c)$
6. (i) $\dfrac{a^2+2ab}{15}$
(ii) 3
(iii) $\dfrac{3c^3}{10}$
(iv) $\dfrac{14c-3c^2}{4}$

21. Linear Equations in one Variable

21.1 What is an Equation ?

An equation is a mathematical sentence involving an equal sign. Thus :

$$4 + 4 = 8 \text{ is an equation.}$$

An algebraic equation is an equation which contains one or more algebraic symbols.
Thus $5x + 3 = 38$ is an algebraic equation,
and $3x^2 + 7x + 8 = 0$ is also an algebraic equation.

The algebraic symbol (like x) in the equation is called the **unknown,** and the process of finding the number it represents is called **solving the equation.** An equation is like **balanced scales.** Just as you have two sides of an equation, so you have two pans in a balance. Just as there is the sign of equality in an equation, so there is the horizontal beam in a balance. Just as the two sides of an equation are equal, so the weights in the two pans are equal in a balanced scale.

An equation is called a **simple equation** if the unknown is raised to the *first power only* or, if it contains fractions, the unknown does not appear in the denominator.

Any equation consists of a **left side**, an equal sign ("=") and a **right side**. Here is the general pattern.

$$\boxed{\text{Left side}} \; = \; \boxed{\text{Right side}}$$

Thus in the equation $x - 2 = 7$, we have

$$\underbrace{x - 2}_{Left\ side} \quad = \quad \underbrace{7}_{Right\ side}$$

Testing whether the value found representing the unknown will satisfy the conditions of the equation is called **checking or verifying the solution.** To check, the value is substituted for the variable in the given equation. If the resulting answers of the two sides are the same, the value found is correct.

21.2 Solving Simple Equations

You will work with four kinds of equations :

Equations involving addition	$x + 2 = 8$
Equations involving subtraction	$y - 3 = 5$
Equations involving multiplication	$6t = 24$
Equations involving division	$\dfrac{p}{2} = 3$

You have learnt in class VI that you solve each type of equation by reducing it to the form.

$x = a$ **number**

This you do by undoing the operation combining the unknown and the arithmetic number by the opposite o inverse operation with the same number not disturbing the balance of the equality.

Study the following pictures carefully. They will help you to understand the basic rules for solving simpl equations.

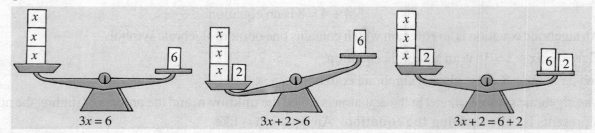

Both sides of an equation remain equal if the same number is added to both sides.

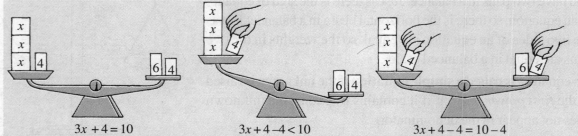

Both sides of an equation remain equal if the same number is subtracted from both sides.

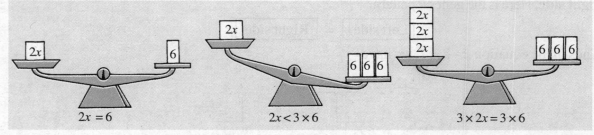

Both sides of an equation remain equal if both sides are multiplied by the same number.

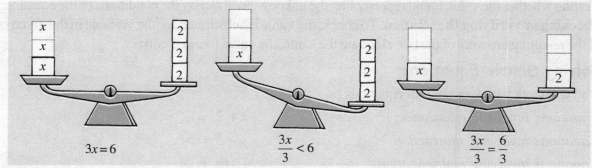

Both sides of an equation remain equal if both sides are divided by the same number.

Using the above rules, we now show how you can solve the four types of equations.

Ex. 1 *Solve : 3 x + 2 = 14.*

Sol. Since $3x + 2$ means that x is multiplied by 3 and then 2 is added to it, we must use the opposite, or invers operation to get back to x. Hence we shall first subtract 2 from both members of the equation. Then we shal divide both members of the new equation by 3, as follows :

$$3x + 2 = 14$$
$$3x + 2 - 2 = 14 - 2$$
$$3x = 12$$
$$\frac{3x}{3} = \frac{12}{3}$$
$$x = 4.$$

> Subtract 2 from both sides

> Divide both sides by 3

∴

Check : $3(4) + 2 = 14$ or $12 + 2 = 14$ or $14 = 14$.

Ex. 2 *Solve* $\dfrac{m}{3} - 7 = 4.$

Sol. In this equation, m has been divided by 3 and then 7 has been subtracted from the result. Using the opposite, or inverse operations, we must first add 7 to both members of the equation. Then we will multiply both members of the new equation by 3. The solution is as under :

$$\frac{m}{3} - 7 = 4$$

$$\frac{m}{3} - 7 + 7 = 4 + 7$$

> Add 7 to both sides

$$\frac{m}{3} = 11$$

$$3 \times \frac{m}{3} = 3 \times 11$$

> Multiply both sides by 3

∴
$$m = 33.$$

Check : $\dfrac{33}{3} - 7 = 4$, $11 - 7 = 4$ or $4 = 4$.

Notice that in solving these two-step equations, we first add or subtract the same number from both members of the equation. Then we either multiply or divide the new equation by the same number.

Ex. 3. *Solve : $7x + 13 = 4x + 43$.*

Sol. Since $7x$ is larger than $4x$, we decide to shift letter terms to the left and number terms to the right side.

$$7x + 13 = 4x + 43$$
$$7x + 13 - 4x = 4x + 43 - 4x$$
$$3x + 13 = 43$$
$$3x + 13 - 13 = 43 - 13$$
$$3x = 30$$
$$\frac{3x}{3} = \frac{30}{3}$$
∴
$$x = 10$$

1. We want to remove $4x$ from the right side, we can do so by subtracting $4x$ from both sides.

2. We want to remove 13 from both sides, we do so by subtracting 13 from both sides.

3. Dividing both sides by 3

Check : Left side $= 7(10) + 13 = 70 + 13 = 83$.
Right side $= 4(10) + 43 = 40 + 43 = 83$.

21.3 Undoing and Balancing Mentally

After having acquired enough practice and understood the method, you can perform the inverse operations mentally. For example, if you have to solve the equation $x - 3 = 5$, you can perform mentally the operation of adding 3 to both sides and write directly $x = 5 + 3$ or 8. Similarly, if you have to solve the equation $6x = 30$, you can divide mentally both sides by 6.

Any number may be transferred from one side of an equation to the other if we change its sign (+ to –, – to +).

21.4 Simplifying Equations Before Solving.

Study the following examples :

Ex. 4 *Solve : x + 5x + 7 = 25.*

Sol.

$$6x + 7 = 25$$

$$\Rightarrow 6x = 25 - 7 = 18$$

$$\therefore \qquad x = 3$$

> Add the similar terms x and $5x$. Think what we did here to both sides of the equation $6x + 7 = 25$. What did we do to both sides of $6x = 18$?

Ex. 5 *Solve : 8y – 3 – 5y = 24.*

Sol.

$$8y - 3 - 5y = 24$$

$$\Rightarrow 8y - 5y - 3 = 24$$

$$\Rightarrow 3y - 3 = 24$$

$$\Rightarrow \qquad 3y = 24 + 3 = 27$$

$$\therefore \qquad y = 9$$

> What did we do in this step to remove 3 from left side ?

Check : Left side = 8(9) – 3 – 5(9) = 72 – 3 – 45 = 72 – 48 = 24 = Right side.

Ex. 6 *Solve : 14 + 2n – 6 + 8n = 4n – 21 + n + 34.*

Sol.

$$14 + 2n - 6 + 8n = 4n - 21 + n + 34$$

$$\Rightarrow \quad 14 - 6 + 2n + 8n = 4n + n - 21 + 34 \Rightarrow 8 + 10n = 5n + 13$$

$$\Rightarrow \quad 10n - 5n = 13 - 8$$

$$\Rightarrow \qquad 5n = 5$$

$$\therefore \quad \Rightarrow \qquad n = \frac{5}{5} \text{ i.e., } \boldsymbol{n = 1.}$$

> Transposing 8 to right side and $5n$ to left side.

Ex. 7 *Solve : 5(p + 4) – 8(4 – p) = 25 – 3(7 – p) + 144.*

Sol.

$$5(p + 4) - 8(4 - p) = 25 - 3(7 - p) + 144$$

$$\Rightarrow \quad 5p + 20 - 32 + 8p = 25 - 21 + 3p + 144$$

$$\Rightarrow \quad 5p + 8p + 20 - 32 = 25 - 21 + 144 + 3p$$

$$\Rightarrow \qquad 13p - 12 = 148 + 3p$$

$$\Rightarrow \qquad 13p - 3p = 148 + 12$$

$$\Rightarrow \qquad 10p = 160$$

$$\therefore p = \frac{160}{10} = \boldsymbol{16.}$$

Check : Left side = 5(16 + 4) – 8(4 – 16) = 5 × 20 – 8(– 12) = 100 + 96 = 196.

Right side = 25 – 3(7 – 16) + 144 = 25 – 3(–9) + 144 = 25 + 27 + 144 = 196.

EXERCISE 21 (a)

Solve the following equations :

(A)

1. $x + 2x = 9$ **2.** $3x - x = 8$ **3.** $x + 3x + 6 = 14$ **4.** $2x + 3x + 5 = 20$ **5.** $7 + 5x - 3x = 21$ **6.** $3(x + 1) = 15$

(B)

Solve. Check your answers.

7. $9x + 5 = 4x + 30$ **8.** $5x + 2 = 3x + 12$ **9.** $6y - 9 = 2y + 15$ **10.** $2x - 3 = 9 - x$ **11.** $6x + 4 = 16$

12. $3x + 5 - x = 17$ **13.** $2(x + 2) + 3 = 9$ **14.** $7 + 3(x + 5) = 31$ **15.** $3x + 2(x + 5) = 40$

16. $x = 17 - 3(2x + 1)$ **17.** $3(2x - 4) = 28 - 2x$

(C)

18. $8x + 2(x - 2) = 35 - 3x$ **19.** $x + 2(3x - 2) + 2x = 14$ **20.** $5(2x + 6) = 38 - 2(5x - 6)$

21. $4y + 8(y - 3) = 36 - 3y$ **22.** $3(8 - z) - 9 = 85 - 17z$

21.5 Fractional Equations

Type 1. Equations involving one fraction.

Ex.1 *Solve :* $\frac{x}{3} + 2x = 14$.

Sol. Multiply both sides of the equation by the denominator.

$$\frac{x}{3} + 2x = 14$$

$$3 \times \frac{x}{3} + 3 \times 2x = 3 \times 14$$

| | Multiplying by 3 |

$$\Rightarrow \quad x + 6x = 42$$

$$\Rightarrow \quad 7x = 42$$

$$\therefore x = \frac{42}{7} = 6.$$

Type 2. Equations involving more than one fraction.

To solve such an equation, multiply both sides by the L.C.M. of the denominators.

Ex. 2 *Solve :* $\frac{x}{2} + \frac{x}{3} = 10$.

Sol. L.C.M. of 2 and 3 = 6. Therefore, multiply both sides by 6.

$$6 \times \frac{x}{2} + 6 \times \frac{x}{3} = 6 \times 10$$

$$\Rightarrow \quad 3x + 2x = 60$$

$$\Rightarrow \quad 5x = 60$$

$$\therefore \quad x = \frac{60}{5} = 12.$$

After acquiring sufficient practice, the operation of multiplying by L.C.M. may be done mentally.

Ex.3 *Solve :* $\frac{3x}{4} + \frac{x}{6} = 22$.

Sol.

$$9x + 2x = 264$$

$$\Rightarrow \quad 11x = 264$$

| What operation did we perform mentally in this step? |

$$\therefore \quad x = \frac{264}{11} = 24.$$

Check : Left side $= \frac{3 \times 24}{4} + \frac{24}{6} = 18 + 4 = 22 =$ Right side

Ex. 4 *Solve :* $\frac{x-3}{5} + \frac{x-4}{7} = 6 - \frac{2x-1}{35}$.

Sol. L.C.M. of 5, 7 and 35 = 35.

Therefore, multiply both sides of the equation by 35.

$$7(x - 3) + 5(x - 4) = 6 \times 35 - (2x - 1)$$

$$\Rightarrow \quad 7x - 21 + 5x - 20 = 210 - 2x + 1$$

$$\Rightarrow \quad 7x + 5x - 21 - 20 = 210 + 1 - 2x$$

$$\Rightarrow 12x - 41 = 211 - 2x$$

$$\Rightarrow 12x + 2x = 211 + 41$$

$$\Rightarrow 14x = 252 \Rightarrow x = \frac{252}{14} = 18$$

$$\therefore \ x = 18.$$

Ex. 5 *Solve : 1.32y + 0.02y = 1.19 + y.*

Sol. $1.32y + 0.02y - y = 1.19$

$$\Rightarrow \quad \frac{132y}{100} + \frac{2y}{100} - y = \frac{119}{100}$$

$$\Rightarrow \quad 132y + 2y - 100y = 119$$

$$\Rightarrow \quad 34y = 119$$

$$\therefore \ y = \frac{119}{34} = \frac{7}{2} = 3\frac{1}{2}.$$

| **Note.** To remove the decimals you could multiply both sides by 100. |

EXERCISE 21 (b)

Solve and check your answers :

1. $\dfrac{2x}{3} = 8$ **2.** $\dfrac{x}{2} + 4x = 18$ **3.** $n + \dfrac{3n}{4} = 14$ **4.** $\dfrac{n}{2} + \dfrac{n}{5} = 7$ **5.** $\dfrac{2m}{3} + \dfrac{3m}{4} = 17$ **6.** $\dfrac{2u}{3} - \dfrac{u}{5} = 14$

7. $\dfrac{x}{2} + \dfrac{x}{3} - \dfrac{3x}{4} = 3$ **8.** $\dfrac{x+3}{7} - \dfrac{2x-5}{3} = \dfrac{3x-5}{5} - 25$ **9.** $\dfrac{3c-2}{7} - \dfrac{5c-8}{4} = \dfrac{1}{14}$ **10.** $\dfrac{x+3}{2} - \dfrac{3x+1}{4} = \dfrac{2(x-2)}{3} - 2$

11. $1.5y + 7 = 0.5y$ **12.** $2.8v = 54 + v$ **13.** $0.26x + 0.09x = 8 - 0.45x$ **14.** $x - 10\%$ of $x = 27$

21.6 Solving Problems

To solve a problem, we first translate it into an equation. Then we solve the equation that we have made. The equations that we will make in this book are like those you have just been solving. The following examples show how to turn word problems into equations.

Ex. 1 *If 14 is added to a number, the sum is 35. Find the number.*

Sol. Let n represent the number. When 14 is added to it, the sum is $n + 14$. The problem states that this sum is equal to 35. Therefore

$$n + 14 = 35$$
$$\Rightarrow n = 35 - 14$$
$$\Rightarrow n = 21 \qquad \therefore \quad \text{The required number is } \mathbf{21}.$$

Ex. 2 *If a number is multiplied by 5, and 8 is subtracted from the product, the result is 12. Find the number.*

Sol. Let x represent the number. Then $5x$ is 5 times the number. If 8 is subtracted from $5x$, the result is $5x - 8$. The problem states that this is equal to 12. Therefore

$$5x - 8 = 12$$
$$\Rightarrow \quad 5x = 12 + 8$$
$$\Rightarrow \quad 5x = 20$$
$$\Rightarrow x = \dfrac{20}{5} = 4$$

$\therefore$ The required number is **4**.

Ex. 3 *One-third of a number is 2 more than one fourth of the number. Find the number.*

Sol. Let the number be x. Then

One third of the number $= \dfrac{x}{3}$, One fourth of the number $= \dfrac{x}{4}$.

The problem states that $\dfrac{x}{3} - \dfrac{x}{4} = 2 \Rightarrow 4x - 3x = 24$ Multiply both sides by 12.
$$\Rightarrow \qquad\qquad x = 24$$

$\therefore$ The required number is **24**.

Ex. 4 *Anuj is now 7 years older than Pramod. If the sum of their ages is 33 years, find the age of each.*

Sol.   Let Pramod's age $= x$ years

Then Anuj's age $=$ Pramod's age $+ 7 = (x + 7)$ years

By the problem, Anuj's age $+$ Pramod's age $= 33$, that is, $x + (x + 7) = 33$

$\Rightarrow \qquad\qquad 2x + 7 = 33 \qquad\qquad \Rightarrow 2x = 33 - 7 = 26 \qquad\qquad \Rightarrow x = 13$

$\therefore$ Pramod's age $=$ **13 years**, Anuj's age $=$ **20 years**.

Ex. 5 *Find the magnitude of each of the three angles formed in the figure.*

Sol. We know that sum of the angles round a point is 360°. Therefore,

$$3x + 4x + 5x = 360°$$
$$\Rightarrow \quad 12x = 360°$$
$$\Rightarrow \quad x = 30°$$

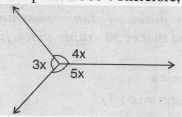

∴ The required angles are $4 \times 30°$, $3 \times 30°$ and $5 \times 30°$, that is, **120°, 90° and 150°.**

21.7 Problems with two unknown numbers

In many simple problems there are two unknowns, one of which may be expressed in terms of the other.

Method. 1. *Let one unknown be x.*

2. *Use the given relationship to write the second unknown in terms of x.*

For example, If Rs 50 are to be divided among two persons and the share of one person is Rs x, then that of the other person will be Rs $(50 - x)$.

Ex. 6 *The sum of two numbers is 11, and one of them is 3 greater than the other. Find the numbers.*

Sol. Let n = the smaller number. Then, $n + 3$ = the larger number, and their sum is $n + n + 3$.

Hence, $n + n + 3 = 11 \Rightarrow 2n + 3 = 11$

$\Rightarrow \quad 2n = 11 - 3 = 8 \Rightarrow n = \dfrac{8}{2} = 4$

First number	n
Second number	$n + 3$

Therefore, the numbers are 4 and $4 + 3$, that is **4 and 7.**

Ex. 7 *Three years ago Somesh was 5 years older than Hema was then. If he is now twice as old as she is, find their present ages.*

Sol. Let x = Hema's age, then $2x$ = Somesh's age

	Present time	3 years ago
Hema's age	x	$x - 3$
Somesh's age	$2x$	$2x - 3$

It is given that

Somesh's age 3 years ago = 5 more than Hema's age 3 years ago.

that is $2x - 3 = x - 3 + 5$

$\Rightarrow 2x - x = -3 + 5 + 3$

$\Rightarrow x = 5$

Therefore, **Hema** is now **5 years** old and **Somesh** is **10 years** old.

Ex. 8 *Length of a rectangle is 5 cm more than twice its breadth. If the perimeter of the rectangle is 52 cm, find its length and breadth.*

Sol. Let the breadth of the rectangle be x cm, then its length = 2 (breadth) + 5 = $(2x + 5)$ cm

∴ Perimeter = 2 (length + breadth) = 2 ($2x + 5 + x$) cm

$= 2(3x + 5)$ cm $= (6x + 10)$ cm

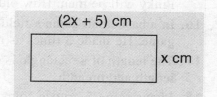

But it is given that perimeter = 52 cm

∴ $6x + 10 = 52 \Rightarrow 6x = 52 - 10 \Rightarrow 6x = 42$

$\Rightarrow x = \dfrac{42}{6} = 7$

∴ Breadth of the rectangle = **7 cm**

and length of the rectangle = $2 \times 7 + 5 =$ **19 cm**.

Check : Perimeter = 2 (length + breadth) = 2(7 + 19) = 2 × 26 = 52 cm.

Ex.9. *A purse contains Rs 250 in notes of denominations of 10 and 50. If the number of 10 - rupee notes is one more than that of 50 - rupee notes, find the number of notes of each denomination.*

Sol. Let the number of 50 - rupee notes = x.

Then, the number of 10 - rupee notes = $(x + 1)$.

According to the problem.

Value of 50 - rupee notes + value of 10 - rupee notes = Rs 250

i.e. $50x + 10 (x + 1) = 250$

$\Rightarrow \quad 5x + (x + 1) = 25$ | Dividing both ides by 10 |

$\Rightarrow \quad 5x + x = 25 - 1 \quad \Rightarrow 6x = 24 \quad \Rightarrow x = \dfrac{24}{6} = 4$

Hence, the number of 50 - rupee notes = 4, and the number of 10 - rupee notes is 4 + 1, i.e. 5.

Check : Total amount in the purse = Four 50 - rupee notes + Five 10 - rupee notes.

$= Rs (50 \times 4 + 10 \times 5) = Rs (200 + 50) = Rs 250.$

EXERCISE 21 (c)

Find the number if :

1. The number decreased by 7 is 25.　　　2. The number increased by 10 is 16.

3. The number is multiplied by 2, and 8 is added to the product, the result is 50.

4. The number is subtracted from 23, the result is 10 less than twice the number.

5. Two thirds of the number is increased by 9, the sum will be 19.

6. The sum of the one-eighth, one-twelfth and one–twentieth parts is 31.

7. Rekha's little sister is now 5 years old. If her age is 2 years more than $\dfrac{1}{4}$ of Rekha's age, how old is Rekha ?

8. One number is 9 more than the other. If their sum is 63, what are the numbers ?

9. The sum of two numbers is 64, and the second number is 16 less than the first. Find the numbers.

10. One number is 7 times another. If 14 is added to the sum of the numbers, the result is 38. Find the numbers.

11. Suman is 7 years older than her sister, and the sum of their ages is 21 years. How old is each ?

12. Find three consecutive numbers whose sum is 108.

　　[**Hint.** Let the consecutive numbers be x, $x + 1$, $x + 2$.]

13. Find two consecutive odd numbers whose sum is 56.

　　[**Hint.** Let the consecutive odd numbers be $2x + 1$, $2x + 3$]

14. Find two consecutive even numbers whose sum is 86.

　　[**Hint.** Let the consecutive even numbers be $2x$, $2(x + 1)$]

15. Sudhir is now 3 times as old as his little brother Pinky, but in 3 more years he will be only twice as old as Pinky will be then. How old are they now?

16. In a basketball game a field goal counts 2 points and a foul shot one point. Ambrish scored 14 points in a game. He made 3 times as many field goals as foul shots. On how many shots of each kind did he score?

17. The length of a rectangle is 6m less than twice its breadth. If the perimeter of the rectangle is 54 m, find its length and breadth.

18. I have some 5 - rupee coins and some 2 - rupee coins. The number of 2 - rupee coins is 4 times that of 5 - rupee coins. If I have Rs 117 in all, find the number of coins of each denominations.

19. A number is divided into two parts such that one part is 10 more than the other. If the two parts are in the ratio 5 : 3 find the number and the two parts.

[**Hint.** Let one number be x, then the other number is $x + 10$. According to the problem $\dfrac{x+10}{x} = \dfrac{5}{3}$ or $3(x + 10) = 5x$].

20. Mahesh left one third of his property for his son, one fourth for his daughter and the remainder for his wife. If wife's share in the property was worth Rs 10 lakh, find the total worth of Mahesh's property.

21. One fourth of a herd of deer have gone to the forest. One third of the total number are grazing in a field and remaining 15 are drinking water on the bank of a river. Find the total number of deer.

22. A man is 27 years older than his son, and in 10 years from now he will be twice as old as his son. How old is each now ?

ANSWERS

EXERCISE 21 (a)

1. $x = 3$ 2. $x = 4$ 3. $x = 2$ 4. $x = 3$ 5. $x = 7$ 6. $x = 4$ 7. $x = 5$ 8. $x = 5$ 9. $y = 6$ 10. $x = 4$ 11. $x = 2$
12. $x = 6$ 13. $x = 1$ 14. $x = 3$ 15. $x = 6$ 16. $x = 2$ 17. $x = 5$ 18. $x = 3$ 19. $x = 2$ 20. $x = 1$ 21. $y = 4$ 22. $z = 5$

EXERCISE 21 (b)

1. $x = 12$ 2. $x = 4$ 3. $n = 8$ 4. $n = 10$ 5. $m = 12$ 6. $u = 30$ 7. $x = 36$ 8. $x = 25$ 9. $c = 2$ 10. $x = 5$ 11. $y = -7$
12. $v = 30$ 13. $x = 10$ 14. $x = 30$

EXERCISE 21 (c)

1. 32   2. 6   3. 21   4. 11   5. 15   6. 120   7. 12 years   8. 27, 36   9. 40, 24   10. 21,3   11. 7 years, 14 years
12. 35, 36, 37   13. 27, 29   14. 42, 44   15. 3years, 9 years   16. 6, 2   17. 11 m, 16 m
18. Nine 5 rupee, coins, Thirty six 2–rupee coins   19. 15, 25   20. 24 lakh   21. 36   22. 44 years, 17 years

---

MINDBENDERS

1. A man is given three coins which look identical, but in fact one of them is an overweight fake. Describe how he could discover the fake using an ordinary balance and only one weighing operation.

2. How many hours are there in February 1999 ?

FUN WITH NUMBERS

1. Write down the next five lines in this pattern

$$1 \times 999 \qquad = 999$$
$$2 \times 999 \qquad = 1998$$
$$3 \times 999 \qquad = 2997$$
$$4 \times 999 \qquad = 3996$$

2.
$$1 + 9 \times 0 \qquad = 1$$
$$2 + 9 \times 1 \qquad = 11$$
$$3 + 9 \times 12 \qquad = 111$$
$$4 + 9 \times 123 \qquad = 1111$$
$$5 + 9 \times 1234 \qquad = 11111$$

Did you know ?

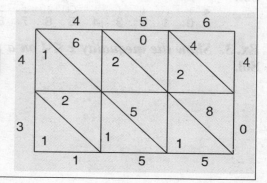

The diagram shows the method of calculation which was used in India during the twelfth century. To evaluate 456×34 set the digits around the outside of the grid. Multiply each pair of digits together, placing the answers inside the grid. Then add along the diagonals, starting from the right; this gives the answer around the outside, 15, 504.

22. Linear Inequations

22.1 Introduction

■ The pictures show apples and bananas. The number of apples is more than the number of bananas. If *a* is the number of apples and *b* is the number of bananas, then ***a is greater than b***. We write ***a > b***.

■ This fish weighs less than 1 kg. You can write
$$f < 1,$$
where *f* is the weight of the fish in kilograms.

>	means 'greater than'	$7 > 3$
<	means 'less than'	$7 < 8$
=	means 'equal to'	$7 + 2 = 9$
≥	means 'greater than or equal to'	
≤	means 'less than or equal to'	

Ex. 1. *Write down the values of x that are whole numbers and satisfy these inequalities x > 4 and x < 8.*

Sol. $x > 4$ so the numbers must be bigger than 4; ∴ The numbers satisfying the inequality $x > 4$ are 5, 6, 7, 8, 9, 10, 11, 12... Since $x < 8$ so the numbers must stop before 8. Therefore the answer is 5, 6, 7.

> A number satisfies an inequality if it makes that inequality true. $x = 5$ satisfies the inequality $x < 8$ because 5 < 8.

EXERCISE 22 (a)

Write down the values of *x* that are integers and satisfy these inequalities.

1. $x > 1$ and $x < 4$ **2.** $x > 0$ and $x < 5$ **3.** $x > 5$ and $x < 10$

4. $x > 25$ and $x < 32$ **5.** $x < 4$ and $x > -2$ **6.** $x < 3$ and $x > -4$

22.2 Showing Inequations on a Number Line

You can show inequations by shading a number line.

Ex. 2. *Draw a number line from 0 to 10. Show the inequation x > 5 on it.*

The open circle means $x = 5$ is not included.

> The thick part of the line represents $x > 5$.

Sol.

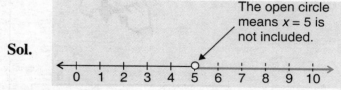

Ex. 3. *Show the inequality x ≤ 4 on a number line.*
Sol.

The filled circle means x = 4 is included.

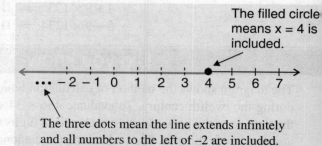

The three dots mean the line extends infinitely and all numbers to the left of –2 are included.

Ex. 4. *Show the inequality –3 ≤ x < 2 on a number line.*

Sol. The inequality $-3 \leq x < 2$ means -3 is less than x or equal to x or we can say that x is greater than or equal to -3. It is also given that x is less than 2.

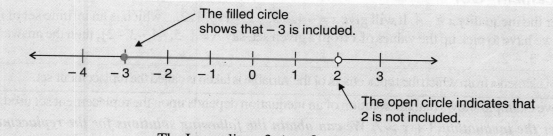

The filled circle shows that -3 is included.

The open circle indicates that 2 is not included.

The Inequality $-3 \leq x < 2$.

EXERCISE 22 (b)

Show the following inequalities on a number line.

1. $x > 3$
2. $x > 6$
3. $x > -2$
4. $x < 5$
5. $x < 0$
6. $x < -4$
7. $x > 4$ and $x < 9$
8. $x > 0$ and $x < 6$
9. $x > -4$ and $x < 1$
10. $x > -7$ and $x < -3$
11. $x \geq 4$
12. $x^3 -1$
13. $x \leq -1$
14. $2 < x < 5$
15. $3 < x < 8$
16. $0 < x < 4$
17. $-4 < x \leq 0$
18. $-5 \leq x < -2$

Write down the inequalities represented by the shading on these number lines :

19. $\begin{array}{c} \longleftarrow \; | \; | \; | \; \circ \; | \; | \; | \; | \longrightarrow \\ -3 \; -2 \; -1 \; 0 \; 1 \; 2 \; 3 \; 4... \end{array}$

20. $\begin{array}{c} \longleftarrow \; | \; | \; | \; | \; \bullet \; | \; | \longrightarrow \\ ...-2 \; -1 \; 0 \; 1 \; 2 \; 3 \end{array}$

21. $\begin{array}{c} \longleftarrow \; | \; | \; \circ \; | \; | \; \bullet \; | \longrightarrow \\ 0 \; 1 \; 2 \; 3 \; 4 \; 5 \; 6 \end{array}$

22. $\begin{array}{c} \longleftarrow \; \bullet \; | \; | \; | \; | \; \circ \; | \; | \longrightarrow \\ -1 \; 0 \; 1 \; 2 \; 3 \; 4 \; 5 \; 6 \end{array}$

22.3 Properties of Inequations

$8 > 4$ is an inequality. It is also a true statement, so $8 > 4$ is a true inequality. $-5 < -1$ is also a true inequality. $0 > -1$ is a true inequality.

Now, examine whether the inequality remains true when you do the following things to it. Take the inequality $8 > 3$.

(i)   add 2 to both sides : $8 + 2 > 4 + 2$ or $10 > 6$ is still true.

Property 1. *An inequality remains true on adding the same number to each side.*

(ii) Subtract 3 from both sides : $8 - 3 > 4 - 3$ or $5 > 1$ is still true.

Property 2. *An inequality remains true on subtracting the same number from each side.*

(iii) Multiply both sides by 4 : $8 \times 4 > 4 \times 4$ or $32 > 16$ is still true.

Property 3. *An inequality remains true on multiplying both sides by the same positive number.*

(iv) Multiply both sides by -2 : $8 \times -2 > 4 \times -2$ or $-16 > -8$ which is **not** true.

In fact, now $-16 < -8$. [> changes to <]

Property 4. *An inequality is reversed on multiplying both sides by the same negative number.*

(v)   Dividing both sides by 2 : $8 \div 2 > 4 \div 2$ or $4 > 2$ which is true.

Property 5. *An inequality remains true on dividing both sides by the same positive number.*

(vi) Dividing both sides by -2 : $8 \div (-2) > 4 \div (-2)$ or $-4 > -2$ which is **not** true. Infact, now $4 < -2$.

Property 6. *An inequality is reversed on dividing both sides by the same negative number.*

Remark : Properties 4 and 6 tell us that we **should not** multiply or divide both sides of an inequality by a negative number unless it is desired to reverse the inequality.

22.4 Replacement Set

Consider the inequality $x \geq -4$. It will give $x = -4, -3, -2, -1, 0, 1, 2,...$ which is an infinite set of integer ≥ -4. If we have to pick up the values of x from a given set, say A = $\{-5, -4, -3, -2\}$, then the answer will b $x = -4, -3, -2$.

> The set of elements from which the replacement of the variable is taken is called the replacement set.

The above example shows that the solution of an inequation depends upon the replacement set used.

Ex. 5. *Consider the inequation $3 + x > 7$. We can obtain the following solutions for the replacement se given.*

$$3 + x > 7 \Rightarrow 3 + x - 3 > 7 - 3 \Rightarrow x > 4.$$

Replacement set	Solutions
A = $\{0, 2, 4, 5, 8, 9\}$	$x = 5, 8, 9$
B = $\{0, 1, 2, 3, 4, 5\}$	5
C = $\{0, 1, 2\}$	ϕ

Since no value of x is possible from the given set C, we say the solution is the empty set.

22.5 Solution Set or the Truth Set

The set of all possible values of x which satisfy a given inequation is called the **solution set** or the **truth set** o the inequation. If a replacement set is given and these values are picked up from the replacement set, the obviously the solution set is a subset of this replacement set.

> The **solution set** *is the subset of the given replacement set consisting of those values of the variable which satisfy the given inequation.*

In solved example 5, the set $\{5, 8, 9\}$ is a solution set of the inequation $3 + x > 7$ when the replacement set i A. As you can see, $\{5, 8, 9\}$ is a subset of $A = \{0, 2, 4, 5, 8, 9\}$.

22.6 Solving Inequations

You can solve inequations exactly in the same way as solving equations by making use of the properties o inequations.

Ex. 6. *Solve the inequation $3x + 2 \geq 14$.*

Sol. $3x + 2 \geq 14$

$\Rightarrow 3x \geq 12.$

$\Rightarrow x \geq 4.$

> The following operations have been done mentally.
> 1. Subtract 2 from both sides.
> 2. Divide both sides by 3

Ex. 7. *Solve $x + 2 \geq 2$,*

(i) $x \in W$ (ii) $x \in N$ (iii) $x \in \{0, -2, -1, 3, 5, 7\}$.

(iv) Show each of the solution sets on the number line.

Sol. $x + 2 \geq 2 \Rightarrow x \geq 2 - 2 \Rightarrow x \geq 0$

∴ (i) Since the replacement set is given to be $\{0, 1, 2, 3...\}$, so that solution set = $\{0, 1, 2, 3...\}$.

(ii) Solution set = $\{1, 2, 3,...\}$. Since $x \in N$, i.e., $x \in \{1, 2, 3, ...\}$, so, 0 has not been included.

(iii) Solution set = $\{0, 3, 5, 7\}$.

Here the values of x have to be picked up from the replacement set $\{0, -2, -1, 3, 5, 7\}$.

(iv) Graphical representation of the solution sets is as under :

For (i) :

The dark dots represent some of the numbers belonging to the solution set. The three dots beyond 3 indicate that the solution set is an infinite set, i.e, whole numbers beyond 3, namely 4, 5, 6, ... belong to the solution set.

For (ii) :

For (iii) :

Ex. 8. *Solve* : $-14 - 15x \geq 3x + 2$. *Show the solution set on the number line.*

Sol. $-14 - 5x \geq 3x + 2$

$\Rightarrow -14 \geq 3x + 5x + 2$ Add $5x$ to both sides

$\Rightarrow -14 \geq 8x + 2$

$\Rightarrow -14 - 2 \geq 8x$ Subtract 2 from both sides

$\Rightarrow -16 \geq 8x$

$\Rightarrow -2 \geq x$ Divide both sides by 8

$\Rightarrow x \leq -2$ Another way of writing $-2 \geq x$ is $x \leq -2$.

> **Note that** on changing sides the direction of the inequality is changed.

The graphical representation of the solution set is shown below :

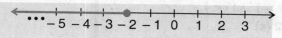

EXERCISE 22 (c)

Solve these inequalities :

1. $3x + 7 < 10$

2. $2x + 7 \leq 9$

3. $2(3x - 1) \geq 10$

4. $3(m - 2) > 9$

5. $5 < p - 1$

6. $-2x \geq -3$

7. $4 - 5x \leq 3x$

8. $4 - 9p > 1 - 11p$

Solve the following inequations and graph the solution set.

9. $x + 3 > 8$ given that $x \in W$

10. $3 - 2x \geq x - 12$, given that $x \in N$.

11. $2(3x - 1) \leq 16$, $x \in N$.

12. $3x \leq 6$, $x \in Z$.

Write down the inequations shown on the following number lines :

13.

14.

15.

16.

ANSWERS

EXERCISE 22 (a)

1. 2, 3   2. 1, 2, 3, 4,   3. 6, 7, 8, 9   4. 26, 27, 28, 29, 30, 31   5. $-1, 0, 1, 2, 3$ 6. $-3, -2, -1, 0, 1, 2$

EXERCISE 22 (b)

1. $x > 3$

2. $x > 6$

3. $x > -2$

4. $x < 5$

5. $x < 0$

6. $x < -4$

7. $x > 4$ and $x < 9$

8. $x > 0$ and $x < 6$

9. $x > -4$ and $x < 1$

10. $x > -7$ and $x < -3$

11. $x \geq 4$

12. $x \geq -1$

13. $x \leq -1$

14. $2 < x < 5$

15. $3 < x < 8$

16. $0 < x < 4$

17. $-4 < x \leq 0$

18. $-5 \leq x < -2$

19. $x > -1$ 20. $x \leq 1$ 21. $x > 2$ and $x \leq 5$ 22. $x \geq -1$ and $x < 4$

EXERCISE 22 (c)

1. $x < 1$ 2. $x \leq 1$ 3. $x \geq 2$ 4. $m > 5$ 5. $p > 6$ 6. $x \leq \dfrac{3}{2}$ 7. $x \geq \dfrac{1}{2}$

8. $p > \dfrac{-3}{2}$ 9. $x > 5, x \in W$

10. $x \leq 5, x \in N$ 11. $x \leq 3, x \in N$

12. $3x \leq 6, x \in Z$ 13. $x \leq 1, x \in Z$ 14. $-2 \leq x \leq 1, x \in Z$

15. $0 < x < 5, x \in W$ 16. $-3 < x < 2, x \in Z$

23. Graphs

23.1 Introduction

Think of the diagram at the right as a class room. The picture shows desks lined up in 5 rows, from left to right, with 7 desks in a row. The teacher asked the students in row number 3 to stand. All the seven students sitting in that row would stand up but if the teacher wants only a particular boy to stand up, then he can say let the boy in the 3rd row and seat 4 stand up. Then only Ankur sitting over there will stand up.

Ankur's location can be given by the number (3,4). Similarly, the positions of all the seats in the class room can be indicated by assigning each location a pair of numbers. Thus the position of seat marked F will be indicated by the number (2,1). Note that the number (1,2) will not indicate F. It will indicate the desk at P. Thus the order in which the numbers are written is important. Such pairs are called *ordered pairs*.

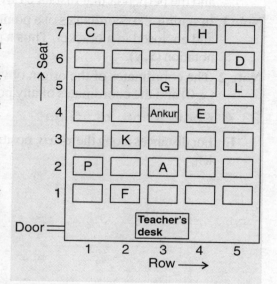

An ordered pair of numbers is needed to locate each student.

Try These   **Oral**

1. Which labelled desk is named by
   (*a*) row 3, seat 2?   (*b*) row 2, seat 3?   (*c*) row 1, seat 7?   (*d*) row 5, seat 6?
2. Give the row number and seat for   :   (*a*) E   (*b*) F   (*c*) G   (*d*) H   (*e*) L.
3. Which desk matches :   (1, 7)? (5, 5)? (2, 1)? (3, 5)? (4, 7)? (5, 6)?

23.2 Co-ordinate Axes

The examples of the classroom suggests a way of fixing the position of a point in a plane using two number lines.

It is done by selecting the *axes of reference* which are formed by combining the two numbers scales at right angles to each other so that their zero points coincide. The horizontal number scale is called the **x-axis** and the vertical number scale the **y-axis.** The point where the two scales cross each other is called the **origin.** The two together are called the *rectangular axes* (so called because they are at right angles to each other.)

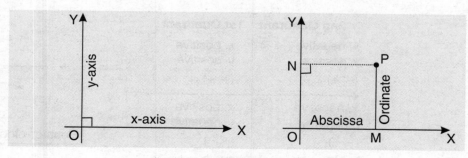

23.3 Coordinates-Definition and Notation

The position of each point of the planes is determined with reference to the rectangular axes by means of a pa of numbers called *coordinates* which are the distances of the point from the axes. The distance OM, which equal to the perpendicular distance PN of the point P from the *y-axis* is called the *x-coordinate* or **abscis** and the perpendicular distance PM of the point P from the *x- axis* is called the *y-coordinate* or **ordinate**.

Note 1. In stating the coordinates of a point, the abscissa precedes the ordinate. The two are separated by a comm and enclosed in a bracket. Thus a point whose abscissa is *x* and whose ordinate is *y* is designated by th notation (*x, y*).

Note 2. The coordinates of the origin obviously are **(0, 0)**. The coordinates of any point on the *x-axis* would b (*x*, 0) and the coordinates of any point on the *y- axis* would be (0, *y*).

23.4 Convention of Signs

1. For distances along the *x-axis,* positive values are measured to the right of the origin and negative values to i left.

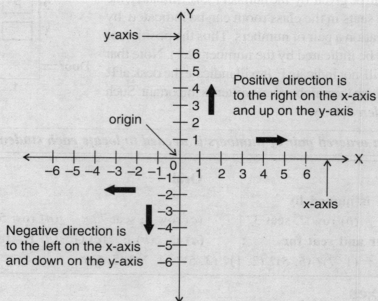

2. For distances along the *y-axis,* positive values are measured upward and negative values downward from th origin.

23.5 Quadrants

The coordinate axes separate the plane into four regions, called *quadrants*. By custom, the quadrants ar numbered I, II, III and IV in the counter clockwise direction as shown in the figure given below.

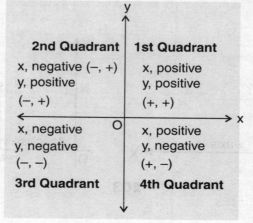

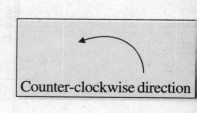

Counter-clockwise direction

23.6 Points on the Axes

(a) *Any point on the x-axis*

The ordinate of every point on *x*-axis is zero. So the coordinates of any point on the x-axis are of the form **(x, 0)**

For example : Each of the points (3, 0), (–4, 0), (7, 0), (–8, 0) lies on the x-axis

(b) *Any point on the y-axis*

The abscissa of every point on *y*-axis is zero so the coordinates of any point on the y-axis are of the form **(0, y)**

For example: Each of the points (0, 2), (0, 6), (0, –1), (0, –4) lies on the y-axis

Ex.1. *Graph (2, 5) and (5, 2).*

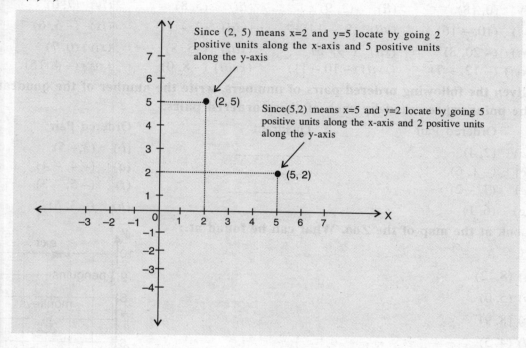

Since (2, 5) means x=2 and y=5 locate by going 2 positive units along the x-axis and 5 positive units along the y-axis

Since(5,2) means x=5 and y=2 locate by going 5 positive units along the x-axis and 2 positive units along the y-axis

Ex.2. *What are the co-ordinates of each point shown in the graph ?*

Sol.

Point	Co-ordinates	Point	Co-ordinates
A	(4, 3)	J	(2, –2)
B	(–4, 3)	K	$\left(-2\frac{1}{2}, -1\frac{1}{2}\right)$
C	(–4, –3)	M	(0, –4)
D	(4, –3)	O	(0, 0)
E	(4, 0)	P	(2, 0)
F	(–4, 0)	Q	(–1, 0)
G	(0, 3)	R	(0, 4)
H	(0, –3)		

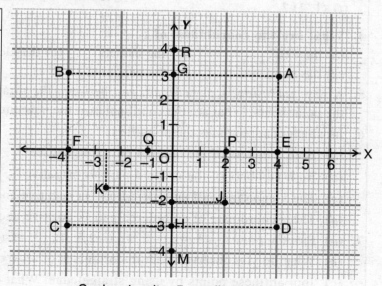

Scale : 1 unit = 5 small squares

Ex.3 *State the quadrants in which the following points lie.*

  (i) A (3, 5)   (ii) B(– 4, –7),   (iii) C (5, –1),   (iv) D (–6, 8)

Sol. (*i*)   Since both *x* and *y* are positive (+, +) the point A lies in the first quadrant.

   (*ii*)   Since both *x* and *y* are negative (–, –), the point B lies in the third quadrant.

   (*iii*)   Since *x* is positive and *y* negative (+, –), the point C lies in the fourth quadrant.

   (*iv*)   Since *x* is negative and *y* positive (–, +), the point D lies in the second quadrant.

EXERCISE 23 (a)

1. **Plot the following points using the same pair of axes and the same scale for each one.**

(*i*) (0, 18)	(*ii*) (2, 9)	(*iii*) (5, 8)	(*iv*) (7, 0)	(*v*) (5, – 8)
(*vi*) (10, – 16)	(*vii*) (8, – 14)	(*viii*) (3, – 11)	(*ix*) (– 5, 6)	(*x*) (– 15, 4)
(*xi*) (– 20, 8)	(*xii*) (–9, 5)	(*xiii*) (–5, 8)	(*xiv*) (0, 7)	(*xv*) (– 8, – 15)
(*xvi*) (– 12, – 7)	(*xvii*) (– 10,– 11)	(*xviii*) (– 8, 0)	(*xix*) (– 4, 15)	(*xx*) (7, – 6)

2. **Given the following ordered pairs of numbers, write the number of the quadrant in which you fin|
the point represented by each of these ordered pairs.**

Ordered Pair	Quadrant	Ordered Pair	Quadrant
(*a*) (2, 4)	_____	(*b*) (3,– 5)	_____
(*c*) (– 1, 6)	_____	(*d*) (– 4, – 4)	_____
(*e*) (7, – 2)	_____	(*f*) (– 5, – 3)	_____
(*g*) (6, 1)	_____	(*h*) (– 3, 5)	_____

3. **Look at the map of the Zoo. What can be found at :**

   (*a*) (8, 2)

   (*b*) (5, 0)

   (*c*) (8, 9)

   (*d*) (4, 5)

   (*e*) (4, 2)

   (*f*) (1, 2) ?

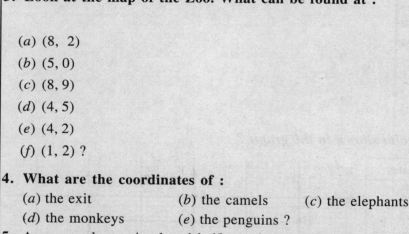
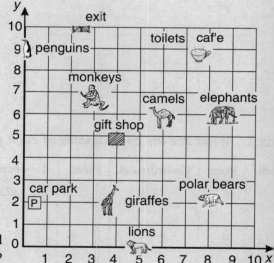

4. **What are the coordinates of :**

   (*a*) the exit   (*b*) the camels   (*c*) the elephants

   (*d*) the monkeys   (*e*) the penguins ?

5. A new enclosure is placed half-way between the giraffes and
the polar bears. What are the coordinates of the new enclosure ?

6. In which quadrant does the point lie if

   (*a*) Both numbers of the ordered pair are positive?

   (*b*) Both numbers of the ordered pair are negative?

   (*c*) The *x*-coordinate of an ordered pair is negative and the *y*-coordinate is positive?

   (*d*) The *x*-coordinate of an ordered pair is positive and the *y*-coordinate is negative ?

7. (*a*) Plot the points (– 5, 4), (– 8, 4), (– 2.5, 4), (0, 4), (3.5, 4), (6, 4).

   (*b*) What do you observe about the ordinates of all six points ?

   (*c*) Join all these points by using straightedge. What do you observe ? The line so obtained is parallel t|
   which axis ?

8. (*a*) Graph the points (3, 7), (3, 2), $\left(3, \dfrac{1}{2}\right)$, (3, 0), (3, – 2), (3, – 8).

(*b*) What pattern do you see in the coordinates of these six points ?

(*c*) Join all these points by using straighedge. What do you observe ? The line so obtained is parallel to which axis ?

9. **In which quadrant or on which axis will (x, y) be graphed if :**

(*a*) $x > 0$ and $y > 0$?   (*b*) $x < 0$ and $y < 0$?   (*c*) $x > 0$ and $y < 0$?

(*d*) $x < 0$ and $y > 0$?   (*e*) $x = 0$?   (*f*) $y = 0$?

23.7 Graph of a Linear Equation

Activity 1. Plot the points A (2, 2), B (4, 4) and C (6, 6) on a grid and join them. You will find that they lie on a straight line. In all these points the *y*-coordinate = *the x*-coordinate. So the equation of the line is $y = x$.

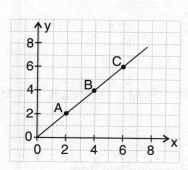

y-coordinate is the
same as x-coordinate

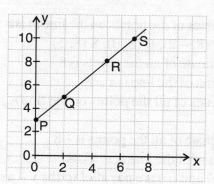

y-coordinate is x-coordinate+3

Activity 2. Plot the points P (0, 3), Q (2, 5), R (5, 8), S(7, 10) and join them, you will find that they lie on a straight line, (0, 3) (2, 5) (5, 8) (7, 10). In all these points the *y* - coordinate is.

+3   +3   +3   +3

x – coordinate + 3. The rule is 'add 3 to the *x* - coordinate'. So the equation of the line is $y = x + 3$.

■ **To find the equation of a sloping line find a rule connecting the x -coordinate and the y - coordinate.**

Ex. 4 *Find the equation of the lines on the following grid.*

Sol. (*a*) The co-ordinates of the points on the line *a* are

A (– 4, 3), B (2, 3), C (5, 3), D (7, 3)

The *y* - coordinate of all the points is 3.

So the equation of the line is $y = -3$.

(*b*) The co-ordinates of points on the line *b* are

A′ (– 4, – 3), B′ (2, – 3), C′ (5, – 3), D′ (7, – 3)

The *y* - coordinate of all the points is – 3.

So the equation of the line is $y = 3$.

The lines (*a*) and (*b*) are parallel to the x – axis. They are horizontal lines.

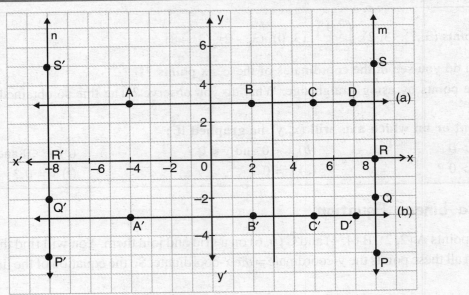

(c) The co-ordinates of the points on the line *m* are
     P (8, – 5), Q (8, – 2), R (8, 0), S (8, 5)
     The *x* - coordinate of all the points is 8
     So the equation of the line is *x* = **8**.

(d) The coordinates of all the points on the line *n* are P' (– 8, – 5), Q' (– 8, – 2), R' (– 8, 0),
     S' (– 8, 5)
     The *x*-coordinate of all the points is – 8.
     So the equation of the line is *x* = **– 8.**
     The lines (*m*) and (*n*) are **parallel to the** *y* **– axis. They are vertical lines.**

> **The equation of a line parallel to the** *x* **axis,** *i.e.,* **a horizontal line is** *y* **= a number.**
>
> **The equation of a line parallel to** *y* **the axis,** *i.e.,* **a vertical line is** *x* **= a number.**

Try These
Find the equation of the lines on this coordinate grid. (**Hint :** Find a rule that connects the *x* and the *y*
coordinates of points on the lines.)

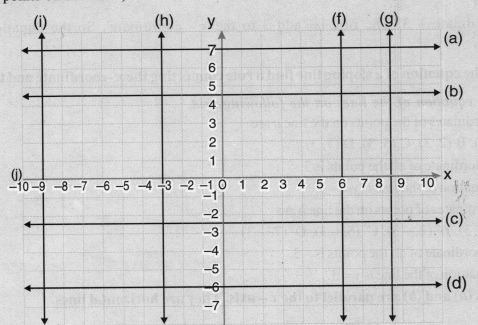

23.8 Drawing Graph of a line from its Equation

If you are asked to draw a line whose equation is given, *use the equation to find the coordinates of a few points on the line*. The graph is obtained on joining these points.

Ex. 1. *Draw the line with the equations*   (a) $x = 3$ (b) $y = 5$

Sol. You need the coordinates of any three points on the line. These will do.

(a) Three points on the line are : A (3, 0), B (3, 2), C (3, 4).
Plot these points and join them up with a straight edge.

(b) Three points on the line are : P (0, 5), Q (4, 5), R (6, 5).
Plot these points and join them up with a straight edge.

Ex. 2. Draw the lines with the equations

(i) $y = x + 2$,   (ii) $y = -\dfrac{1}{2}x + 3$,   (iii) $y = 3x - 5$

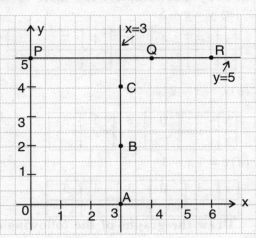

Sol. When you are required to draw a sloping line, use a table of values. Choose some value for x, such as 0, 1, 2, 3, 4, and 5 and draw a table like this :

x	1	2	3	4	5
y					

(i) $y = x + 2$

Work out $x + 2$ for each x–value.

For example :

When $x = 0$, $y = 0 + 2 = 2$,
when $x = 2$, $y = 2 + 2 = 4$.

Step 1. Prepare a table as under :

x	0	2	5
y	2	4	7

Step 2. Plot the points and join them up with a straight edge.

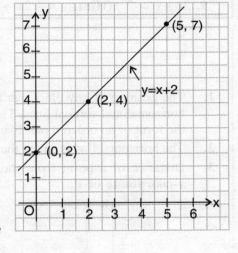

(ii) $y = -\dfrac{1}{2}x + 3$

The table of values is

x	0	4	6
y	3	1	0

(iii) $y = 3x - 5$

The table of values is

x	1	2	4
y	– 2	1	7

Plots the points (1, –2), (2, 1) and (4, 7) and join.

Plots the points (0, 3), (4, 1) and (6, 0) and join them with a straightedge.

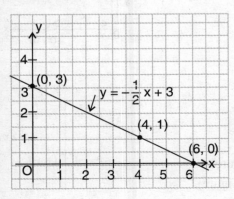

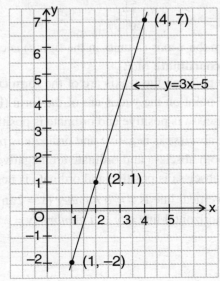

EXERCISE 23 (b)

1. Draw the straight lines for each of the following equations.

   (a) $x = 5$ (b) $x = 8$ (c) $x = -6$ (d) $x = 0$

   (e) $y = 4$ (f) $y = 7$ (g) $y = -5$ (h) $y = 0$

2. Copy and complete the table of values for each equation.

   (a) $y = x + 5$

x	–3	–1	0	4	7
y					

(b) $y = x - 2$

x	–2	0	3	5	8
y					

(c) $\left(y = -\dfrac{1}{3}x + 2 \right)$

x	–6	–3	0	3	9
y					

(d) $y = 2x - 3$

x	–1	0	3	4	5
y					

Draw the graphs of the following equations.

   3. $y = x + 4$ **4.** $y = x - 5$ **5.** $y = 3x$ **6.** $y = \dfrac{1}{2}x$ **7.** $y = 2x - 4$ **8.** $y = 3x - 4$

   9. $2x + y = 7$ (**Hint.** $y = -2x + 7$)   **10.** $x + y = 6$ **11.** $8x + y = -7$.

LOOKING BACK

Summary of Key Facts

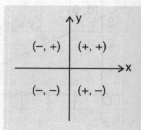

1. The position of any place can be located by knowing 'its' distances from two intersecting horizontal and vertical lines. These lines are called **coordinate axes** and the distances put in the form of an ordered pair like (2, 3) the **coordinates** of the point.

2. The horizontal line is called the **x-axis** and the vertical line the **y-axis.**

3. Distance of a point from the y-axis (2 units in the figure) is called the **abscissa** *or* **x-coordinate of P.**

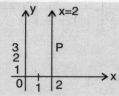 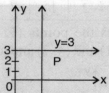

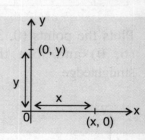

4. Distance of a point from the x-axis (3 units in the figure) is called the **ordinate** or the **y-coordinate** of P.

5. The coordinates of any point on the x-axis are of the form (**x, 0**)

6. The coordinates of any point on the y-axis are of the form (**0, y**)

7. (*i*) In first quadrant abscissa is positive and ordinate is positive.

   (*ii*) In second quadrant abscissa is negative and ordinate is positive.

   (*iii*) In third quadrant both abscissa and ordinate are negative.

   (*iv*) In fourth quadrant abscissa is positive and ordinate is negative.

8. (*i*) The equation of a vertical line is $x = a$ *number* ($x = 2$ in the figure).

   (*ii*) The equation of a horizontal line is $y = a$ *number* ($y = 3$ in the figure).

ANSWERS

Try these

1. (a) A (b) K (c) C (d) D 2. (a) row 4, seat 4 (b) row 2, seat 1 (c) row 3, seat 5 (d) row 4, seat 7
(e) row 5, seat 5 3. C, L, F, G, H, D.

EXERCISE 23 (a)

2. (a) I (b) IV (c) II (d) III (e) IV (f) III (g) I (h) II
3. (a) Polar bears (b) Lions (c) Cafe (d) Gift shop (e) Giraffes (f) Car park
4. (a) (3, 10) (b) (6, 6) (c) (9, 6) (d) (3, 7) (e) (0, 9)
5. (6,2) 6. (a) I (b) III (c) II (d) IV
7. (b) y-coordinate is same (c) x-axis 8. (b) x-coordinate is same (c) y-axis
9. (a) I (b) III (c) IV (d) II (e) y-axis (f) x-axis

Try These

1. (a) $y = 7$ (b) $y = 4\frac{1}{2}$ (c) $y = -2\frac{1}{2}$ (d) $y = -6$ (f) $x = 6$ (g) $x = 8.5$
(h) $x = -3$ (i) $x = -9$ (j) $y = 0$

EXERCISE 23 (b)

2. (a)

x	–3	–1	0	4	7
y	2	4	5	9	12

(b)

x	–1	0	3	4	5
y	– 4	– 2	1	3	6

(c)

x	– 6	–3	0	3	9
y	4	3	2	1	–1

(d)

x	–1	0	3	4	5
y	–5	–3	3	5	7

24. Relations and Mappings

24.1 Ordered Pairs

In daily life, there are situations in which order is important and in others it is not.

For example :

When we take off our shoes, it does not matter whether we remove the shoe on our right first. We w ultimately get both shoes off. The end result is not affected by the order in which we perform the steps. On t other hand, if we have the pair of socks and shoe, the order in which they are put on is not only important b essential also.

Study the following examples :

1. The table below shows how four children are paired with their ages.

Child :	Anju	Suman	Aadhar	Aparna
Age :	8	7	6	10

   This pairing can be shown by means of the following ordered pairs :

   (Anju, 8),   (Suman, 7),   (Aadhar, 6),   (Aparna, 10)

   In the ordered pair (Anju, 8), Anju is the **first component** and 8 is the **second component**

2. The association of some countries with their capitals form the set of ordered pairs as given below :

   (India, New Delhi),   (France, Paris)   (England, London),   (Nepal, Kathmandu)

3. By forming pairs of a few numbers and their squares, we obtain the following set of ordered pairs.

   $\{(1, 1), (2, 4), (3, 9), (4, 16), (5, 25), (6, 36), (7, 49)\}$.

> **An ordered pair is a pair of objects whose components** occur in a special order.
> *It is written by listing the two components in the specified order, separating them by a comma and enclosing the pair in parentheses. In the ordered pair (a, b), a is called the first component and the second component.*

Remark : Ordered pairs can have the same first and second components such as (2, 2), (5, 5).

Ex. 1. Let $A = \{a, b\}$. Then all its possible ordered pairs are $(a, a), (b, b), (a, b), (b, a)$.

Ex. 2. Let A be the set of first five natural numbers and B be the set of cubes of these numbers, then the set of ordere pairs of these numbers and their cubes is $\{(1, 1), (2, 8), (3, 27), (4, 64), (5, 125)\}$.

Ex. 3. Let $A = \{a, b, c\}$ and $B = \{1, 2, 3, 4\}$. Then all possible ordered pairs such that in each ordered pair the fir component is an element of set A and the second component is an element of set B are obtained by pairing eac element from set A with each element from set B. This can be done by the following scheme :

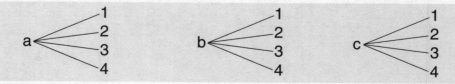

The ordered pairs are

$(a, 1), (a, 2), (a, 3), (a, 4), (b, 1), (b, 2), (b, 3), (b, 4), (c, 1), (c, 2), (c, 3), (c, 4)$.

EXERCISE 24 (a)

1. The following table shows the weights of six persons. Write this information in the form of a set of ordered pairs taking the person as the first component of each ordered pair.

Person :	Akhil	Sumit	Pradeep	Ranjana	Manju	David
Weight :	51	49	58	45	46	63

2. For each set, list the set of all first components and the set of all second components.

   (a) {(4, 10), (5, 8),(6, 6),(7, 4)}   (b) {(10,3), (5, 7), (3,8), (1,9), (2,10)}.

3. Form a set of ordered pairs where the first component is a member of {1, 3, 5, 7} and the second component is related to the first as given.

   (a) The second component is I less than the first. (b) The second component is square of the first.

   (c) The difference of the components is 0.   (d) The product of the components is 0.

   (e) The product of the components is the opposite of the first component.

4. Name the ordered number pair for the point :

   (a) K   (b) G   (c) D   (d) N

   (e) R   (f) A   (g) J   (h) B

   (i) L   (j) E   (k) F   (l) T

   (m) Q   (n) P   (o) H   (p) I

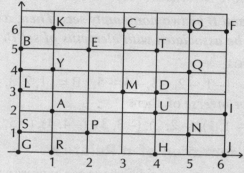

5. You can use the number plane shown in Q. 4 to play a spelling game. In this game, an ordered pair is written in place of a letter. For example, (3, 3), (1, 2), (5, 1), spells MAN.

   Use ordered number pairs to write the word.

   (a) CAT   (b) PEN   (c) HAND   (d) BALL   (e) STREET   (f) ELEPHANT   (g) TEA

6. Name the word.

   (a) (6,0), (5,6), (1,6), (2,5)   (b) (0,5), (5,6), (1,4)

   (c) (2,1), (2,5), (5,1), (3,6), (6,2), (0,3)   (d) (1,0), (1,2), (6,2), (5,1)

   (e) (3,6), (5,6), (6,6), (6,6), (2,5), (2,5)   (f) (5,4), (4,2), (2,5), (0, 1), (4,5), (6,2), (5,6), (5,1).

24.2 Relation

A. Study the following sentences :

1. Jawahar Lal Nehru was the father of Indira Gandhi.

2. New Delhi is the Capital of India.

3. 52 is greater than 43.

4. The line AB is parallel to the line CD.

5. {a, b} is a subset of {a, b, c}

   All these sentences express **relationship** between two objects. Intuitively, we can say that the **word "relation",** implies an association of two objects (people, numbers, ideas, etc.) according to some property possessed by them.

   We also say that relation between two elements is a **rule** by which first element is associated with the second element.

   Thus, the number 6, 36 are associated by the rule, 36 is square of 6 : Aadhar and Ananya are associated by the rule that Aadhar is the brother of Ananya.

B. Now Consider the Sentence

'x is the capital of y'

A few ordered pairs satisfying this sentence are (Colombo, Ceylon) , (London, England), (Beijing, China (Tokyo, Japan), Similarly, the ordered pairs {(8, 6), (7, 3) (2, 1) (1, 0)} satisfy the sentence '*x* is greater th *y*', while (6, 8), (3, 7), (1, 2), (0, 1) do not.

From the above you can conclude that you can always form a set of ordered pairs from the given relation.

> **Definition : A relation** *is a set of ordered pairs. Any set of ordered pairs is, therefore, a relation. The set of first components of the ordered pairs is called the* **domain** *and the set of second components called the* **range**.

In the relation {(6, 8), (3, 7), (1, 2) (0, 1)} the domain is {6, 3, 1, 0} and the range is {8, 7, 2, 1}.

24.3 Relation Between Two Sets

Let A and B be two non-empty sets. Then, a relation R from A to B is a rule by which elements of s A can be associated with elements of set B.

For example:

Let A = {– 1, – 2, – 3, – 4, – 5,} B = {1, 2, 3, 4, 5,}, and R be the relation from A to B is the *opposite additive inverse* of, then,

R = {(– 1, 1), (– 2, 2), (– 3, 3), (– 4, 4), (– 5, 5)}.

24.4 Representation of a Relation

There are two ways in which we can express a relation.

A. Roster Form : In this form, a relation *R* from set *A* to set *B* is expressed as a set of ordered pairs whose fir components are taken from set *A* and second components from set *B* so that these components satisfy th given relation (i.e. the given rule).

For example :

1. Let *A* = {Dollar, Rupee, Yen, Euro}, *B* = {Japan, Germany, India, U.S.A} and the relation *R is the Curren of*, then

   R = {(Dollar, U.S.A), (Rupee, India), (Yen, Japan), (Euro, Germany)}.

2. Let *A* = {25, 36, 81, 100}, *B* {9, 6, 5, 10,} and *R* be the relation *'is the square of'*, the *R* = {(25, 5), (36, 6), (81, 9), (100, 10)} :

B. By arrow diagrams: In constructing the arrow diagrams, the related elements should be paired and if th relation is from A to B the arrowhead should indicate the direction from A to B.

Set A	is the Capital of	Set B
Bhopal		Rajasthan
Chennai		Arunachal Pradesh
Jaipur		West Bengal
Kolkata		Madhya Pradesh
Itanagar		Tamil Nadu

The symbol → (called an arrow) represents the relation *is the capital* of.

From the diagram, the following set of ordered pairs can be formed.

{(Bhopal, Madhya Pradesh), (Chennai, Tamil Nadu), (Jaipur, Rajasthan), (Kolkata, West Bengal (Itanagar, Arunachal Pradesh)}.

Ex. 1. *Let A = {5, 7, 9} and B = {3, 8, 10} and R be the relation less than from A to B. (i) Write R in roster form (ii) Represent R by an arrow diagram. (iii) Find the domain and range of R.*

Sol. Given : $A = \{5, 7, 9\}$, $B = \{3, 8, 10\}$ and R is the relation *'is less than'* from A to B.

(i) **Roster Form :** To write R in roster form, we form a set of ordered pairs whose first components belong to set A and second components are taken from set B in such a way that first component is less than second component. Thus,

$R = \{(5, 8), (5, 10), (7, 8), (7, 10), (9, 10)\}$.

(ii) **Arrow diagram:** Write the elements of the two sets in column form and draw arrows from elements of A to those of B, satisfying the relation less than.

(iii) Domain of $R = \{5, 7, 9\}$

Range of $R = \{3, 8, 10\}$

Ex. 2. *Let A = {2, 3, 4, 5}, B = {2, 4, 9, 10, 11, 12} and R the relation 'is a factor of' from A to B. Represent R in (i) roster form, (ii) by arrow diagram and write the domain and range of R.*

Sol. Given $A = \{2, 3, 4, 5\}$, $B = \{2, 4, 9, 10, 11, 12\}$ and R the relation *'is a factor of'* from A to B.

(a) (i) **Roster Form :** We form a set of ordered pairs whose first component belongs to set A and second component is taken from set B in such a manner that the first component is a factor of second component. We start with the first element '2' of set A.

∴ $R = \{(2, 2), (2, 4), (2, 10), (2, 12), (3, 9), (3, 12), (4, 4), (4, 12), (5, 10)\}$.

(b) **By Arrow diagram :** Write the elements of the two sets in column form and draw arrows from elements of set A to those of set B satisfying the given relation.

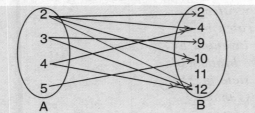

as Domain of $R = \{2, 3, 4, 5\}$, Range of $R = \{2, 4, 9, 10, 12\}$

EXERCISE 24 (b)

1. **Copy these sets and draw an arrow from each town in set A to the State in set B in which the town is situated**

Set A	Set B
Lucknow	Rajasthan
Shimla	Karnatak
Bangalore	Uttar Pradesh
Patna	Himachal Pradesh
Bhubaneshwar	Orissa
Jaipur	Bihar

Complete this sentence : The diagram shows the relation '............' from set A to set B.

2. **Copy and complete arrow diagrams for the relations between the members of the given set in each case**

    (*a*) **Set A**   *is the square of*   **Set B**   (*b*) **Set A**   *is greater than*   **Set B**

    | 100 | 3 | | 3 | 3 |
    | 16 | 10 | | 5 | 6 |
    | 25 | 9 | | 7 | 8 |
    | 81 | 4 | | 9 | 13 |
    | 9 | 5 |

    Write out the set of ordered pairs for both (*a*) and (*b*).

3. **Let A = {a, b, c, d}, B = {x, y, z}. Tell which of the following relations are from A to B.**

    (*i*) $R_1 = \{(a, x), (a, z), (b, y), (c, z),\}$.

    (*ii*) $R_2 = \{(x, b), (y, a), (z, c), (x, d),\}$.

    (*iii*) $R_3 = \{(a, z), (b, x), (c, x), (d, y),\}$.

    (*iv*) $R_4 = \{(a, x), (b, y), (d, z)\}$.

4. **Let A = {Prem, Anil, Shyam}, B = {11, 8, 13, 5}. Tell which of the following relations are from B to A.**

    (*i*) $R_1 = \{(Anil,5), (Prem,11), (Shyam, 13)\}$.

    (*ii*) $R_2 = \{(5, Shyam), (8, Prem), (11, Shyam)\}$.

    (*iii*) $R_3 = \{(13, Anil), (5, Prem), (11, Shyam), (8, Anil)\}$.

    (*iv*) $R_4 = \{(11, Prem), (11, Anil), (5, Shyam)\}$.

5. **Renu was asked to make up a set of ordered pairs. In some cases she wrote the pairs in the wrong order. Study the following table and write true or false.**

	Ordered pair	**Relation**
(*a*)	(12, 3)	*is a factor of*
(*b*)	(Geetanjli, Tagore)	*was written by*
(*c*)	(Lollipops, Children)	*are eaten by*
(*d*)	(James Watt, steam engine)	*was invented by*
(*e*)	(Sudha, Lalit)	*is the brother of*
(*f*)	(India, U.P.)	*is a state in*
(*g*)	(1, 5)	*is less than*

6. Let A = {1, 5, 6, 9, 10,} Write set A in column form and make an arrow diagram to show the relation 'is four more than' on the set A.

7. **List the ordered pairs in the relation:**

    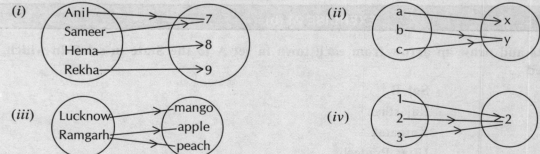

8. **Let A = {4, 6, 8, 9, 18}, B = {2, 3, 6, 12, 16, 36, 48, 54}. Form the following relations from A to B and express them in roster form.**

    (*i*) R_1 relation *'is a multiple of'*   (*ii*) R_2 relation *'is a factor of'*

    (*iii*) R_3 relation *'is a square of'*   (*iv*) R_4 relation *'is one half of'*

    Find the domain and range of the relation in each case.

9. Use the set of ordered pairs {(1, 2), (1, 4), (1, 8), (1, 18), (1, 20), (2, 2), (2, 4), (2, 8), (2, 18), (2, 20), (3, 18), (5, 20), (6, 18),} to find the following relations.
   (i) R_1 relation 'is a factor of.'
   (ii) R_2 relation 'is one fourth of'.

10. Let A = {1, 8, 27, 70, 125}, B = {1, 2, 3, 4, 5}. Let R be the relation 'is a cube of' from A to B.
    Represent R in (i) roster form, (ii) by arrow diagram. Find domain (R) and range (R).

11. Given the following relations, find the rule :
    (a) {(0, 3), (1, 4), (2, 5), (3, 6)......}
    (b) {(0, 0), (1, – 3), (2, – 6), (3, – 9), (4, –12), (5, – 15)}

12. Given A = { –2, –1, 0, 1, 2}, list the ordered pairs determined by each of the following relations applied on A.
    (i) R_1 = 'is less than'
    (ii) R_2 = 'is the square of'
    (iii) R_3 = 'is the additive inverse of'
    (iv) R_4 = 'is equal to'

24.5 Mapping

A Mapping is a special relation from a set A to set B which is formed by some rule in such a manner that.
(i) Every member of set A is associated with a unique element of set B.
(ii) No member of Set A remains unassociated.
Illustrations : Consider the relation displayed by the following arrow diagrams.
(a) Relation R_1 **'is the mother tongue of'**
In this relation :
(i) Every member of set A is associated with a unique member of set B.
(ii) No member of set A is left out.

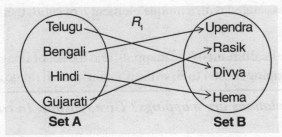

Therefore, this relation is a mapping.
R_1 = {(Telugu, Divya), (Bengali, Upendra), (Hindi, Hema), (Gujarati, Rasik)}.
Note that different ordered pairs, have different first components, In other words we can say that no two different ordered pairs have the same first component
(b) Relation R_2 'is the square of'

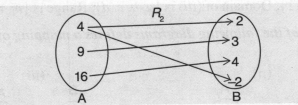

In this relation : Every member of set A **is not** associated with a unique element of set B. Thus, 4 is associated with –2, and 2. So, this relation is not a mapping.
In roster form, R_2 = {(4, –2), (4, 2), (9, 3), (16, 4),}. Here two different ordered pairs (4, –2) and (4, 2) have the same first component.

(c) Relation R_3 'is the cube of'

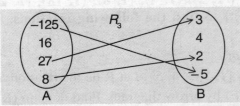

In this relation no arrow starts from the element '16' of set A, i.e, this element is not used up.

In roster form, $R_3 = \{(-125, -5), (8, 2), (27, 3)\}$. Domain of $R_3 = \{-125, 8, 27\}$ which is not equal to A. Therefore, this relation is not a mapping even though all other members of set A have association with members of set B.

(d) Relation R_4 '**Plays**'

The arrow diagram (i) represents a mapping while diagram (ii) does not represent a mapping.

Notice that while for a mapping from A to B to be defined, all elements of set A should be used up. It does not matter whether all the elements of set B are used up or not.

> Let A, B be two non-empty sets, then a **mapping** from A to B is a rule which associates every element of set A to a unique element of set B.
>
> If an element a of set A is associated with a unique element b of set B, then b is called the **image** of a under the mapping.
>
> The elements of set A form the **domain** of the mapping and the set of images in set B form the **range** of the mapping. **Note that** in a mapping from A to B, while domain = set A, range may or may not be equal to set B.

Ex. 1. *Which of the following relations are mappings? Give reasons. In case of a mapping, determine its domain and range:*

(i) *{(1, – 2), (3, 7), (4, – 6), (8, 11)}*   (ii) *{(1, 0), (1, –1), (2, 3), (4, 10)}*

(iii) *{(a, m), (b, n), (c, m), (d, n)}*

Sol. (i) and (iii) are mappings because no two of their ordered pairs have the same first component. (ii) is not a mapping since the two ordered pairs (1, 0) and (1, –1) have the same first component. Domain of (i) is {1, 3, 4, 8}, Range is {–2, 7, –6, 11}, Domain of (iii) is {a, b, c, d}, Range is {m, n}.

Ex. 2. *State whether or not each of the following diagrams defines a mapping of* A = {a, b, c} *to* B = {x, y, z}.

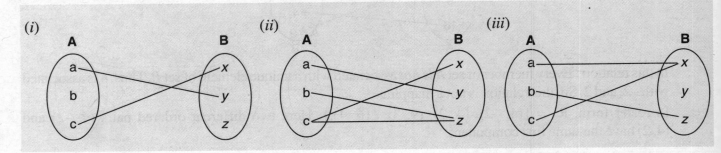

l. (*i*) No, because the domain set *A* is not entirely used up.

(*ii*) No, because element *c* of the domain set is not assigned to a unique element of set B. It is assigned to two elements *x* and *z*, yielding two ordered pairs with the same first component.

(*iii*) Yes, because a given association is a mapping even if (*a*) two or more elements of the first set A are assigned to the same element of the second set, (*b*) the second set B is not entirely used up.

EXERCISE 24 (c)

1. **Which of the following relations represents mapping ?**

(*i*) {(2,2), (2,3), (2,4), (2,5)}   (*ii*) {(*a*, *b*), (*b*, *c*), (*c*, *d*), (*d*, *e*)}

(*iii*) {(1, 2), (3, 1), (1, 3), (4, 1)}   (*iv*) {(1, 2), (2, 2), (3, 2), (4, 2)}

2. **Which of the following arrow-diagrams represents a mapping? Give reasons in each case.**

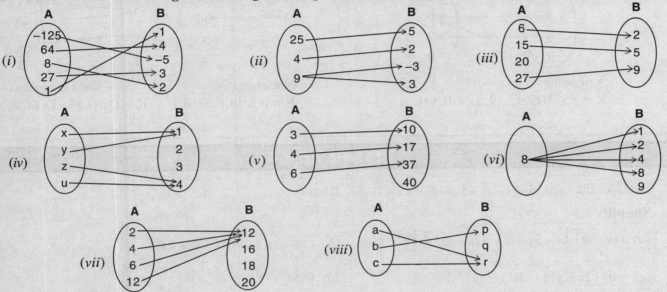

3. Let A = {1, 2, 3, 4, 5, 6, 7,}, B = {4, 9, 10}. Let R = {(2,4), (3,4), (4,4), (5,4), (6,4)} Is R a mapping from A to B? Given reason.

4. Let A = {6, 7, 8, 9}, and B = {6, 9, 10, 11, 12}. Let R = {(6, 6), (6, 9), (7, 10), (8, 11), (9, 12),} Is R a mapping from A to B? Give reason.

5. Let R = $x \rightarrow x^2 - 2$ where $x \in \{-1, -2, 0, 2\}$. (*i*) List the elements of R (*ii*) Is R a mapping ?

6. Let R = $x \rightarrow 2x - 3$, where $x \in \{1, 2, 3\}$. (*i*) List elements of R. (*ii*) Is R a mapping ?.

7. The domain of a mapping is the set of positive integers less than 12. If the mapping is defined by $x \rightarrow |x - 4|$, where $x \in A$, find all ordered pairs satisfying the mapping.

8. **Determine which of the following are mappings.**

(*i*) P is the set of parents and Q is the set of children. R = {(*x*, *y*), *x* ∈ P, *y* ∈ Q, *x* is the parent of *y*}.

(*ii*) B is the set of buttons, and C is the set of coats. R = {(*x*, *y*) : *x* ∈ B, *y* ∈ C, *x* is sewn onto *y*}

LOOKING BACK

Summary of Key Facts

1. An **ordered pair** is a pair of objects whose components occur in a specified order. In the ordered pair. (*a*, *b*), a is called the **first component** and b the **second component.**

2. A **relation** is an association between two objects.

3. Let A and B be two non-empty sets, then a **relation,** R from A to B is a rule by which elements of set A can be associated with elements of set B. This association yields a set of ordered pairs.

4. A **relation** is a **set of ordered pairs.** The set of first components of the ordered pairs is called

the **domain** and the set of second components is called the **range**.

Thus, {(5, 7), (6, 8), (7, 9), (9, 11)} is a relation whose domain is {5, 6, 7, 9} and range is {7, 8, 9, 11}

5. Let A, B be two non-empty sets, then a **mapping** from A to B is a rule which associates every element of set A to a unique element of set B.

Thus, for a mapping to be defined from set A to set B it is essential that

(*i*) All elements of set A are used up, i.e., domain of the mapping = set A.

(*ii*) An element of set A is not assigned to more than one element of set B, i.e., no two ordered pairs of the mapping should have the same first component.

For example

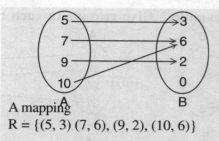

A mapping
R = {(5, 3) (7, 6), (9, 2), (10, 6)}

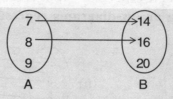

Not a mapping
R = {(7, 14,) (8, 16)}

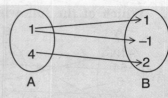

Not a mapping
R = {(1, 1), (1 −1), (4, 2)}

UNIT REVIEW-4

1. Subtract the sum of $4x - x^2 + 5$ and $-4x - 3 + 6x^2$ from 6.

2. **Simplify :**

   (a) $11x - 2\left[4x - 3y - (5y + 2x - \overline{x - y})\right]$

   (b) $(2x - 5)(5x + 6) - 5(2x - 1)^2$

   (c) $-4[-(2x + y) + (-3)(x - y)]$

   (d) $(-5x^2 y) \times \left(\dfrac{-2}{3} xy^2 z\right) \times \left(\dfrac{8}{15} xyz^2\right) \times \left(\dfrac{-z}{4}\right)$

3. **Multiply :**

   (a) $(2x - 3y)(x^3 - 3x^2 y + 6xy^2 - y^3)$

   (b) $(x^4 + x^2 + 1)(x^4 - x^2 + 1)$

   (c) $(3a + 2b)(2a - 3b)(4a + 5b)$

4. **Divide :**

   (a) $25y^4 + 30y^3 + 15y^2$ by $5y^2$

   (b) $(8x^2 - 6x - 9)$ by $(4x + 3)$

5. **Expand :**

   (a) $\left(6x + \dfrac{y}{5}\right)^2$

   (b) $\left(5a^2 - \dfrac{6}{7} b\right)^2$

   (c) $\left(3x + \dfrac{1}{3x}\right)^2$

   (d) $\left(\dfrac{x}{y} - \dfrac{y}{x}\right)^2$

6. **Factorize :**

   (a) $ab + ac + a^2$

   (b) $pq - q^2 + rp - qr$

   (c) $x^2 y^2 + xy - a\, xy - a$

   (d) $144 - 169x^2$

   (e) $12a^2 - 27$

   (f) $a^4 - 64$

   (g) $x^3 - \dfrac{x}{25}$

7. **Evaluate using algebraic identities :**

   (a) 71^2

   (b) $61^2 - 39^2$

   (c) 51×49

8. If $x + \dfrac{1}{x} = 4$, find the value of $x^2 + \dfrac{1}{x^2}$.

9. **Simplify :**

   $(5x + 3y)^2 - (2x - 3y)^2 - (4x - 7y)(4x + 7y)$. Find the value of the result if $x = 1$, $y = -1$

10. Solve for a :

(a) $a - (2a + 5) - 5(1 - 2a) = 2(3 + 4a) - 3(a - 4)$

(b) $\frac{5}{7}(3a - 2) = \frac{3}{4}(a + 1) + \frac{2}{3}a$

(c) $2.4(3 - a) - 0.6(2a - 3) = 0$

11. Solve : $3 - 2x \geq x - 17$ $\quad x \in W$

12. Frame a formula for :

The sum of r and s is 6 less than the sum of twice p plus 3 times q.

13. For $S = \frac{n}{2}(a + b)$, (i) find S when $a = 3, b = 18, n = 50$ $\quad$ (ii) find n when $S = 24, a = 3, b = 5$

14. Change the subject of the formula $y = mx + c$ to x.

15. Divide 34 into two parts in such a way that $\left(\frac{4}{7}\right)$th of one part is equal to $\left(\frac{2}{5}\right)$th of the other.

16. Raj's age is four times the difference of his age after four years and his age three year back. How old is he?

17. The adjacent arrow diagram represents a relation. Represent the relation in roster form. Is this relation a mapping? Give reasons for your answer.

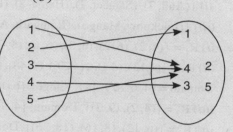

18. Draw the graph of $x - 3y = 0$.

Find the product using identity : $\quad$ **19.** $\left(3x + \frac{4y}{5}\right)\left(3x - \frac{4y}{5}\right)$ $\quad$ **20.** $(x + 1)(x - 1)(x^2 + 1)$

ANSWERS
EXERCISE 24 (a)

1. {(Akhil, 51), (Sumit, 49), Pradeep, 58), (Ranjna, 45), (Manju, 46), (David, 63)}

2. (a) {4, 5, 6, 7} ; {10, 8, 6, 4} $\quad$ (b) {10, 5, 3, 1, 2}, {3, 7, 8, 9, 10}

3. (a) {(1, 0). (3, 2), (5, 4), (7, 6)} $\quad$ (b) {(1, 1), (3, 9), (5, 25), (7, 49)} $\quad$ (c) {(1, 1), (3, 3), (5, 5), (7, 7)}

(d) {(1, 0), (3, 0), (5, 0), (7, 0)} $\quad$ (e) {(1, − 1), (3, − 1), (5, − 1), (7, − 1)}

4. (a) (1,6) $\quad$ (b) (0, 0) $\quad$ (c) (4,3) $\quad$ (d) (5, 1) $\quad$ (e) (1,0) $\quad$ (f) (1, 2) $\quad$ (g) (6,0) $\quad$ (h) (0, 5)

(i) (0,3) $\quad$ (j) (2, 5) $\quad$ (k) (6,6) $\quad$ (l) (4, 5) $\quad$ (m) (5,4) $\quad$ (n) (2, 1) $\quad$ (o) (4,0) $\quad$ (p) (6, 2)

5. (a) (3,6), (1,2),(4,5) $\quad$ (b) (2,1), (2, 5), (5, 1), $\quad$ (c) (4,0), (1,2),(5,1), (4, 3) $\quad$ (d) (0,5), (1, 2), (0, 3),(0,3)

(e) (0,1), (4,5),(1,0), (2, 5), (2, 5), (4, 5) $\quad$ (f) (2,5),(0, 3),(2, 5),(2, 1),(4, 0),(1, 2),(5, 1),(4, 5).

(g) (4, 5), (2, 5), (1, 2)

6. (a) JOKE $\quad$ (b) BOY $\quad$ (c) PENCIL $\quad$ (d) RAIN $\quad$ (e) COFFEE $\quad$ (f) QUESTION

EXERCISE 24 (b)

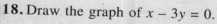

1.

Set A	Set B
Lucknow	Rajasthan
Shimla	Karnataka
Bangalore	Uttar Pradesh
Patna	Himachal Pradesh
Bhubaneshwar	Orissa.
Jaipur	Bihar

2 (a).

Set A	Set B
100	3
16	10
25	9
81	4
9	5

2. (b)   Set A   Set B

   The set ordered pairs for (a) is {(100, 10), (16, 9), (25, 4), (81, 9), (9,3)}

   The set of ordered pairs for (b) is {5, 3}, (7, 3), (7,6), (9,3), (9,6),(9, 8)}

3. (i) R_1, (iii) R_3 and (iv) R_4.   4. (ii) R_2, (iii) R_3 and (iv) R_4

5. (a) False,   (b) True,   (c) True,   (d) False,   (e) False,   (f) False,   (g) True.

6. Set A   Set B

7. (i) {(Anil, 7), (Sameer, 7), (Hema, 8), (Rekha, 9)}   (ii) {(a, x), (b, y), (c, y),}

   (iii) {(Lucknow, Mango), (Ramgarh, Apple), (Ramgarh, Peach),}   (iv) {(1, 2), (2, 2), (3, 2),}

8. (i) R_1 = {(4, 2), (6, 2), (6, 3), (6, 6), (8, 2), (9, 3), (18, 2), (18, 3), (18, 6)}, Domain = {4, 6, 8, 9, 18}, Range = {2, 3, 6}

   (ii) R_2 = {(4,12), (4,16), (4, 36), (4, 48), (6, 6), (6, 12), (6, 36), (6, 48), (6, 54), (8, 16), (8, 48), (9, 36), (9, 54), (18, 36), (18, 54),

   Domain = {4, 6, 8, 9, 18}, Range ={6, 12, 16, 36, 48, 54}.

   (iii) R_3 = {(4, 2), (9, 3)}, Domain, {4, 9}, Range = {2, 3}.

   (iv) R_4 = {(6, 12), (8, 16), (18, 36)}, Domain {6, 8, 18} Range {12, 16, 36}.

9. R_1 = {(1, 2), (1, 4), (1, 8), (1, 18) (1, 20), (2, 2), (2, 4), (2, 8), (2, 18), (2, 20) (3, 18), (5, 20), (6, 18)}

   (ii) R_2 = {(1, 4), (2, 8), (5, 20),}.

10. (i) R = {(1, 1), (8, 2), (27, 3), (125, 5)}   (iii)

    Domain (R) = {1, 8, 27, 125}

    Range (R) = {1, 2, 3, 5}.

11. (a) is 'three less than', i.e; $y = x - 3$

    (b) $y = -3x$

12. (i) R_1= {(−2, −1), (−2, 0), (−2, 1), (−2, 2), (−1, 0), (−1, 1), (−1, 2), (0, 1), (0, 2), (1, 2)}

    (ii) $R_2 = \phi$ (iii) R_3 = {(−2, 2), (−1, 1), (2, −2), (1, −1)}   (iv) R_4 = {(−2, −2), (−1, −1), (0, 0), (1, 1), (2, 2)

EXERCISE 24 (c)

1. (ii) & (iv).   2. (i), (iv), (v), (vii), (viii)   3. No, because domain (R) ≠ A

4. No, since 6 ∈ A has two images in B. namely, 6 and 9.   5. (i) {(−1, −1), (−2, 2), (0, −2), (2, 2)}   (ii) Yes

6. (i) {(1, −1), (2, 1), (3, 3), (ii) yes

7. **Hint :** Domain = {1, 2, 3, 4, 5, 6, 7, 8, 9, 10, 11}. According to the given mapping,

   1 → |1 − 4| = |− 3| = 3, 2 → |2 − 4| = |−2| = 2, 3 → |3 − 4| = | −1| = 1, 4 → |4 − 4| = 0, 5 → |5 − 4| = 1, and so on.

   The ordered pairs satisfying the given mapping are

   (1, 3), (2, 2), (3, 1), (4, 0), (5, 1), (6, 2), (7, 3), (8, 4), (9, 5), (10, 6), (11, 7).

8. (i) No,   (ii) Yes.

UNIT REVIEW – 4

1. $-5x^2 + 4$ 2. (a) $5x + 18y$ (b) $-10x^2 + 7x - 35$ (c) $20x - 8y$ (d) $-\dfrac{4}{9}x^4 y^4 z^4$

3. (a) $2x^4 - 9x^3 y + 21x^2 y^2 - 20 xy^3 + 3y^4$ (b) $x^8 + x^4 + 1$ (c) $24a^3 + 10a^2 b + 49ab^2 - 30b^3$

4. (a) $5y^2 + 6y + 3$ (b) $2x - 3$

5. (a) $36x^2 + \dfrac{12}{5}xy + \dfrac{y^2}{25}$ (b) $25a^4 - \dfrac{60a^2b}{7} + \dfrac{36}{49}b^2$ (c) $9x^2 + 2 + \dfrac{1}{9x^2}$ (d) $\dfrac{x^2}{y^2} - 2 + \dfrac{y^2}{x^2}$

6. (a) $a(a+b+c)$ (b) $(p-q)(q+r)$ (c) $(1+xy)(xy-a)$ (d) $(12+13x)(12-13x)$ (e) $3(2a+3)(2a-3)$

   (f) $(a^2+8)(a^2-8)$ (g) $x\left(x+\dfrac{1}{5}\right)\left(x-\dfrac{1}{5}\right)$

7. (a) 5041 (b) 2200 (c) 2499 8. 14. 9. $5x^2 + 42xy + 49y^2$; 12

10. (a) 7 (b) 3 (c) 2.5 11. $\{0, 1, 2, 3, 4, 5, 6\}$ 12. $(r+s) = (2p+3q) - 6$

13. (i) 525 (ii) 6 14. $x = \dfrac{y-c}{m}$ 15. 14, 20 16. 28 years.

17. $\{1, 4), (2, 1), (3, 4)\ (4, 3)\ (5, 4)\}$; yes because in no ordered pair, first element is the same. Moreover, all elements in the first set are used up.

19. $9x^2 - \dfrac{16y^2}{25}$ 20. $(x^4 - 1)$

UNIT V : GEOMETRY

25. Basic Geometrical Concepts Lines and Angles

In this chapter we shall revise some fundamental geometrical concepts and terms, which you have alread studied in class VI.

25.1 Line, Plane, Line Segment and Ray

Point

A point indicates an exact location in space. It is depicted by a fine dot made by a sharp pencil on a sheet of paper. Points are represented by capital letters of the English alphabet and are written next to the dot depicting the point. In the given figure, *P* represents a point.

Thus a point is the simplest of all geometrical figures having a position but no dimensions (length, breadth and height).

Line

A line is a straight path that extends endlessly in both the directions. The crease in the paper when it folded or the edge of a ruler etc. are examples of a line. A line has no end points and does not have a defini length. Lines are represented by small letters of the English alphabet as *l, m, n,...* etc.

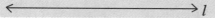

There can be unlimited number of lines passing through a given point *P*.

There can be exactly one line that passes through two given points.

The given figure shows a line represented by the letter *l*.

The two arrow heads show that the line is extending indefinitely in both the directions.

Plane

A plane is a flat surface which extends indefinitely in all directions. The walls and floors of your room, the surface of a sheet of paper, surface of a table top etc. are all examples of a plane. A plane has no thickness. Two planes intersect in a line. We can represent a part of a plane by a parallelogram.

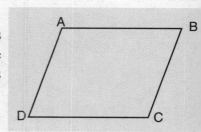

Line Segment

A line segment $\overline{AB}$ is a straight path containing points *A* and *B* and all the points between *A* and *B*. The poin *A* and *B* are called **end points** of the line segment $\overline{AB}$. The distance between *A* and *B* is called the length o $\overline{AB}$. *A* and *B* being fixed points, the distance between them is fixed and hence a line segment has a defini length. *Thus a line segment can be defined as a portion of a line having a definite length*.

When two fixed points are given, one and only one line segment can be drawn with these two points as en points. The given figure represents a line segment $\overline{AB}$.

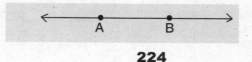

Ray

The part of a line that extends indefinitely in one direction from a given point O is called a ray. A ray has only one end point. The given figure shows the ray $\overrightarrow{OA}$

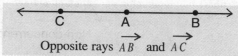

$\overrightarrow{OA}$ and $\overrightarrow{AO}$ are two different rays. A ray has no definite length. An unlimited number of rays can be drawn from the same initial point.

Two rays $\overrightarrow{AB}$ and $\overrightarrow{AC}$ are said to be opposite rays if they are collinear and point A is the only common point of the two rays.

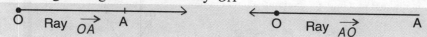

Opposite rays $\overrightarrow{AB}$ and $\overrightarrow{AC}$

25.2 Summary of Line Notations

$\overline{AB}$ denotes the line segment between A and B

AB denotes the length or the measure of the line segment AB.

$\overleftrightarrow{AB}$ denotes the line determined by A and B.

$\overrightarrow{AB}$ denotes the ray having end point A and passing through B.

$\overrightarrow{BA}$ denotes the ray having end point B and passing through A. We will denote line segment $\overline{AB}$ by AB.

25.3 Properties of Lines

1. An unlimited number of lines can be drawn through a given point.

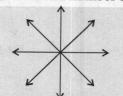

2. Two points determine a unique line.

3. Two lines in a plane either intersect each other at exactly one point or are parallel.

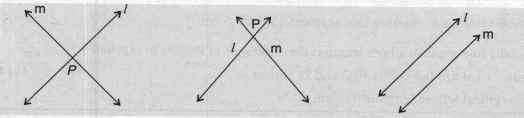

If two lines intersect each other, then the common point P (as in the first two figures) is known as the point of intersection.

25.4 Collinear Points

Three or more points which lie on the same line are called collinear points, and the line is called the **line of collinearity.**

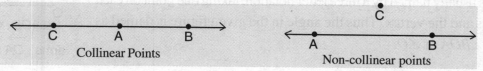

Collinear Points   Non-collinear points

25.5 Concurrent Lines

Three or more lines in a plane are concurrent if all of them pass through the same point, the common point
called the **point of concurrency.**

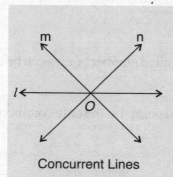

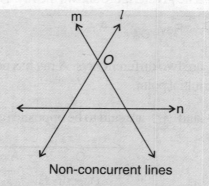

Concurrent Lines   Non-concurrent lines

EXERCISE 25 (a)

1. What is the difference between a ray and a line ?
2. How many lines can be drawn through two different points ?
3. In how many points can two distinct lines at most intersect ?
4. Give two examples each of (*i*) intersecting lines and (*ii*) parallel lines from your environment.
5. How many **line segments** are possible with three collinear points ?
6. **Write names of the following :**
   (*i*) Five line segments   (*ii*) Five rays
   (*iii*) Four collinear points   (*iv*) A pair of non-intersecting lines in the given figure.
7. **Fill in the blanks :**
   (*i*)   A ray has _____ length.
   (*ii*) A line segment has _____ end points.
   (*iii*) Ray $\overrightarrow{AB}$ is _____ as ray $\overrightarrow{BA}$.
   (*iv*) Concurrent lines pass through a _____ point.
   (*v*)   Three or more points in a plane are said to be _____ if they lie on the
           same line.
   (*vi*) Two planes intersect in a _____.
8. A line segment $\overline{AB}$ = 6.4 cm. Another line segment $\overline{CD}$ = 3.6 cm.

   Find the length of the line segment whose length is the difference of lengths of $\overline{AB}$ and $\overline{CD}$.
9. In the given figure, what are the points P, O and Q known as ?
10. Construct a line segment whose length is 6.3 cm.

Fig. Q. 6

Fig. Q. 9

25.6 Angle

An angle is an inclination between two rays with the same initial point. The
initial point is the **vertex** and the two rays are the **arms** of the angle. An angle
is represented by the symbol ∠.

An angle is usually named by a three letter notation, taking one point on each
of the arms and the vertex. Thus the angle in the given figure is named as
∠AOB or ∠BOA or ∠O.

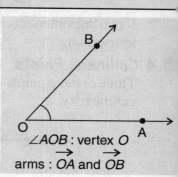

∠AOB : vertex O

arms : $\overrightarrow{OA}$ and $\overrightarrow{OB}$

25.7 Angle as Rotation

An angle is also thought of as the figure formed by rotating a single ray about its vertex.

The amount of rotation is called the measure of the angle.

The **degree** symbolized as ° is a unit for measuring angles. One complete turn or rotation about the vertex is divided into 360 equal parts; each part being called 1°. 1° is further divided into 60 equal parts, each part being called a **minute** and 1′ (**one minute**) is further divided into 60 equal parts, each part being called 1″ (**one second**).

> ∴ **1 rotation = 360°, 1° = 60', 1' = 60''**

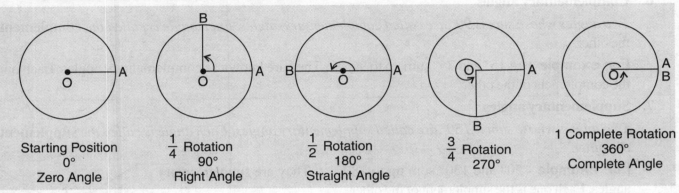

25.8 Types of Angles

1. **Acute angle :** An angle whose magnitude is more than 0° but less than 90° is called an acute angle.

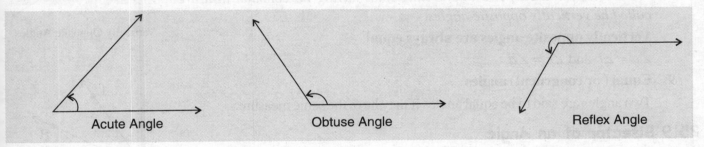

2. **Obtuse angle :** An angle whose magnitude is more than 90° but less than 180° is called an obtuse angle.

3. **Reflex angle :** An angle whose magnitude lies between 180° and 360° is called a reflex angle.

4. **Adjacent angles :** Two angles like ∠AOB and ∠BOC with a common vertex O, a common arm $\overrightarrow{OB}$ and the other arms lying on the opposite sides of the common arm form a pair of adjacent angles.

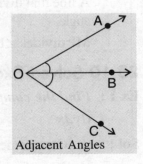

Adjacent Angles

5. **Linear pair :** Adjacent angles whose two non-common arms are opposite rays (i.e. lie on the same straight line), form a linear pair.

∠AOC and ∠BOC form a linear pair.

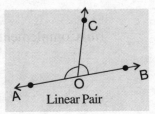

Linear Pair

■ *The sum of the measures of the angles of a linear pair is 180°.*

$\angle AOC + \angle BOC = 180°$.

■ *The sum of the angles at a point on one side of a straight line = 180°.*

$\angle x + \angle y + \angle z = 180°$.

■ *The sum of the angles round a point = 360°.*

$\angle x + \angle y + \angle z + \angle w = 360°$.

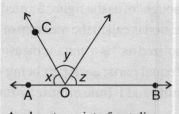

Angles at a point of a st. line on the same side. Sum = 180°

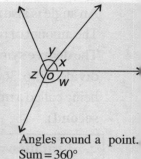

Angles round a point. Sum = 360°

6. **Complementary angles**

*Two angles whose sum is 90° are called complementary angles. Each angle is called the **complement** of the other.*

For example : ∵ 15° and 75° sum up to 90°, ∴ They are known as complementary angles. Each one is the complement of the other.

7. **Supplementary angles**

*Two angles whose sum is 180° are called supplementary angles. Each angle is called the **supplement** of the other.*

For example : 50° and 130° sum up to 180°; ∴ They are supplementary angles. Each one is the supplement of the other.

8. **Vertically opposite angles**

The angles formed by two intersecting lines having no common arm are called be vertically opposite angles.

Vertically opposite angles are always equal.

$\angle a = \angle b$ and $\angle c = \angle d$.

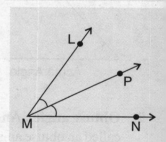

Vertically Opposite Angles

9. **Equal (or congruent) angles**

Two angles are said to be equal angles if they have the same measure.

25.9 Bisector of an Angle

A line that divides an angle into two equal angles is called the bisector of that angle.

MP divides $\angle LMN$ into two equal parts such that $\angle LMP = \angle PMN$.

25.10 Solved Examples

Ex 1 : *Find the complement of :*

    (i) 48°   (ii) 25° 42'   (iii) 60° 45' 22"

Sol : (i) Complement of 48°   = 90° − 48° = **42°**

    (ii) Complement of 25° 42' = 90° − 25° 42'

                          = 89° 60' − 25° 42' = **64° 18'**. | ∵ 90° = 89° 60' |

    (iii) Complement of 63° 45' 22" = 90° − 63° 45' 22"

                            = 89° 59' 60" − 63° 45' 22" = **26° 14' 38"**. | ∵ 90° = 89° 59' 60" |

Ex 2 : *Find the supplement of :*

    (*i*) *79°*   (*ii*) *98° 43'*   (*iii*) *109° 52' 23"*.

Sol :   (*i*) Supplement of 79°   = 180° − 79° = **101°**.

      (*ii*) Supplement of 98° 43' = 180° − 98° 43'

                          = 179° 60' − 98° 43' = **81° 17'**. $\boxed{\because \ 180° = 179°\ 60'}$

      (*iii*) Supplement of 109° 43' 25" = 180° − 109° 43' 25"

                       = 179° 59' 60" − 109° 43' 25" = **70° 16' 35"**. $\boxed{\because \ 180° = 179°\ 59'\ 60"}$

Ex 3 : *Two complementary angles are in the ratio 7 : 8. Find the angles.*

Sol :   Let the angles be 7*x*° and 8*x*°

      ∵ The given angles are complementary

      ∴ 7*x* + 8*x* = 90° ⇒ 15*x* = 90°   ⇒ *x* = 6° ⇒ 7*x* = 42° and 8*x* = 48°

      Hence, the required angles are **42°** and **48°**.

Ex 4 : *An angle is 30° less than two times its supplement. Find the angles.*

Sol :   Let one angle be *x*°. The supplement of this angle is (180 − *x*)°.

      ∴ According to the question

      x = 2 (180 − *x*) − 30 ⇒ *x* = 360 − 2*x* − 30 ⇒ *x* + 2*x* = 330

      ⇒ 3*x* = 330 ⇒ *x* = 110° ⇒ supplement = 180° − 110° = 70°

      ∴ Required angles are **110°** and **70°**.

EXERCISE 25 (b)

1. (*a*) **State the angle through which the line AB has turned in the following case:**

    (*b*) **Measure the angles labelled in the diagrams below to the nearest degree.**

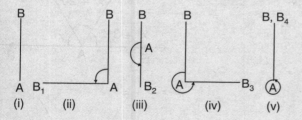

(i)   (ii)   (iii)   (iv)   (v)

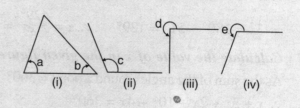

(i)   (ii)   (iii)   (iv)

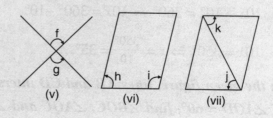

(v)   (vi)   (vii)

2. Name the type of angle in each case.

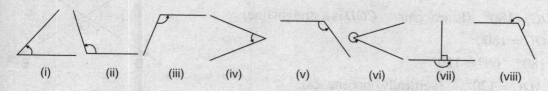

(i)   (ii)   (iii)   (iv)   (v)   (vi)   (vii)   (viii)

3. Find the complement of :

    (*i*) 35°   (*ii*) 90°   (*iii*) 30° 29'   (*iv*) 58° 45'   (*v*) 35° 30' 25"   (*vi*) 70° 48' 22".

4. **Find the supplement of :**

    (i) 72°   (ii) 113°   (iii) 132° 45'   (iv) 105° 25'   (v) 85° 45' 30"   (vi) 165° 10' 26".

5. Two supplementary angles are in the ratio 3 : 7. Find the angles.

6. Two complementary angles are in the ratio 2 : 3. Find the angles.

7. If an angle is 30° less than its complement, find its measure.

8. An angle is 40° more than its supplement, find the angle.

9. If $(2x – 10°)$ and $(x – 5°)$ are complementary angles, find x.

10. If $(3x + 40°)$ and $(x – 20°)$ are supplementary angles, find x.

11. An angle is 30° less than three times its complement. Find the angle.

12. An angle is 8 times its complement. Find the angle.

Ex 5 : *In the given figure, AB and AC are opposite rays.*

$\angle BAD = 5x° – 30°$, $\angle CAD = 2x°$. *Find the value of x ?*

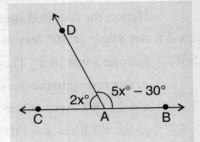

Sol :   Rays AB and AC are opposite rays

∴ BAC is a straight line

⇒ $\angle BAD$ and $\angle CAD$ form a linear pair.

⇒ $\angle BAD + \angle CAD = 180°$

i.e. $5x – 30° + 2x = 180° \Rightarrow 7x = 180° + 30° = 210°$

∴ $x = \dfrac{210°}{7} = \mathbf{30°}$.

Ex 6 : *In the given figure, find x.*

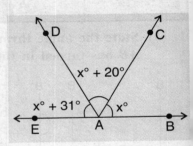

Sol :   As the sum of the angles at a point on a straight line $= 180°$

∴ $x + 31° + x + 20° + x = 180°$ ⇒ $3x + 51° = 180°$

⇒ $3x = 180° – 51° = 129°$ ∴ $x = \dfrac{129°}{3} = \mathbf{43°}$.

Ex. 7 : *Calculate the value of x in the given figure.*

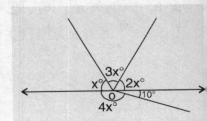

Sol :   As the sum of the angles round a point $= 360°$

∴ $x + 3x + 2x + 10° + 4x = 360°$

⇒ $10x + 10° = 360° \Rightarrow 10x = 360° – 10°$

⇒ $10x = 350° \Rightarrow x = \dfrac{350°}{10} = \mathbf{35°}$.

Ex. 8 : *In the given figure, lines AB and CD intersect at O.*

If $\angle AOD = 60°$, find $\angle BOC$, $\angle AOC$ and $\angle BOD$.

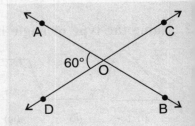

Sol : $\angle BOC = \angle AOD = 60°$ (vert. opp. ∠s)

$\angle AOD + \angle AOC = 180°$ (Linear pair ∵ COD is a straight line)

⇒ $60° + \angle AOC = 180°$

⇒ $\angle AOC = 180° – 60° = \mathbf{120°}$

∴ $\angle BOD = \angle AOC = \mathbf{120°}$ (vertically opposite ∠s).

1. Calculate the value of *x*.

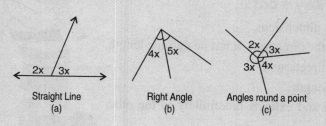

Straight Line   Right Angle   Angles round a point
(a)   (b)   (c)

2. In the given figure *AB* and
     AC are opposite rays.
     If *x* = 32°, find *y*.
     If *y* = 27°, find *x*.

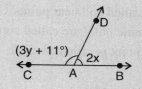

3. In the given figure find
     the value of *x*.

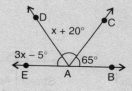

4. Determine *x*.

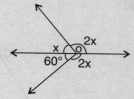

5. In the given figure,
     POS is a line, find *x*.

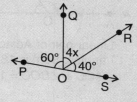

6. In the figure line AB and *CD*
     intersect at *O*. ∠*BOC* = 36°.
     Find ∠*x*, ∠*y* and ∠*z*.

7. In the given figure,
     find the value of *y*.

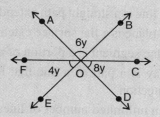

8. In the given figure, if
     ∠*AOC* + ∠*BOD* = 266°,
     find all the four angles.

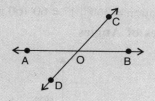

9. In the given figure, if
     ∠*AOC* + ∠*BOC* + ∠*BOD* = 338°,
     find all the four angles.

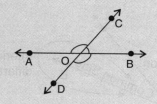

10. In the given figure, *PQ* and RS are two
     lines intersecting each other at point '*O*'.
     If ∠*ROT* = 90°, find the values of *x*, *y*
     and *z*.

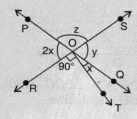

LOOKING BACK

Summary of Key Facts

1. Point indicates an exact location in space and has no dimensions.
2. A line is a straight path extending indefinitely in both the directions. It has no definite length.
3. A plane is a flat surface extending indefinitely in all directions.
4. Line segment is a portion of a line having a definite length.
5. Ray is a part of a line that has one fixed end point and extends indefinitely in the other direction.
6. An unlimited number of lines as well as rays can be drawn through a fixed point.
7. Two lines in a plane either intersect each other at exactly one point or are parallel to each other.
8. Three or more points which lie on the same line are called collinear points.
9. Three or more lines in a plane passing through the same point are called concurrent lines.
10. A figure formed by two rays having the same initial point is called an angle.
11. The unit of angle measure is degree denoted by °.

    1 rotation = 360°, 1° = 60' (60 minutes), 1' = 60" (60 seconds)

12. **Types of Angles**

Acute angle More than 0° and Less than 90°	Right angle Equal to 90°	Obtuse angle More than 90° and Less than 180°	Straight Angle Equal to 180°	Reflex angle More than 180° and Less than 360°

13. **Types of Angles**

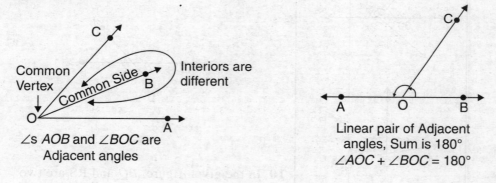

∠s *AOB* and ∠*BOC* are
Adjacent angles

Linear pair of Adjacent
angles, Sum is 180°
∠*AOC* + ∠*BOC* = 180°

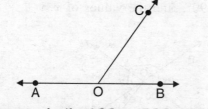

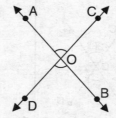

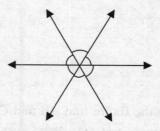

Conversely, if ∠*AOC* + ∠*BOC* = 180°
Then *AOB* is a st. Line

Vertically
Opposite Angles are equal
∠*AOC* = ∠*BOD*, ∠*AOD* = ∠*BOC*

Sum of angles
round a point is 360°

14.	**Complementary Angles** whose sum is 90° e.g. 30° and 60°	15.	**Supplementary Angles** whose sum is 180° e.g. 50° and 130°

16. The sum of angles at a point on a straight line is 180°.

$\angle x + \angle y + \angle z = 180°$

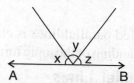

MENTAL MATHS 17

1. Find x in the given figure :

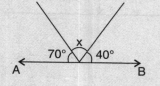

2. In the following figure, find y.

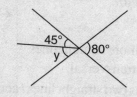

3. Find the supplement of $\angle x$ and $\angle y$.

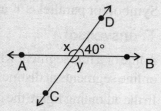

4. The complement of an angle is 65°. Find the angle.
5. Angles forming a linear pair are supplementary. True or False?
6. Find the complement of 89° 60'.
7. What kind of angle is the angle whose magnitude is 210° ?

ANSWERS

EXERCISE 25 (a)

1. A line extends endlessly in both the directions and has no end points. A ray has one initial point and extends indefinitely in one direction.

2. One   3. One

4. (i) Adjacent edges of a cuboid, adjacent sides of a table top.   (ii) Railway track, opposite sides of a rectangular field.

5. Three   6. (i) AC, BQ, RS, AR, CS   (ii) BR, DS, QC, BA, DC   (iii) C, D, Q, S   (iv) AR and CS

7. (i) indefinite   (ii) Two   (iii) not the same   (iv) Common   (v) Collinear   (vi) Line.

8. 2.8 cm.   9. Non-collinear points

EXERCISE 25 (b)

1. (a) (i) 0°   (ii) 90°   (iii) 180°   (iv) 270°   (v) 360°

2. (1) Acute angle   (2) Obtuse angle   (3) Obtuse angle   (4) Acute angle   (5) Obtuse angle   (6) Reflex angle
   (7) Straight angle   (8) Reflex angle

3. (i) 55°   (ii) 0°   (iii) 59° 31'   (iv) 31° 15'   (v) 54° 29' 35"   (vi) 19° 11' 38"

4. (i) 108°   (ii) 67°   (iii) 47° 15'   (iv) 74° 35'   (v) 94° 14' 30"   (vi) 14° 49' 34"

5. 54°, 126°   6. 36°, 54°   7. 30°, 60°   8. 110°, 70°   9. $x = 35°$ 10. $x = 40°$ 11. 60°   12. 80°

EXERCISE 25 (c)

1. (a) $x = 36°$ (b) $x = 10°$ (c) $x = 30°$ 2. (i) $y = 35°$ (ii) $x = 44°$ 3. $x = 25°$ 4. $x = 60°$

5. $x = 20°$ 6. $\angle x = 36°, \angle y = 144°, \angle z = 144°$ 7. $y = 10°$ 8. $\angle AOC = \angle BOD = 133°, \angle AOD = \angle BOC = 47°$

9. $\angle AOC = \angle BOD = 158°, \angle BOC = \angle AOD = 22°$ 10. $x = 30°, y = 60°, z = 120°$.

MENTAL MATHS – 17

1. $x = 70°$ 2. $y = 35°$ 3. 40°   4. 25°   5. True   6. 0°   7. Reflex.

26. Parallel Lines

26.1 Introduction

You have already studied parallel lines is class 6. Let us revise what you have learnt there and help you strengthen your understanding of the topic further.

26.2 Definition of Parallel Lines

Two lines or line segments in a plane which do not intersect and whose perpendicular distance between them remains constant are called parallel lines.

Symbol for parallel is 'll' and is read as *parallel to.*

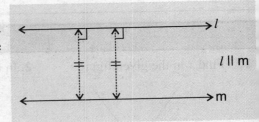

$l \parallel m$

26.3 Transversal

A line or a line segment which intersects two or more straight lines or line segments at distinct points is known as a transversal.

In the adjoining figure the line **'n'** which intersects two straight lines *l* and *m* at *P* and *Q* respectively is called the **transversal.**

The **eight angles** which are formed when a transversal cuts two lines have been categorised as :

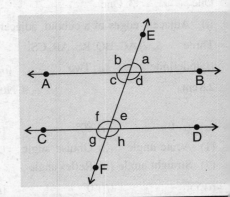

1. **Alternate Angles**

   ($\angle 3$, $\angle 5$) and ($\angle 4$, $\angle 6$) are two pairs of alternate angles.

2. **Corresponding Angles**

   ($\angle 1$, $\angle 5$), ($\angle 2$, $\angle 6$), ($\angle 4$, $\angle 8$) and ($\angle 3$, $\angle 7$) are four pairs of corresponding angles.

3. **Co-interior Angles**

   ($\angle 4$, $\angle 5$) and ($\angle 3$, $\angle 6$) are two pairs of co-interior angles.

26.4 Properties of Angles Related to Parallel Lines

Let *AB* and *CD* be two parallel lines cut by a transversal *EF*. Then

(i) *Alternate angles are equal :*

   $\angle d = \angle f$ and $\angle c = \angle e$

(ii) *Corresponding angles are equal :*

   $\angle a = \angle e$, $\angle d = \angle h$, $\angle b = \angle f$, $\angle c = \angle g$

(iii) *Co-interior angles are supplementary :*

   $\angle d + \angle e = 180°$ and $\angle c + \angle f = 180°$

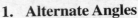

Conversely, *If a transversal intersects two straight lines such that :*

(i) *a pair of alternate angles is equal,*

or (ii) *a pair of corresponding angles is equal,*

or (iii) *sum of the interior angles on the same side of the transversal (co-interior angles) is equal to 180°*

then the two straight lines are parallel to each other.

26.5 Solved Examples

Ex. 1: *Calculate all the marked angles in the given figure.*

Sol :   Given $l \parallel m$

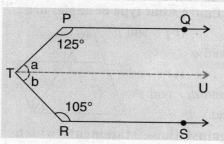

$\angle a = 75°$ *(vertically opposite angles)*

$\angle d = \angle a = \mathbf{75°}$.   *(corresponding angles)*

$75° + \angle b = 180°$ *(linear pair)*

$\therefore \angle b = 180° - 75° = \mathbf{105°}$.

$\angle c = \angle d = \mathbf{75°}$.   *(vertically opposite angles)*

Ex. 2 : *In the figure (i) PQ $\parallel$ RS, find the value of x.*

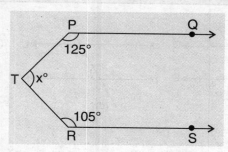

Fig. (i)   Fig. (ii)

Sol :   In the fig. (ii) Draw $TU \parallel PQ \parallel RS$

$PQ \parallel TU$ and PT is the transversal

$\therefore a + 125° = 180° \Rightarrow a = 180° - 125° = 55°$ *(co-interior angles)*

Similarly $TU \parallel RS$ and TR is the transversal

$\Rightarrow b + 105° = 180° \Rightarrow b = 180° - 105° = 75°$ *(co-interior angles)*

$\therefore x = a + b = 55° + 105° = \mathbf{160°}$.

Ex. 3 : *In the figure, if $\angle 2 = 120°$ and $\angle 5 = 60°$, show that p $\parallel$ q.*

Sol : $\angle 1 + \angle 2 = 180°$ *(linear pair)*

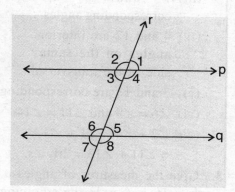

$\Rightarrow 120° + \angle 1 = 180°$

$\therefore \angle 1 = 180° - 120° = 60°$

Given $\angle 5 = 60°$

$\angle 1$ and $\angle 5$ are corresponding angles and $\angle 1 = \angle 5$

$\therefore p \parallel q$.

Ex. 4 : *In the figure given that PQ $\parallel$ MN. If $\angle 1 = (120° - 2x°)$ and*

   $\angle 5 = 4x°$, find the measures of $\angle 1$ and $\angle 5$.

Sol. : $PQ \parallel MN$ and t is the transversal

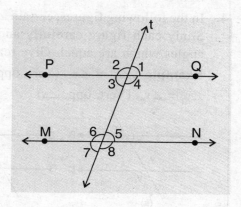

$\therefore$ corresponding angles $\angle 1$ and $\angle 5$ are equal.

$\therefore 120 - 2x = 4x \Rightarrow 120 = 2x + 4x$

$\Rightarrow 6x = 120 \Rightarrow x = 20$

$\therefore \angle 1 = 120° - 2x = 120° - 40° = \mathbf{80°}$

Hence, $\angle 5 = \angle 1 = \mathbf{80°}$.

Ex. 5 : *In the given figure. ∠DCE = 65° and ∠ACD = 35°. Find x, y and z.*

Sol :   *AB ∥ CD* and *AC* is the transversal (Parallel lines are denoted by arrows)

∴ ∠y = 35°   (*alternate interior angles*)

AB ∥ CD and *BE* is the transversal

∴ ∠x = 65°   (*corresponding angles*)

65° + 35° + z = 180°   (*angles at a point on a straight line*)

⇒ 100° + z = 180°

⇒ z = 180° − 100° = **80°**.

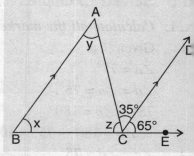

EXERCISE 26

1. In the following figure what type of angles are :

(i)   *a* and *f*   (ii) *b* and *p*

(iii)   *x* and *p*, *y* and *q*

(iv)   *b* and *e*   (v) *c* and *q*

(vi)   *b* and *x*, *y* and *d*, *c* and *y*

(vii) *c* and *d*, *t* and *y* ?

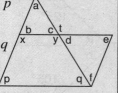

2. Write 'true' against those statements which are correct and 'false' against those which are wrong. Refer to the given figure :

(i)   1 and 2 are adjacent angles.

(ii)   5 and 10 are alternate angles.

(iii)   7 and 8 are corresponding angles.

(iv)   4 and 12 are interior angles on the same side of the transversal.

(v)   3 and 13 are corresponding angles.

(vi)   ∠6 = ∠9 and ∠11 = ∠14.

(vii) ∠2 + ∠4 = ∠1 + ∠3 = ∠11 + ∠13 = 2rt. ∠s

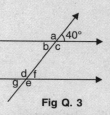

3. Give the measures of angles *a*, *b*, *c*, *d*, *e*, *f*, *g*, in the adjoining figure.

Fig Q. 3

4. In the following figures, certain angles are marked. Study each figure carefully and write down the angles which are equal. Give reasons.

Example : ∠x₁ = ∠x₂ (Vert. opp. ∠s)

∠y₁ = ∠y₂ (Vert. opp. ∠s)

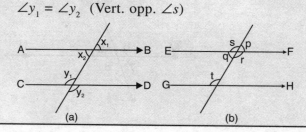

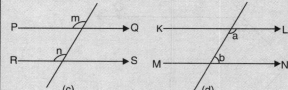

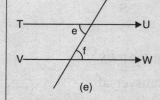

(c)   (d)

(e)   (f)

5. Examine whether *AB* and *CD* are parallel in each of the following cases.

(a) ∠b = 60°, ∠y = 60°

(b) ∠b = 50°, ∠z = 50°

(c) ∠a = 40°, ∠y = 40°

(d) ∠b = 100°, ∠x = 80°

(e) ∠c = 70° ∠x = 70°

(f) ∠a = 30°, ∠x = 30°

(g) ∠b = 82°, ∠w = 82°

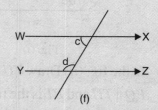

6. A st. line cuts two other st. lines and the following are the pairs of alternate angles in different cases. Show in which of these cases the two straight lines are parallel :

(a) 35°, 36°   (b) 80°, 80°   (c) 57°,69°

(d) 119°, 119°

7. A straight line cuts two other straight lines and the following are the pairs of corresponding angles in different cases. Show in which of the cases the two straight lines are parallel.

(a) 121°, 105°   (b) 90°, 90°   (c) 103°, 97°

(d) 70°, 70°

8. A straight line cuts two other straight lines and the following are the pairs of co-interior angles in different cases. Show in which of the cases the two straight lines are parallel.

(a) 120°, 50° (b) 135°, 45° (c) 90°, 90°
(d) 20°, 159° (e) 55°, 125° (f) 40°, 140°
. Prove that the dotted lines in the following diagrams are parallel. Give reasons.

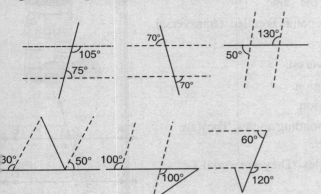

0. In the following figure, AB ∥ CL. Find ∠ACD.

1. Find the sizes of the unknown angles in the figures (i) to (iv).

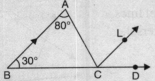

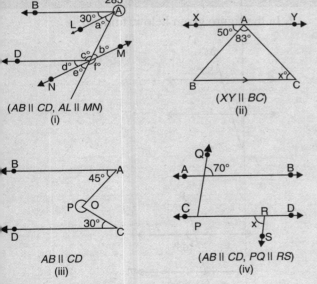

(AB ∥ CD, AL ∥ MN)
(i)

(XY ∥ BC)
(ii)

AB ∥ CD
(iii)

(AB ∥ CD, PQ ∥ RS)
(iv)

12. Find x in the following figures.

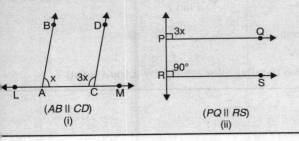

(AB ∥ CD)
(i)

(PQ ∥ RS)
(ii)

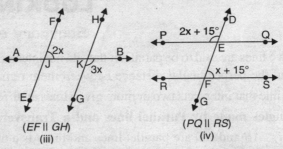

(EF ∥ GH)
(iii)

(PQ ∥ RS)
(iv)

13. In the figure given below DE ∥ AB, ∠DEC = 55° and ∠EDC = 40°. Find the values of a and b.

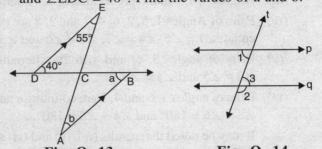

Fig. Q. 13

Fig. Q. 14

14. In the figure, ∠1 = 61° and ∠2 = 118°, is p ∥ q ? Give reasons.

15. In the given figure, p ∥ q and r ∥ s. Find the angles a, b and c.

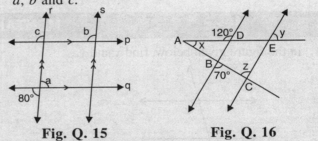

Fig. Q. 15

Fig. Q. 16

16. In the figure BD ∥ CE, find x, y and z.

17. In the given figure, AB ∥ CD ∥ EF, find the angles x and y.

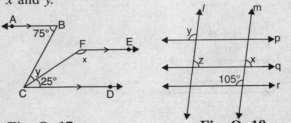

Fig. Q. 17

Fig. Q. 18

18. In the given figure p ∥ q ∥ r and l ∥ m, find x, y and z.

19. Given l ∥ m and p ∥ q, find x and y.

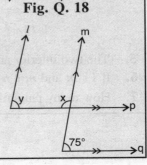

Fig. Q. 19

LOOKING BACK

Summary of Key Facts

1. Two lines are said to be parallel if they do not intersect even when extended indefinitely, and the perpendicular distance between them remains the same.

2. A line that intersects two or more given lines at different points is called a transversal.

3. **Angles made by Parallel lines and a Transversal**

    (*i*) *AB* and *CD* are parallel lines and line *l* is a transversal.

    (*ii*) Angles 1, 2, 8 and 7 are located in the exterior region.

    (*iii*) Angles 3, 4, 5 and 6 are located in the interior region.

    (*iv*) Pairs of Angles 1, 5; 2, 6; 4, 7 and 3, 8 are corresponding angles. They are equal; $\angle 1 = \angle 5$, $\angle 4 = \angle 7$, $\angle 2 = \angle 6$ and $\angle 3 = \angle 8$.

    (*v*) Pairs of angles 3, 5, and 4, 6 are alternate angles. They are equal *i.e.* $\angle 3 = \angle 5$ and $\angle 4 = \angle 6$.

    (*vi*) Pairs of angles 3, 6 and 4, 5 are co-interior angles. Their sum is 180°. Thus, $\angle 3 + \angle 6 = 180°$ and $\angle 4 + \angle 5 = 180°$.

    It may be noted that results (*iv*), (*v*) and (*vi*) above hold in case of parallel lines only. They will not be valid if two non-parallel lines are cut by a transversal.

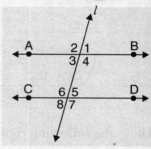

MENTAL MATHS – 18

1. In the figure given below, find *x* and *y*.

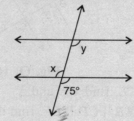

2. In the figure given below, find $\angle d$.

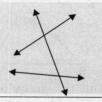

3.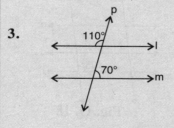

    Is *l* ∥ *m*?

4.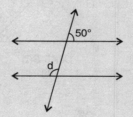

    Find *x*.

5. The two interior angles lying on the same side of the transversal are ....

6. If *l* ∥ *m* and *m* ∥ *n* then ....

7. How many pairs of corresponding angles are formed when two parallel lines are cut by a transversal ?

ANSWERS

EXERCISE 26

1. (i) alt. $\angle s$ (ii) corr. $\angle s$ (iii) co.-int. $\angle s$ (iv) alt. $\angle s$ (v) corr. $\angle s$ (vi) Adj. Supp. $\angle s$ (vii) Vert. Opp. $\angle s$.

2. (i) True   (ii) True   (iii) False   (iv) True   (v) True   (vi) True   (vii) True.

3. $a = c = d = e = 140°$, $b = f = g = 40°$

4. (a) $\angle x_1 = \angle x_2$, $\angle y_1 = \angle y_2$, (vert. opp. $\angle s$)   (b) $\angle p = \angle q$, $\angle r = \angle s$ (vert. opp. $\angle s$); $\angle r = \angle t$ (alt. $\angle s$); $\angle s = \angle t$ (corr. $\angle s$)
    (c) $\angle m = \angle n$ (corr. $\angle s$);   (d) None equal   (e) $\angle e = \angle f$ (alt. $\angle s$)   (f) None equal.

5. (a) Yes   (b) No   (c) No.   (d) Yes   (e) Yes   (f) Yes   (g) Yes.

6. (b) and (d)   7. (b) and (d)   8. (b), (c), (e), (f)   10. $110°$.

11. (i) $a = b = e = 45°$, $c = 105°$, $d = 30°$, $e = 45°$, $f = 135°$ (ii) $x = 47°$ (iii) $p = 285°$ (iv) $x = 70°$

12. (i) $45°$ (ii) $30°$ (iii) $36°$ (iv) $50°$ 13. $a = 40°$, $b = 55°$

14. No, alternate angles $\angle 1$ and $\angle 3$ are not equal. ($\angle 3 = 180° - \angle 2 = 180° - 118° = 62°$)   15. $a = 80°$, $b = 100°$, $c = 100°$

16. $x = 50°$, $y = 60°$, $z = 70°$ 17. $x = 155°$, $y = 50°$ 18. $x = 75°$, $y = 105°$, $z = 75°$ 19. $x = 105°$, $y = 75°$.

MENTAL MATHS - 18

1. $x = 75°$, $y = 75°$ 2. $\angle d = 130°$ 3. Yes   4. $x = 75°$ 5. Supplementary   6. $l \parallel n$ 7. Four.

INTERESTING FACTS

- The number 10 is used as a convenient base to count with, but the Gauls of ancient France, the Mayas of Central America, and other peoples used a base of 20. The Sumerians, the Babylonians, and others after them used a base of 60 - convenient because 60 can be evenly divided by 2, 3, 4, 5, 6, 10, 12, 15, 20, and 30. Thus 60 survives in the division of hours into minutes and minutes into seconds, and the division of the circle into 360 (60 × 6) degrees.

- The modern decimal position system, in which the placing of numerals indicates their value (units, tens, hundreds etc.), was the invention of the Indians, around 800 A.D. Their invention of the symbol for zero greatly simplified arithmetic computation. By comparison, the Roman numeral system containing no zero was awkward.

- The number system was invented by India. The digit zero is also an invention of the Indians.

27. Basic Constructions

We shall review some basic constructions which are used quite often in geometry.

27.1 To Construct an Angle Equal to the Given Angle ABC at a Point Q Outside it.

Step 1 : Draw a ray *QR*.

Step 2 : With *B* as centre and a convenient radius draw an arc which cuts *AB* at *F* and *BC* at *E*.

Step 3 : With *Q* as centre and the same radius as in **step 2**, draw an arc of sufficient length cutting *QR* at *M*.

Step 4 : With *M* as centre and radius *EF*, draw an arc cutting the previous arc at *N*.

Step 5 : Join *QN* and extend it to form ray *QP*.

∠*PQR* is the required angle, equal to ∠*ABC*.

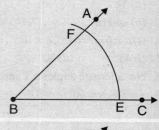

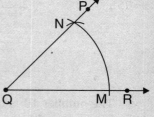

27.2 To Bisect a Given Angle ABC.

Step 1 : With *B* as centre and a suitable radius, draw an arc that intersects *BA* and *BC*. Name the points of intersection as *P* and *Q*.

Step 2 : With *P* as centre and a radius greater than half *PQ* draw an arc.

Step 3 : With *Q* as centre and the same radius draw another arc to cut the first arc. Name the point of intersection of the two arcs as *R*.

Step 4 : Join *BR*. Then ray *BR* bisects ∠*ABC*. It is called the angle bisector.

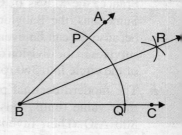

27.3 To Draw the Perpendicular Bisector of a Given Line Segment.

Let *AB* be the given line segment.

Step 1 : With *A* as centre and radius equal to more than half the length of *AB*, draw two arcs one above *AB* and one below *AB*.

Step 2 : With *B* as centre and the same radius (as in step 1), draw two arcs to cut the first two arcs. Name the points of intersection as *P* and *Q*.

Step 3 : Join *PQ* to cut *AB* at *M*. Measure *AM* and *MB*.

AM = *MB* and ∠*PMA* = ∠*PMB* = 90°.

∴ *PQ* is the perpendicular bisector of *AB*.

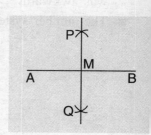

27.4 To Draw a Perpendicular to a Given Line.

(a) **At a point on the line**

Let *AB* be the given line segment and *P* a point on it.

Step 1 : With *P* as centre and any suitable radius draw an arc to cut line *AB* at points *M* and *N*.

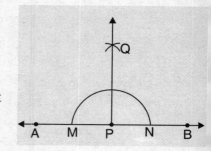

Step 2 : With M and N as centres and radius more than half of MN, draw two arcs to intersect at Q.

Step 3 : Join PQ.

Then ray PQ is the perpendicular to the line AB at P.

(b) **From a point outside the line :** Let l be the given line and P a point outside it.

Step 1 : With P as centre and a suitable radius, draw an arc to cut the line l at X and Y.

Step 2 : With X and Y as centres and a radius of more than half XY, draw two arcs to intersect each other at M.

Step 3 : Join PM. Then $PM \perp l$.

27.5 To Construct a Line Parallel to a Given Line from a Point Outside it.

Let l be a given line and P a given point outside it.

Step 1 : Mark any point A on l and join PA.

Step 2 : With A as centre and with any convenient radius, draw an arc to cut PA at M and l at N.

Step 3 : With P as centre and with the same radius draw an arc to cut PA at B.

Step 4 : With B as centre and MN as radius draw an arc to cut the previous arc at Q.

Step 5 : Joint PQ and produce it both ways. Then line m as shown is parallel to given line l. **(Why ?)**

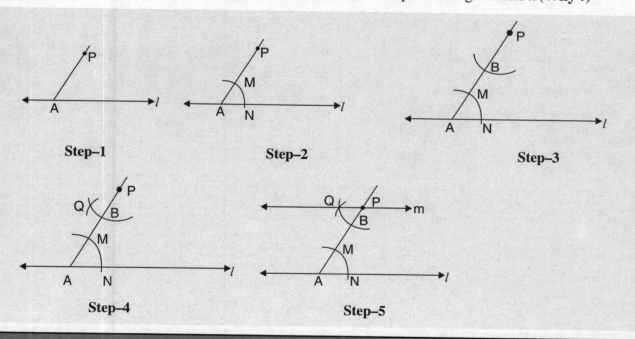

| Step–1 | Step–2 | Step–3 |

| Step–4 | Step–5 |

1. Draw angle $\angle PQR = 125°$ with the help of a protractor. Construct $\angle AOB = \angle PQR$. Measure it and check.

2. Construct an angle of $75°$. Draw its angular bisector.

3. Construct an angle of $120°$. Divide it into four equal parts using compasses. Verify using a protector that each part is equal to $30°$.

4. Draw a line segment 6.8 cm long and draw its perpendicular bisector using compasses and ruler.

5. Draw a line segment AB = 8.2 cm. Mark a point M on AB such that AM = 5.7 cm. Draw a ray perpendicular to AB at M.

6. Draw a line segment PQ = 6.5 cm. Mark a point O below it at a sufficient distance. Draw a perpendicular from O to PQ.

7. Draw a line segment PQ = 7 cm. Mark a point O above it. Through O draw a line parallel to PQ.

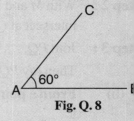
Fig. Q. 8

8. Draw a line segment AB = 7 cm. Draw AC making an angle of 60° with AB. Mark AC = 4 cm. Through *C*, draw *a* line parallel to AB.

DID YOU KNOW

- The World's first university was established in Takshila in 700 BC. More than 10,500 students from all over the world studied more than 60 subjects. The University of Nalanda built in the 4th century was one of the greatest achievements of ancient India in the field of education.

- Bhaskaracharya rightly calculated the time taken by the earth to orbit the sun in (5th century) hundreds of years before the astronomer Smart. His calculation was -Time taken by the earth to orbit the sun =365.258756484 days.

- Latest researches point out that infinite series were invented by Indians and not by Newton and Leibnitz at least 200 years before them.

28. Triangles

28.1 Triangle

A closed figure formed by joining three non-collinear points is called a triangle. We can also define a triangle as a plane figure bounded by three line segments It is denoted by the symbol Δ.

In the adjoining figure Δ PQR is formed by the three non-collinear points P, Q and R. The line segments PQ, QR and PR form the sides of the triangle PQR.

Δ PQR has :

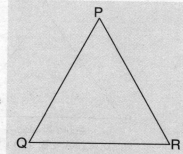

(*i*)   Three vertices namely. P, Q and R,

(*ii*) Three sides namely, PQ, QR and PR,

(*iii*) Three angles namely, $\angle$P, $\angle$Q and $\angle$R.

The three angles and the three sides are known as the **parts** or **elements** of the triangle. Hence a triangle has six parts.

- Points which lie inside the triangle are said to be in the **interior region.** Points S and T lie in the interior of Δ PQR.

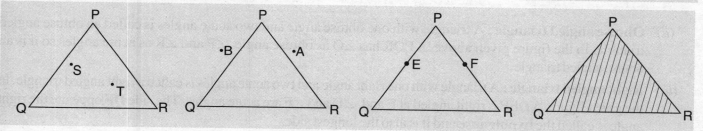

- Points which lie outside the triangle are said to be in the **exterior region.** Points A and B lie in the exterior of Δ PQR.
- Points lying on the sides of the triangle are said to be on the **boundary region.** Points E and F are on the boundary of Δ PQR.
- The interior and boundary of a triangle together make the triangular region.

28.2 Classification of Triangles

■ According to Sides

Triangles can be classified into three types according to their sides.

(*i*) **Scalene triangle :** A triangle with three unequal sides is called a scalene triangle. In the given diagram $AB \neq BC \neq AC$, $\therefore$ Δ ABC is scalene triangle.

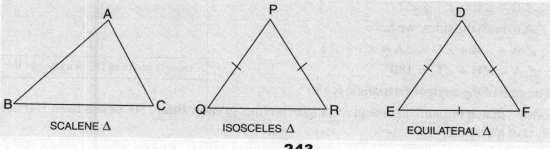

SCALENE Δ ISOSCELES Δ EQUILATERAL Δ

243

(ii) **Isosceles triangle :** A triangle with two equal sides is called an isosceles triangle. In the given figure PQ = QF so ΔPQR is an isosceles triangle.

(iii) **Equilateral triangle :** A triangle with three equal sides is called an equilateral triangle. In the given figur DE = EF = DF, $\therefore$ Δ DEF is an equilateral triangle.

■ According to Angles

(i) **Acute angled triangle :** A triangle with all three acute angles is an acute angled triangle. In the given figure a the angles i.e. $\angle$A, $\angle$B and $\angle$C are less than 90°. $\therefore$ ΔABC is an acute angled triangle.

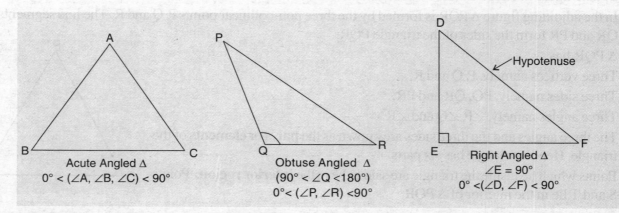

Acute Angled Δ
$0° < (\angle A, \angle B, \angle C) < 90°$

Obtuse Angled Δ
$(90° < \angle Q < 180°)$
$0° < (\angle P, \angle R) < 90°$

Right Angled Δ
$\angle E = 90°$
$0° < (\angle D, \angle F) < 90°$

(ii) **Obtuse angled triangle :** A triangle with one obtuse angle and two acute angles is called an obtuse angle triangle. In the figure given above, Δ PQR has $\angle$Q as obtuse angle, $\angle$P and $\angle$R as acute angles so it is a obtuse angled triangle.

(iii) **Right angled triangle :** A triangle with one right angle and two acute angles is called a right angled triangle. I the given figure, Δ DEF is right angled at E and, $\angle$D and $\angle$F are acute angles. The side **DF** opposite the rig angle is called the **hypotenuse** and it is also the longest side.

28.3 Angle Sum Property of a Triangle

Theorem 1. *The sum of the angles of a triangle is 180°.*

    Given : ΔABC

    To prove : $\angle$A + $\angle$B + $\angle$C = 180°

    Construction : Through A draw a line DE || BC

    Proof : DE || BC, AB is the transversal

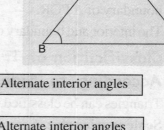

        $\therefore$ $\angle$ B = $\angle$1   ... *(i)*   Alternate interior angles

        $\because$ DE || BC, AC is the transversal

        $\therefore$ $\angle$C = $\angle$2   ... *(ii)*   Alternate interior angles

Adding *(i)* and *(ii)*, we have

        $\angle$ B + $\angle$C = $\angle$1 + $\angle$2

Adding $\angle$ A to both the sides, we have

        $\angle$ A + $\angle$B + $\angle$C = $\angle$A + $\angle$1 + $\angle$2

    $\Rightarrow$ $\angle$ A + $\angle$B + $\angle$C = **180°**.   A straight angle as DE is a straight line

Hence, The sum of the angles of a triangle is 180°.

Thus it follows that, if the sum of three given angles is either **greater than** 180° or **less than** 180°, then they are not parts of a triangle.

    Note :   **A Triangle can have only one right angle.** (not more than one).

28.4 Solved Examples

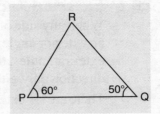

Ex. 1 : *In a △ PQR, ∠P = 60° and ∠Q = 50°, find ∠R.*

Sol : By the angle sum property of a triangle, in △ PQR

$$\angle P + \angle Q + \angle R = 180°$$
$$60° + 50° + \angle R = 180°$$
$$110° + \angle R = 180° \Rightarrow \angle R = 180° - 110° = \mathbf{70°}$$

Ex. 2 : **Is it possible to have a triangle whose angles measure**

       (i) 60°, 90°, 40°   **(ii) 65°, 30°, 85°**

Sol : (i) $60° + 90° + 40° = 190° > 180°$

       By angle sum property it is not possible.

       So a triangle cannot have angles of measures 60°, 90°, and 40°.

      (ii) $65° + 30° + 85° = 180°$

       ∴   By angle sum property it is possible.

       So a triangle with angles of measure 65°, 30°, and 85° is possible.

Ex. 3: *The angles of a triangle are in the ratio 3:5:10. Find the measure of each angle of the triangle.*

Sol : Let the measures of the given triangle be $3x, 5x, 10x$. Then by angle sum property,

    $3x + 5x + 10x = 180° \Rightarrow 18x = 180° \Rightarrow x = \mathbf{10°}$

    ∴ The required angles are $3 \times 10°, 5 \times 10°, 10 \times 10°$ i.e. **30°, 50°, 100°**.

    Alternatively, The sum of the angles of a triangle = 180°

    Sum of the ratios = 3 + 5 + 10 = 18

    ∴ The angles of the triangle are $\dfrac{3}{18} \times 180°$, $\dfrac{5}{18} \times 180°$, and $\dfrac{10}{18} \times 180°$, i,e, 30°, 50° and 100°.

Ex. 4 : *In a right angled triangle, the two acute angles are in the ratio 2 : 3. Find these angles.*

Sol : Let the two acute angles be $2x, 3x$. ∵ it is a right ∠d △ ∴ the third angle = 90°.

    By Angle Sum Property

    $90° + 2x + 3x = 180° \Rightarrow 5x = 180° - 90° \Rightarrow 5x = 90° \Rightarrow x = \dfrac{90°}{5} = 18°$

    ∴ The required angles are $2 \times 18°, 3 \times 18°$, i.e., **36°** and **54°**.

    Alternative Method: Since it is a right angled triangle, so the sum of the remaining two angles = 90°. The measure of these remaining angles are in the ratio 2 : 3.

    Sum of the ratios = 2 + 3 = 5

    ∴ One angle = $\dfrac{2}{\cancel{5}_1} \times \cancel{90°}^{18} = (2 \times 18°) = 36°$ and the other angle = $\dfrac{3}{5} \times 90° = 3 \times 18° = 54°$.

28.5 Inequality Property

The sum of any two sides of a triangle is always greater than the third side.

Ex. 5 : *Can 3 cm, 9 cm and 5 cm represent the sides of a triangle?*

Sol : $3 + 9 = 12 > 5$

    $9 + 5 = 14 > 3$

    $3 + 5 = 8 < 9$

    Since sum of the sides 3 cm and 5 cm is less than the third side i.e. 9 cm, therefore sides with measures 3 cm, 9 cm and 5 cm cannot be the sides of a triangle.

28.6 Exterior Angle of a Triangle

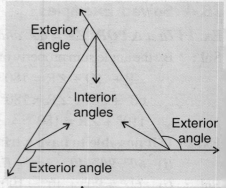

When any side of a triangle is extended beyond the vertex it forms an exterior angle with the other side at the same vertex. To get the exterior angles, the sides of the triangle are to be produced in one direction only, either in clockwise or anticlockwise.

There are six exterior angles and three interior angles.

The two interior angles opposite to the given exterior angle are called **interior opposite angles**.

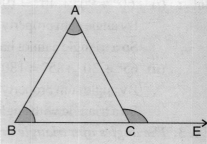

If the side BC of a $\triangle$ ABC is produced to E, then $\angle$ACE is the exterior angle of $\triangle$ ABC at C.

Angles A and B are called interior opposite angles.

Theorem 2 : *If a side of a triangle is produced, then the exterior angle so formed is equal to the sum of the two interior opposite angles.*

Given : $\triangle$ ABC whose side BC has been produced to D forming exterior angle $\angle$ACD.

To Prove : $\angle ACD = \angle A + \angle B$

Proof : In $\triangle$ ABC

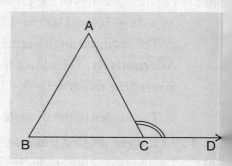

$\angle A + \angle B + \angle ACB = 180°$ .... (1)   (Angle sum property)

also $\angle ACB + \angle ACD = 180°$ .... (2)   (Linear pair)

From (1) and (2)

$\angle A + \angle B + \angle ACB = \angle ACB + \angle ACD$

$\Rightarrow \angle A + \angle B = \angle ACD$

$\Rightarrow \angle ACD = \angle A + \angle B.$ **Hence Proved.**

28.7 Remember

1.   All the angles of a scalene triangle are of different measures.
2.   (*i*) Two angles of an isosceles triangle are equal as angles opposite equal sides are equal.
     (*ii*) In a right angled isosceles triangle, each of the equal angles measures 45°.
3.   All the three angles of an equilateral triangle are equal each measuring 60°.

Remark : Same markings show equal sides in a triangle.

Ex. 6. *Calculate the value of x in each of the given figures :*

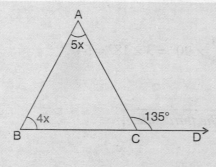

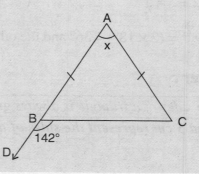

Sol : (*i*) The exterior angle = sum of interior opposite $\angle s$

$\therefore \ 135° = 5x + 4x \Rightarrow 9x = 135° \Rightarrow x = \dfrac{135°}{9} = \mathbf{15°}.$

(*ii*) ∠CBD + ∠ABC = 180° ⇒ 142° + ∠ABC = 180° ⇒ ∠ABC = 180° – 142° = **38°**.

∵ AB = AC ∴ ∠ACB = ∠ABC ⇒ ∠ACB = 38°

(Angles opposite to equal sides are equal).

In △ ABC

x + ∠ABC + ∠ACB = 180°   (Angle sum property)

⇒ x + 38° + 38° = 180° ⇒ x + 76° = 180° ⇒ x = 180° – 76° = **104°**.

EXERCISE 28 (a)

1. In the figure, drawn at the right *AB* = *BC*, *AC* = *AE*, *CE* = *AE*, *AF* = *EF*, ∠ABC = 90°, ∠CDE = 90°.
Name the triangles that are :

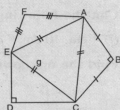

(*i*) isosceles,   (*ii*) equilateral,

(*iii*) right angled,   (*iv*) right angled and isosceles.

2. **Find the unknown lettered angle.**

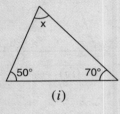   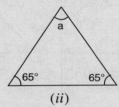   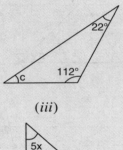   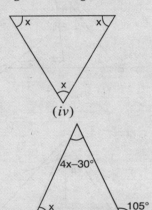

   (*i*)   (*ii*)   (*iii*)   (*iv*)

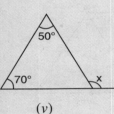   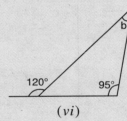   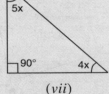

   (*v*)   (*vi*)   (*vii*)   (*viii*)

3. The angles of a triangle are in the ratio 2 : 3 : 4. Determine the angles.

4. One angle of a triangle is 50° and the other two are in the ratio 6 : 7. Find the angles.

5. The two acute angles of an obtuse angled triangle, whose obtuse angle measures 125°, are in the ratio 2 : 3. Find the angles.

6. Of the three angles of a triangle, one is twice the smallest and the other is three times the smallest. Find the angles.

7. One of the exterior angles of a triangle is 80° and the interior opposite angles are in the ratio 3 : 5. Find the angles of the triangle.

8. **Find the value of x in each case :**

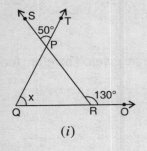   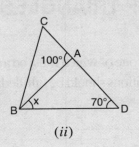   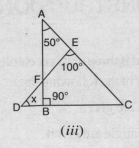   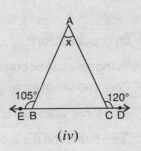

   (*i*)   (*ii*)   (*iii*)   (*iv*)

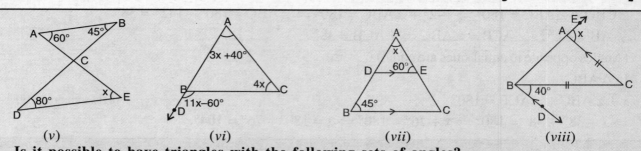

(v)   (vi)   (vii)   (viii)

9. **Is it possible to have triangles with the following sets of angles?**

(i) 70°, 40°, 80°   (ii) 45°, 65°, 70°   (iii) 29° 30', 60° 10', 90° 20'

10. **Can the following represent the sides of a triangle?**

(i) 4 cm, 10 cm, 7 cm   (ii) 6.3 cm, 5.2 cm, 8.3 cm.   (iii) 3 cm, 6 cm, 9cm.

11. **Find the unknown angles in the following figure.**

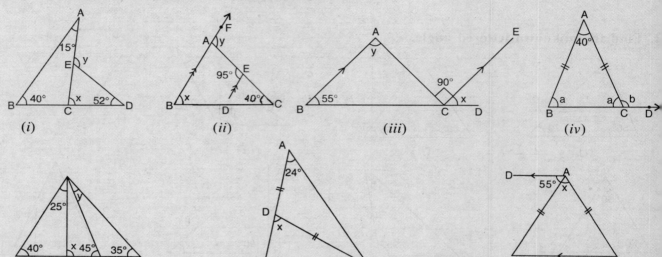

(i)   (ii)   (iii)   (iv)

(v)   (vi)   (vii)

12. In an isosceles triangle each of the base angles is twice the vertical angle. Find all the angles of the triangle.

13. **Fill in the blanks :**

(i) Each angle of a equilateral triangle is _____ .

(ii) The vertical angle of an isosceles triangle is 40°. Each of the base angles is _____.

(iii) A triangle cannot have more than _____ right angle.

(iv) An exterior angle of a triangle is always _____ than either of the interior opposite angles.

CONSTRUCTION OF TRIANGLES

28.8 Introduction

A triangle can be constructed if three of its six elements, one of which must be a side are given. Therefore for the construction of a triangle any of the following three conditions should be fulfilled.

(i) The three sides of a triangle are given.

(ii) Two sides and the included angle are given.

(iii) One side and two angles are given.

28.9 To construct a triangle when the lengths of three sides are given.

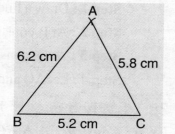

Ex. 1 : *Construct a triangle ABC with AB = 6.2 cm, BC = 5.2 cm and AC = 5.8 cm.*

Sol : **Step 1 :** Draw a line segment BC = 5.2 cm.

Step 2 : With B as centre and radius 6.2 cm, (= AB) draw an arc.

Step 3 : With C as centre and radius 5.8 cm (= AC), draw another arc cutting the previous arc at A.

Step 4 : Join AB and AC. Then Δ ABC is the required triangle.

28.10 To construct a triangle when lengths of two sides and the included angle is given.

Ex. 2 : *Construct a triangle ABC with AB = 5.4 cm, BC = 4.5 cm and ∠B = 75°.*

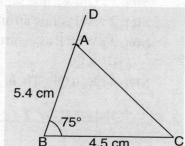

Sol : **Step 1 :** Draw a line segment BC = 4.5 cm.

Step 2 : At B construct ∠CBD = 75°.

Step 3 : With B as centre draw an arc of radius 5.4 cm to cut BD at A.

Step 4 : Join AC. Then ABC is the required triangle.

28.11 To construct a triangle when one side and two angles are given.

Ex. 3 : *Construct a triangle PQR with QR = 6.3 cm, ∠Q =105° and ∠R = 40°.*

Sol : **Step 1 :** Draw a line segment QR = 6.3 cm.

Step 2 : At Q construct ∠BQR = 105°.

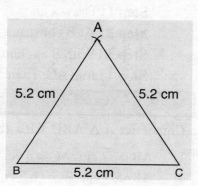

Step 3 : At R draw ∠ARQ = 40° with the protractor.

Step 4 : Let BQ and AR intersect at P.

Then PQR is the required triangle.

28.12 Construction of an equilateral triangle

Ex. 4 : *Construct an equilateral triangle ABC such that the length of one of its sides is 5.2 cm.*

Sol : Since all the three sides of an equilateral triangle are equal,

∴ AB = BC = AC = 5.2 cm for Δ ABC.

Now to do the construction, follow the steps of construction Ex 1.

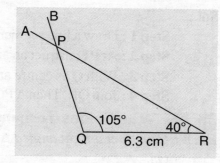

28.13 To construct an isosceles triangle, when base and one base angle are given.

Ex. 5 : *Construct an isosceles triangle PQR with base PQ = 6.4 cm, and ∠P = 30°.*

Sol : Since the base angles of an isosceles triangle are equal ∴ ∠P = ∠Q = 30°.

Step 1 : Draw a line segment PQ = 6.4 cm.

Step 2 : At P, construct ∠BPQ = 30°

Step 3 : At Q, construct ∠AQP = 30°.

Step 4 : Let AQ and BP intersect at R. Then, PQR is the required triangle.

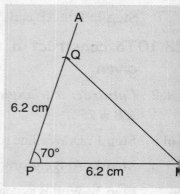

28.14 When one of the equal sides and vertical angle are given.

Ex. 6 : *Construct A Δ PQR with one of its equal sides PQ = 6.2 cm and the vertical angle ∠P = 70°.*

Sol : Since Δ PQR is an isosceles triangle with vertical angle ∠P = 70°, ∴ the sides PQ and PR are equal and
PQ = PR = 6.2 cm.

Step 1 : Draw a line segment PR = 6.2 cm.

Step 2 : At P, draw an angle ∠APR = 70°.

Step 3 : With P as centre and radius = 6.2 cm, draw an arc to cut AP at Q.

Step 4 : Join QR. Then, Δ PQR is the required triangle.

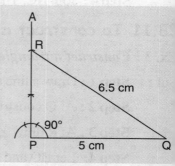

CONSTRUCTION OF A RIGHT ANGLED TRI-ANGLE.

28.15 When one side and hypotenuse are given.

Ex. 7 : *Construct a Δ PQR right angled at P where PQ = 5 cm and QR = 6.5 cm.*

Sol :

Step 1 : Draw a line segment PQ = 5cm.

Step 2 : At P construct an angle ∠APQ = 90°.

Step 3 : With Q as centre and radius = 6.5 cm, draw an arc to cut AP at R.

Step 4 : Join QR. Then Δ PQR is the required triangle.

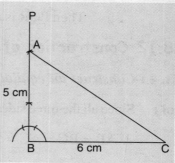

28.16 When sides forming the right angle are given.

Ex. 8 : *Construct a right angled Δ ABC in which ∠B = 90°, BC = 6 cm, AB = 5 cm.*

Sol :

Step 1 : Draw a line segment BC = 6 cm.

Step 2 : At B construct ∠PBC = 90°.

Step 3 : With B as centre and radius = 5 cm, draw an arc to cut PB at A.

Step 4 : Join AC. Then Δ ABC is the required triangle.

EXERCISE 28 (b)

Construct a Δ ABC with the following measures.

1.   AB = 7 cm, AC = 6 cm, BC = 9 cm. Measure ∠A, ∠B and ∠C.

2.   AB=5.5 cm, BC = 6.5 cm, CA = 5 cm.

3.   AB = BC = AC = 5.8 cm. Name the type of triangle formed and also measure ∠A, ∠B and ∠C.

4.   AB = 6 cm, AC = 8 cm, ∠BAC = 50°.

5.   ∠ABC=75°, AB = 6.5 cm, BC = 8.2 cm.

  .   AB = 7.4cm, ∠BAC = 45°, ∠ABC = 60°.

  .   BC = 6.3 cm, ∠ABC = 30°, ∠ACB = 75°.

  .   Construct a triangle PQR such that PQ = PR = 3 cm and ∠P = 120°. Measure ∠Q and ∠R. Name the type of triangle PQR.

  .   Construct an isosceles △ ABC with base BC = 4.5 cm and one of the base angles = 65°.

0.   Construct a right angled triangle PQR right angled at Q with PQ = 6 cm and QR = 6.5 cm.

1.   Draw △ *PQR* in which ∠Q = 80°, ∠R = 55° and *QR* = 4.5 cm. Draw the perpendicular bisector of side *QR*.

2.   Draw a △ *ABC*, in which ∠*C* = 90° and *AC* = *BC* = 4 cm.

3.   Construct an isosceles right triangle with the equal sides of length 5 cm each.

4.   Draw a △ *ABC* in which BC = 5.2 cm, ∠*B* = 100° and ∠*A* = 60°. Draw the perpendicular from *B* to *AC*.

5.   Construct a right angled △ *ABC*, right angled at *B*, when *AC* = 10 cm, *AB* = 8 cm.

6.   Construct a right angled △ *ABC*, right angled at *C* in which hyp. *AB* = 12 cm, side *AC* = 8 cm.

7.   Construct a △ *ABC* with *BC* = 5.5 cm, ∠A = 60°, ∠B = 45° (**Hint** : you need ∠C. We have ∠*A* + ∠*B* + ∠*C* = 180° ⇒ 60° + 45° + ∠*C* = 180° ⇒ ∠*C* = 180° − 105°= 75°).

LOOKING BACK

Summary of Key Facts

1. A closed figure bounded by three line segments is called a triangle.

2. A triangle with all three unequal sides is called a scalene triangle.

3. A triangle with two equal sides is called an isosceles triangle.

4. A triangle with all three sides equal is called an equilateral triangle.

5. A triangle with each angle less than 90° is an acute angled triangle.

6. A triangle with one of its angles greater than 90° is called an obtuse angled triangle.

7. A triangle with one angle equal to 90° is called a right angled triangle.

8. Sum of the angles of a triangle in equal to 180°.

9. In a triangle, the sum of any two sides is always greater than the third side.

10. Exterior angle of a triangle is equal to the sum of its interior opposite angles.

MENTAL MATHS – 19

1. Two angles of a triangle are 70° and 20°, find the third angle and name the triangle.

2. Is △ *ABC* isosceles?

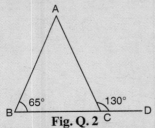

Fig. Q. 2

3. Can an obtuse angled triangle be an isosceles triangle?

4. Each angle of an equilateral triangle measures _____.

5. In the given figure find *x* and *y*.

Fig. Q. 5

6. The hypotenuse of a right angled triangle is the longest side. **True or False ?**

7. **Find** *x*:

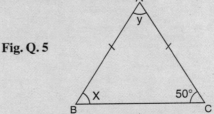

Fig. Q. 7

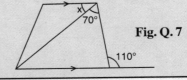

ANSWERS

EXERCISE 28 (a)

1. $(i)\ \Delta\ ABC,\ \Delta\ AFE$ $(ii)\ \Delta\ AEC$ $(iii)\ \Delta\ ABC,\ \Delta\ EDC$ $(iv)\ \Delta\ ABC$

2. $(i)\ x=60°$ $(ii)\ a=50°$ $(iii)\ c=46°$ $(iv)\ x=60°$ $(v)\ x=120°$ $(vi)\ b=25°$ $(vii)\ 50°,40°$ $(viii)\ 27°,78°$

3. $40°,60°,80°$ 4. $60°,70°$ 5. $22°,33°$ 6. $30°,60°,90°$ 7. $30°,50°,100°$

8. $(i)\ x=80°$ $(ii)\ x=30°$ $(iii)\ x=40°$ $(iv)\ x=45°$ $(v)\ x=25°$ $(vi)\ x=25°$ $(vii)\ x=75°$ $(viii)\ x=110°$

9. (i) No (ii) Yes (iii) Yes

10. (i) Yes (ii) Yes (iii) No.

11. $(i)\ x=55°,y=107°$ $(ii)\ x=55°,y=95°$ $(iii)\ x=55°,y=90°$ $(iv)\ a=70°,b=70°$

    $(v)\ x=65°,y=10°$ $(vi)\ x=48°,y=84°$ $(vii)\ x=70°.$

12. $72°,72°,36°$

13. $(i)\ 60°$ $(ii)\ 70°$ (iii) one (iv) greater

MENTAL MATHS – 19

1. $90°$, Right angled triangle   2. Yes   3. No   4. $60°$ 5. $x=50°,y=80°$ 6. True

7. $x=40°.$

29. Congruence of Triangles

29.1 Concept of Congruence

Study carefully the following 12 figures :

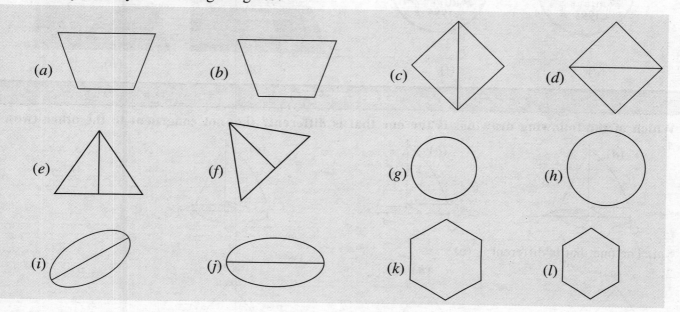

(a) (b) (c) (d)

(e) (f) (g) (h)

(i) (j) (k) (l)

If you cut these figures out, you will find that Fig. (a) and (b) are of the same size and shape. That is to say we can put Fig. (a) on top of Fig. (b) and they fit exactly. Similarly, Fig. (c) fits exactly on Fig. (d), Fig. (e) fits exactly on Fig. (f). Fig. (g) and Fig. (h) although look very much alike yet they do not fit exactly on each other. Similarly, Fig. (i) and Fig. (j), Fig. (k) and Fig. (l) do no fit exactly on any other figure given above.

> *In Geometry, when two figures fit exactly on each other, we call them congruent figures or we say that they are in congruence.*

For example: Figs. (a) and (b) are congruent figures. But Fig. (g) and Fig. (h) are not congruent figures. Two photographs of the same size obtained from the same 'negative' are another example of congruent figures.
The following pictures also show congruent figures.

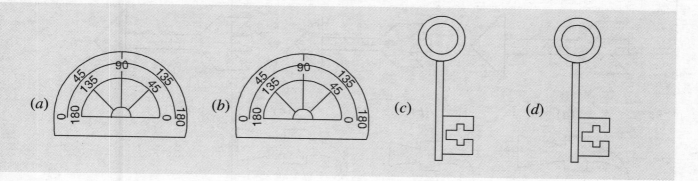

(a) (b) (c) (d)

(e)   (f)   (g)   (h)

EXERCISE 29 (a)

Which of the following drawings is the one that is different? (i.e. not congruent to the other two).

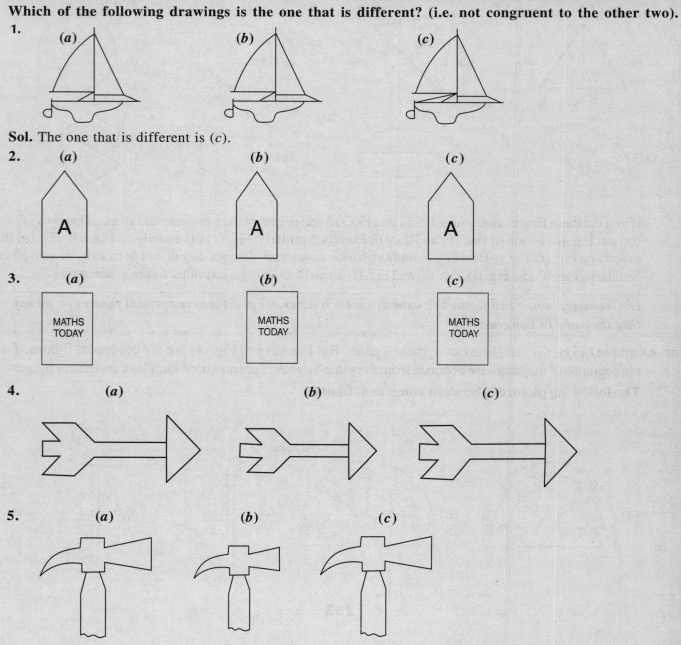

1. (a)   (b)   (c)

Sol. The one that is different is (c).

2. (a)   (b)   (c)

3. (a)   (b)   (c)

4. (a)   (b)   (c)

5. (a)   (b)   (c)

6. Pair each given figure with a congruent figure from the collection at the right

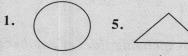

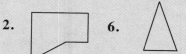

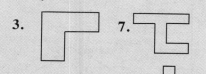

1. 5.

2. 6.

3. 7.

4. 8.

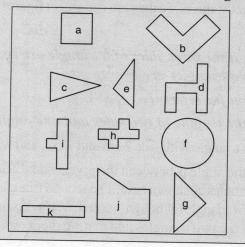

29.2 Congruent Triangles

Two triangles are congruent if they are exactly identical (i.e. if they are of the same shape and size).

Trace $\triangle ABC$ and $\triangle XYZ$. Cut them out and place one over the other. Do they fit exactly ? You will notice that $\angle A = \angle X$, $\angle B = \angle Y$, $\angle C = \angle Z$, $AB = XY$, $BC = YZ$ and $AC = XZ$. These equal angles and sides will coincide when one triangle is placed or *superposed* over the other.

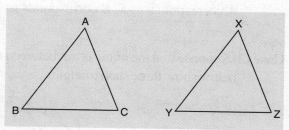

It is by the method of **superposition,** that is, by placing one figure on to another that we can establish whether the given figures are congruent or not. In two congruent figures, the sides and angles that coincide by superposition are said to *correspond.* They are also called **corresponding sides and corresponding angles respectively.**

Here, since the two triangles ABC and XYZ are congruent, therefore, their corresponding angles and corresponding sides are equal. We write in short form as

$$\triangle ABC \cong \triangle XYZ$$

(The symbol $\cong$ means "is congruent to")

Note. In congruent triangles, the corresponding sides are opposite equal angles, and corresponding angles are opposite equal sides.

Using arrows to indicate corresponding parts, we have

$$\angle A \leftrightarrow \angle X \qquad AB \leftrightarrow XY$$
$$\angle B \leftrightarrow \angle Y \qquad BC \leftrightarrow YZ$$
$$\angle C \leftrightarrow \angle Z \qquad CA \leftrightarrow ZX$$

29.3 Conditions of Congruence of Triangles

Now we shall state the various tests of congruence of triangles as theorems.

(1) Given the lengths of the three sides (SSS)

Draw separately two triangles ABC and XYZ on a sheet of paper, with $AB = XY = 4$ cm, $BC = YZ = 6$ cm and

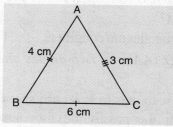

$CA = ZX = 3$ cm. Cut these triangles out, and place them one over another. We find that these two triangles ca be fitted exactly, therefore they are congruent figures.

$$\Delta ABC \cong \Delta XYZ$$

In general, if the three sides of a triangle are equal to the corresponding sides of another triangle, then the two triangles are congruent.
Abbreviation for reference : (SSS)

(2) Given the lengths of two sides and one angle (SAS)

Construct a triangle with side 2 cm and 3 cm, and with an angle of 30°.

Case (1) Suppose the angle is between the given sides. There are two possible triangles as shown here. The second triangle is congruent to the first triangle (although "turned over"). You may test this by copying the two triangles and cutting them out. Do they fit exactly. ?

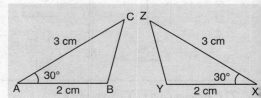

A corresponds to X, B corresponds to Y, C corresponds to Z.

$$\Delta ABC \cong \Delta XYZ \quad \text{(SAS)}$$

Case (2) Suppose that the angle is not between the given sides. Then there are several possible triangles. The figure below show three such triangles.

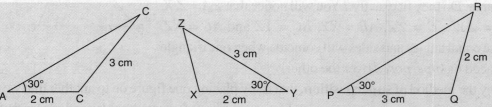

As can be clearly seen, the triangles are of different sizes and therefore are not congruent. Thus two triangle need not be congruent if the lengths of two sides and a non-included angle (i.e. the angle is not between the tw given sides) of one triangle are equal to the lengths of two sides and a non-included angle of the other triangle

If two triangles have two corresponding sides equal and the angle included between them als equal, the two triangles are congruent.
Abbreviation for reference : (SAS)

Case (3). Given the length of one side and the size of two angles (ASA).

(a) Suppose we wish to construct a triangle with one side 2 cm, and two angles 30° and 40°. Some possibilities are :

These two triangles are congruent.

$\Delta ABC \cong \Delta PRQ$ (**ASA** — *Two angles and the included side*)

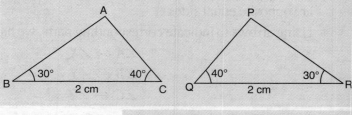

(b) A corresponds to P, B corresponds to R and C corresponds to Q..

Again the two triangles are congruent

$\Delta ABC \cong \Delta PRQ$ (**AAS** — *Two angles and the side opposite to one of them*)

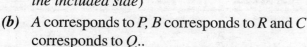
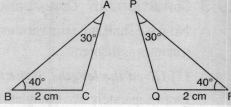

Note that A corresponds to P, B corresponds to R, C corresponds to Q. Work out further possibilities for yourself. You will find that the triangles in each case are congruent.

> *If two triangles have one side equal and two corresponding angles equal, the two triangles are congruent.*
> *Abbreviation for reference : (ASA) or (AAS)*

Note : 1. The two equal sides must be corresponding sides, i.e. opposite to angles which are known to be equal. For example, in the adjoining figure, $\angle A = \angle Q$, $\angle C = \angle R$, and side AB = side PR. These triangles are not congruent because the equal sides AB and PR are not opposite to equal angles. If instead of PR, the side PQ were equal to the side AB, the triangles would be congruent.

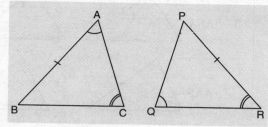

2. By '$\angle$ sum property of a Δ', you can always find the third angle of a triangle whose two angles are known.

Case (4). *Given the hypotenuse and one side of a right-angled triangle. (RHS)*

Construct a right angled triangle given that the hypotenuse is 7 cm and one side is 4 cm.

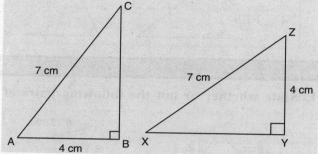

Two possible triangles can be constructed out of this given data as shown here. You will find that the two triangles are congruent (check this out).

$$\Delta ABC \cong \Delta ZYX \ (RHS)$$

> *If the hypotenuse and one side of a right-angled triangle are equal to the hypotenuse and one side of another right-angled triangle, the two triangles are congruent.*
> *Abbreviation for reference : (RHS)*

Case (5). *Given the three angles of a triangle*

Construct a triangle whose angles are 80°, 60° and 40°. Here it is possible to draw an infinite number of triangles satisfying the above data. The figures below-show four such triangles.

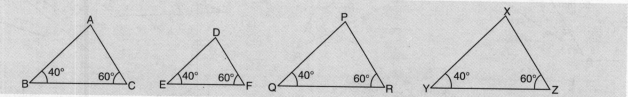

All the triangles drawn are of the same shape but not of the same size. We say that the triangles are **similar** but not congruent. Thus two triangles need not be congruent if their corresponding angles are equal.

29.4 Summary

The **four tests for congruent triangles** may be summarized in the following table:

1. **SSS**		Three sides correspondingly equal.

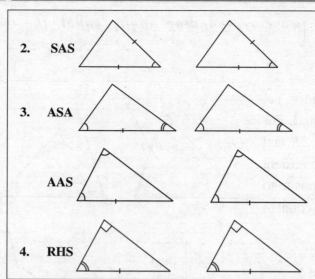

2. **SAS**   Two sides and the included angle correspondingly equal.

3. **ASA**   Two angles and the included side correspondingly equal.

AAS   Two angles and the side opposite to one of them correspondingly equal.

4. **RHS**   Hypotenuse and one side correspondingly equal.   (rt. ∠d Δs)

EXERCISE 29 (b)

1. State whether or not the following pairs of triangles are congruent. If they are, give reasons.

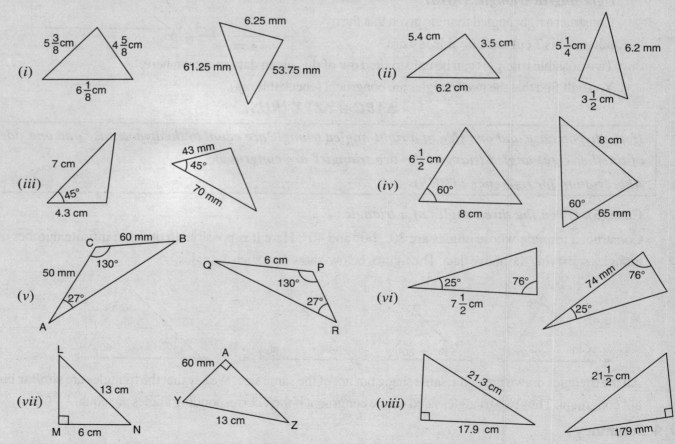

2. Show by comparing angles and sides, which of the triangles given here are congruent to each other

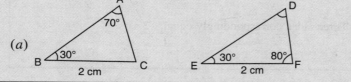

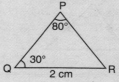

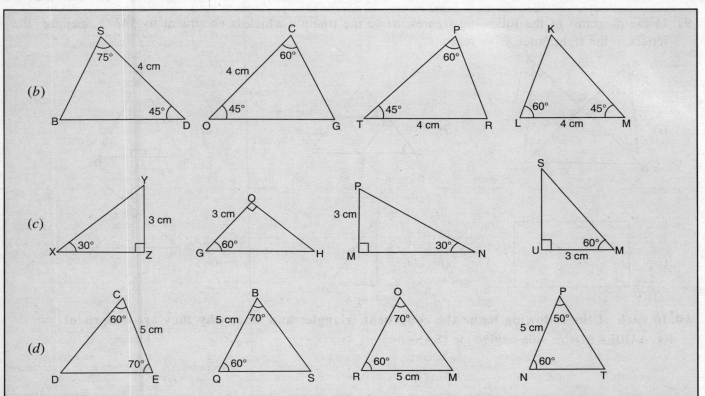

(b)

(c)

(d)

3. **In the following figure, state the condition you would use to show that △ABC and △CDE are congruent.**

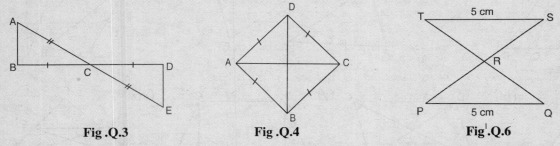

Fig .Q.3   **Fig .Q.4**   **Fig .Q.6**

4. In the figure, ABCD is a rhombus. Are △ADC and △ABC congruent ? What can you say about △ABD and △BCD?

5. If △ABC and △XYZ are equilateral triangles and AB = XY, state the conditions (s) under which △ABC and △XYZ are congruent.

6. In this figure, TS ∥ PQ and TS = PQ. Prove that the triangles PQR and RST are congruent.

7. △PRQ ≅ △LMN. If PQ = 6 cm, PR = 5 cm and ∠P = 50°, find NL and ∠L if LM = 5 cm and QR = MN.

8. △PQR ≅ △XYZ. Study the triangles carefully and then find ∠X and ∠Y.

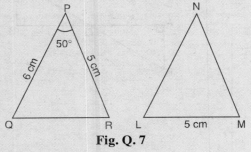

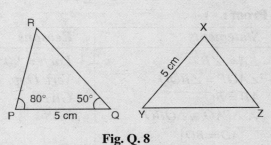

Fig. Q. 7   **Fig. Q. 8**

9. In the diagrams of the following figures, name the triangle which is congruent to ΔABC, keeping the letters in the right order. Give reasons.

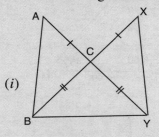 (i)

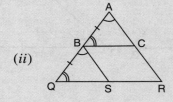 (ii)

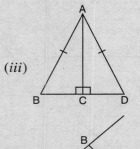 (iii)

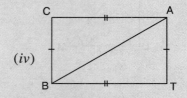 (iv)

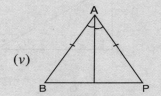 (v)

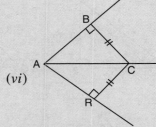 (vi)

10. In each of the following name the congruent triangles and state why they are congruent.

    Ex. $\Delta ABE \cong \Delta DCE$; side-angle-side (SAS)

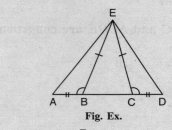
Fig. Ex.

(i)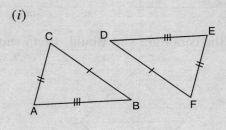

(ii)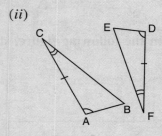

(iii)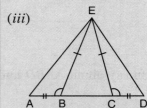

(iv)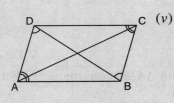

(v)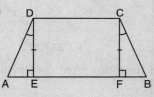

(vi)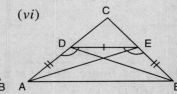

29.5 Application of Congruence Theorems in Proving Results

Ex. 1. *AP and BQ are perpendiculars to AB. It is also given that AP = BQ. Prove that O is the mid-point of the line segments AB and PQ.*

Sol.   Given $AP \perp AB$, $BQ \perp AB$, $AP = BQ$.

    To prove : $AO = BO$, $PO = QO$.

    Proof :

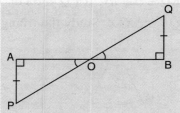

Statements	Reasons
$\angle A = \angle B$	Each = 90°
$\angle AOP = \angle BOQ$	Vert. Opp. $\angle$s
$AP = BQ$	Given
$\therefore \Delta PAO \cong \Delta QBO$	AAS
$\begin{aligned} AO &= BO \\ \therefore PO &= QO \end{aligned}$	Corresponding parts of congruent Δs.
Proved	

Ex.2. *AB and CD intersect each other at O and O is the mid-point of both AB and CD. Prove that AC = BD and AC ∥ BD.*

Sol. **Given.** $AO = BO$ and $CO = DO$.

To prove: $AC = BD$ and $AC \parallel BD$.

Proof:

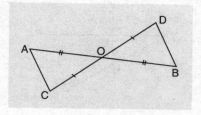

Statements	Reasons
In Δs *AOC* and *BOD*	
$AO = BO$	*Given*
$\angle AOC = \angle BOD$	*Vert. opp. Δs*
$CO = DO$	*Given*
$\therefore \Delta AOC \cong \Delta BOD$	*SAS*
$\therefore AC = BD$ and $\left.\begin{array}{l}\\ \angle CAO = \angle DBO\end{array}\right\}$	*Corresponding parts of congruent Δs.*
$\therefore AC \parallel BD$	$\angle CAO$ and $\angle DBO$ are alt. $\angle s$.
Proved	

Ex.3. *AX is the bisector of ∠BAC; P is any point on AX. Prove that the perpendiculars drawn from P to AB and AC are equal.*

Given: An angle *BAC* bisected by *AX*. From any point *P* on *AX*, *PM* and *PN* are drawn perpendiculars to *AB* and *AC* respectively.

To prove : $PM = PN$.

Proof:

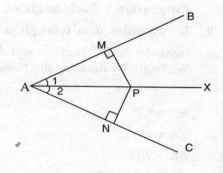

Statements	Reasons
$\angle M = \angle N$	*Each is 1 rt. $\angle$*
$\angle 1 = \angle 2$	*AX bisects $\angle BAC$*
$AP = AP$	*Common (Given)*
$\Delta AMP \cong \Delta ANP$	*(AAS)*
$PM = PN$	*Corresponding parts of congruent Δs.*
Proved	

EXERCISE 29 (c)

1. *AB* and *CD* bisect each other at *K*. Prove that $AC = BD$.

2. The sides *BA* and *CA* have been produced such that $BA = AD$ and $CA = AE$. Prove that $DE \parallel BC$.

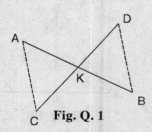

Fig. Q. 1

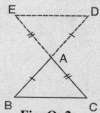

Fig. Q. 2

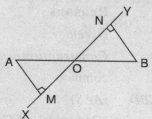

Fig. Q. 3

3. Prove that Δs *OAM* and *OBN* are congruent and hence prove that $AM = BN$. *AB* and *MN* bisect each other at *O*.

4. $\angle XYZ$ is bisected by *YP*. L is any point on *YP* and *MLN* is perpendicular to *YP*. Prove that $LM = LN$.

5. Prove that *AP* bisects ∠*BAC*.

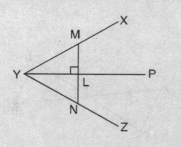 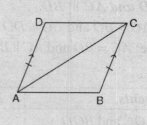 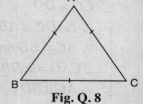

Fig. Q. 4   **Fig. Q. 5**   **Fig. Q. 6**

6. In the figure, *AD = BC* and *AD ∥ BC*. Prove that A*B = DC*.

7. In the given figure, triangles *ABC* and *DCB* are right angled at *A* and *D* respectively and *AC = DB*. Prove that △*ABC* ≅ △*DCB*.

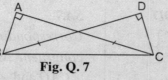

Fig. Q. 7

8. Find the size of each angle of an equilateral triangle.

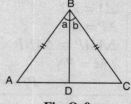

Fig. Q. 8

This can be found from the following considerations:

(*i*) Why is ∠*B* = ∠*C*? Why is ∠*C* = ∠*A* ? Why is ∠*A* = ∠*B*?

∴ ∠*A*=∠*B*=∠*C*

(*ii*) What is ∠*A* + ∠*B* + ∠*C* equal to?

∴ Each angle = ... ?

Conclusion : Each angle of an equilateral triangle is 60°.

9. **If two sides of a triangle are equal, then the angles opposite those sides are equal.**

Isosceles △*ABC* is given and *AB = BC*. We wish to prove that ∠*A* = ∠*C*. We begin by drawing the bisector of ∠*B*, namely *BD*.

	Reasons
AB = CB	*Given*
∠*a* = ∠*b*	*Construction*
BD = BD	*Common*
∴ △*ABD* ≅ △*CBD*	(SAS)
∴ ∠*A* = ∠*C*	(Corr. ∠s of Cong. △s)

Fig. Q. 9

10. **If two angles of a triangle are equal the sides opposite those angles are also equal.**

A △*ABC* is given in which ∠*A* = ∠*C*. We wish to prove that AB = BC. In this case also, we begin by drawing the bisector of ∠*B*, namely *BD*.

	Reasons
∠*A* = ∠*C*	*Given*
∠*a* = ∠*b*	*Construction*
BD = BD	common
∴ △*ABD* ≅ △*CBD*	(AAS)
∴ *AB = CB*	(Corr. sides of Cong. △s)

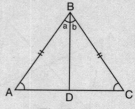

Fig. Q. 10

LOOKING BACK
Summary of Key Facts

1. A plane figure F_1 is said to be congruent to F_2, if F_1, when superposed over F_2, fits it exacly. The symobl $\cong$ is used to indicate' is congruent to':

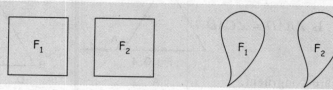

2. **Congruence of triangles: Two triangles are congruent if pairs of corresponding sides and correspondig angles are equal.**
Thus, $\triangle ABC \cong \triangle DEF$ if $\angle A = \angle D$, $\angle B = \angle E$, $\angle C = \angle F$, $AB = DE$, $AC = DF$ and $BC = EF$.

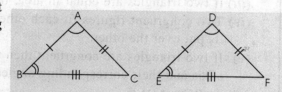

3. **Conditions of congruence of triangles;** Two triangles are congruent if.

(i)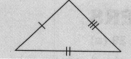

Three sides of one are equal to the three sides of the other (**SSS condition**)

(ii)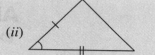

Two sides and included angle of one are respectively, equal to the two sides and the included angle of the other (**SAS condition**)

(iii)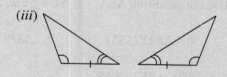

Two angles and the included side of one are respectively equal to the two angles and the included side of the other (**ASA condition**)

(iv)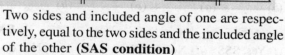

Two angles and a side of one are respectively equal to the two angles and corresponding side of the other (**AAS conditon**)

(v)

Two right triangles are congruent if the hypotenuse and one side of a triangle are respectively equal to the hypotenuse and a corresponding side of the other (**RHS conditon**).

4. Two congruent figures are equal in area but two figures, equal in area need not be congruent, e.g., the two rectangles shown in the figure have equal area but they are obviously not congruent.

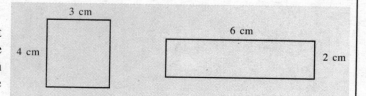

MENTAL MATHS -20

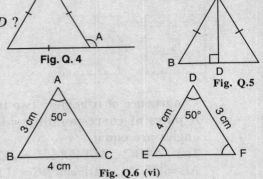

1. One of the equal angles of an isosceles triangle is 50°. Find all the angles of this triangle.
2. In a $\triangle ABC$, $AC = BC$ and $\angle C = 110°$. Find the angles A and B.
3. One angle of an equilateral $\triangle$ is 60°, what are the measures of the remaining two angles ?
4. Find $\angle A$ if the given triangle is equilateral.
5. Answer yes or no : $AB = AC$ and $AD \perp BC$. Is $\angle BAD = \angle CAD$?
6. **State true or false :**
   (*i*) All squares are congruent.
   (*ii*) If two squares have equal areas, they are congruent.
   (*iii*) If two triangles are equal in area, they are congruent.
   (*iv*) Two congruent figures fit each other exactly when one is put over the other.
   (*v*) If two triangles are congruent then their corresponding sides and their corresponding angles are equal.
   (*vi*) $\triangle ABC \cong \triangle DEF$.

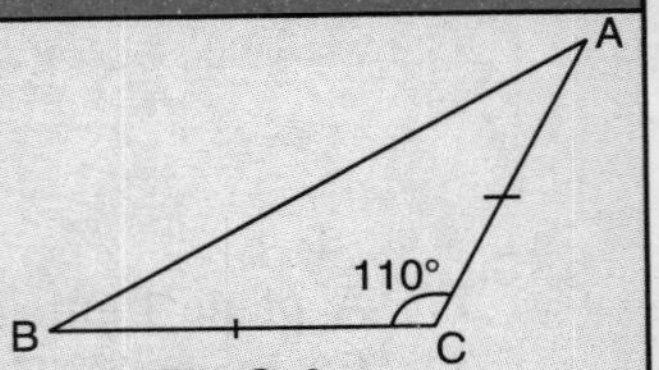

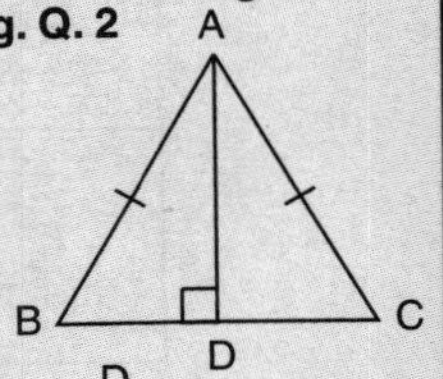

Fig. Q. 2

Fig. Q. 4

Fig. Q.5

Fig. Q.6 (vi)

ANSWERS

EXERCISE 29 (a)

2. **(b)**   3. **(a)**   4. **(b)**   5. **(b)**   6. (1) *f* (2) *j* (3) *b* (4) *e* (5) *g* (6) *c* (7) *d* (8) *h*

EXERCISE 29 (b)

1. (*i*) Yes, SSS (*ii*) No (*iii*) Yes, SAS (*iv*) No (*v*) Yes, AAS (*vi*) No (*vii*) Yes, RHS (*viii*) No
2. (*a*) $\triangle ABC \cong \triangle DEF$ (*b*) $\triangle SBD \cong \triangle RPT$ (*c*) all are congruent (*d*) $\triangle CDE \cong \triangle QSB$
3. SAS   4. Yes, yes congruent   5. SSS, ASA, SAS   6. Use the condition ASA   7. $NL = 6$ cm, $\angle L = 50°$
8. $\angle X = 80°$, $\angle Y = 50°$
9. (*i*) $\triangle XYC$ (SAS)   (*ii*) $\triangle BQS$ (AAS)   (*iii*) $\triangle ADC$ (RHS)   (*iv*) $\triangle BAT$ (SSS)   (*v*) $\triangle APC$ (SAS)
   (*vi*) $\triangle ARC$ (RHS)
10. (*i*) $\triangle ABC \cong \triangle EDF$; SSS   (*ii*) $\triangle BAC \cong \triangle EDF$; ASA   (*iii*) $\triangle CED \cong \triangle BEA$; SAS
    (*iv*) $\triangle ADB \cong \triangle CBD$; SAS, $\triangle DAB \cong \triangle BCD$; ASA   (*v*) $\triangle ADE \cong \triangle BCF$; ASA   (*vi*) $\triangle ADE \cong \triangle BED$; SAS

MENTAL MATHS - 20

1. 50°, 50°, 80° 2. 35°, 35° 3. 60°, 60° 4. 120° 5. yes
6. (*i*) False   (*ii*) True   (*iii*) False   (*iv*) true   (*v*) True   (*vi*) False

30. Polygons

30.1 Simple Closed Figures

Which figures can you trace completely and return to the point from where you began *without* retracing any points or lifting the pencil? The figures in which this is possible are called *simple closed figures*. Figures *A*, *B*, *E* and *I* are simple closed figures.

A simple closed figure separates the plane into two regions. One of the regions is the **interior** and the other region is the **exterior** of the simple closed curve. The figure is the **boundary** of each of these regions.

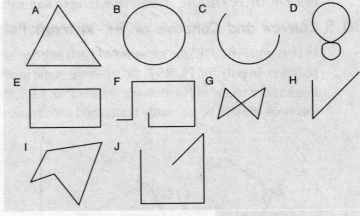

- **Plane Figure.** A plane figure is one whose all points lie in the same plane. All figures drawn above are plane since all points of each figure lie in the same plane, namely, the plane of the page.

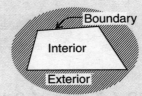

30.2 Polygons

Study, the figures below.

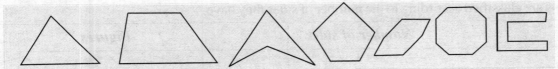

Are all of the figures above simple closed figures?

A *simple closed plane figure formed by line segments is called* **a Polygon**. The *line segments* are called *sides* of the figure. Each **end-point** of a side is called a **vertex** of the polygon.

The following figures are not polygons.

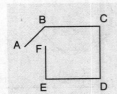

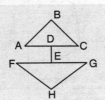

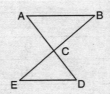

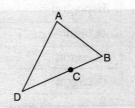

| Sides *AB* and *EF* do not intersect another side at each of their end points. | Side *DE* does not intersect sides *AC* and *FG* at their endpoints | Side *AC* intersects more than one side at vertex *C*. | Sides *CD* and *CB* are collinear (though *ABCD* is not a four sided polygon, *ABD* is a three sided one.) |

30.3 Vertices and Diagonals

Each line bounding the polygon, is called a **side** and the common point of intersection of two sides is called a **vertex** (plural is vertices). If two sides have a common end point, they are called **adjacent sides**. A line joining the non-adjacent vertices of a polygon is called a **diagonal** of the polygon.

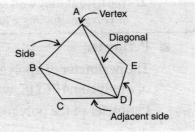

265

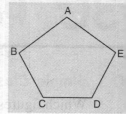

30.4 Naming a Polygon

A polygon is named by using its vertices, the letters representing the vertices being taken consecutively. Thus, we can name the pentagon drawn at the right as *ABCDE* or *BCDEA* or *CDEAB*, or *DEABC*. It will be wrong to name it as *ABDCE* or *AECBD*.

30.5 Convex and Concave or Re-entrant Polygons

In polygon ABCDE, the measure of each interior angle is less that 180°. Such a polygon is called a conve polygon. In polygon PQRST, the measure of the interior angle QRS is more that 180°. If a polygon has at leas one interior angle with a measure greater than 180°, the polygon is called a concave or a re-entrant polygon. I this book we will be primarily concerned with convex polygons.

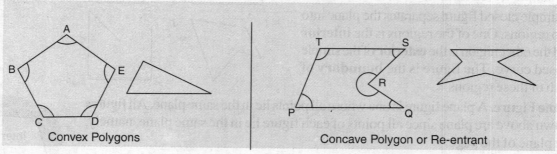

Convex Polygons   Concave Polygon or Re-entrant

30.6 Types of Polygons

Polygons are classified according to the number of sides they have.

Name	Number of sides	Figures
triangle	3	
quadrilateral	4	
pentagon	5	triangle quadrilateral pentagon hexagon
hexagon	6	
heptagon	7	
octagon	8	
nonagon	9	heptagon octagon decagon
decagon	10	

Note: 1. The term *polygon* comes from the Greek words *polys* meaning *many*, and *gonia*, meaning *angle*. Though we classify polygons according to the number of sides they have, the names we use for them, except for quadrilateral, do not reflect this fact.

2. You have already worked with one kind of polygon, i. e., triangles. In this chapter, we will introduce you to other kinds of polygons starting with quadrilateral.

■ **Perimeter**

The **perimeter** of a polygon is the sum of the lengths of its sides. To find the perimeter of a polygon *ABCDE*, we add the lengths of the sides.

Perimeter of the polygon $ABCDE = AB + BC + CD + DE + EA$

$$= 5 + 6 + 7 + 2.5 + 3 = 23.5 \text{ units.}$$

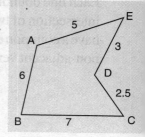

0.7 Regular Polygons

A regular polygon is a polygon with all its sides and all its angles equal. (both equilateral and equiangular).

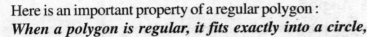

Square	Rectangle	Rhombus
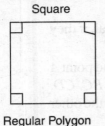	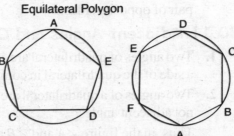	
Regular Polygon	Equiangular Polygon	Equilateral Polygon

Here is an important property of a regular polygon :

When a polygon is regular, it fits exactly into a circle,

_i.e._ we can draw a circle passing through each vertex of the polygon.

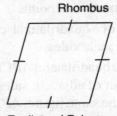

Now Try these.

Oral

1. (a) In the polygon at the right, (i) name its sides (ii) name its vertices.

   (b) Is polygon *AMECIN* a name for this polygon? Why?

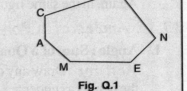

   Fig. Q.1

2. Name and spell the words used for a figure having (a) 5 sides, (b) 6 sides, (c) 7 sides (d) 8 sides, (e) 9 sides, (f) 10 sides.

3. Name all the diagonals of the polygon shown here.

4. For each convex polygon, draw all possible diagonals
   (i) quadrilateral   (ii) pentagon   (iii) hexagon.

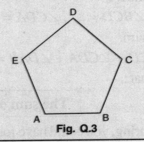

   Fig. Q.3

30.8 Quadrilateral

If *A*, *B*, *C* and *D* are coplanar points, such that (i) no three of them are collinear and (ii) the line segments *AB*, *BC*, *CD*, and *DA* do not intersect except at their end points, then the figure made up of the four line segments, is called the **quadrilateral** (**Abbreviation : quad**). The points *A*, *B*, *C* and *D* are called its **vertices**.

A quadrilateral is named by listing its vertices, starting at any vertex and reading clockwise or counter-clockwise. So *ABCD*, *BCDA* and *ADCB* name the same figure.

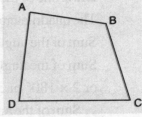

30.9 Sides, Angles and Diagonals of a Quadrilateral

(a) The four line segments *AB*, *BC*, *CD* and *DA* are called its sides.

(b) The four angles ∠*DAB*, ∠*ABC*, ∠*BCD* and ∠*CDA* are called its angles; and

(c) A line segment joining two non-consecutive vertices is called a **diagonal**.

   AC and *BD* are the two diagonals of the quad. *ABCD*.

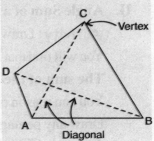

30.10 Adjacent Sides and Opposite Sides

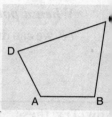

1. Two sides of a quadrilateral are said to be *adjacent sides* of the quadrilateral, if they have a common end point.

2. Two sides of a quadrilateral are said to be opposite sides of the quadrilateral, if they are not adjacent sides.

   Thus in the quadrilateral *ABCD* shown here, *AB* and *AD* have a common end point *A* so are a pair of adjacent sides. So also are the pairs of sides *AB*, *BC* and *BC*, *CD*. Again, in the same figure. *AB*, *DC* are a pair of opposite sides. *BC*, *AD* are the other pair of opposite sides.

30.11 Adjacent Angles and Opposite Angles

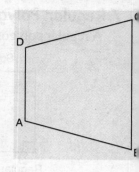

1. Two angles of quadrilateral are said to be adjacent angles of the quadrilateral, if they have a side of the quadrilateral in common.

2. Two angles of a quadrilateral are said to be opposite angles of the quadrilateral, if they are not adjacent angles.

   Thus, in the figure ∠*A* and ∠*B* are a pair of adjacent angles of the quadrilateral *ABCD*. They have side *AB* in common. Similarly, ∠*B*, ∠*C*; ∠*C*, ∠*D*; and ∠*D*, ∠*A* are the other pairs of adjacent angles.

   Again, in the same figure, ∠*A* and ∠*C* are a pair of opposite angles, so also are the pair of angles ∠*B* and ∠*D*

30.12 Angles of a Polygon

I. Angle : Sum of a Quadrilateral

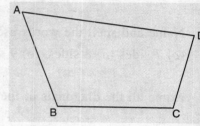

Activity : Draw any quadrilateral *ABCD*. Measure its angles and write the results as under :

∠*ABC* = ...°, ∠*BCD* = ...°, ∠*CDA* = ...°, ∠*DAB* = ...°

Now find the sum.

∠*ABC* + ∠*BCD* + ∠*CDA* + ∠*DAB* = ...°.

You will find that :

> **The sum of the angles of a quadrilateral is 360°.**

Without measuring, you could have found the sum as under :

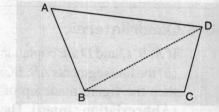

Draw one of the diagonals, say *BD*.

The quadrilateral is divided into 2 triangles.

Sum of the angles of 1 triangle = 2*rt*. ∠*s* or 180°

Sum of the angles of 2 triangles = 2 × 2*rt*. ∠*s* = 4*rt*. ∠*s*

or 2 × 180° or 360°.

∴ Sum of the angles of the quadrilateral = 4*rt*. ∠*s* or 360°.

II. Angle Sum of a Pentagon.

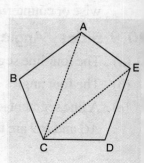

Activity: Draw any pentagon. Measure its angles. Find the sum of these angles.

You will find that :

The sum of the angles of a pentagon is 6*rt*. ∠*s* or 540°.

You can reason out as under :

Draw any pentagon *ABCDE*. Join its one vertex, say, *C* to the opposite vertices by diagonals *CE* and *CA* as shown. The pentagon is divided into 3 triangles

The sum of the angles of 1 triangle = 2*rt*. ∠*s* or 180°.

∴ The sum of the angles of 3 triangles = 3 × 2rt. ∠s = 6rt. ∠s or 540°.

∴ The sum of the angles of a pentagon = 6rt. ∠s or 540°

III. Angle Sum of a Hexagon.

Activity : Draw any hexagon. Measure its angles. Find the sum of these angles. You will see that :

The sum of the angles of a hexagon is 8rt. ∠s or 720°.

Without measuring, you can find the sum by arguing as under :

Draw any hexagon *ABCDEF*. Join one of its vertices, say A, to the opposite vertices by diagonals *AC*, A*D* and A*E* as shown.

The hexagon is divided into 4 triangles.

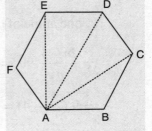

The sum of the angles of 1 triangle = 2rt. ∠s or 180°.

∴ The sum of the angles of 4 triangles = 4 × 2rt. ∠s = 8rt. ∠s or 720°.

∴ The sum of the angles of the hexagon is 8rt. ∠s or 720°.

30.13 Angle sum of any Polygon

You have found out the sum of the angles of a quadrilateral, a pentagon and a hexagon by the method of drawing diagonals through one vertex. Did you notice that by drawing the diagonals, the given polygon is divided into triangles whose number is 2 less than the number of sides of the polygon. Thus a quadrilateral is divided into 4 – 2, that is 2 triangles, a pentagon is divided into 5 – 2, that is 3 triangles, a hexagon is divided into 6 – 2, that is 4 triangles.

Looking at the above pattern, you can say that a polygon containing n sides will be divided into $(n-2)$ triangles.

Since the sum of the angles of these $(n-2)$ triangles $= 2(n-2)$ rt. ∠s $= (2n-4)$ rt. ∠s.

Therefore,

> 1. *The sum of the interior angles of a polygon containing n sides = (2n – 4) rt. ∠s or (2n – 4). 90°.*
>
> 2. *Each interior angle of a regular polygon = $\dfrac{2n-4}{n}$ rt. ∠s or $\dfrac{2n-4}{n}$. 90°.*

30.14 Solved Examples

Ex. 1. *Find the sum of the interior angles of a 9-gon.*

Sol. Sum of the Int. ∠s of a polygon = $(2n-4)$rt. ∠s

∴ Sum of the int. ∠s of a 9-gon = $(2 × 9 – 4)$rt. ∠s = 14rt. ∠s = 14 × 90° = **1260°.**

Ex. 2. *Find the size of each interior angle of a regular polygon with 12 sides.*

Sol. Sum of int. ∠s = $(2 × 12 – 4)$rt. ∠s = 20rt. ∠s = 20 × 90°= 1800°

∴ Each int. ∠ = $\dfrac{1800°}{12}$ = **150°.**

Ex. 3. *How many sides has a polygon if the sum of its interior ∠s is 20rt. ∠s?*

Sol. Let the polygon have n sides. Then, $(2n-4)$ rt ∠s = 20 rt ∠s

$2n – 4 = 20 \Rightarrow 2n = 20 + 4 = 24 \Rightarrow n = 12$

∴ The polygon has **12 sides.**

Ex. 4. *Each interior angle of a polygon is 140°. Find the number of sides.*

Sol. Let the polygon have n sides.

Given : Each interior $\angle = 140°$

Sum of all the angles of the polygon $= (2n - 4) . 90°$.

$\therefore$ one angle of the polygon $= \dfrac{2n - 4}{n} . 90°$.

$\therefore \quad \dfrac{2n - 4}{n} . 90° = 140° \Rightarrow \dfrac{2n - 4}{n} = \dfrac{140}{90} \Rightarrow \dfrac{2n - 4}{n} = \dfrac{14}{9}$

$\Rightarrow 9(2n - 4) = 14n \Rightarrow 18n - 36 = 14n \Rightarrow 18n - 14n = 36 \Rightarrow 4n = 36 \Rightarrow n = \dfrac{36}{4} = 9$.

$\therefore$ The polygon has **9 sides**.

Ex. 5. *Is it possible to have a regular polygon if each interior angle is 105° ?*

Sol. If each int. $\angle$ is 105°, the sum of int. angles of a polygon of n sides is equal to $n \times 105°$.

$\therefore \quad (2n - 4) \times 90° = n \times 105° \Rightarrow 180n - 360 = 150n \Rightarrow 180n - 105n = 360 \quad \therefore \quad 75n = 360$

$\therefore \quad n = \dfrac{360}{75} = 4\dfrac{4}{5}$, which is not a whole number. Therefore no polygon is possible with each of its interior angle equal to 105°.

		EXERCISE 30 (a)		

1. Copy and complete the table.

	Convex polygon	Number of sides	Number of triangles	Sum of interior angles
(i)	triangle			
(ii)	Quadrilateral	4		
(iii)	Pentagon			
(iv)			4	
(v)		7		
(vi)			6	
(vii)	nonagon			
(viii)	decagon			
(ix)	12-gon			
(x)			15	
(xi)	20-gon			
(xii)				3600
(xiii)				6120
(xiv)				9000

2. Find the sum of interior angles of a polygon with :

   (*a*) 15 sides   (*b*) 19 sides   (*c*) 23 sides   (*d*) 75 sides

3. Three of the angles of a quadrilateral are 65°, 90°, 150°. Find the fourth angle.

4. If in the quardrilateral *ABCD* the angle A = 98° and the angle *B* = 105°, how many degrees are there in the sum of the angles *ADC* and *BCD*.

5. Four of the angles of a pentagon are 42°,105°,63°,86°. Find the fifth angle.

6. Five of the angles of a hexagon are 120°, 150°, 92°, 79°, 135°. Find the sixth angle.

7. By drawing diagonals, through one of the vertices, find the sum of the angles of an octagon.

8. Find the number of sides of the polygon if the sum of its interior angles is :

   (a) 12rt. ∠s   (b) 20rt. ∠s   (c) 16rt. ∠s   (d) 24rt. ∠s

9. Each angle of a polygon is 160°. How many sides has it?

10. The angles of a quadrilateral are $x°$, $5x°$, $4x°$, and $2x°$. Find the value of x.

11. The angles of a hexagon are $6x°$, $4x°$, $5x°$, $6x°$, $7x°$, and $8x°$. Find the value of x.

12. One angle of a seven sided polygon is 114°, and each of the other six angles is $x°$. Find x.

13. Calculate the size of each interior angle of a regular

   (i) 15-gon   (ii) 20-gon   (iii) 90-gon.

14. Can regular polygons be described whose interior angles are (i) 110°, (ii) 140°? Give reasons for your answer.

15. A regular polygon has n sides, and each interior angle = 172°. Find n.

30.15 Types of Quadrilaterals

There are various types of quadrilaterals whose description is given below :

30.16 Parallelogram

A quadrilateral with both pairs of opposite sides are parallel is called a parallelogram. The short form is 'll gm'.

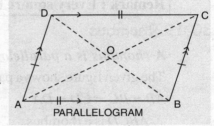
PARALLELOGRAM

ABCD is a parallelogram with *AB* ll *CD* and *AD* ll *BC*.

Properties of a parallelogram

Parallelogram *ABCD* has the following properties.

1. *Opposite sides are parallel,* i.e., *AB* ll *CD* and *AD* ll *BC*

2. *Opposite sides are equal in length,* i.e., *AB* = *CD* and *AD* = *BC*

3. *Opposite angles are equal,* i.e., *∠A* = *∠C* and *∠B* = *∠D*

4. *Adjacent angles are supplementary,* i.e., *∠A* + *∠B* = 180°, *∠B* + *∠C* = 180°, *∠C* + *∠D* = 180°, *∠D* + *∠A* = 180°.

5. *Diagonals bisect each other,* i.e., *AO* = *OC* and *BO* = *OD*.

6. *Each diagonal divides it into two congruent triangles,* i.e., *ΔABC* ≅ *ΔADC* and *ΔABD* ≅ *ΔBDC*.

30.17 Rectangle

A rectangle is a parallelogram each of whose angles measures 90°.

Thus in the given parallelogram *ABCD*, *∠A* = *∠B* = *∠C* = *∠D* = 90°.

∴ *ABCD* is a rectangle

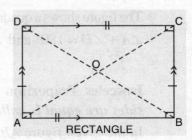
RECTANGLE

Properties of a Rectangle

The properties of rectangle *ABCD* are as under :

1. *Opposite sides are parallel,* i.e., *AB* ll *CD* and *AD* ll *BC*.

2. *Opposite sides are equal,* i.e., *AB* = *CD* and *AD* = *BC*.

3. *All the angles are equal to 90°,* i.e,. *∠A* = *∠B* = *∠C* = *∠D* = 90°.

4. *Diagonals are equal,* i.e., *AC* = *BD*.

5. *Diagonals bisect each other,* i.e., *AO* = *OC* and *BO* = *OD*.

30.18 Square

A parallelogram with all sides equal and each angle measuring 90° is called a square.

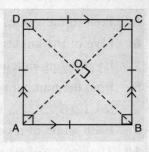

The adjoining figure shows a parallelogram *ABCD* with all sides equal, i.e., $AB = BC = CD = DA$ and each angle = 90°, i.e., $\angle A = \angle B = \angle C = \angle D = 90°$.

∴ *ABCD* is a square.

Properties of a Square.

The properties of square *ABCD* can be listed as under :

1. *Opposite sides are parallel* i.e, $AB \parallel CD$ and $AD \parallel BC$.
2. *All sides are equal* i.e, $AB = BC = CD = DA$.
3. *All angles are equal* to 90°, i.e. $\angle A = \angle B = \angle C = \angle D = 90°$.
4. *Both the diagonals are equal*, i.e. $AC = BD$.
5. *The diagonals bisect each other at right angles*, i.e. $AO = OC$, $BO = OD$ and $\angle AOC = \angle BOC = \angle COD = \angle DOA = 90°$.

   Remark : Every square is a rectangle

30.19 Rhombus

A rhombus is a parallelogram with all sides equal.

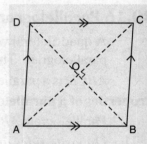

The given figure shows a parallelogram *ABCD* with all sides equal, i.e.,

$AB = BC = CD = DA$

∴ *ABCD* is a rhombus.

Properties of a Rhombus

The properties of a rhombus *ABCD* are listed below :

1. *Opposite sides are parallel*, i.e., $AB \parallel CD$ and $BC \parallel AD$.
2. *All sides are equal*, i.e., $AB = BC = CD = DA$.
3. *Diagonals bisect each other at right angles*, i.e.,
   $AO = OC$, $BO = OD$ and $\angle AOB = \angle BOC = \angle COD = \angle DOA = 90°$.

   Note : The diagonals of a rhombus are not equal.

30.20 Trapezium

A quadrilateral with exactly one pair of parallel sides is called a trapezium.

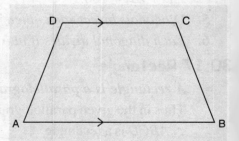

The figure shows a quadrilateral *ABCD* with $AB \parallel CD$ ∴ it is a trapezium.

$\angle A + \angle D = 180°$ and $\angle B + \angle C = 180°$ ∵ $AB \parallel CD$

   co-interior angles are supplementary

Isosceles Trapezium : *A trapezium in which the non-parallel sides are equal is called an isosceles trapezium.*

In the given figure $AB \parallel DC$ and $AD = BC$, therefore *ABCD* is an isosceles trapezium.

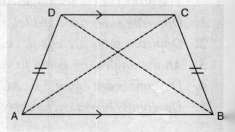

Properties : In an isosceles trapezium *ABCD*, $\angle A = \angle B$, $\angle C = \angle D$ and diagonal AC = diagonal BD.

30.21 Kite

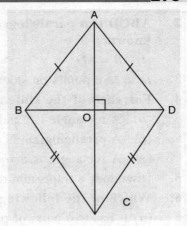

A Kite is a quadrilateral in which two pairs of adjacent sides are equal.

In the adjoining figure ABCD is a quadrilateral in which AB = AD and BC = CD

∴ ABCD is a kite.

Property : *Diagonals of a kite intersect each other at right angles.*

$\angle AOB = \angle BOC = \angle COD = \angle DOA = 90°.$

This chart shows how special parallelograms are related.

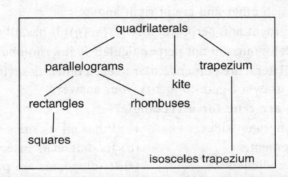

EXERCISE 30 (b)

1. Complete the table given below :

	Properties	Parallelogram	Rectangle	Square	Rhombus
1.	Opposite sides are parallel	Yes			
2.	Opposite sides are equal				Yes
3.	Adjacent sides are equal		No		
4.	Opposite angles are equal	Yes			
5.	Each interior angle is 90°			Yes	
6.	Diagonals are equal	No		Yes	
7.	Diagonals bisect each other				Yes
8.	Diagonals bisect at right angles		No		
9.	Diagonals bisect interior angles			Yes	

2. **ABCD is a parallelogram. What special name will you give it, if the following additional facts are known :**

   (*i*) *AB = AD*   (*ii*) ∠*BAD* is a right angle   (*iii*) *AB = AD* and ∠*BAD* = rt.∠ ?

3. *D, E* are points on sides *AB, AC* of Δ*ABC* such that *DE* || *BC*. What is quadrilateral *BCED* called?

4. **For each of the statements given below, indicate whether it is true (T) or false (F).**

   (*a*) A rectangle is a parallelogram.   (*b*) A square is a rectangle.

   (*c*) A parallelogram is a rhombus.   (*d*) A square is a rhombus.

   (*e*) A rectangle is a square.   (*f*) A square is a parallelogram.

5. How does a trapezium differ from a parallelogram?

6. **Which of the following are true for a rhombus ?**

   (*a*) It has two pairs of parallel sides.   (*b*) It has two pairs of congruent angles.

   (*c*) It has two pairs of congruent sides.   (*d*) Two of its angles are right angles.

   (*e*) Its diagonals bisect each other and are at right angles.

   (*f*) Its diagonals are congruent and perpendicular.   (*g*) It has all its sides of equal length.

7. The diagonals of a parallelogram are not perpendicular. Is it a rhombus ? Why or why not?

8. The diagonals of a quadrilateral are perpendicular to each other. Is such a quadrilateral always a rhombus ? If your answer is a 'no', draw a figure to justify your answer.

9. **Which of the following are true for a rectangle?**

   (*a*) It has two pairs of congruent sides.   (*b*) It has all its sides of equal lengths.

   (*c*) Its diagonals are congruent.   (*d*) Its diagonals bisect each other.

   (*e*) Its diagonals are perpendicular.   (*f*) Its diagonals are perpendicular and bisect each other.

   (*g*) Its diagonals are congruent and bisect each other.

   (*h*) Its diagonals are congruent, and perpendicular and bisect each other.

10. Repeat question 9 for a square, in place of a rectangle.

11. A window frame has one diagonal longer than the other. Is the window frame a rectangle? Why or why not?

12. *ABCD* **is a rectangle,** *EFGH* **is a rhombus and** *PQRS* **is a square.**

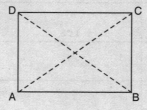 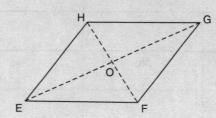 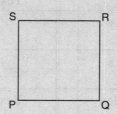

   Complete the following :

   (*i*) *FH* ⊥ ....   (*ii*) *GE* bisects ....

   (*iii*) If ∠*FEH* = 130°, ∠*EHG* = ...   (*iv*) If *AC* = 4, *BD* = ...

   (*v*) If *PQ* = 4, *PS* = ...   (*vi*) If ∠*EHG* = 48°, ∠*HGF* = ...

   (*vii*) If *HE* = 12, *GH* = ...   (*viii*) ∠*EOF* = ...

30.22 Solved Examples

Ex. 1. *The adjacent angles of a parallelogram are as 2 : 3. Find the measure of all the angles.*

Sol.   Suppose *ABCD* is the parallelogram and the two adjacent angles *A* and *B* are as 2 : 3.

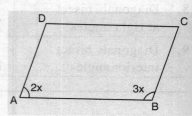

Suppose $\angle A = 2x$ and $\angle B = 3x$

Since $\angle A$ and $\angle B$ are a pair of adjacent interior angles and $AD \parallel BC$.

$$\therefore \ \angle A + \angle B = 180° \implies 2x + 3x = 180°$$

$$\implies 5x = 180° \implies x = \frac{180°}{5} = 36°$$

$$\therefore \ \angle A = 72° \text{ and } \angle B = 108°$$

Again, since opposite angles of a ∥ gm are equal,

$$\therefore \ \angle C = \angle A = 72° \text{ and } \angle D = \angle B = 108°$$

Ex. 2. *The ratio of two sides of a ∥ gm is 3 : 5, and its perimeter is 48 cm. Find the sides of the ∥ gm.*

Sol. Let the two sides of the ∥ gm be $3x$ cm and $5x$ cm.

Since the opposite sides of a ∥ gm are equal, therefore, the other two sides are $3x$ cm and $5x$ cm.

Now, perimeter of ∥ gm = 48 cm

$$\therefore \ 3x + 5x + 3x + 5x = 48 \quad \text{or} \quad 16x = 48 \quad \therefore \ x = \frac{48}{16} = 3$$

Hence the sides of the ∥ gm are 9 cm, 15 cm, 9 cm and 15 cm.

Ex. 3. *The point of intersection of diagonals of a quadrilateral divides one diagonal in the ratio 2 : 3, Is it a ∥ gm? Why or why not?*

Sol. No, it is not a ∥ gm, because the diagonals of a ∥ gm are bisected at their point of intersection.

Ex. 4. *One of the diagonals of a rhombus is congruent to one of its sides. Find the angles of the rhombus.*

Sol. Let $ABCD$ be a rhombus in which diagonal $BD = AB = AD$ $\therefore \triangle ABD$ is an equilateral triangle.

$$\therefore \ \angle BAD = 60°$$

Also, $\angle BAD + \angle ABC = 180°$

$$\therefore \ \angle ABC = 180° - \angle BAD = 180° - 60° = 120°$$

| ∵ each angle of an equilateral $\triangle$ is 60° |
| adj. int. angles, $AD \parallel BC$ |

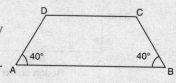

Since opposite angles of a rhombus are equal

$$\therefore \ \angle BCD = \angle BAD = 60° \text{ and } \angle ADC = \angle ABC = 120°$$

Hence, the angles of the rhombus are 60°, 120°, 60° and 120°.

EXERCISE 30 (c)

1. The measure of one angle of a parallelogram is 80°. What are the measures of the remaining angles?

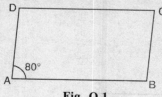

Fig. Q.1

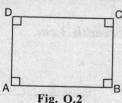

Fig. Q.2

2. Two adjacent angles of a parallelogram are congruent. What is the measure of each?

3. Two adjacent sides of a parallelogram are 5 cm and 6 cm repectively. Find its perimeter.

4. The perimeter of a ∥ gm is 180 cm. One of its sides is greater than the other by 30 cm. Find the lengths of the sides of the parallelogram.

5. $ABCD$ is a trapezium in which $AB \parallel DC$. If $\angle A = \angle B = 40°$, what are the measures of the other two angles ?

6. Calculate the angles marked with small letters in the following diagrams.

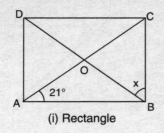

(i) Rectangle

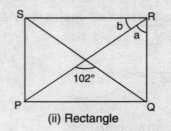

(ii) Rectangle

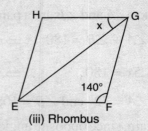

(iii) Rhombus

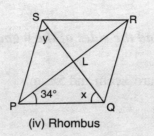

(iv) Rhombus

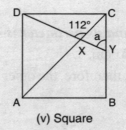

(v) Square

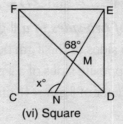

(vi) Square

7. Find each angle of a parallelogram if two consecutive angles are in the ratio 1:3.

8. Find the sizes of the angles of a parallelogram if one angle is 20° less than twice its adjacent angle.

9. *ABCD* is a rhombus. ∠*BAC* is 37°. Draw a sketch and find the four angles of the rhombus.

10. *ABCD* is a parallelogram. Find *x, y* and *z*.

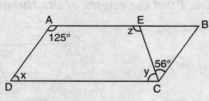

Fig. Q. 10

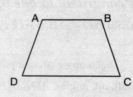

Fig. Q. 11

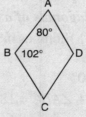

Fig. Q. 12

11. *ABCD* is an isosceles trapezium. ∠*BAD* is three times the size of ∠*ADC*. Find the angles of the trapezium

12. Find the size of the two unmarked angles in the kite.

13. If an angle of a rhombus is 50°, find the size of the angles of one of the four triangles which are formed by the diagonals.

30.23 Construction of Rectangles

I. Adjacent sides are given.

Construct a rectangle of length 5 cm and breadth 3 cm.

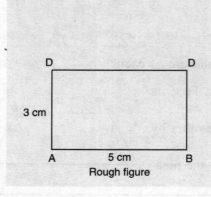

Rough figure

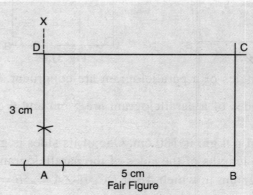

Fair Figure

Step 1. Draw AB = 5 cm.

Step 2. At A draw $AX \perp AB$.

Step 3. From AX cut off AD = 3 cm.

Step 4. With 3 cm radius and centre B draw an arc.

Step 5. With radius 5 cm and centre D, draw another arc cutting the arc drawn in Step 4 at C.

Step 6. Join BC and DC.

Then $ABCD$ is the required rectangle.

II. A side and length of one diagonal are given.

Construct a rectangle of length 4.5 cm and length of the diagonal 6 cm.

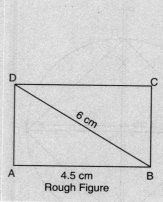

Rough Figure

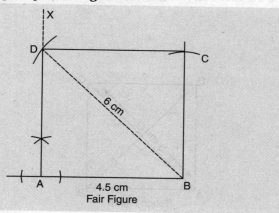

Fair Figure

Step 1. Draw AB = 4.5 cm.

Step 2. At A draw $AX \perp AB$.

Step 3. With B as centre and radius 6 cm draw an arc cutting AX at D.

Step 4. With B as centre and radius equal to AD draw an arc. With D as centre and radius 4.5 cm draw an arc cutting the previous arc at C.

Step 5. Join BC and DC

Thus $ABCD$ is the required rectangle.

30.24 Construction of Squares

I. Having given one side.

Construct a square of side 4 cm.

You can construct a square of given side length in the same manner as you constructed a rectangle.

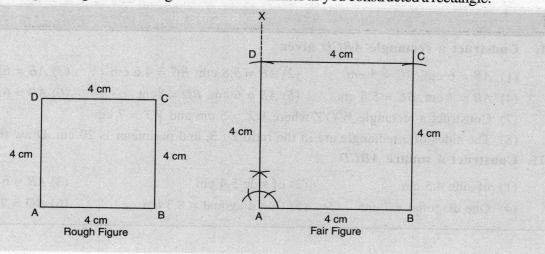

Step 1. Draw $AB = 4$ cm.

Step 2. At A, draw $AX \perp AB$.

Step 3. From AX, cut off $AD = 4$ cm.

Step 4. With B and D as centres and radii 4 cm each, draw two arcs cutting each other at C.

Step 5. Join BC and DC.

Then $ABCD$ is the required square.

II. Having given a diagonal.

Construct a square whose one diagonal is 5 cm.

Use the fact that (*i*) the diagonals of a square are equal. (*ii*) They bisect each other at right angles.

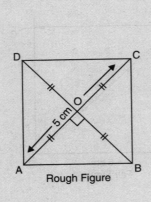

Rough Figure

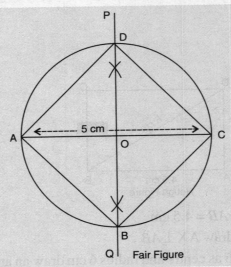

Fair Figure

Step 1. Draw a diagonal $AC = 5$ cm.

Step 2. Draw PQ the perpendicular bisector of AC.

Step 3. Let PQ cut AC at O.

Step 4. With O as centre and OA radius draw a circle.

Let this circle cut QP at points B and D.

Step 5. Join AB, BC, CD and DA.

Then $ABCD$ is the required square.

EXERCISE 30 (d)

I. Construct a rectangle *ABCD* given

   (1) $AB = 6$ cm, $BC = 5$ cm   (2) $AB = 5.8$ cm, $BC = 4.6$ cm   (3) $AB = 6.3$ cm, $BC = 5.1$ cm

   (4) $AB = 7$ cm, $BC = 5.5$ cm   (5) $AB = 6$ cm, $BD = 8$cm   (6) $AB = 6.4$ cm, $AC = 7.8$ cm

   (7)   Construct a rectangle *WXYZ* where $WX = 5$ cm and $WY = 7$ cm.

   (8)   The sides of a rectangle are in the ratio 2 : 3, and perimeter is 20 cm. Draw the rectangle.

II. Construct a square *ABCD*

   (1)   of side 4.5 cm   (2)   of side 5.4 cm   (3) $AB = 6$ cm

   (4)   One diagonal = 7 cm   (5)   One diagonal = 8.3 cm   (6) $BD = 7.5$ cm

LOOKING BACK
Summary of Key Facts

1. A simple closed figure formed by three or more line segments is called a polygon.
2. If the measure of each interior angle of a polygon is less then 180°, then it is called a convex polygon.
3. If the measure of at least one interior angle of a polygon is greater then 180°, then it is a concave or rentrant polygon.
4. A polygon with all sides and all angles equal is called a regular polygon.
5. Sum of the interior angles of a polygon with n sides = $(2n - 4) \times 90°$.
6. Each interior angle of a regular polygon with n sides = $\dfrac{2n-4}{n} \times 90°$.
7. A quadrilateral is a closed figure bounded by four line segments.
8. A parallelogram is a quadrilateral whose opposite sides are parallel and equal.
9. A rectangle is a parallelogram whose each angle measures 90°.
10. A square is a parallelogram whose all sides are equal and each angle measures 90°.
11. A rhombus is a parallelogram with all sides equal.
12. A trapezium is a quadrilateral with one pair of opposite sides parallel.
13. A trapezium whose non parallel sides are equal is called an isosceles trapezium.
14. A kite is a quadrilateral with two pairs of adjacent sides equal, but opposite sides unequal.

MENTAL MATHS–21

1. Three angles of a quadilateral are 140°, 60°, 80°, Find the fourth angle.
2. A quadrilateral having angles as 60°, 200°, 40°, 60° is a concave quadrilateral. True or false?
3. The sum of the interior angles of a polygon with 10 sides is ... .
4. How many pairs of opposite angles are there in a quadrilateral?
5. All the angles of a quadrilateral are equal. Find each angle.
6. A square has equal diagonals bisecting each other at right angles. True or false ?
7. The adjacent angles of a rhombus are equal, find all the angles.
8. The diagonal of a parallelogram divides it into _____ triangles.

ANSWERS

ry These

(*a*) (*i*) *CA, AM, ME, EN, NI, IC.* (*ii*) *C, A, M, E, N, I* (*b*) No, vertices not named in order.

(*a*) pentagon, (*b*) Hexagon, (*c*) heptagon (*d*) octagon (*e*) nonagon (*f*) decagon

(*a*) *AC, AD, BD, BE, CE*

EXERCISE 30 (a)

Convex Polygon	Number of sides	Number of triangles	Sum of inteior angles				
(*i*) Triangle	3	1	180°	(*iv*) Hexagon	6	4	720°
(*ii*) Quadrilateral	4	2	360°	(*v*) Heptagon	7	5	900°
				(*vi*) Octagon	8	6	1080°
iii) Pentagon	5	3	540°	(*vii*) nonagon	9	7	1260°
				(*viii*) 10-gon	10	8	1440°
				(*ix*) 12-gon	12	10	1800°

(x) 17-gon	17	15	2700°	
(xi) 20-gon	20	18	3240°	
(xii) 22-gon	22	20	3600°	
(xiii) 36-gon	36	34	6120°	
(xiv) 52-gon	52	50	9000°	

2. (a) 2340°　　(b) 3060°　　(c) 3780°　　(d) 13140°
3. 55°　　4. 157°　　5. 244°　　6. 144°　　7. 12 rt ∠s
8. (a) 8　　(b) 12　　(c) 10　　(d) 14
9. 18　　10. x = 30°　　11. x = 20°　　12. x = 131°
13. (i) 156°　　(ii) 162°　　(iii) 176°
14. (i) No　　(ii) Yes, 9-gon　　15. 45

EXERCISE 30 (b)

	Properties	Parallelo-gram	Rectangle	Square	Rhombus
1.	Opposite sides are parallel	Yes	Yes	Yes	Yes
2.	Opposite sides are equal	Yes	Yes	Yes	Yes
3.	Adjacent sides are equal	No	No	Yes	Yes
4.	Opposite angles are equal	Yes	Yes	Yes	Yes
5.	Each interior angle is 90°	No	Yes	Yes	No
6.	Diagonals are equal	No	Yes	Yes	No
7.	Diagonals bisect each other	Yes	Yes	Yes	Yes
8.	Diagonals bisect at right angles	No	No	Yes	Yes
9.	Diagonals bisect interior angles	No	No	Yes	Yes

2. (i) Rhombus　(ii) Rectangle　(iii) Square
3. Trapezium.
4. (a) T　(b) T　(c) F　(d) T　(e) F　(f) T
5. A trapezium has one pair of opposite sides parallel, while a parallelogram has two pairs of opposite sides parallel.
6. (a) T　(b) T　(c) T　(d) F　(e) T　(f) F　(g) T
7. No
8. Yes, it is always a rhombus
9. (a) T　(b) F　(c) T　(d) T　(e) F　(f) F　(g) T　(h) T
10. (a) T　(b) T　(c) T　(d) T　(e) T　(f) T　(g) T　(h) T
11. No
12. (i) EG　　(ii) HF at right angles　　(iii) 50°
 (iv) 4　　(v) 4　　(vi) 132°　　(vii) 12
 (viii) 90°

EXERCISE 30 (c)

1. 100°, 80° and 100°　　2. 90° each　　3. 22 cm　　4. 30 cm, 60 cm, 30 cm, 60 cm　　5. ∠C = ∠D = 140°
6. (i) 69° [**Hint.** Use the fact that diagonals of a rectangle being equal, ΔAOB is isosceles. Also, ∠ABC = 90°]
 (ii) a = 51°, b = 39°　　(iii) 20°　　(iv) x = y = 56°　　(v) 67°　　(vi) 113°

7. 45°, 135°, 45°, 135°　　8. $66\frac{2°}{3}, 113\frac{1°}{3}, 66\frac{2°}{3}, 113\frac{1°}{3}$　　9. ∠A = 74°, ∠B = 106°, ∠C = 74°, ∠D = 106°

10. x = 55°, y = 69°, z = 111°　11. ∠A = 135°, ∠B = 135°, ∠C = 45°, ∠D = 45°　　12. 102°, 76°　　13. 25°, 65°, 90°

MENTAL MATHS – 21

1. 80°　　2. True　　3. 1440°　　4. Two　　5. 90°　　6. True　　7. 90° each　　8. two congruent

INTERESTING INFORMATION

1. The mathamatician Gauss, who died in 1814, wanted a 17-sided polygon drawn on his tombstone, but it too closely resembled a circle for the sculptor to carve.

2. The US Defence Department Building, the Pentagon, has the largest ground area covered by any office building : 604 600 m², and 27 km of corridors.

3. **Mystic hexagon.** A mystic hexagon is a regular hexagon with all its diagonals drawn.

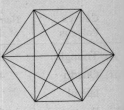

ENRICHMENT
(TESSELLATIONS)

Shapes tessellate when they fit together exactly, without any gaps, or overlapping.

'Tessellate' means to cover a plane surface by repeated use of a single shape without gaps or overlapping.

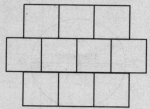

circles do not tessellate.

Squares tessellations

We can also have tessellations made up of more than one shape. This tessellation is made using squares and regular octagons.

1. In the diagram A-1, show, by drawing a diagram, which of the regular polygons can tessellate.

2. A square, a regular hexagon and a regular dodecagon can be tessellated. The diagram (A-2) shows part of the tessellation. Only four sides of the dodecagon have been drawn.

   Add two more squares and one more hexagon to the diagram to show how the tessellation will continue.

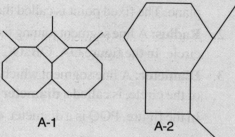

A-1   A-2

ANSWERS

1.

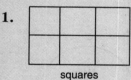

squares
tessellate

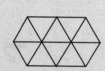

triangles
tessellate

hexagons
tessellate

2.

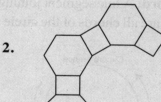

31 . Circles

31.1 Revision

Recall the following concepts or definitions which you have learnt in earlier classes.

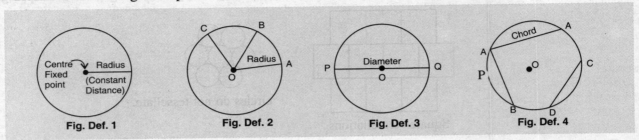

| Fig. Def. 1 | Fig. Def. 2 | Fig. Def. 3 | Fig. Def. 4 |

1. A circle is a simple closed curve all of whose points are at a constant distance from a fixed point in the same plane. The fixed point is called the **centre** of the circle.

2. **Radius:** A line segment joining the centre of a circle with any point on it is called a radius (plural: **radii**) of that circle. In the figure OA, OB, OC are all radii of the circle with centre O. **All radii of a circle are equal.**

3. **Diameter:** A line segment which passes through the centre of a circle and has the end points on the boundary of the circle, is called a **diameter** of the circle.

   In the figure, POQ is a diameter. of the circle with centre O. Clearly,

$$\boxed{\textbf{diameter} = \textbf{2} \times \textbf{radius}}$$

4. **Chord:** A line segment joining any two points on a circle is called a chord of that circle In the figure, PA, PB, CD are all chords of the circle with centre O.

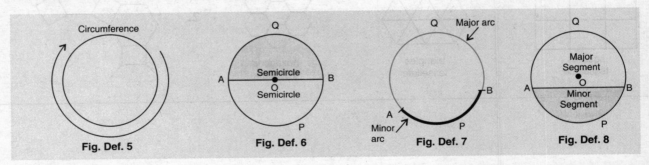

| Fig. Def. 5 | Fig. Def. 6 | Fig. Def. 7 | Fig. Def. 8 |

5. **Circumference:** The distance around the circle is called its **circumference.** It is the perimeter of the circle. If you run around a circle, you will cover a distance equal to its circumference.

6. **Semicircle :** A diameter of a circle divides the circle into two equal parts. Each part is called a semi-circle.

7. **Arc :** An arc is a part of a circle included between two points on the circle. In the figure APB is an arc of the circle. It is denoted by $\overarc{APB}$. It is less than a semi-circle and is called a **minor arc**. The other arc is AQB. It is greater than a semi-circle and is called a **major arc**.

8. **Segments :** A chord AB of a circle divides the circular region into two parts. Each part is called a segment of the circle. The bigger part AQB containing the centre of the circle is called the **major segment** and the smaller part which does not contain the centre is called the **minor segment** of the circle.

9. **Secant :** A line which intersects a circle at two distinct points is called a secant. PQ is a secant intersecting the circle at A and B.

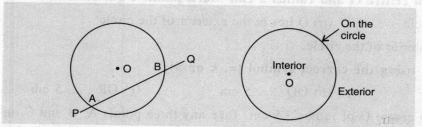

10. A point lies in the 'interior of a circle', 'on the circle', or 'in the exterior of the circle' according as its distance from the centre is less than, equal to or greater then the radius of the circle.

31.2 Angle in a Semi-Cirlce

Draw a circle with centre O. Draw its diameter AB. Then AXB and AYB are two semi-circles. Mark any point C on the semi-circle AXB. Join AC and CB. Then, ∠ACB is said to be an angle in a semi-circle.

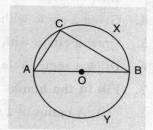

Activity: Draw two circles with centres O and M. Draw a diameter in each of these circles. Then each circle is divided into two semi-circles.

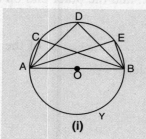

(i)

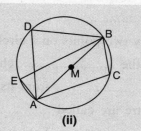

(ii)

Take any three different points C, D and E in each of these semi-circles. Join each of these points with A and B. Now, measure angles C, D and E and record your results as under :

Figure	∠C	∠D	∠E	Conclusion: Is ∠C = ∠D = ∠E = 90°?
Fig. (i)	.....	.....	.....	yes/no
Fig. (ii)	.....	.....	.....	yes/no

Hence, we have the following result.

> **Angle in a semi-circle is a right angle.**

Ex. *In the adjoining figure, O is the centre of the circle and ∠Q = 30°, find ∠P.*

Sol. PQ passes through centre O ∴ PQ is a diameter.

∴ ∠PRQ is an angle in a semi-circle.

∴ ∠PRQ = 90°

But ∠P + ∠Q + ∠R = 180° (angle sum property of a Δ)

∴ ∠P + ∠30° + ∠90° = 180°.

⇒ ∠P = 180 – 30° – 90° = 180° – 120° = **60°**

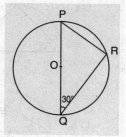

EXERCISE 31

1. **Draw a circle with centre O and radius 5 cm. Mark points PQR such that**

   (*i*) P lies on the circle   (*ii*) Q lies in the exterior of the circle.

   (*iii*) R lies in the interior of the circle.

   Fill in the blanks using the correct symbol (=, < or >)

   (*a*) OP .... 5 cm   (*b*) OQ ...... 5 cm   (*c*) OR ...... 5 cm

2. Draw a circle with centre O of radius 3.5 cm. Take any three points A, B and C on the circumference. Measure OA, OB and OC. Write your conclusion in the form of a statement.

3. Draw circles of radii 3cm, 4.5 cm and 5.2 cm each having the same centre O. What is the name given to such circles.

4. Given a circle with centre O and radius 3cm, what is the length of the longest chord of the circle.

5. Draw a circle with PQ as diameter where PQ = 5 cm.

6. Draw a semi circle with centre O and radius 6 cm.

7. **Fill in the blanks :**

   (*i*) A radius of a circle is a line segment with one end at the .... and the other end on the ....

   (*ii*) All radii of a circle are ....

   (*iii*) The line segment joining any two points on a circle is called the .... of the circle.

   (*iv*) The diameter of a circle is the .... chord of the circle.

   (*v*) Every point on the circle is .... from its centre.

   (*vi*) Circle having the same centre are called .... circles.

   (*vii*) The radius of a circle whose diameter is 7 cm is ....

8. **Answer True (T) or False (F).**

   (*i*) The centre of a circle is a point on the circle.

   (ii) Diameter = 2 × radius.

   (iii) A radius is a chord of the circle.

   (*iv*) A chord of a circle divides it onto two parts, each of these being called the segment of the circle.

   (*v*) A line segment joining any two points on a circle is called the secant of the circle.

   (*vi*) The distance around the circle is called a semi-circle.

9. **O is the centre of the circle in each figure. Find the size of each lettered angle.**

   (*i*)   (*ii*) 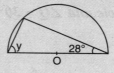   (*iii*)   (*iv*)

     (*v*)   (*vi*)

ANSWERS

EXERCISE 31

1. (*a*) =   (*b*) >   (*c*) <   3. Concentric circles   4. 6 cm.

7. (*i*) centre, circle   (*ii*) equal   (*iii*) chord   (*iv*) longest   (*v*) equidistant   (*vi*) concentric   (*vii*) 3.5 cm

8. (*i*) F   (*ii*) T   (*iii*) F   (*iv*) T   (*v*) F   (*vi*) F

9. (*i*) 55°   (*ii*) 62°   (*iii*) $a = 42°, x = 55°$ (*iv*) $p = 60°, q = 30°, r = 60°$ (*v*) $a = 40°, b = 40° c = 50°$

(*vi*) $x = 70°, y = 70°$

MATHS FOR FUN

DID YOU KNOW?

Scientists require power of concentration, but even that can be carried too far. In 1807, the mathematcian Johan Karl Friedrich Gauss was caught up in a problem while his wife lay sick upstairs. When the doctor told him his wife was dying, Gauss waived him away and, never looking up from his problem muttered. Tell her to wait a moment till I am through.

32. Symmetry

32.1 Line Symmetry

1. Pradeep watched a butterfly land and then fold its wings.

    Do the two wings seem to match exactly ?

    Think of the line along the fold. It divides the butterfly into two equal parts.

    This is a **line of symmetry.** You can say that the butterfly has line symmetry.

2. Trace the figure and the dotted line. Then fold your tracing along the dotted line. Is the figure divided into two equal halves? If it is so, the figure has line symmetry. The dotted line along which you folded the figure is the line of symmetry.

> *If you can fold a figure so that both halves fit exactly on one another, the figure is symmetrical. The fold is called a line of symmetry.*

Many things in nature are symmetrical. Animals and humans have symmetrical shapes (though sometimes only approximately symmetrical). Flowers and leaves very often have exact symmetrical shapes. Man has designed buildings so that often either the whole structure or part of it is symmetrical. This is done not only for the beauty of design but also because the use of symmetry produces better buildings.

32.2 Number of Lines of Symmetry

A figure may have one line of symmetry, two lines of symmetry, three or more lines of symmetry or no line of symmetry.

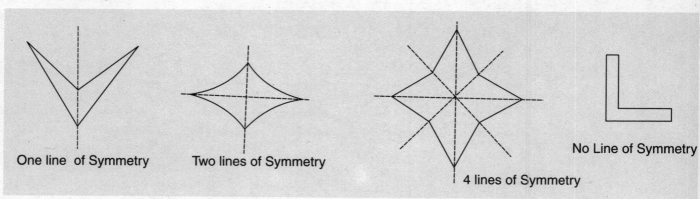

One line of Symmetry   Two lines of Symmetry   4 lines of Symmetry   No Line of Symmetry

286

32.3 Symmetry of the Letters

The following letters of the English alphabet are symmetrical about the dotted line (or lines).

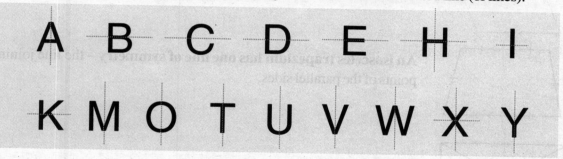

Each of the following letters has no line of symmetry :

F G J L N P Q R

32.4 Symmetry of Some Geometrical Figures

In each case, the line of symmetry is shown by a dotted line (or lines)

1. **An angle** (with equal arms) has one line of symmetry, the bisector of the angle.

2. **A scalene triangle** has no line of symmetry.

3. **An isosceles triangle** has one line of symmetry the bisector of its angle included between the equal sides. It is also the perpendicular bisector of the base.

4. **An equilateral triangle** has three lines of symmetry which are the bisectors of the angles. They are also the perpendicular bisectors of its sides.

5. **A scalene quadrilateral** has no line of symmetry.

6. **A parallelogram** has no line of symmetry.

7. **An isosceles trapezium has one line of symmetry** – the line joining the mid-points of the parallel sides.

8. **A rectangle** has two lines of symmetry – the lines joining the mid-points of opposite sides.

9. **A rhombus** has two lines of symmetry – the diagonals of the rhombus.

10. **A square** has four lines of symmetry – the lines joining the mid-points of opposite sides, and the diagonals.

11. **A kite** has one line of symmetry – the diagonal that bisects the pair of angles contained by equal sides.

12. **An arrowhead** has one line of symmetry – the diagonal as shown.

13. **A semi-circle** has one line of symmetry – the perpendicular bisector of the diameter.

14. **A regular pentagon** has five lines of symmetry – the angle bisectors. They are also the perpendicular bisectors of its sides.

15.

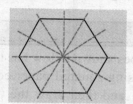

A regular hexagon has six lines of symmetry-the three diagonals through the centre and the three lines joining the mid-points of opposite sides.

16.

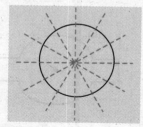

A circle has an infinite number of lines of symmetry-all lines along diameters.

32.5 Remarks

1. From the illustrations given above, it can be seen that a line of symmetry may be horizontal, vertical or oblique.
2. (*i*) A triangle can never have exactly two lines of symmetry.

   (*ii*) A quadrilateral can never have exactly three lines of symmetry.

   (*iii*) A regular polygon of *n* sides has *n* lines of symmetry.

Ex. 1. *Draw the lines of symmetry of the following figures.*

(*i*)

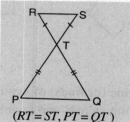

(RT = ST, PT = QT)

(*ii*)

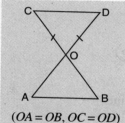

(OA = OB, OC = OD)

(*iii*)

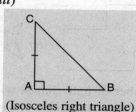

(Isosceles right triangle)

Sol. (*i*) *MN* - the angular bisector of ∠*RTS* (or ∠*PTQ*) is the line of symmetry.

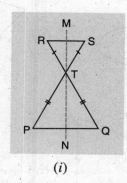

(*i*)

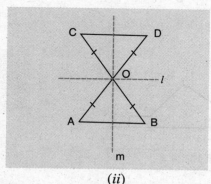

(*ii*)

(*ii*) The two lines of symmetry are *l* and *m*, which are the angular bisectors of ∠*AOC* and ∠*AOB* respectively.

(*iii*) Δ*ABC* is an isosceles right triangle with *AB* = *AC*. The line *l*. which is the angular bisector of ∠*A* is the line of symmetry.

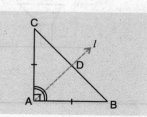

EXERCISE 32

1. Some of the shapes below have one axis of symmetry and some have more. State which of the drawings. (*i*) to (*viii*) have an axis of symmetry.

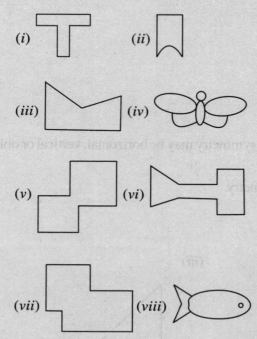

(*i*)   (*ii*)

(*iii*)   (*iv*)

(*v*)   (*vi*)

(*vii*)   (*viii*)

2. A number of half-shapes with the line of symmetry indicated by dotted line are shown below. Draw the complete symmetrical shape using squared paper.,

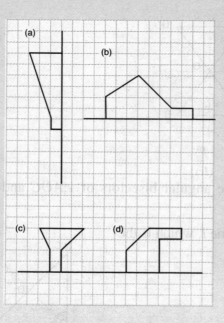

3. Each of the shapes shown below has two lines of symmetry. Using squared paper copy each of these shapes and then draw the two lines of symmetry.

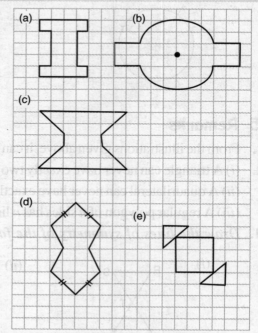

4. Draw the line (or lines) of symmetry if any, of the following shapes and count their number.

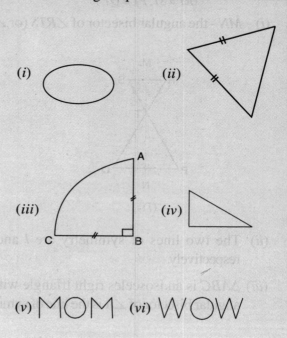

(*i*)   (*ii*)

(*iii*)   (*iv*)

(*v*) MOM   (*vi*) WOW

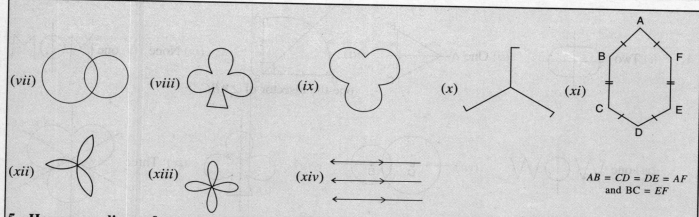

(vii)   (viii)   (ix)   (x)   (xi)

A

B   F

C   E

D

(xii)   (xiii)   (xiv)

AB = CD = DE = AF
and BC = EF

5. How many lines of symmetry do the following geometrical figures have ? Fill in the blanks.

1.   A scalene triangle _____   2.   An isosceles triangle _____
3.   An equilateral triangle _____   4.   A parallelogram _____
5.   A rectangle _____   6.   A rhombus _____
7.   An angle with equal arms _____   8.   A square _____
9.   A right triangle with equal legs _____   10.   An isosceles trapezium _____
11. A regular pentagon _____   12.   A regular hexagon _____
13. A circle _____   14.   A semi-circle _____

LOOKING BACK

Summary of Key Facts

1.   When a straight line divides a shape into two identical (congruent) shapes, the they are said to be **symmetrical** about the line. The line is called a **line of symmetry.** It is usually shown by a dotted line.

2.   A simple test to determine if a figure has a line symmetry is to fold the figure along the supposed line of symmetry. If the two halves of the figure coincide, the figure has line symmetry about that line, otherwise not.

ANSWERS

EXERCISE 32

1.   (i)   (ii)   (iv)   (vi)   (viii)

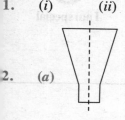

2.   (a)   (b)   (c)   (d)

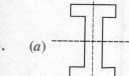 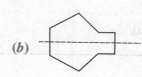 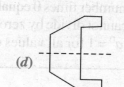 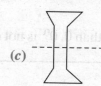

3.   (a)   (b)   (c)   (d)   (e)

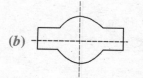 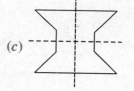 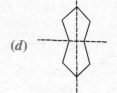 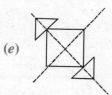

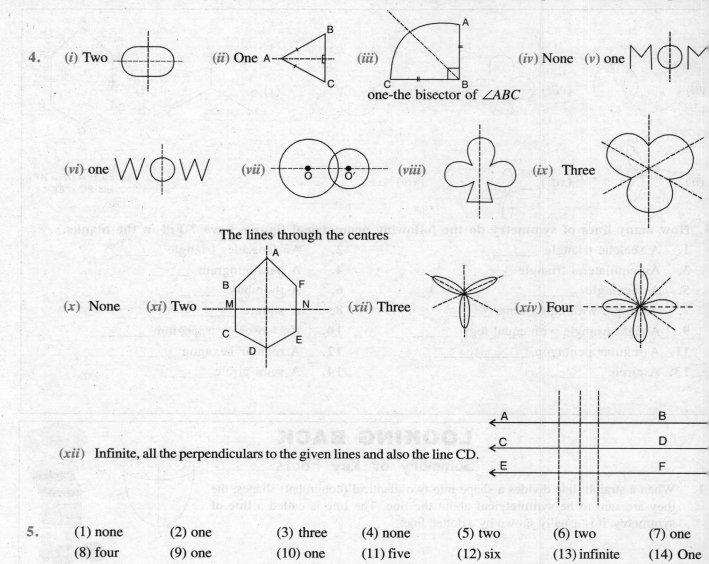

4. (i) Two   (ii) One   (iii)   (iv) None   (v) one

one-the bisector of $\angle ABC$

(vi) one   (vii)   (viii)   (ix) Three

The lines through the centres

(x) None   (xi) Two   (xii) Three   (xiv) Four

(xii) Infinite, all the perpendiculars to the given lines and also the line CD.

5.   (1) none   (2) one   (3) three   (4) none   (5) two   (6) two   (7) one

     (8) four   (9) one   (10) one   (11) five   (12) six   (13) infinite   (14) One

ZERO IS A SPECIAL NUMBER

Can you think of a number which is neither positive nor negative ? Zero is a special number. It is neither positive nor negative.

We say that a number is postive if it is greater than zero (thus zero cannot be positve), and a number is negative if it is less than zero (thus zero cannot be negative).

0 is the additive identity (which means adding 0 to a number doesn't change the number). Any number times 0 equals 0.

You cannot divide by zero

Also $a^0 = 1$ for all values of a other than 0, 0^0 is not defined.

0

I am special

33. Reflection

33.1 Introduction

The concept of reflection is a familiar one.

When you look into a mirror, the image that you see behind the mirror is the image that you see after reflection in the mirror. An image in the mirror is as far behind the mirror as the object is in front. That is why when you move towards the mirror, your image also seems to come closer.

Experiments in physics show that if A' is the **image of** A upon reflection in mirror m, then the line m is the perpendicular bisector of the line AA'. The line m is called the **mirror line** or the **reflection line**. As you will study later in this chapter this line is also called the line of symmetry.

If A' is the image of A after reflection in the line m, then the point A is called the **pre-image** of the point A'.

> *A reflection in a line produces a* **mirror image**. *The image is the same size but it is a reflection of the original shape.*

33.2 How to obtain the Image of a point after Reflection

To find the image of a point P after reflection in a line m, we mark a point P' on the other side of m at the same distance from the line as the original point such that the line joining the two points is perpendicular to the reflection line, that is $PP' \perp m$ and $PO = OP'$.

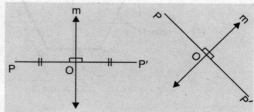

In the adjoining figure, X_1Y_1 is the image of XY under reflection in line m.

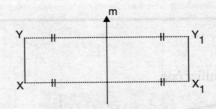

Images are as far behind the mirror line as the objects are in front.

If a point P lies on the reflection line m, then P is its own image.

Ex. 1. *Reflect this shape in the line of symmetry:*

Sol.

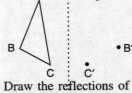

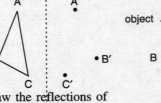

Draw the reflections of the points...

... and join them up.

The reflection of the point A is the point A'. You say 'A dash'.

Note that each point of the reflection is the same distance from the line of symmetry as the original point and AA', BB' and CC' are all perpendiculars to line m.

Ex. 2. **Reflect the given shape in the line m and *draw the image of* :**

    (*i*) *shape ABCDEF*   **(*ii*) *quadrilateral ABCD***

Sol. **(*i*)** The given shape is *ABCDEF*. You have to draw image after reflection in line m

    Step 1. Since point A lies on the mirror line its image is A itself. Similarly, image of F is itself.

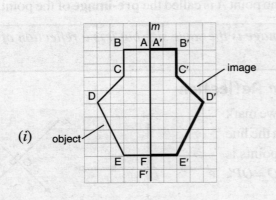

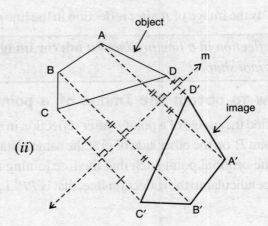

Draw a line from B at right angles to m. Extend the line to a point the same distance on the other side and lab the point B'. Repeat this for the points $C, D, E, and F$. Join the points to make the **reflected shape $A'B'C'D'E'F$**

(*ii*)   The given shape is *ABCD*. You have to draw its image after reflection in line m.

    Draw perpendicular from A to line m. Extend the line to a point the same distance on the other side and lab it A'. Repeat this for the points B, C and D. Join the points to make the **reflected image $A'B'C'D'$**.

eflect the shapes below in the mirror line and draw the images.

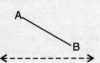

1.

2.

3.

4.

5.

3.3 Reflection in Coordinate axes

■ Reflection in the x–axis

Study the figure show alongside.

The figure shows the reflection of a few points in the *x*–axis. The image of point A(2, 3) is A′ (2, –3), that of B (4, –2) is B′ (4,2) and that of C (–3,–1) is C′ (–3,1). The point D is its own image as it lies on the mirror line i.e; the *x*–axis.

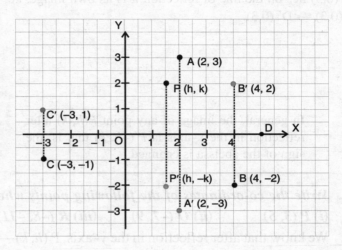

In general, the image of any point P(*h,k*) after reflection in the x–axis is P′ (*h,–k*), that is, the sign of the ordinate is changed.

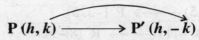

$$P\,(h, k) \longrightarrow P'\,(h, -k)$$

Change sign of the ordinate *k*.
REFLECTION IN the *x*-axis

Ex. 1. *Write the co-ordinates of the following points when reflected in x–axis:*

    (i) P(5, 7)   *(ii) Q (–3, 6)*   *(iii) R (8, –15)*   *(iv) H (–3, –8)*   *(v) A (5, 0)*

ol.   We know that after reflection in the *x*-axis, P (*h, k*) ⟶ P′(*h,– k*)

     ∴ After reflection in x–axis

(*i*)   P (5, 7) ⟶ P′ (5,–7)   (*ii*)   Q (–3, 6) ⟶ Q′ (–3,–6)

(*iii*)   R (8, –15) ⟶ R′ (8,15)   (*iv*)   H(–3, –8) ⟶ H′ (–3, 8)

(*v*)   Since point A lies on the *x*-axis, it is its own image i.e; A (5, 0) → A′ (5, 0)

■ **Reflection in y–axis.**

Study the figure shown alongside:

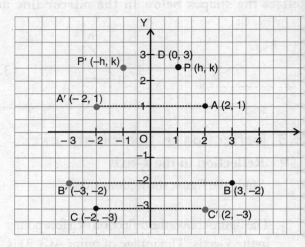

The figure shows the reflection of a few points in the y–axis. The image of point A(2, 1) is A′ (–2, 1), that of B(3, –2) is B′ (–3, –2) and that of C(–2, –3) is C′ (2, –3). Since the point D (0,3) lies on the line of reflection it is its own image, i.e; D(0,3) → D′ (0,3).

In general, the image of any point $P(h, k)$ after reflection in the y–axis is $P'(-h, k)$ that is, the sign of the abcissa is changed.

$$P(h, k) \longrightarrow P'(-h, k)$$

Change sign of the abscissa

REFLECTION IN the y-axis

Ex. 2. *Write the co-ordinates of the following points when reflected in the y–axis:*

   (i) P (3, 5)   **(ii) Q (–7, 9)**   **(iii) R (–8, –11)**   **(iv) M (4, 0)**   **(v) A (0, –6)**

Sol. We know that after reflection in the y–axis, $P(h, k) \longrightarrow P'(-h, k)$

   ∴ After reflection in the y–axis

   (i) $P(3, 5) \longrightarrow P'(-3, 5)$ (ii) $Q(-7, 9) \longrightarrow Q'(7, 9)$

   (iii) $R(-8, -11) \longrightarrow R'(8, -11)$ (iv) $M(4, 0) \longrightarrow M'(-4, 0)$

   (v) Since point A lies on the y–axis, which is the line of reflection, therefore it is its own imag i.e; $A(0, -6) \longrightarrow A'(0, -6)$.

EXERCISE 33 (b)

1. **State the co-ordinates of:**
   (*a*) points (i) (6,8)   (ii) (4, –5)   (iii) (–9,10)   (iv) (–2, –3) under reflection is the x-axis.
   (*b*) points (*i*) (3, 6)   (ii) (2, –5)   (iii) (–8, –14)   (iv) (–7, 9) under reflection in the y-axis

2. Write down the co-ordinates of the image of the poin (5, –6) when:
   (*i*) reflected in the x-axis   (*ii*) reflected in the y-axis
   (*iii*)reflected in the x-axis followed by the reflection in the y-axis;

3. (i) Point P(a, b) is reflected in the x-axis to P_1 (6, –4). Write down the values of *a* and *b*.
   (ii) P_2 is the image of P when reflected in the y-axis. Write down the co-ordinates of P_2.

4. A point P is reflected in the x-axis. Co-ordinates of its image are (7, – 5). Find the coordinates of P.
   Find the co-ordinates of the image of P under reflection in the y-axis.

5. Parallelogram ABCD has vertices A (–3, 2), B (5, 2), C (7, –1), D (–1, –1). Determine the image A′, B′, C′, D′ of A, B, C, D respectively under reflection in the x-axis.

6. The vertices of a △ ABC are A (2, 5), B (–3, 2) and C (6, 1). The figure is first reflected in the y-axis and then the new figure obtained is reflected in the x-axis. Draw the image figures.

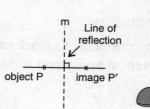

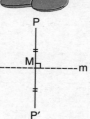

LOOKING BACK

Summary of Key Facts

1. The **reflection** (or image) of a point P in a line *m* is a point P' such that line *m* is the perpendicular bisector of the line segment PP'.

2. To find the reflection (or image) of a point P in a line *m*, drop perpendicular PM from P on *m* and extend it to P' such that PM = MP'. Then, P' is the image of P and AB is the reflection or **mirror line**.

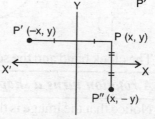

3. (*i*) A point P(x, y) has its image P''(x, −y) when reflected in the x-axis.
   (*ii*) A point P(x, y) has its image P'(−x, y) when reflected in the y-axis.

ANSWERS

EXERCISE 33 (a)

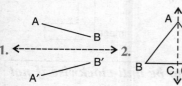 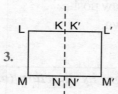 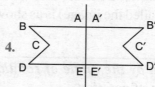 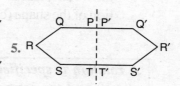

EXERCISE 33 (b)

1. (*a*) (*i*) (6, −8),   (*ii*) (4, 5),   (*iii*) (−9, −10),   (*iv*) (−2, 3)
   (*b*) (*i*) (−3, 6),   (*ii*) (−2, −5),   (*iii*) (8 −14)   (*iv*) (7,9)

2. (*i*) (5, 6),   (*ii*) (−5, −6),   (*iii*) (− 5, 6)

3. (*i*) a = 6, b = 4,   (*ii*) (−6, 4)   4. P (7, 5), Reflection in y-axis (−7, 5)

5. A(−3, −2), B(5, −2), C(7, 1), D(−1, 1)

6. On reflection in the y–axis A' (−2, 5), B' (3, 2) C' (−6, 1). Then on reflection in x–axis, A'(−2, −5), B'(3, −2), C'' (−6, −1)

34. Rotation

34.1 Introduction

The minute hand of a clock **rotates** (turns) about a point near one of its ends. A blade of a pair of scissors rotates about a point part way along its length.

 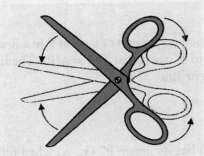

The clock hand and the scissors blade **turn through an angle** about a fixed point.

> *A rotation turns a shape through an angle about a fixed point.*

Notice that the image is the same shape and size as the original shape.

Activity :

Draw a shape like the one shows in Fig. (i) on a piece of card board and take its cut-out. Mark the point O on it. Keeping it fixed, rotate the cut out through half a turn (180°) clockwise. You will see that the new position of the shape (called the image) is as shown.

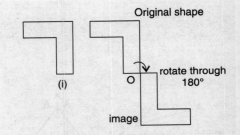

> *A rotation is specified by the angle of rotation, its direction (assumed to be anti-clockwise if not stated) and the centre of rotation.*

Thus in the figure at the right, the shape A has been given a rotation of 60°, anticlockwise about the point P. After a rotation the pre-image and the image are congruent.

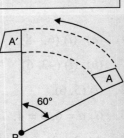

34.2 To Construct the Image of a Figure Under Rotation

Study the following examples :

Ex. 1. *Show the image of segment AB under a clockwise rotation of 90° about a given point O.*

Sol. Let *AB* be the given segment and *O* the point about which *AB* is rotated clockwise through 90°.

We have to show the image of AB after this rotation.

Method :

Step 1. Join *OA* and *OB*.

Step 2. Draw $\angle AOA' = 90°$ making $OA' = OA$.

Step 3. Draw $\angle BOB' = 90°$ making $OB' = OB$.

Step 4. Join A' to B'.

Then $A'B'$ is the image of AB after a clockwise rotation of $90°$ about the point O.

The point O is the centre of rotation. You can check by measurement that $A'B' = AB$.

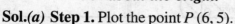

Ex. 2. **(a)** *Show the image of a point P (6, 5) under an clockwise rotation of 90° about the origin.*

(b) *Show the image of a point P (4, 5) under an anticlockwise rotation of 90° about the origin.*

Sol.(a) **Step 1.** Plot the point P (6, 5).

Step 2. Join OP.

Step 3. Construct $\angle POP' = 90°$ making $OP' = OP$. Then $P'(5 - 6)$ is the image of P.

(b) **Step 1.** Plot the point P (4, 5).

Step 2. Join OP.

Step 3. Construct $\angle POP' = 90°$ making $OP' = OP$. Then $P'(-5, 4)$ is the image of P.

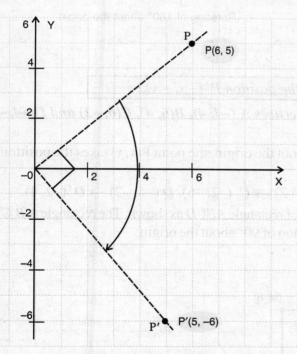

Clockwise Rotation of 90°

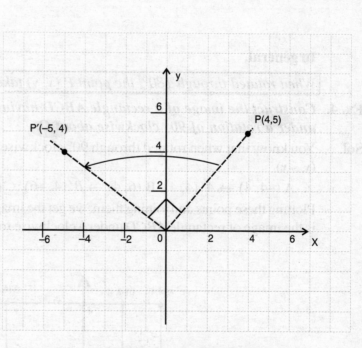

Anticlockwise Rotation of 90°

Notice that point P (6, 5) takes the position (5, –6) under clockwise rotation of 90° and point P'(4, 5) takes the position (–5, 4) under anticlockwise rotation of 90°.

In general,

(i) *When rotated thought 90° clockwise, point P(x, y) takes the position P'(y, – x).*

(ii) *When rotated through 90° anticlockwise, point P (x, y) takes the position P' (– y, x).*

Aid to Memory :

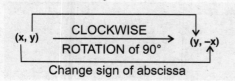

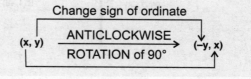

Notice that in both cases, **abscissa becomes ordinate and ordinate becomes abscissa in the image point.**

Ex. 3. *Show that the image of a point P (4, 5) under a rotation of 180° about the origin.*

Sol.   1. Plot the point $P(4, 5)$.

2. Construct $\angle POP' = 180°$ making $OP' = OP$.

(Note that the position of P' is the same for both clockwise and anticlockwise rotations.

Then, $P'(-4, -5)$ is the image of P.

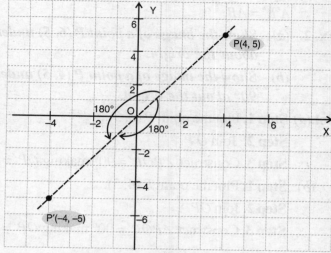

Rotation of 180° about the origin

In general,

When rotated through 180°, the point P (x, y) takes the position P′(− x, − y).

Ex. 4. *Construct the image of a rectangle ABCD having vertices A (−4, 4), B(6, 4), C(6, −2) and D(−4, −2) under a rotation of 90° clockwise about O.*

Sol.   You know that when rotated through 90° clockwise about the origin, the point P(x, y) takes the position P′ (y, −x)

∴ $A(-4, 4) \rightarrow A'(4, 4)$, $B(6, 4) \rightarrow B'(4, -6)$, $C(6, -2) \rightarrow C'(-2, -6)$, $D(-4, -2) \rightarrow D'(-2, 4)$.

Plotting these points and joining them, we get the image of rectangle $ABCD$ as shown. The rectangle $A'B'C'D'$ is the image of rectangle $ABCD$ under a clockwise rotation of 90° about the origin.

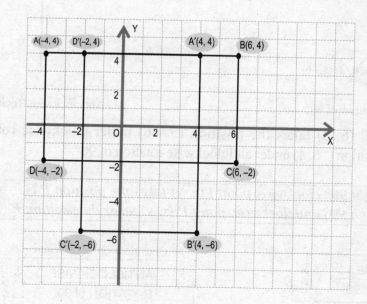

EXERCISE 34

Plot the following points on a graph paper and show their images under the indicated rotations.

1. *A* (3, 5) through 90° clockwise.

2. *B* (– 4, –6) through 90° clockwise.

3. *P* (7, –4) through 90° clockwise.

4. *D* (–5, –6) through 90° anticlockwise.

5. *K* (3, –4) through 90° anticlockwise.

6. *H* (–6, –8) through 180°

7. *R* (0, 6) through 180°

8. Plot the points *P*(–3, 4) and *Q* (4, 6) on the graph paper. Rotate the line segment *PQ* about the origin through (*i*) 90° clockwise (ii) 180° to the position *P' Q'*. Write down the coordinates of *P'* and *Q'* in each case. Are *PQ* and *P' Q'* equal.

9. Δ*ABC* has vertices *A* (3, 3), *B*(6, 3) and *C*(6, 5). Plot these points on graph paper and join then to form Δ*ABC*. Draw the image of Δ*ABC* after a rotation of 90° about the origin and mark it *A' B' C'*. Write down the coordinates of *A'*, *B'* and *C'*.

   [**Note :** Rotation is assumed to be anticlockwise if not stated.]

10. A square *PQRS* has vertices *P* (4, 3), *Q*(–3, 3), *R*(–3, –4) and *S*(4, –4). It is rotated through 180° about the origin. *O*. Construct its image *P'Q'R'S'*.

LOOKING BACK

Summary of Key Facts

1. A rotation is defined by the angle of rotation, direction of rotation (assumed to be anti-clockwise if not stated) and the centre of rotation.

(*i*) A point *P* (*x*, *y*) takes the position (*y*, –*x*) when rotated clockwise through 90°.

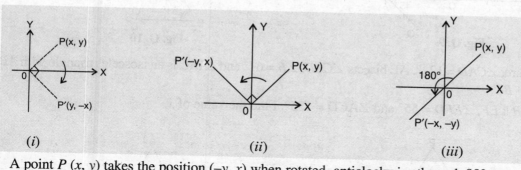

| (*i*) | (*ii*) | (*iii*) |

(*ii*) A point *P* (*x*, *y*) takes the position (–*y*, *x*) when rotated anticlockwise through 90°.

(*iii*) A point *P* (*x*, *y*) takes the position (–*x*, –*y*) when rotated clockwise through 180°.

UNIT REVIEW – 5

1. If two angles are supplementary and one angle is 20° more than three times the other, find the angles.

2. In the adjoining diagram find the value of *x* and *y*.

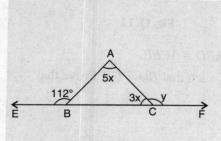

Fig. Q. 2

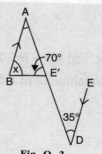

Fig. Q. 3

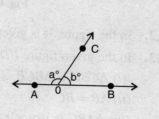

Fig. Q. 4

3. In the given figure $AB \parallel DE$. find the value of x.

4. In the given figure, $\angle AOC$ and $\angle BOC$ form a linear pair. If $a - b = 80°$, find the value of a and b.

5. In the figure, $PQ \parallel MN$. Find the value of x.

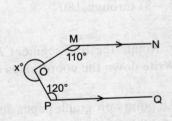

Fig. Q. 5

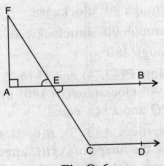

Fig. Q. 6

6. In the figure, $AB \parallel CD$ and $\angle F = 40°$. Find $\angle ECD$.

7. Construct an isosceles triangle having base $AB = 5.3$ cm and $\angle B = 75°$. Measure $\angle C$.

8. Construct a triangle PQR given $PQ = 5.6$ cm, $\angle P = 45°$ and $\angle Q = 60°$. Measure $\angle R$. From R draw a perpendicular to PQ.

9. In the diagram $AB \parallel CD \parallel FG$ and $DE \parallel CF$. Find x, y and z.

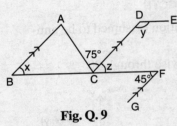

Fig. Q. 9

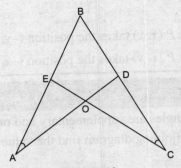

Fig. Q. 10

10. In the given figure, $\angle CAD = 122°$, AE bisects $\angle CAD$, $\angle B = 61°$ and $\triangle ABC$ is an isosceles triangle with $AB = AC$. Prove that $AE \parallel BC$.

11. In the figure, $AB \parallel EF$, $\angle EFD = 55°$ and $\angle ACD = 135°$. Find the value of x.

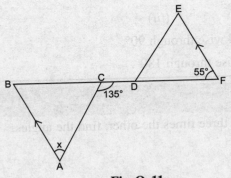

Fig. Q. 11

Fig. Q. 12

12. In the figure, it is given that $\angle A = \angle C$ and $AB = BC$. Prove that $\triangle ABD \cong \triangle CBE$.

13. In the given figure BD and CE are two altitudes of a triangle ABC, such that $BD = CE$. Prove that

    (i) $\triangle CBD \cong \triangle BCE$

    (ii) $AB = BC$

    (iii) $\triangle ABC$ is isosceles.

14. In the given figure, it is given that $AB = CD$ and $AD = BC$. Prove that $\triangle ADC \cong \triangle CBA$.

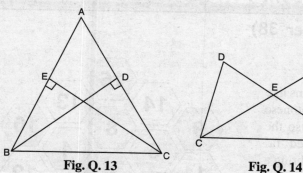

Fig. Q. 13

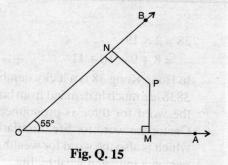

Fig. Q. 14

Fig. Q. 15

15. In the given figure, find the measure of $\angle MPN$.

16. Find the measure of each angle of a regular polygon having 18 sides.

17. Construct a square, one of whose diagonals is 4.5 cm.

18. Construct a rectangle $ABCD$ in which $AB = 5.3$ cm and diagonal $AC = 6.3$ cm. Measure AD.

19. A hexagon has two equal angles of 95° each, other two equal angles each of 105° each. Find the measure of the remaining two equal angles.

20. Triangle ABC is formed by joining the points A (1, 1), B (2, 1) and C (1, 2). Draw this triangle on the graph paper.

(a) Draw the image of $\triangle ABC$ after reflection in the x – axis and mark it as $A'B'C'$.

(b) Draw the image of $\triangle ABC$ after reflection in the y – axis and mark it as $A''B''C''$.

21. From the word **EXACT,** write down all the letters that have.

(i) a vertical line of symmetry.

(ii) a horizontal line of symmetry.

(iii) both

22. P' is the image of $P(-5, -8)$ in the x–axis and P'' is the image of P' in the y–axis. What are the coordinates of P' and P''?

ANSWERS

EXERCISE 34

1. A′ (5, –3)
2. B′ (–6, 4)
3. P (–4, –7)
4. D′ (6, –5)
5. K′ (4, 3)
6. H′ (6, 8)
7. (0, –6)
8. (i) P′ (4, 3), Q′ (6, –4)

   (ii) P′ (3, –4), Q′ (–4, –6) ; yes PQ = P′ Q′
9. A′ (–3, 3), B′ (–3, 6), C′ (–5, 6)

10.

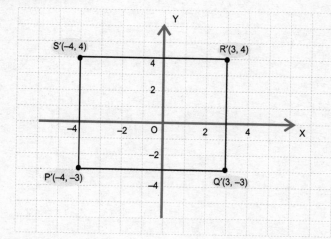

UNIT REVIEW– 5

1. 40°, 140°
2. $x = 14°$, $y = 138°$
3. $x = 75°$
4. $a = 130°$, $b = 50°$
5. $x = 230°$
6. $\angle ECD = 130°$

9. $x = 45°$, $y = 135°$, $z = 45°$
11. $x = 80°$
15. 125°
16. 160°
19. 160° each.

22. P′ = (–5, 8), P″ = (5, 8)

FUN WITH NUMBERS

(The Number 38)

$38 = 2 \times 19$

$\quad = 8 + 9 + 10 + 11$

In Hong Kong 38 is a lucky number and car registrations like 3838 are much in demand from business people. In Cantonese the word for three is pronounced 'sam' which is also the Cantonese word for life. Similarly, eight is pronounced 'fa' which is also the word for wealth. So lucky 38 should bring a person a long and wealthy life.

■ Every row of numbers in this magic hexagon adds up to the same total 38. There are 15 different ways you can make 38.

This pattern was discovered by an American railway clerk named Clifford. Adams It took him 47 years to discover this arrangement. It was proved later by one Charles Trigg that no other magic hexagon of any size was possible.

The only possible magic hexagon.

35. Perimeter and Area

35.1 Perimeter

The total boundary length of a closed figure is called its perimeter. The commonly used units of perimeter are metre (m) and centimetre (cm).

35.2 Area

The amount of surface enclosed by a closed figure is called its area. The units of area generally used are cm^2 and m^2.

35.3 Perimeter and Area of a Rectangle

Let us take a rectangle ABCD with length = l units and breadth = b units.

$$\text{Perimeter} = AB + BC + CD + DA$$
$$= (l + b + l + b) \text{ units}$$
$$= 2(l + b) \text{ units} = 2(\text{length} + \text{breadth})$$
$$\textbf{Area} = (l \times b) \text{ sq units} = \text{length} \times \text{breadth}$$

$$\therefore \textbf{Length} = \frac{\textbf{Area}}{\textbf{Breadth}}, \textbf{Breadth} = \frac{\textbf{Area}}{\textbf{Length}}$$

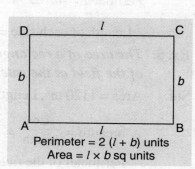

Perimeter = 2 ($l + b$) units
Area = $l \times b$ sq units

35.4 Perimeter and Area of a Square

Let us take a square ABCD with one side = a units.

$$\text{Perimeter} = AB + BC + CD + DA$$
$$= (a + a + a + a) \text{ units} = \textbf{4a units.}$$
$$\textbf{Area} = (a \times a) \text{ sq. units.} = \textbf{\textit{a}}^2 \textbf{ sq units.}$$

$$\therefore \textbf{Side of square} = \sqrt{\textbf{Area}}.$$

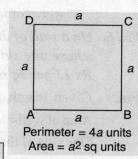

Perimeter = 4a units
Area = a^2 sq units

35.5 Measures of Area

1 cm = 10 mm	$\Rightarrow$	1cm^2 = 10 mm × 10 mm = 100 mm^2
1dm = 10 cm	$\Rightarrow$	1 dm^2 = 10 cm × 10 cm = 100 cm^2
1 m = 100 cm	$\Rightarrow$	1 m^2 = 100 cm × 100 cm = 10000 cm^2
1 dam = 10 m	$\Rightarrow$	1 dam^2 = 10 m × 10 m = 100 m^2
1 km = 1000 m	$\Rightarrow$	1 km^2 = 1000 m × 1000 m = 1000000 m^2

1 Are = 100 m^2

1 hectare (1 ha) = 100 m × 100 m = **10000 m^2**

35.6 Solved Examples

Ex. 1. *A rectangular garden is 42 m long and 25 m wide. Find its perimeter and area :*

Sol.   Length = 42 m, breadth = 25 m

Perimeter = 2 (length + breadth)

= 2 (42 + 25) m = (2 × 67) m = **134 m.**

Area = length × breadth

= (42 × 25) m^2 = **1050 m^2.**

Ex. 2. *The area of a rectangular plot is 630 m². Its breadth is 15 m. Find its length and perimeter.*

Sol. Area = 630 m² and breadth = 15 m $\quad \therefore$ Length $= \dfrac{\text{Area}}{\text{breadth}} = \dfrac{630}{15} = $ **42 m.**

Length of rectangular plot = 42 m.

$\therefore$ Perimeter $= 2(42 + 15)$ m $= 2 \times 57$ m = **114 m.**

Ex. 3. *Find the area, in hectare, of a square field whose one side measures 125 m.*

Sol. Area of the square field $= (\text{side})^2 = (125 \times 125)$ m² $= 15625$ m²

10000 m² $= 1$ hectare $\therefore 15625$ m² $= \dfrac{15625}{10000}$ hectare = **1.5625 ha.**

Ex. 4. *The perimeter of a square garden is 444 m. Find the area of the garden ?*

Sol. Let the length of one side of the garden be *a* m.

Perimeter $= 4a \Rightarrow 4a = 444 \Rightarrow a = \dfrac{444}{4} = 111$ m.

$\because$ Length of each side = 111 m. $\quad \therefore$ Area $= (\text{side})^2 = (111 \times 111)$ m² = **12321 m².**

Ex. 5. *The area of a rectangular field is 1120 m². Its length is 40 m. Find the cost of fencing the boundary of the field at the rate of Rs 3.20 per metre.*

Sol. Area = 1120 m², Length = 40 m

$\therefore$ breadth $= \dfrac{\text{Area}}{\text{length}} = \dfrac{1120}{40}$ m = 28 m.

$\therefore$ Perimeter of the field $= 2 (40 + 28)$ m $= 2 \times 68$ m = 136 m

$\therefore$ The cost of fencing the boundary of the given field = Rs (136×3.20) = **Rs 435.20.**

Ex. 6. *On a wall of dimensions 10.5 m long and 8.5 m wide, square shaped wall poster is stuck at the centre whose one side is 2.5 m. If the remaining part of the wall is to be painted with pink colour costing Rs 12 per sq m find the amount spent.*

Sol. Given, length of wall = 10.5 m, breadth of wall = 8.5 m.

Area of wall= length × breadth $= (10.5 \times 8.5)$ m² $= 89.25$ m²

One side of the poster = 2.5 m.

$\therefore$ Area of the poster$= (2.5 \times 2.5)$m² $= 6.25$ m²

$\therefore$ Area of remaining part of the wall = Area of the wall – Area of the poster $= 89.25$ m² $- 6.25$ m² $= 83$ m².

Amount spent in painting the remaining wall = Rs (12×83) = **Rs 996.**

Ex. 7. *Find the area of the shaded figure :*

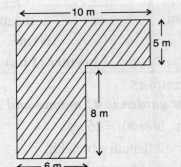

Sol. The figure can be divided into two rectangles by drawing dotted line.

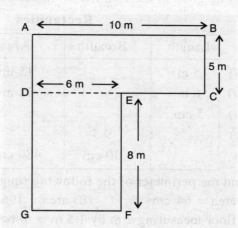

Area of rectangle ABCD = (10 × 5) m² = 50 m²
Area of rectangle DEFG = (6 × 8) m² = 48 m²
∴ Area of the given figure = (50 + 48) m² = **98 m²**.

Ex. 8. *The cost of cultivating a square field at the rate of Rs 360 per hectare is Rs 3240. What is the cost of putting a fence around it at the rate of Rs 15 per metre.*

Sol. Area of the square field $= \dfrac{\text{Total cost}}{\text{Cost per hectare}} = \dfrac{3240}{360} = 9$ ha.

∴ Area of the square field = 90000 m² (∵ 1 hectare = 10000 m²)

⇒ Side of the square field = $\sqrt{90000}$ = 300 m.

∴ Perimeter of the square field = (4 × 300) m = 1200 m.

∴ The cost of putting a fence round the square field = Rs (15 × 1200) = **Rs 18000.**

Ex. 9. *A room measures 12 m × 9 m. The floor of the room is to be covered by marble tiles measuring 45 cm by 30 cm. How many tiles are needed?*

Sol. No of tiles needed $= \dfrac{\text{Area of the floor}}{\text{Area of one tile}} = \dfrac{12 \times 9}{0.45 \times 0.3}$

$= \dfrac{12 \times 9}{\dfrac{45}{100} \times \dfrac{3}{10}} = \dfrac{12 \times 9 \times 100 \times 10}{45 \times 3} = \textbf{800.}$

EXERCISE 35 (a)

1. Find (*a*) the perimeter (*b*) the area of each shape.

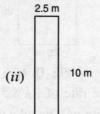
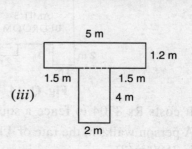

(*i*) 5 cm, 3 cm   (*ii*) 2.5 m, 10 m   (*iii*) 5 m, 1.2 m, 1.5 m, 1.5 m, 4 m, 2 m

2. Find (*i*) the area (*ii*) the perimeter of the square PQRS if its one side equals.

(*i*) 20 cm   (*ii*) 15 cm   (*iii*) 1.2 m   (*iv*) 25 mm

3. Copy and complete the following table :

Rectangles

	Length	Breadth	Area	Perimeter
(*i*)	5 m		15 m^2	
(*ii*)	8 m		32 m^2	
(*iii*)	5 cm			16 cm
(*iv*)		9.5		49 cm
(*v*)		30 cm	480 cm^2	

4. Find the perimeter of the following squares :

(*i*) area = 64 cm^2 (*ii*) area = 196 cm^2 (*iii*) area = 2.25 m^2 (*iv*) area = 5.76 m^2

5. A floor measuring 2 m by 1.5 m is to be covered with tiles measuring 25 cm square. How many tiles will be needed ?

6. A metal plate measuring 32 cm by 12 cm is cut up into small squares of side length 4 cm. How many squares will be cut ?

7. Which of the following has a larger area and by how much ?

(*i*) A rectangle of length 24 cm and breadth 17 cm.

(*ii*) A square of side 21 cm.

8. Find the area, in hectare, of a field whose length is 240 m and breadth 110 m.

9. The area of a rectangular field is 0.5 ha. If one side is 12.5 m, find the other side in metres.

10. A rectangular piece of plastic sheet measures 1 m by 70 cm. Find its cost at the rate of Rs 80 per square metre.

11. The length and breadth of a playground are 80 m and 35 m respectively.

(*i*) Find the cost of levelling it at Rs 4.50 per square metre.

(*ii*) How long will a boy take to go three times round the field, if he walks at the rate of 1.5 m per second ?

12. How many envelopes can be made out of a sheet of paper 125 cm by 85 cm; supposing one envelope requires a piece of paper of size 17 cm by 5 cm?

13. Two plots of land have the same perimeter. One is a square of side 60 m, while the other is a rectangle whose breadth is 1.5 dam. Which plot has the greater area and by how much?

14. Find the area of the floor in Amit's bedroom shown in the figure.

15. Find the area of the stage and the floor space in hall.

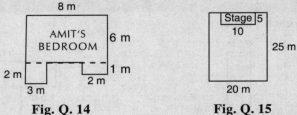

Fig. Q. 14   **Fig. Q. 15**

16. It costs Rs 8704 to fence a square field at the rate of Rs 8.5 per metre. Find the area of the field.

17. A person walks at the rate of 4 km/hr. How long will he take to go round a square park 5 times, whose area is 2500 m^2?

35.7 Areas of Rectangular Paths

Type 1 : *Paths running around (inside or outside) a rectangular shape.*

Ex. 1. *A garden is 90 m long and 75 m broad. A path 5 m wide is to be built outside all around it along its border. Find the area of the path.*

Sol. Let ABCD represent the garden and the shaded region as shown in the figure the path around it. From the figure, we have

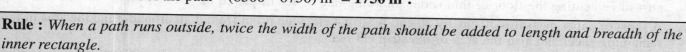

$$\text{Area of the path} = \begin{pmatrix} \text{Area of the} \\ \text{Rectangle} \\ \text{EFGH} \end{pmatrix} - \begin{pmatrix} \text{Area of the} \\ \text{Rectangle} \\ \text{ABCD} \end{pmatrix}$$

EF = 75 m + 5 m + 5 m = 85 m, EH = 90 m + 5m + 5m = 100 m

$\Rightarrow$ Area of the rectangle EFGH = 85 m × 100 m = 8500 m^2

Area of the rectangle ABCD = 90 × 75 m^2 = 6750 m^2

$\therefore$ Area of the path = (8500 – 6750) m^2 = **1750 m^2**.

> **Rule :** *When a path runs outside, twice the width of the path should be added to length and breadth of the inner rectangle.*

Ex. 2. *A path 1 m wide is built along the border inside a square park of side 30 m. Find the cost of covering the remaining portion of the park by grass at the rate of Rs 2 per sq m.*

Sol. Let ABCD represent the park. Then the shaded portion represents the path 1 m wide. The unshaded portion EFGH is the remaining portion. From the figure

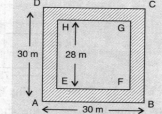

EF = 30 m – 1 m – 1 m = 28 m

EH = 30 m – 1 m – 1 m = 28 m

Area of the remaining portion (EFGH) = (28 × 28) m^2 = 784 m^2

Cost of covering 1 m^2 of area by grass = Rs 2

$\therefore$ Cost of covering 784 m^2 of area by grass = Rs (784 × 2) = **Rs 1568**.

> **Rule :** *When the path runs inside, twice the width of path should be subtracted from the length and breadth of the outer rectangle.*

Type 2. Central Paths, *i.e., when paths are constructed in the centre of the field.*

Ex. 3. *A grassy plot is 80 m × 60 m. Two cross paths each 4 m wide are constructed at right angles through the centre of the field, such that each path is parallel to one of the sides of the rectangle. Find the total area used as path.*

Sol. From the figure,

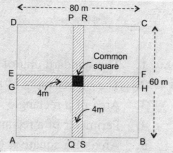

Area of the path EFHG   = (80 × 4) m^2 = 320 m^2

Area of the path PQRS   = (60 × 4) m^2 = 240 m^2

Area of the common square   = (4 × 4) m^2 = 16 m^2

Area of two cross paths   = (320 + 240 – 16) m^2 = 544 m^2

Hence the total area of the paths = **544 m^2**.

> **Note :** From the figure, we observe that the dark shaded area (4 m × 4 m) has been taken twice, because it has been included in both paths EFHG and PQSR. So in order to get the total area of the cross paths, we need to subtract this area from the sum of the areas of the two paths.

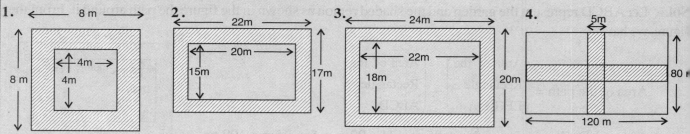

EXERCISE 35 (b)

Find the area of the shaded portion in each case.

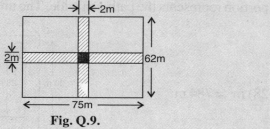

5. A photograph of sides 35 cm by 22 cm is mounted onto a frame of external dimension 45 cm by 30 cm. Find the area of the border surrounding the photograph.

6. A verandaah 1.25 m wide is constructed all along the outside of a room 5.5 m long and 4 m wide. Find the cost of cementing the floor of this verandah at the rate of Rs 15 per sq m.

7. A sheet of paper measures 30 cm by 20 cm. A strip 4 cm wide is cut from it all around. Find the area of the remaining sheet and also the area of the strip cut out.

8. The side of a square flower-bed is 1 m 80 cm long. It is enlarged by digging a strip 20 cm wide all around it. Find the area of the enlarged flower-bed and also the increase in area of the flower-bed.

9. Find the area of the crossroads at right angles to each other through the centre of the field.

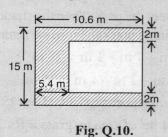

Fig. Q.9.   **Fig. Q.10.**

10. Find the area of the shaded portion. All corners are right-angled.

11. A rectangular lawn 80 m × 60 m has two roads each 10 m wide running in the middle of it, one parallel to the length and the other parallel to the breadth. Find the cost of gravelling them at Rs 1.20 per sq metre.

12. A floor which measures 15 m × 8 m is to be laid with tiles measuring 50 cm by 25 cm. Find the number of tiles required. Further, if a carpet is laid on the floor so that a space of 1 m exists between its edges and the edges of the floor, what fraction of the floor is uncovered ?

LOOKING BACK

Summary of Key Facts

1. The standard unit of area is 1 sq cm or 1 cm^2.
2. The bigger units of area are 1 m^2, **are, hectare,** etc.
3. Area of a rectangle = length × breadth.
4. Perimeter of a rectangle = 2 (lengh + breadth) = 2 ($l + b$)
5. Area of a square = (side)^2
6. Perimeter of a square = 4 × side
7. Area of a rectangular path inside (or outside) a rectangular field

                   = Area of the outer rectangle – Area of the inner rectangle.

8. Area of cross paths = Area of all the rectangles making the paths – Area of the common rectangles (or squares)

MENTAL MATHS – 22

1. Area of a square is 169 cm². Find its side.

2. The perimeter of a rectangle is 36 m. Its length is 10 m. What is its breadth?

3. 48 cm² = _____ mm²

4. 5 hectare = _____ m²

5. The perimeter of a square garden is 36 m. Find its area.

6. A room is 25 m long and 10 m wide. A 20 m² carpet is laid on the floor. How much area is not carpeted ?

7. The area of a square garden is 400 m². Find the distance travelled by a person if he takes 20 rounds of the garden.

8. Area of a rectangle is 24 x^2 m². Length = 6 xm, find the breadth.

ANSWERS

EXERCISE 35 (a)

1. (*i*) 16 cm, 15 cm²   (*ii*) 25 m, 25 m²   (*iii*) 20.4 m, 14 m²

2. (*i*) 80 cm, 400 cm²   (*ii*) 60 cm, 225 cm²   (*iii*) 4.8 m, 1.44 m²   (*iv*) 100 mm, 625 mm²

3. (*i*) Breadth = 3 m, Perimeter = 16 m   (*ii*) Breadth = 4 m, Perimeter = 24 m   (*iii*) Breadth = 3m, Area = 15 m²

   (*iv*) Length = 15 cm, Area = 142.5 cm²   (*v*) Length = 16 cm, Perimeter = 92 cm

4. (*i*) 32 cm   (*ii*) 56 cm   (*iii*) 6 m   (*iv*) 9.6 m   5. 48   6. 24

7. Square by 33 cm²   8. 2.64 ha   9. 400 m   10. Rs 56   11. (*i*) Rs 12600   (*ii*) 7 min 40 sec

12. 125   13. Area of square plot greater by 2025 m²   14. 56 m²   15. Stage → 50 m², Floor area → 450 m²

16. 65536 m²   17. 15 min

EXERCISE 35 (b)

1. 48 m²   2. 74 m²   3. 84m²   4. 975 m²   5. 580 cm²   6. Rs 450   7. 264 cm², 336 cm²

8. 4.84 m², 1.6 m²   9. 270 m²   10. 101.8 m²   11. Rs 1560   12. 960, $\dfrac{7}{20}$

MENTAL MATHS–22

1. 13 cm   2. 8 m   3. 4800 mm²   4. 50000 m²   5. 81 m²   6. 230 m²   7. 1.6 km

8. 4 x m.

Volume and Surface Area
36. of Solids

36.1 Cuboid

A **cuboid** is a rectangular solid. A brick, a book, a match box and an almirah all have the form of a cuboid.

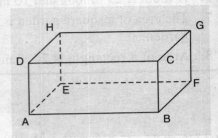

The figure here shows a cuboid having eight **vertices** *A, B, C, D, E, F, G* and *H*. It has **six faces** which are the rectangles *ABCD, EFGH, CDHG, ABFE, ADHE* and *BCGF*. It has **twelve edges** which are the line segments *AB, BC, CD, DH, HG, GC, GF, AE, DA, HE, BF* and *EF*. The vertices *A, B, F, E, D, C, G, H* are its corners.

36.2 Cube

A cube is a rectangular solid whose all edges are equal. A chalk-box, a die, a packing case having all sides equal, a room measuring $4 \text{ m} \times 4 \text{ m} \times 4 \text{ m}$ all have the form of a cube. The figure at the right shows a cube whose **six faces** are the squares *ABCD, CDEF, EFGH, ABGH, BCFG* and *ADEH*.

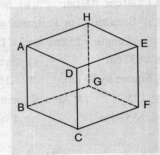

Its **edges** are *AB, BC, CD, DE, EF, FG, GH, HA, AD, HE, BG* and *CF* which are all equal line segments.

36.3 Volume

The capacity of a solid (how much it will hold, or how much space a solid occupies) is called the **volume** of the solid. You may also say that measurement of the interior of a solid figure is called its volume.

To measure the volume of a solid, a unit of measure is needed.

To measure the length of a line, (one dimension), we used as a measurement, a part of a line.

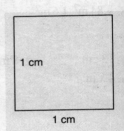

To measure the area of a plane figure, such as a rectangle, (two dimensions), we used as a measuring unit, a part of the plane.

Now to measure the volume of a solid, (three dimensions), we shall use a part of a solid as our measuring unit. This unit of measure for the volume of a solid is a cube. Common units of volume are the cubic centimetre (cm^3) and the cubic metre (m^3).

Here is a picture of a 1 centimetre cube.

Each of its edges is 1 cm long.

This cube has a volume of 1 cubic centimetre (1 cm^3).

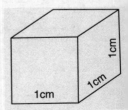

Volume = 1 cm³

The measure of the volume of a soild is the number of cubes contained in it.

Let us now find the volume of an empty box which is 4 cm long, 3 cm wide, and 2 cm high.

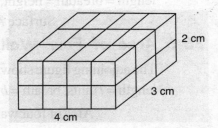

We place a layer of cubes at the bottom of the box. This layer contains 12 cubes. Since the box is 2 cm high, we could place 2 layers of 12 cubes each in the box. Hence the box will hold 2 layers of 12 cubes, or 24 cubes. ($2 \times 12 = 24$). The volume of the box is 24 cm cubes or 24 cubic centimetres. It is written as $V = 24\ cm^3$.

It the number of units in the length, width, and height were multiplied ($4 \times 3 \times 2 = 24$), the result would be equal to the number of cubes in the solid.

If we denote the volume by V and the length, breadth and height by l, b and h respectively, we can write the following formula for volume of a cuboid :

	$V = lbh$
i.e.,	$V = length \times breadth \times height$
	$= Area\ of\ the\ base \times height\ (Ah)$
Volume of cube	$= a^3\ where\ a\ denotes\ its\ edge.$
Also,	$l = \dfrac{V}{b \times h},\ b = \dfrac{V}{l \times h},\ h = \dfrac{V}{l \times b}$
and	$a = \sqrt[3]{V}\ ;\ i.e.\ one\ edge\ of\ a\ cube = cube\ root\ of\ its\ volume.$

emember that

A 10 cm cube holds 1 litre of water. Since a 10 cm cube has a volume of

($10cm \times 10cm \times 10cm$) = $1000\ cm^3$, therefore,

$$\boxed{1\ litre = 1000\ cm^3 = 1\ dm^3}$$

Also $1m^3 = 1m \times 1m \times 1m = 100\ cm \times 100\ cm \times 100\ cm$

$$= 1000000\ cm^3 = (1000 \times 1000)\ cm^3 = 1000 \times 1\ litre = 1000\ litres = \mathbf{1\ kilolitre = 1\ k}l$$

$$\boxed{1\ k\ l = 1m^3}$$

6.4 Surface Area of a cuboid

The sum of the areas of all the six faces of a cuboid is its total surface area. The given diagram shows a cuboid with length = l units, breadth = b units and height = h units.

There are three pairs of congruent faces : Front and back, Right and Left and, Top and Bottom.

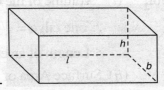

Area of (front or back) = $l \times h$

Area of (Right or left) = $b \times h$

Area of (top or bottom) = $l \times b$

∴ Total surface area of the cuboid = Area of front and back faces + Area of Right and left faces + Area of top and bottom faces.

$$= 2\ lh + 2bh + 2\ lb$$

$$= 2\ (lh + bh + lb)$$

36.5 Surface Area of a Cube

Sum of the areas of all six faces of a cube is its total surface area. Since a cube has all its dimensions equal, i. length = breadth = height, therefore, its each surface is a square. Number of faces in a cube being six

Surface Area of a cube = 6 × Area of one face = 6 × (side)²

36.6 Area of Four Walls of a Room :

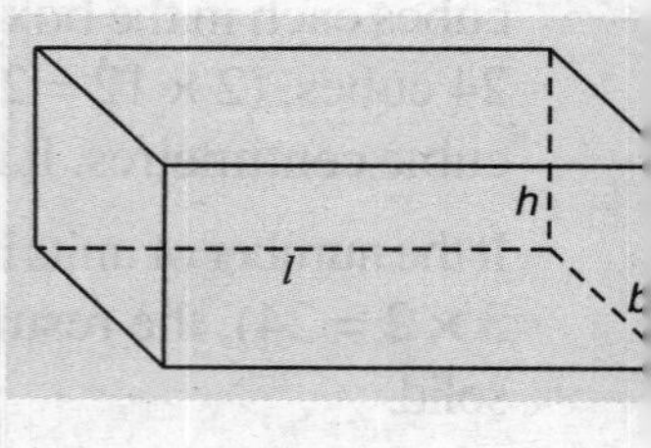

The adjoining figure shows a rectangular room with
length = *l* units, breath = *b* units and height = *h* units.

Area of four walls = Area of front and back walls +
                    Area of left and right walls

= 2 *lh* + 2*bh*

= 2 (*l* + *b*) × *h*

= *Perimeter of the floor × height of the room*

Surface area of a cuboid	= **2 (*lb* + *bh* + *lh*) sq units**
	= **2 (length × breadth + breadth × height + length × height)**
Surface area of a cube	= **6*a*² sq units**
	= **6 (side)²**
Area of four walls	= **2 (*l* + *b*) × *h***
	= **Perimeter of the floor × height of the room.**

36.7 Solved Examples

EX. 1. *Find the volume and surface area of a cuboid whose dimensions are :*

(a) **Length = 9 cm, breadth = 3.5 cm, height = 4cm**

(b) **Length = 1.6 m, breadth = 80 cm, height = 120 cm.**

Sol. (a) Given *l* = 9 cm, *b* = 3.5 cm, *h* = 4 cm

Volume of the cuboid   = *l* × *b* × *h* = (9 × 3.5 × 4) cm³ = **126 cm³**.

Surface Area of the cuboid   = 2 (*l b* + *bh* + *l h*) = 2 (9 × 4 + 3.5 × 4 + 9 × 3.5) cm²

= 2 (36 + 14 + 31.5) cm² = 2 × 81.5 cm² = **163 cm²**.

(b) Given *l* = 1.6 m, *b* = 80 cm = 0.8m, *h* = 120 cm = 1.2 m.

Volume of the cuboid   = *l* × *b* × *h* = (1.6 × 0.8 × 1.2)m³ = **1.536 m³**.

Surface Area of the cuboid   = 2 (*lb* + *bh* + *lh*) = 2 (1.6 × 0.8 + 0.8 × 1.2 + 1.6 × 1.2) m²

= 2 (1.28 + 0.96 + 1.92) m² = 2(4.16) m² = **8.32 m²**.

Ex. 2. *The Volume of a cube is 512 cm³. Find :*

(i) *the length of an edge*   (ii) *surface area of the cube.*

Sol.   (i)   Volume of the cube = (edge)³ = 512 cm³ = 2³ × 4³

∴ one edge = $\sqrt[3]{512}$ = 2 × 4 = 8cm.

∴ Length of an edge of the cube = **8 cm**.

(ii) Surface Area of the cube = 6 × edge² = (6 × 8 × 8) cm² = **384 cm²**

Ex. 3. *A beam 11 m long, 40 cm wide and 30 cm deep is made of wood which weighs 25 kg per m³. Find th weight of the beam ?*

Sol. $l = 11$m, $b = 40$ cm $= \dfrac{40}{100}$ m $= 0.4$ m, $h = 30$ cm $= \dfrac{30}{100}$ m $= 0.3$ m.

Volume of the beam $= l \times b \times h = (11 \times 0.4 \times 0.3)$ m^3. $= 1.32$m^3.

1 m^3 of beam weighs 25 kg

$\therefore$ 1.32 m^3 of beam weighs (1.32×25) kg $=$ **33 kg.**

Ex. 4. *Rain falls in a tank of base area 30 m × 24 m. Find the height to which it will fill the tank if the total volume of water is 36 m³.*

Sol. Volume of water in the tank $=$ base area $\times$ height of the tank

$\therefore$ 36m$^3 = 30$m $\times 24$m $\times$ height $\Rightarrow$ height $= \dfrac{36}{30 \times 24}$ m $= \dfrac{1}{20}$ m $= \dfrac{1}{20} \times 100$ cm $=$ **5cm.**

Ex. 5. *A hall has dimensions 34m × 24m × 8m. Find the cost of white washing the four walls at the rate of Rs 10 per m².*

Sol. Given $l = 34$ m, $b = 24$ m and $h = 8$m.

Area of 4 walls $= 2 (l + b) h = 2 (34 + 24) \times 8$ m$^2 = (58 \times 16)$m$^2 = 928$m^2

$\therefore$ Cost of white washing the four walls at the rate of Rs 10 per m$^2 = $ Rs $928 \times 10 = $ **Rs 9280.**

Ex. 6. *A village has a water tank measuring 25m by 16 m by 8 m, which is full of water. How many persons can use the water if each person requires 200 litres of water?*

Sol. Given for the water tank : $l = 25$ m, $b = 16$m, $h = 8$m

Volume of the water tank $= l \times b \times h = (25 \times 16 \times 8)m^3 = 3200$ m^3

1m$^3 = 100 \times 100 \times 100$ cm^3 $= 1000000$ cm^3

$\therefore$ Volume of the water tank $= 3200 \times 1000000$ cm^3

Water required by one person $= 200$ litres $= 200 \times 1000$ cm^3 $\boxed{\because\ 1\ \text{litre} = 1000\ \text{cm}^3.}$

Number of people who can use the tank $= \dfrac{\text{Volume of water tank}}{\text{Water required by one person}}$

$= \dfrac{3200 \times 1000000}{200 \times 1000} = $ **16,000.**

Ex. 7. *Find the volume of wood required to make a closed box with external dimensions 30 cm by 25 cm by 20 cm where the thickness of wood is 3 cm.*

Sol. External length $= 30$ cm, External breadth $= 25$ cm, External height $= 20$ cm

To get the internal dimensions, we subtract double the thickness from each external dimension.

$\therefore$ Internal length $= 30$ cm $- 6$ cm $= 24$ cm, Internal breadth $= 25$ cm $- 6$ cm $= 19$ cm

Internal height $= 20$ cm $- 6$ cm $= 14$ cm.

External volume of the box $= (30 \times 25 \times 20)$ cm$^3 = 15000$ cm^3

Internal volume of the box $= (24 \times 19 \times 14)$ cm$^3 = 6384$ cm^3

$\therefore$ Volume of wood $=$ External volume $-$ Internal volume

$= 15000$ cm$^3 - 6384$ cm$^3 = $ **8616 cm³.**

Ex. 8. *A metal cube of edge 0.9m is melted and cast into cuboids whose dimensions are 30 cm by 15 cm by 10 cm. Find the number of cuboids.*

Sol.   **Cube :** Edge = 0.9 m = 90 cm, $\therefore$ Volume = $(90 \times 90 \times 90)$cm^3 = 729000cm^3.

Cuboid : l = 30 cm, b = 15 cm, h = 10 cm $\therefore$ Volume = $(30 \times 15 \times 10)$ = 4500cm^3

$\therefore$ Number of cuboids = $\dfrac{\text{Volume of cube}}{\text{Volume of one cuboid}} = \dfrac{729000}{4500}$ = **162.**

Ex. 9. *A swimming pool is 20m in length, 15m in breadth, 4 m in depth. Find the cost of cementing its floor and walls at the rate of Rs 12 per square metre.*

Sol. l = 20 m, b = 15 m, h = 4 m

Area of the floor	= $l \times b$ = (20×15)m^2 = 300m^2
Area of four walls	= $2 \times h(l + b)$ = $2 \times 4(20 + 15)$m^2 = (8×35) m^2 = 280m^2

$\therefore$ Total area to be cemented   = 300 m^2 + 280m^2 = 580 m^2

Cost of cementing 1m^2 surface area = Rs 12

$\therefore$ Cost of cementing 580m^2 surface area = Rs (12×580) = **Rs 6960.**

EXERECISE 36

1. **Find the volume and surface area of a cuboid whose dimensions are :**
   (*a*) length = 9cm, breadth = 6 cm, height = 4cm
   (*b*) length = 10.5m, breadth = 5m, height = 220 cm.

2. **Find the volume and surface area of a cube whose edge measures :**
   (*a*) 8 cm   (*b*) 11 m   (*c*) 0.7m.

3. The volume of a soap cake is 160cm^3. Its length and width are 10 cm and 5cm. find its height.

4. The surface area of a cube is 384 cm^2. Find its volume.

5. The volume of a cube is 1331 m^3. Find its surface area.

6. A cuboidal vessel is 10 cm long and 8 cm wide. How high should it be made so that it may hold 480 cubic centimetre of a liquid?

7. The area of the four walls of a room is 168m^2. The breadth and height of the room are 8 m and 6m respectively. Find the length of the room ?

8. A classroom is 12 m long, 7m wide and 4m high. Find the cost of repairing the walls and ceiling at the rate of Rs 15 per square metre.

9. Find the volume of the wood used to make a closed box of inner dimensions 35cm × 15cm × 24cm, the thickness of wood being 2cm.

10. The floor of a rectangular hall has a perimeter of 300 m, its height is 8m. Find the cost of white washing the four walls (including door, windows etc.) at the rate of Rs 9 per m^2.

11. How many bricks each measuring 25cm × 11.25 cm × 6cm will be needed to build a wall 8m long, 6m high and 22.5 m thick ?

12. A cuboidal block of metal measuring 60 cm × 40 cm × 0.5m was melted and recast into cubical blocks each with an edge of length 5 cm.
    (a) Find the number of cubes that can be made.
    (b) What is the cost of polishing the surfaces of the cubes at the rate of Rs 1.25 per cm^2 ?

13. The paint in a certain container is sufficient to paint an area equal to 1464 m^2. How many bricks of dimensions 11.5 cm × 10 cm × 6 cm can be painted out of this container?

4. Three cubes each of side 5 cm are placed together. Find the volume and surface area of the cube thus formed.

5. A rectangular water tank has 16200 litres of water. The floor of the water tank is 4.5m × 3m. Find the height of water in the tank.

6. In a shower, 5 cm of rainfall was there. Find the volume of water that fell on 2 hectares of land.
   [**Hint** 1 hectare = 10000 m².].

7. How many cubes of edge 8cm can be placed in a rectangular box of dimensions 32 cm by 24 cm by 20 cm?

8. A rectangular room is 8m long, 5m wide and 4m high. It has two doors 1.5m by 2m each and two windows 2m by 1.8m each. Find the cost of white washing the walls and ceiling of the room at the rate Rs 50 per m².

LOOKING BACK

Summary of Key Facts

1. Volume of a cuboid = (length × breadth × height) cubic units = Area of base × height.
   Total Surface Area of a cuboid = 2 (*lb* + *bh* + *lh*) square units.

2. Volume of a cube = (edge)³ cubic units.
   Total surface area of a cube = $6a^2$ square units where a = edge.

3. Area of 4 walls of a room = 2 (l + b) h Sq units = Perimeter of floor × height of room.

4. $1m^3 = 100 \text{ cm} \times 100 \text{ cm} \times 100cm = 1000000cm^3$, 1 litre = 1000 cm³, 1 m³ = 1000 litres
   = 1 kilo litre

MENTAL MATHS – 23

1. Find the volume of a cube whose one edge is 5cm.

2. The surface area of a cube is 24m².Find its volume.

3. Area of the floor of a swimming pool is 120m² and its height is 6m. Find the volume of the swimming pool.

4. The volume of a water tank is 4m³. What is its capacity in litres ?

5. The capacity of a cubical mug is 1 litre. Find its edge.

6. How many cubes each of side 3cm can be made from a cuboid whose dimensions are 10 cm by 9 cm by 3 cm ?

7. The edge of a cube is 6x cm. What is its volume?

8. How many cubical blocks of edge 3cm can be cut from another cubical block of edge 6cm.

9. The perimeter of the floor of a room is 100 m. Its height is 8 m. Find the area of the four walls of the room.

UNIT REVIEW – 6

1. Find the area and perimeter of   (a) [diagram: 8 m, 6 m, 2 m, 4 m, 4 m, 2 m, 6 m]   (b) [diagram: 3 cm, 6 cm, 6 cm, 5 cm, 3 cm, 6 cm, 10 cm]

2. A rectangle has the area equal to that of a square of side 80 cm. If the breadth of the rectangle is 20cm, find its length.

3. Find the height of the wall whose length is 4m and which can be covered by 2400 tiles of size 25 cm by 20 cm.

4. Find the area in cm² of a rectangle whose
   (a) length = 78 mm   breadth = 2.3 dm.
   (b) length = 5 m   breadth = 1.9 cm.

5. The area of a rectangular garden is 5 ares. If its length is 25 m, find its breadth.

6. What happens to the area of a square if its side is tripled ?

7. The total cost of flooring a room with Rs 7 per square metre is Rs 4340. The length of the room is 31m, find its breadth.

8. A hollow cubic container, without lid, has its inner surface area as 20cm². Find the edge of the container?

9. If the sum of all the edges of a cube is 36 cm, find the volume of the cube.

10. A cuboidal block of silver is 10cm long, 5 cm broad and 4.5 cm in height. From it, beads of volume 1.5 cm³ each are to be made. Find the number of beads that can be made from the block.

11. The outer dimensions of a closed wooden box are 12 cm by 10cm by 9cm. Thickness of wood is 1.5 cm. Find the total cost of wood required to make the box if 1cm³ of wood costs Rs 3.00.

12. How many planks each of which is 3m long, 15 cm broad and 6 cm thick can be prepared from a wooden block 9 m long, 75 cm broad, 54 cm thick ?

13. The capacity of a certain cuboidal tank is 45000 litres of water. Find the height of the tank if its base measures 9m by 2.5m.

14. Cubes A,B and C having edges 3 cm, 4 cm and 5 cm are melted and a new cube is formed. Find the edge of the new cube.

15. A birthday cake measuring 60 cm by 40 cm by 15 cm was ordered for a party. If each child in the party enjoys 240 cm³ of cake and the cake is finished, how many children attended the party ?

16. A village having a population of 3600, requires 125 litres of water per head per day. It has a tank 25 m long, 18 m broad and 5 m high. For how many days the water of the tank will last?

17. Two cubes each of volume 512 cm³ are joined end to end. Find the surface area of the resulting cuboid.

ANSWERS

EXERCISE - 36

1. (a) V = 216 cm³, SA = 228cm²   (b) V = 115.5 cm³,SA = 173.2m²

2. (a) V = 512 cm², SA=384cm²   (b) V=1331 m³, SA = 726 m²   (c) V = 0.343 m³, SA =2.94 m²

3. 3.2 cm   4. 512 cm³   5. 726 m²   6. 6cm   7. 6m   8. Rs 3540   9. 8148cm³

10. Rs 21600   11. 640000   12. (a) 960   (b) Rs 180000   13. 30,000   14. V = 375cm³, SA = 350 cm²

15. 1.2m   16. 1000 m³   17. 30   18. Rs 6540

MENTAL MATHS – 23

1.   125cm³   2. 8m³   3. 720 m³   4. 4000 litres   5. 10 cm   6.10   7. 216 x³ cm³   8. 8   9. 800 m²

UNIT REVIEW – 6

1. (a) A = 32m², Perimeter = 38m (b) A = 68 cm², Perimeter = 48cm   2. 320 cm   3. 30 m

4. (a) 179.4 cm² (b) 950 cm²   5. 20 m   6. 9 times   7.20 m   8. 2 cm   9. 27 cm³

10. 150   11. Rs 2106   12. 135   13. 2 m   14. 6 cm   15. 150   16. 5   17. 640 cm²

UNIT - VII STATISTICS

37. Frequency Distribution and Mean

37.1 Introduction

Statistics may be defined as the science of collection, presentation, analysis and interpretation of numerical data. Information is collected, presented and organized in the form of tables, graphs etc., analysed and then inferences are drawn from them.

(Plural of 'Datum')

37.2 Data

Considering the weights of 25 students of a class, measured in kg, we get the following information :

35, 28, 26, 30, 32, 35, 26, 31, 36, 28, 29, 30, 27, 26, 36, 30, 25, 28, 29, 28, 27, 28, 30, 32, 31

This collection of a particular type of information in the form of numerical figures is called **data.**

This data obtained in the original form is called **raw** *(or ungrouped)* **data.**

Each numerical figure in the data is called an **observation.**

37.3 Array

It is very difficult to draw any inference from this raw data. So we arrange it in *ascending* or *descending order* of size. The above data arranged in ascending order is :

25, 26, 26, 26, 27, 27, 28, 28, 28, 28, 28, 29, 29, 30, 30, 30, 30, 31, 31, 32, 32, 35, 35, 36, 36

> ***Arranging the observations of a data in ascending or descending order is called an array.***

38.4 Range

By presenting the data in the above manner we can get some information about the data.

Lowest weight = 25 kg   Highest weight = 36 kg

> ***The difference between the highest and lowest values of the observations in a given data is called its* range.**

Here the range = 36 – 25 = 11

37.5 Frequency Distribution

***The number of times a particular observation occurs is called its* frequency.**

The frequency of 26 kg in the above data is 3 and the frequency of 28 is 5.

We may represent the above data in a tabular form showing the frequency of each observation beside it as under :

Weights of children (in kg)	Tally Marks	Fequency
25	I	1
26	III	3
27	II	2
28	THL	5
29	II	2
30	IIII	4

31	||	2
32	||	2
35	||	2
36	||	2

The table showing the frequencies of various observations of data is called a **frequency distribution table** *or simply* **frequency table.**

We take each observation from the data and count them with the help of strokes called **tally marks.** For convenience we use tally marks in bunches of five i.e. the fifth one crossing the four diagonally.

HHH Five

Ex. 1. ***The marks scored by 35 students in a mathematics test were as under :***

60, 65, 100, 70, 85, 75, 95, 90, 65, 70, 80, 95, 70, 75, 75, 70, 80, 80, 70, 75, 85, 85, 70, 90, 75, 75, 80,
80, 85, 85, 90, 75, 75, 80, 80.

Prepare a frequency distribution table for the above data.

Sol. It is convenient first to arrange the given data is ascending order.

60, 65, 65, 70, 70, 70, 70, 70, 70, 75, 75, 75, 75, 75, 75, 75, 75, 80, 80, 80, 80, 80, 80, 80, 85, 85, 85, 85,
85, 90, 90, 90, 95, 95, 100.

The frequency distribution table for the above data is given below :

Score (s)	Tally	Frequency
60	|	1
65	||	2
70	HHH |	6
75	HHH |||	8
80	HHH ||	7
85	HHH	5
90	|||	3
95	||	2
100	|	1
Total		35

37.6. Mean

The *arithmetic mean* in statistics is the same as *'average'* in arithmetic.

37.7 Mean of Ungrouped or raw data

The mean of a set of data is found out by dividing the sum of all the observations by the total number of observations in the data. We denote the mean by $\overline{x}$ (read "x bar").

$$\text{Mean} = \overline{x} = \frac{\textbf{Sum of all the observations}}{\textbf{Number of observations}}$$

Ex.1. ***The daily maximum temperature recorded in °C at Delhi during the first week of July, 2005 was as under: 39, 37, 38, 28, 30, 35, 36. Find the mean temperature recorded.***

Sol. Mean temperature $= \dfrac{\text{Sum of observations}}{\text{Number of observations}}$

$= \dfrac{39 + 37 + 38 + 28 + 30 + 35 + 36}{7} = \dfrac{243}{7} = \textbf{34.7° C.}$

Ex. 2. *Following are the ages (in years) of 10 teachers in a school.*

  32, 41, 27, 54, 36, 25, 28, 57, 40, 38

  (i) *What is the age of the oldest teacher and that of the youngest teacher ?*

  (ii) *Find the range of the ages of the teachers.*

  (iii) *Find the mean age.*

Sol.   Arranging in ascending order, we get 25, 27, 28, 32, 36, 38, 40, 41, 54, 57

   From the above, we find that

   (i) Age of the oldest teacher   = 57 years

      Age of the youngest teacher = 25 years

   (ii) Range = (57 – 25) years   = **32 years.**

   (iii) Mean age = $\dfrac{\text{Sum of observations}}{\text{Number of observations}}$

   $= \dfrac{32 + 41 + 27 + 54 + 36 + 25 + 28 + 57 + 40 + 38}{10} = \dfrac{378}{10}$ years = **37.8 years.**

> **Note:** that for finding mean, it is not necessary to arrange the given data in an ascending or descending order.

37.8. Mean of Grouped Data

   If the observations $x_1, x_2, x_3, \ldots\ldots x_n$ have frequencies $f_1, f_2, f_3, \ldots\ldots f_n$ respectively, then their mean is given by the formula :

   $\text{Mean} = \bar{x} = \dfrac{f_1 x_1 + f_2 x_2 + f_3 x_3 + \ldots\ldots + f_n x_n}{f_1 + f_2 + f_3 + \ldots\ldots + f_n}$

   $= \dfrac{\sum fx}{\sum f}.$

$$\boxed{\bar{x} = \dfrac{\Sigma fx}{\Sigma f}}$$

   Σ (read as sigma) is a Greek letter which represents sum.

   In the above formula, Σfx represents the sum of the products of various values of f and x, i.e., $f_1 x_1, f_2 x_2, f_3 x_3$, etc. Σf represents the sum of the frequencies f_1, f_2, f_3, etc.

Ex. 3. *The heights in cm of 50 boys are given below. Calculate the mean height.*

Height	:	150	151	152	153	154	155
Frequency	:	**3**	**12**	**9**	**6**	**15**	**5**

Sol.   To calculate the mean, we construct the following table.

Height (in cm) (x)	Frequency (f)	(fx)
150	3	150 × 3 = 450
151	12	151 × 12 = 1812
152	9	152 × 9 = 1368
153	6	153 × 6 = 918
154	15	154 × 15 = 2310
155	5	155 × 5 = 775
Total	$\sum f = 50$	$\sum fx = 7633$

$\therefore \text{Mean} = \dfrac{\sum fx}{\sum f} = \dfrac{7633}{50} = 152.66 \text{ cm} = \textbf{152.7 cm}$ (correct to 1dp).

1. **Find the mean of each of the following set of numbers**
   (*a*) First 5 natural numbers   (*b*) First 7 whole numbers   (*c*) First 4 prime numbers
   (*d*) 1.3 cm, 5.7 cm, 9.8 cm, 6.4 cm, 6.9 cm   (*e*) Rs 7, Rs 19, Rs 31, Rs, 43, Rs 70

2. Seema obtained the following scores (out of 100) on a set of spelling tests :
   80, 85, 90, 71, 60, 100. What is her mean score ?

3. Shaleen's last six batting scores were 138, 144, 155, 142, 167, 172. What was his mean score ?

4. Madhu worked $2\dfrac{1}{2}$ hours on Monday, $3\dfrac{1}{4}$ hrs. on Tuesday, and $2\dfrac{3}{4}$ hrs. on Wednesday. What is the
   mean number of hours she worked on these three days?

5. Ayushree sat for six tests and Ananya sat for seven tests. Their percentage scores were:
   Ayushree :   68   75   70   45   57   77
   Ananya :   87   64   53   74   81   86
   Who has the higher mean score ?

6. Find the mean of first ten odd natural numbers.

7. If the mean of 16, 14, *x*, 23, 20 is 18, find the value of *x*.

8. If the mean of *x*, *x* + 2, *x* + 4, *x* + 6, *x* + 8 is 24, find *x*.

9. Madhu practised on her sitar 45 minutes, 30 minutes, 60 minutes, 50 minutes and 20 minutes. What was
   her mean practice time ?

10. Nisha scored 73, 86, 78 and 75 marks in four tests. What is the least number of marks she can score in
    her next test, if she has to have a mean score of 80 marks in five tests ?
    Find the mean of the following frequency distributions: (Use the formula Mean = $\dfrac{\sum fx}{\sum f}$)

11. | *x* | : 2 | 5 | 7 | 8 |
    |---|---|---|---|---|
    | *f* | : 2 | 4 | 6 | 3 |

12. | Weight (kg) | : | 30 | 31 | 32 | 33 | 34 |
    |---|---|---|---|---|---|---|
    | Number of students | : | 8 | 10 | 15 | 8 | 9 |

13. | *x* | : | 0.1 | 0.2 | 0.3 | 0.4 | 0.5 | 0.6 |
    |---|---|---|---|---|---|---|---|
    | *f* | : | 20 | 60 | 20 | 40 | 10 | 50 |

14. The marks scored in a test by a class of 25 boys are as follows :
    24   25   23   20   20   19
    22   20   24   22   18   23
    23   18   20   16   25   24
    17   18   23   22   23   20   24
    Draw a frequency table and caluclate the mean.

LOOKING BACK

Summary of Key Facts

. The collection of a particular type of information in numerical figures is called **data** e.g. heights of a particular number of students, marks of students in a particular subject etc.

. The data obtained initially are called **raw-data.**

. Arranging numerical figures of a data in ascending or descending order is called an **array.**

. The difference between the highest and lowest values of observations in a given set of data, is called the **range** of the data e.g. if highest marks in Mathematics in a class = 100 and lowest marks = 22, then range = 100 – 22 = 78 marks.

. The number of times a particular observation occurs is called its **frequency.**

. Mean of ungrouped data = $\bar{x} = \dfrac{\text{Sum of observations}}{\text{Number of observations}}$.

. Mean of grouped data = $\bar{x} = \dfrac{\sum fx}{\sum f}$,

Where f is the frequency corresponding to the observation x and Σ represents the **Sum.**

MENTAL MATHS – 24

. Find the range of the following data :

40, 65, 25, 30, 15, 55, 70, 5

. A die was thrown 15 times and the following outcomes were noted : (dice' is plural of 'die')

4, 3, 5, 2, 1, 1, 3, 4, 6, 2, 3, 5, 6, 5, 4.

Find the frequency of (*i*) 5 and (*ii*) 1 in the above data.

. Find the mean of the first 5 even members.

. Find the value of x if the arithmetic mean of 3, 5, 6, 2, 10 and x is 5.

. Find the mean from the following frequency distribution table :

x	15	40	30	10	20
f	20	10	5	15	30

ANSWERS

EXERCISE 37 (b)

(*a*) 3   (*b*) 3   (*c*) 4.25   (*d*) 6.02 cm   (*e*) Rs 34

81   3. 153   4. $2\frac{5}{6}$ hours.   5. Ananya   6. 10   7. 17   8. 20   9. 41 minutes.

). 88 marks   11. 6   12. 32 kg.   13. 0.355   14. 21.32 marks

MENTAL MATHS – 24

5   2. (*i*) 3   (*ii*) 2   3. 6   4. $x = 4$ 5. 20

38. Graphical Representation of Data

38.1 Introduction

The two forms which are generally used for presenting data are:

(i) Tables   (ii) Graphs.

We have dealt with the preparation of frequency distribution tables in the last chapter. Here we shall review th different types of graphs you have already studied in class VI, for representing the data pictorially. Thoug there are various types of graphs used to represent statistical data, we shall limit our study to the following:

(a) Bar Graphs   (b) Line Graphs   (c) Pie Chart.

38.2. Bar Graph

A bar graph is a pictorial representation of the numerical data by a number of bars of uniform width (wit different height), erected horizontally or vertically with equal spacing between them.

The examples given below will help you to revise the concept of bar graphs and the method of drawing then

Ex.1. *The following table shows the number of books of different subjects in a library.*

Subject	Physics	Chemistry	Biology	History	Geography	English	Maths	Compute
No. of Books	100	125	75	75	50	200	250	17

Draw a bar graph to represent the above data :

Sol. Take the subjects along the x – axis and the number of books along the y-axis. Construct the bars of sam width, with same distance between them.

Take the scale as 25 books = 5 small divisions or $\frac{1}{2}$ cm.

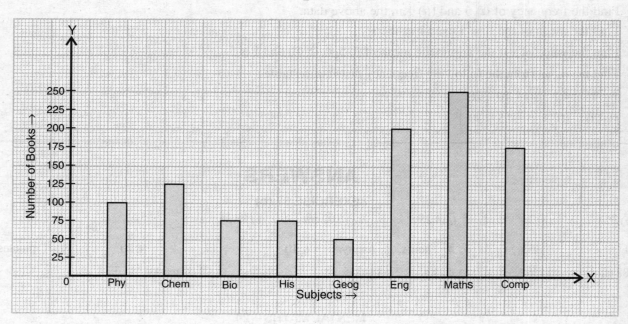

x. 2. *The following table shows the expenditure pattern of a family :*

Items	Food	Clothing	Rent	Education	Miscellaneous
Expenditure (inRs)	3500	2000	1500	2500	1000

Draw a bar graph to represent the above data.

ol. Take Items along the x–axis and expenditure along the y-axis. Here we take the scale as 1 cm = Rs 1000 or 10 small divisions = Rs 1000.

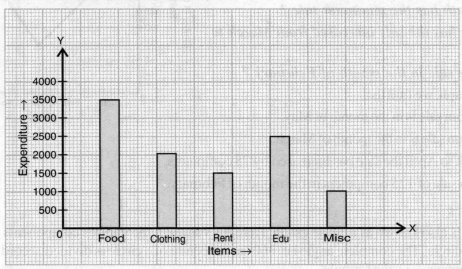

8.3. Line Graph

In a line graph, points are plotted on a graph paper with the help of two variables i.e. one along the x – axis and the other along the y – axis. Then these points are joined in pairs by lines to obtain line graphs.

x. 3. *The maximum temperature on first 10 days of June, 2005 in Delhi is given below.*

Date :	1	2	3	4	5	6	7	8	9	10
Max. Temp (in °C)	41	40.5	42	39	40	43	44	41.5	38	40

Draw a line graph to represent the above information.

Sol. Take dates along the x – axis and maximum temperatures along the y – axis. Take 10 small divisions or 1 cm = 1°C. Plot the points (1, 41), (2, 40.5), (3, 42), (4, 39), (5, 40), (6, 43) (7, 44), (8, 41. 5), (9, 38), (10, 40) and join them by line segments as shown. A **Kink (or break)** is indicated near the Origin in the direction of y – axis to show that the graph is drawn to scale beginning at 38, not at the origin.

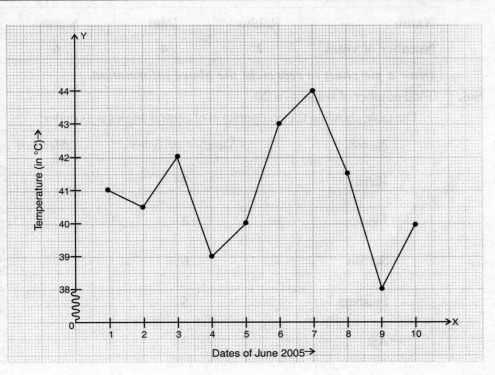

Ex. 4. *The adjoining line graph shows the number of computers sold by a shop during the first five months of the year.*

Answer the following questions by seeing the graph.

(*i*) *Which month has the maximum sale?*

(*ii*) *Which month has the minimum sale?*

(*iii*) *How much has the sale increased from March to April?*

(*iv*) *What is the sale in the month of February?*

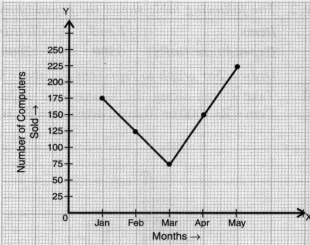

Sol. From the graph, we find that

(*i*) The maximum sale is in the month of May.

(*ii*) The minimum sale is in the month of March.

(*iii*) From March to April the sale has increased by 75 computers.

(*iv*) There was a sale of 125 computers in the month of February.

38.4 Pie Charts

A Pie chart is also known as a circle graph. Here the values of the various components are represented by sectors of a circle. The complete angle i.e. 360° at the centre of a circle is divided according to values of the various components by the formula.

$$\text{Central angle for a component} = \left(\frac{\text{Value of the component}}{\text{Total value}} \times 360\right)^{\circ}$$

It is called a pie chart because it resembles a 'pie.'

Ex. 5. *The following table shows the votes received by the students who stood for the election of the class monitor.*

Name	Rahim	John	Suman	Prashant	Ajit
Number of votes	2	4	6	5	3

Draw a pie chart to represent the above information.

Sol. Total number of students is 20.

∴ The table showing the computation of central angles is as under:

Name	Number of votes	Measure of the central angle
Rahim	2	$\frac{2}{20} \times 360° = 36°$
John	4	$\frac{4}{20} \times 360° = 72°$
Suman	6	$\frac{6}{20} \times 360° = 108°$
Prashant	5	$\frac{5}{20} \times 360° = 90°$
Ajit	3	$\frac{3}{20} \times 360° = 54°$

Draw a circle of any convenient radius. Now divide the interior of this circle into sectors of angles 36°, 72°, 108°, 90° and 54° with the help of your protractor. You will obtain the circle graph as shown on the right.

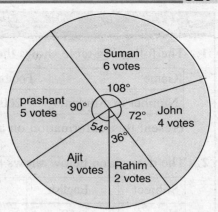

x. 6. *The way Mr. Sharma spends his allowance is given below. Draw the pie chart.*

Item	Per cent
Lunch	*25 %*
Hobby	*20 %*
Recreation	*40 %*
Saving	*15 %*
Total	*100 %*

ol. Represent the above information by a pie chart

Item	*Per cent*	*Fractional part*	*Central angle*
Lunch	25%	$\dfrac{25}{100} = \dfrac{1}{4}$	$\dfrac{1}{4} \times 360° = 90°$
Hobby	20%	$\dfrac{20}{100} = \dfrac{1}{5}$	$\dfrac{1}{5} \times 360° = 72°$
Recreation	40%	$\dfrac{40}{100} = \dfrac{2}{5}$	$\dfrac{2}{5} \times 360° = 144°$
Saving	15%	$\dfrac{15}{100} = \dfrac{3}{20}$	$\dfrac{3}{20} \times 360° = 54°$

Draw a circle of any convenient size.

Divide it into sectors of angles, 90°, 72°, 144° and 54°.

You obtain the required pie chart.

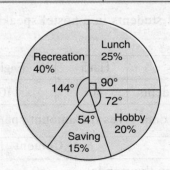

EXERCISE 38

1. The following table shows the number of students in a school playing five different games.

Game	Football	Hockey	Cricket	Tennis	Squash
Number of Students	200	175	250	75	50

Present this information on a bar graph.

2. The data given below shows the number of students opting for different subjects in a college.

Subject	English	Maths	Physics	Chemistry	Commerce
Number	50	60	45	25	40

(i) Consrtruct a bar graph for the above data.

(ii) Represent the above data also with the help of a line graph.

3. The following table gives the number (approx.) of competitors of different countries that took part in the Commonwealth Games held during the year 1986.

Country's name	U.K	Australia	U.S.A	China	Korea	Russia	Germany
Number of competitors	86	105	138	128	150	214	160

Draw a bar graph to represent the above data (Take scale 1 cm = 20 persons)

4. Draw the temperature-time line graph for the following data.

Time (in hours) :	5:00	8:00	11:00	14:00	17:00	20:00
Temperature in °C :	29	30	32	35	31	28

5. The number of acidents in a city during the first six months are given below:

Month	January	February	March	April	May	June
Number of accidents	45	35	39	46	25	32

Present the above information by a line graph.

6. The number of students in a hostel speaking different languages is given below. Present the data in a pie chart.

Language	Hindi	English	Marathi	Tamil	Bengali	Total
Number of students	40	10	8	8	6	72

7. The following data gives the amount spent on the construction of a house. Draw a pie chart.

Item	Cement	Timber	Bricks	Labour	Steel	Misc
Expenditure (in thousands)	50	35	45	70	50	60

8. The expenditure of a firm under different heads in term of percentage expenditure is given below. Draw a pie chart.

Item	Wages	Rent	Maintenence	Miscelleneous
Percentage	50	25	12.5	12.5

UNIT REVIEW – 7

1. The following data gives the number of students in classes 7A, 7B, 7C, 7D and 7E of a particular school.

Class	7A	7B	7C	7D	7E
Number of Students	30	32	35	33	28

Represent the above information by (i) bar graph (ii) line graph.

2. The survey of the favourite food-items of 50 children is given below. Represent the given data by a line graph.

Food Item	Pizza	Burger	Icecream	Chaat	Noodles
Number of Children	11	13	12	5	9

3. The number of students interested in taking part in various hobbies from class 7 of a particular school is as under:

Hobby	Music	Pottery	Dance	Drama	Social service
Number of students	20	25	27	28	20

Represent the above data by (*i*) Bar graph (*ii*) Line graph (*iii*) Pie chart.

4. Following data gives runs scored by various players in a particular match.

Player	Tendulkar	Ganguly	Dravid	Sehwag	Laxman	Yuvraj
Runs scored	30	25	56	75	48	15

[**Hint :** Take 1 cm or 10 small divisions = 10 runs)

Depict the above data by (*i*) Bar graph (*ii*) Line graph.

ANSWERS

EXERCISE 38

1.

2. (i)

(ii)

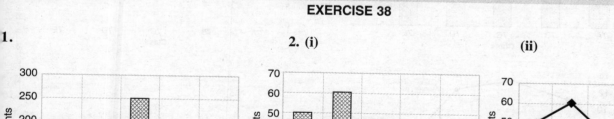
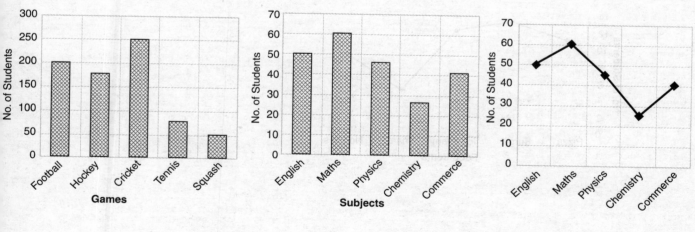

3.

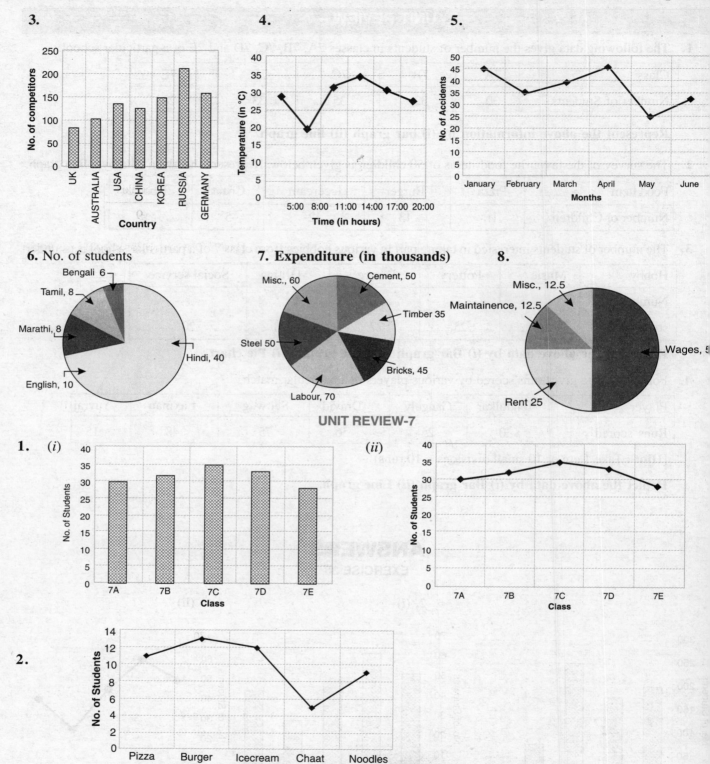

4.

5.

6. No. of students

7. Expenditure (in thousands)

8.

UNIT REVIEW-7

1. (*i*)

(*ii*)

2.

(i)

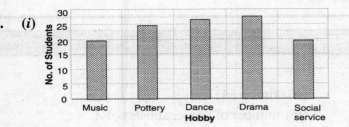

(ii)

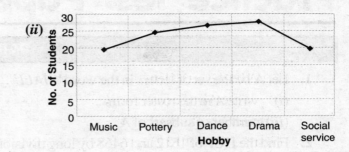

(iii)

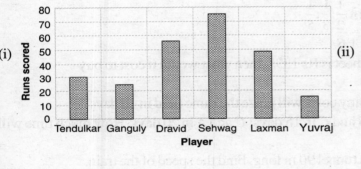

4. (i)

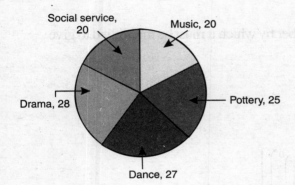

(ii)

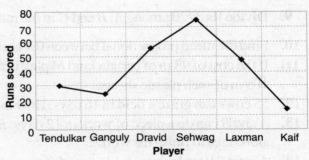

Practice Test Papers

1. Let A be the set of letters in the word "*HALL*".
   (*i*) write *A* in the roster form   (*ii*) find $n(A)$
   (*iii*) number of subsets of *A*   (*iv*) number of proper subsets of *A*.

2. Find the HCF of 1512 and 6468 by long division method.

3. **Simplify** : $\left(\dfrac{14}{0.35} + \dfrac{9}{0.36}\right) \div \left(\dfrac{14}{0.35} - \dfrac{9}{0.36}\right)$

4. Express 10584 in prime factors. What is the least number by which it must be multiplied to give
   (*i*) a perfect square   (*ii*) a perfect cube.

5. Write three fractions between $\dfrac{3}{7}$ and $\dfrac{9}{11}$.

6. **Express** (*i*) 2.15   (*ii*) $32.\overline{7}$ as fractions.

7. **Simplify** : $(6^2 - 2^2) \times \left(\dfrac{2}{3}\right)^{-3} + \left[(6^0 + 7^0) \div \left(8^0 + \left(\dfrac{1}{3}\right)^0\right) \right]$

8. Find the square root of 207025 by long division.

9. Divide Rs 3720 among *A*, *B* and *C* in the ratio $\dfrac{1}{2} : \dfrac{1}{3} : \dfrac{1}{5}$.

10. Find the mean proportional between 0.4 and 1.6.

11. If the cost of 93 m of certain kind of plastic sheet is Rs 1395, then what would it cost to buy 105 m of such plastic sheets.

12. 55 cows can graze a field in 16 days. How many cows will graze the same field in 10 days?

13. *A* and *B* can do a piece of work in 12 days; *B* and *C* in 15 days; *C* and *A* in 20 days. How much time will *A* alone take to finish the work ?

14. A train 210 m long took 12 seconds to pass a tunnel 90 m long. Find the speed of the train.

15. An alloy of copper and tin contains 105 parts of copper and 15 parts of tin. Find the percentage of copper in the alloy.

16. By selling a cycle for Rs 2640, Karim loses 12%. For how much should he sell it to gain 12%?

17. At what rate per cent per annum will Rs 1600 amount to Rs 2832 in $5\dfrac{1}{2}$ years ?

18. **Simplify** : $-6a^2(b - b^2) - 3b^2(2a^2 - a) - 2ab(b - a)$.

19. **Expand** : $(a^2b - bc^2)^2$.

20. **Simplify using** $(a - b)(a + b) = a^2 - b^2$
    (a) $(44)^2 - (39)^2$ (b) 90×110

21. **Factorize** : (a) $x^3 - y^2 + x - x^2y^2$ (b) $81x^4 - 121x^2$.

22. In the given figure : $PL \perp OB$ and $PM \perp OA$ such that $PL = PM$. Is $\Delta\, PLO \cong \Delta PMO$?
    Give reasons in support of your answer.

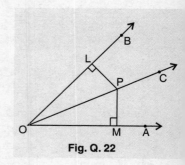

Fig. Q. 22

332

23. ABC is a Δ inscribed in a circle with centre O. If $\angle ABC = 40°$, find $\angle ACB$.

24. Construct a ΔPQR such that $PQ = 5.3$ cm. $\angle P = 65°$ and $\angle Q = 65°$. Draw its line (or lines) of symmetry.

25. The cover of a safety matchbox is 7 cm long, 4 cm wide and 2 cm high and its ends are open. Find the area of the exterior surface of the cover.

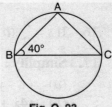

Fig. Q. 23

PAPER – 2

1. Let ξ = {natural numbers upto 10}, A = { even numbers}, B = {factors of 18}
   Find: (i) $A \cup B$ and $A \cap B$ (ii) A' and B'
          (iii) $(A \cup B)'$ and $A' \cap B'$ (iv) $(A \cap B)'$ and $A' \cup B'$
   Hence show that $n(A \cup B) = n(A) + n(B) - n(A \cap B)$.

2. Simplify : $20 - [6 - 4 + \{8 \div 2 - (2 \text{ of } 3 - \overline{3-2})\}]$

3. Find the greatest number of four digits which is exactly divisible by 6, 12, 15 and 18.

4. Find the greatest number which divides 1384 and 1456 leaving remainders 4 and 1 respectively.

5. Monica's monthly salary is Rs 24000. She spends $\frac{1}{4}$ of the salary on food and out of the remaining $\frac{1}{6}$ on rent

   and $\frac{1}{9}$ on the education of the children.

   Find : (i) how much does she spend on each part ?

          (ii) how much money is still left with her ?

6. **Work out :** $0.04 \times 0.89 \times 0.037$ and write your answer correct to two significant figures.

7. Convert $3.1\overline{3}$ to the form p/q.

8. **Evaluate :** $\dfrac{\sqrt[3]{9261} - \sqrt[3]{1728}}{\sqrt[3]{27} + \sqrt[3]{216}}$.

9. Mr. Lal weighed 85 kg. He reduced his weight in the ratio 17 : 13 Find his new weight.

10. 200 children in a hostel have provisions for 25 days. If 50 more children join them, how long will the provisions last now ?

11. The average weight of 20 students of a class is 35 kg. If one more student with weight 24.5 kg joins the class, what is the average weight of the students now?

12. **Simplify :** $(1^0 + 2^0 + 3^0) \div 3^{-1} \times \left[\left(\frac{2}{3}\right)^2 \div \left(\frac{6}{7}\right)^{-1}\right]$.

13. A car travels at 70 km/hr for $1\frac{1}{2}$ hours and at 90 km/hr for the next $2\frac{1}{2}$ hours. Find the average speed of the car.

14. If 75% of a number is added to 75, the result is the number itself. Find the number.

15. A discount of 12% is allowed on the marked price of an article. Find the marked price if the S.P = Rs 440.

16. If $s = \dfrac{n}{2}(a + l)$, express l in terms of s, n and a and find the value of l when $s = 30$, $n = 6$ and $a = 3$.

17. **Simplify :**

    (a) $(x - y)(x^2 + xy + y^2) - (x + y)(x^2 - xy + y^2)$

    (b) $(4x + 7y)^2 + (4x - 7y)^2 - [(4x + 7y)(4x - 7y)]$.

18. If $x + \dfrac{1}{x} = 9$, find the value of $x^2 + \dfrac{1}{x^2}$.

19. **Solve for x :** $\dfrac{5}{7}(3x - 2) = \dfrac{3}{4}(x + 1) + \dfrac{2}{3}x$.

20. A is twice as old as B is now. 6 years ago A was three times as old as B was then. What are their ages now?

21. Solve the linear inequation : $2x + 2 \leq 9, x \in W$.

22. Calculate the lettered $\angle^s$ in each case :

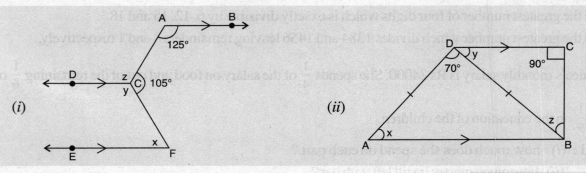

(iii) O is the centre of the circle, calculate the measure of $\angle PAB$.

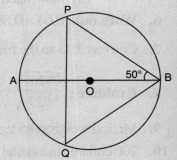

23. In the adjoining figure AO bisects $\angle A$ and $\angle ABO = \angle ACO$. Prove $\triangle ABO \cong \triangle ACO$ and hence prove $OB = OC$.

24. A rectangular park measures 28 m by 14m. A path 2.5 m is constructed all around it. Find the cost of paving the path with cement tiles 47 cm by 40 cm at the rate of Rs 4.80 per tile.

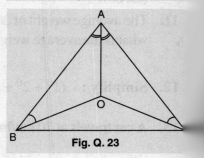

Fig. Q. 23

25. The following table shows the marks obtained (out of 20) by students in a test:

Marks	:	0	6	8	10	11	12	14	15
No. of students	:	4	5	6	3	4	3	2	3

Find the mean of the marks obtained.

PAPER – 3

1. From the adjoining Venn diagram find :

   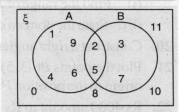

   (i) A (ii) B (iii) ξ

   (iv) A' (v) B' (vi) $A \cup B$

   (vii) $A \cap B$ (viii) $(A \cup B)'$ (ix) $(A \cap B)'$

2. Two numbers are co-prime and their L.C.M is 4800. If one of the numbers is 75, find the other.

3. **Simplify :** $\left[\left(3 - \dfrac{4}{5}\right) \div \left(2 + \dfrac{4}{7}\right)\right] \div \left[\left(2 - \dfrac{4}{13}\right) + \left(\dfrac{1}{2} + \dfrac{1}{9}\right)\right]$.

4. If 28 cows cost Rs 58,800, what will 11 cows cost? How many cows can be bought for Rs 52,500?

5. **Find the quotient of :**   (i) $1735.5 \div 3.25$ (ii) $672.88 \div 6.47$

6. Find the ratio of the area of a square of side 4 cm to the area of a square of side 6 cm.

7. If $a : b = 1\dfrac{1}{4} : 2\dfrac{1}{4}$ and $b : c = 3 : 4\dfrac{1}{2}$, express $a : b : c$ in simplest terms.

8. If 60% of students in a school are boys and the total number of girls in the school is 460, find the number of boys in the school.

9. If the cost price of 72 oranges is the same as the selling price of 64 oranges, find the gain per cent.

10. Divide $10b^2 + 9b + 8$ by $5b - 3$ and verify the result using Dividend = Divisor × Quotient + Remainder.

11. **Simplify :** $(2x + 3y)(3x + 4y) - (7x + 3y)(x + 2y)$

12. The length of a rectangle is 5 cm more than its breadth. If the perimeter of the rectangle is 70 cm, find its length and breadth.

13. In the adjoining figure $\angle ABP = \angle ACQ$,
    $\angle BAC = 68°$. Find $\angle ABC$, $\angle CBR$, $\angle RBP$ and $\angle PBA$.

    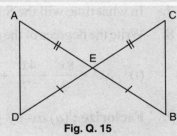

    Fig. Q. 13

14. The interior angle of a regular polygon is 156°, find the number of sides in the polygon.

15. In the adjoining figure, AB and CD intersect each other at E, such that $DE = BE$ and $EA = EC$, Show that $AD = CB$.

    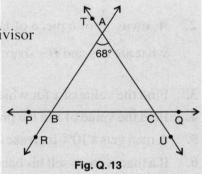

    Fig. Q. 15

16. If $PA = PB$, find :

    (a) $\angle DAP$ (b) $\angle CBP$

    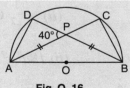

    Fig. Q. 16

    (c) $\angle CAB$ (d) $\angle DBA$

17. Change the subject of the formula $A = a(1 + 2kt)$ to k and evaluate k when $A = 35$, $a = 5$ and $t = 3$.

18. Using special products, **simplify :**

    (a) $\left(\dfrac{1}{4}x + \dfrac{2}{5}y\right)\left(\dfrac{1}{4}x - \dfrac{2}{5}y\right)$ (b) 9.4×8.6

19. The mapping is $R : x \rightarrow$ highest prime factor of x.
    (i) Find the range of R when the domain is $\{12, 13, 14, 15, 16, 17\}$.
    (ii) State the domain of five integers for which range is $\{3\}$.

20. Construct a right angled $\triangle PQR$ such that $PQ = 4.5$ cm. $\angle P = 90°$ and $\angle R = 60°$. Measure the hypotenuse QR.

21. Plot the points $P(-3, 5)$ and $Q(4, -6)$ on the graph paper. Rotate the line segment PQ through $180°$ about the origin to the position $P'Q'$. Write down the coordinates of P' and Q'. Are PQ and $P'Q'$ equal?

22. Rs 4000 amount to Rs 5000 in 5 years. What will Rs 3500 amount to at the same rate of simple interest in 3 years?

23. Draw an equilateral triangle on a side of length 5.6 cm. Draw all its lines of symmetry.

24. Construct a frequency table for the following data :
    25, 33, 24, 29, 30, 29, 24, 29, 24, 23, 21, 23, 21, 33, 23, 24, 28, 30, 29, 33.

25. The number of various cars sold by an auto dealer are given below:

Name of car :	Palio	Alto	Wagon-R	Matiz	Swift	Santro
Number of car :	150	200	250	100	40	260

Represent this information on a pie chart.

PAPER – 4

---

1. A wire in the form of a square encloses the area A^2 cm^2. What is the length of the wire?

2. A owns $\dfrac{3}{7}$ of a piece of land, B owns $\dfrac{2}{5}$ of it and C owns the remainder. If C's share is worth Rs 72000 what are A's and B's share worth?

3. Find the value of x for which $(2x + 3) : (5x + 10) = 1 : 4$.

4. Find the value of x in the proportion $x : \pi : : r^3 : r$.

5. A man gets a 10% increase in his salary. His new salary is Rs 10,285. What was his original salary?

6. If a man were to sell his handcart for Rs 720, he would lose 25%. What must he sell it for to gain 25%?

7. In what time will the S.I. on Rs 800 at 12.5% per annum be Rs 125?

8. Write the degrees of the polynomials given below.

    (i) $5x^4 - \dfrac{8x^3}{3} + \dfrac{4x^2}{7} + 3x - \dfrac{5}{2}$ (ii) $\dfrac{1}{x^2}(x^3 - x^4 + x^8)$

9. **Factorize :** (a) $ax - by + bx - ay$ (b) $18a^2 x^2 - 32$

10. The angle A of a triangle is $\dfrac{2}{3}$ times angle B and angle B is $\dfrac{3}{4}$ times angle C. Find the angle of the triangle.

11. A cistern can be filled by a tap in 4 hours and emptied by an outlet pipe in 6 hours. How long will it take to fill the cistern if both the tap and the pipe are opened together?

12. Walking at a speed of 5.4 km/hr, Rohan takes 40 minutes to reach his school from his house. What time will it take if he runs at 8 km/hr?

13. Draw a triangle ABC with $BC = 4.3$ cm, $AB = 3.8$ cm and $\angle B = 120°$. Also draw a perpendicular from A on BC (extended if necessary).

14. $\triangle ABC$ is an isosceles triangle with $AB = AC$ and $\angle A = 50°$ as shown in the given figure. Bisectors of $\angle B$ and $\angle C$ meet at O. Find:

    (a) $\angle ABC$ (b) $\angle OBC$ (c) $\angle ACB$

    (d) $\angle OCB$ (e) Is $OB = OC$ (f) $\angle BOC$

15. $\triangle ABC$ is isosceles with $AB = AC$

    AD is the perpendicular from A on BC. Is

    (i) $\triangle ABD \cong \triangle ACD$?

    (ii) State the pairs of matching parts used to answer.

    (iii) Is $BD = DC$?

16. The dimensions of a metallic cuboid are : 100 cm $\times 80$ cm $\times 64$ cm. It is melted and recast into a cube. Find the surface area of the cube.

17. The length and breadth of a room are in the ratio $3 : 2$. Its area is 216 m^2. Find its perimeter.

18. The following data shows the average age of men in various countries in a certain year.

Country :	India	Nepal	China	Pakistan	U.K.	U.S.A
Average Age : (in years)	58	53	62	55	68	72.

Represent the above information by a line graph.

19. The weights in kg of 60 workers in a factory are given in the following frequency table. Find the mean weight of a worker.

Wt. (in kg) (x) :	60	61	62	63	64	65
No. of workers (f) :	5	8	14	16	10	7

20. In the adjoining figure AC is the diameter of the circle whose centre is O. If $\angle ACD = 35°$ and $\angle CAB = 80°$, find $\angle BCD$ and $\angle BAD$.

21. Evaluate $\sqrt{0.008464}$ by long division.

22. Find the smallest number by which 53240 must be divided so that the quotient is a perfect cube.

23. Let $A = \{a, b, d, e\}$ and $B = \{d, e, f, g,\}$ be two subsets of the universal set $\xi = \{a, b, d, e, f, g,\}$. Verify the following :

    (i) $(A \cup B)' = A' \cap B'$ (ii) $(A \cap B)' = (A' \cup B')$

24. Solve $3 - x > -2$, $x \in N$.

25. (a) Draw the lines of symmetry in the given figure.

    (b) Mark the image of the point $(6, -3)$ on a graph paper when it is rotated about the origin through $90°$ in a clockwise direction.

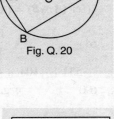
Fig. Q. 20

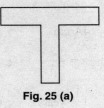
Fig. 25 (a)

ANSWERS

PAPER – 1

1. (i) $A = \{h, a, l\}$ (ii) 3   (iii) 8   (iv) 7

2. 84   3. $4\frac{1}{3}$ 4. (i) 6   (ii) 7

5. $\frac{15}{25}, \frac{12}{18}, \frac{21}{29}$ 6. (i) $\frac{43}{20}$ (ii) $\frac{295}{9}$

7. 109   8. 455

9. $A \to$ Rs 1800, $B \to$ Rs 1200, $C \to$ Rs 720

10. 0.8   11. Rs. 1575   12. 88 cows   13. 30 days

14. 90 km/hr.   15. 87.5%   16. Rs 3360   17. 14%

18. $(-4a^2b + ab^2)$ 19. $a^4b^2 - 2a^2b^2c^2 + b^2c^4$

20. (a) 415   (b) 9900

21. (a) $(x^2 + 1)(x - y^2)$ (b) $x^2(9x - 11)(9x + 11)$

22. Yes, $\because PL = PM, \angle PLO = \angle PMO = 90°$,
$OP = OP$ (common) $\therefore \Delta PLO \cong \Delta PMO$ (R.H.S)

23. $\angle ACB = 50°$ 24. 84 cm²

PAPER – 2

1. (i) $A \cup B = \{1, 2, 3, 4, 6, 8, 9, 10\}, A \cap B = \{2, 6\}$
(ii) $A' = \{1, 3, 5, 7, 9\}$
$B' = \{4, 5, 7, 8, 10\}$
(iii) $(A \cup B)' = \{5, 7\}$ $A' \cap B' = \{5, 7\}$
(iv) $(A \cap B)' = \{1, 3, 4, 5, 7, 8, 9, 10\}$
$A' \cup B' = \{1, 3, 4, 5, 7, 8, 9, 10\}$

2. 19   3. 9900   4. 15

5. Food $\to$ Rs 6000, Rent $\to$ Rs 3000 Ed. $\to$ Rs 2000
(iii) Rs 13000

6. 0.0013   7. $\frac{141}{45}$ 8. 1   9. 65 kg

10. 20 days   11. 34.5 kg   12. $\frac{24}{7}$ 13. 82.5 km/hr

14. 300   15 Rs 500   16. $l = \frac{2s}{n} - a, l = 7$

17. (a) $-2y^3$ (b) $16x^2 + 147y^2$ 18. 79   19. $x = 3$

20. $B = 12$ years, $A = 24$ years.   21. $\{0, 1, 2, 3\}$

22. (i) $x = 50°, y = 130°$ $z = 125°$
(ii) $x = 55°, y = 55°, z = 35°$
(iii) 40°

24. Rs 6000   25. 8.7

PAPER – 3

1. (i) $A = \{1, 2, 4, 5, 6, 9\}$
(ii) $B = \{2, 3, 5, 7\}$
(iii) $\xi = \{0, 1, 2, 3, 4, 5, 6, 7, 8, 9, 10, 11\}$
(iv) $A' = \{0, 3, 7, 8, 10, 11\}$
(v) $B' = \{0, 1, 4, 6, 8, 9, 10, 11\}$
(vi) $A \cup B = \{1, 2, 3, 4, 5, 6, 7, 9\}$
(vii) $A \cap B = \{2, 5\}$
(viii) $(A \cup B)' = \{0, 8, 10, 11\}$
(ix) $(A \cap B)' = \{0, 1, 3, 4, 6, 7, 8, 9, 10, 11\}$

2. 64   3. $\frac{13}{35}$ 4. Rs 23100; 25 cows

5. (i) 534 (ii) 104   6. 4 : 9   7. 10 : 18 : 27

8. 690   9. gain = 12.5%

10. $Q = 2b + 3, R = 17$ 11. $-x^2 + 6y^2$

12. $b = 15$ cm, $l = 20$ cm

13. $\angle ABC = 56°, \angle CBR = 124°, \angle RBP = 56°$,
$\angle PBA = 124°$

14. 15   16. (a) 50° (b) 50° (c) 20° (d) 20°

17. $k = \frac{A - a}{2at}; k = 1$

18. (a) $\frac{1}{16}x^2 - \frac{4}{25}y^2$ (b) 80.84

19. (i) $\{3, 13, 7, 5, 2, 17\}$
(ii) $\{3, 6, 9, 12, 18\}$

21. $P' = (3, -5), Q' = (-4, 6)$; yes

22. Rs 525

Fig. Q. 25

PAPER – 4

1. 4A cm   2. A $\to$ Rs 180000, B $\to$ Rs 168000

3. $x = -\frac{2}{3}$ 4. $x = \pi r^2$ 5. Rs 9350   6. Rs 1200

7. $1\frac{1}{4}$ years   8. (a) 4   (b) 6

9. (i) $(a + b)(x - y)$ (ii) $2(3ax + 4)(3ax - 4)$

10. 40°, 60°, 80°   11. 12 hours.   12. 27 minutes.

14. (a) $\angle ABC = 65°$ (b) $\angle OBC = 32.5°$ (c) $\angle ACB = 65°$
(d) $\angle OCB = 32.5°$ (e) Yes   (f) $\angle BOC = 115°$

15. (i) Yes (ii) $AB = AC, AD = AD, \angle ADB \cong \angle ADC$ (RHS)
(iii) Yes

16. 38400 cm²   17. 60 m   19. 62.65 kg

20. $\angle BAD = 115°$ $\angle BCD = 65°$

21. 0.092   22. 5   24. $\{1, 2, 3, 4, \}$ 25. $(-3, -6)$

NOTE / ROUGH WORK

NOTE / ROUGH WORK